The
BIOLOGY
and
CHEMISTRY
of the
UMBELLIFERAE

Supplements to the Journals
of the Linnean Society of London

Already published:

New Research in Plant Anatomy

The full texts of papers read and submitted
for a symposium arranged by the
Society's Plant Anatomy Group and held in
London September 1970. Published as
Supplement 1 to the *Botanical Journal of
the Linnean Society* Vol. **63**, 1970

Early Mammals

The full texts of papers read and submitted
for a symposium held in London
in June 1970. Published as Supplement 1
to the *Zoological Journal of the Linnean Society*
Vol. **50**, 1971

Forthcoming titles:

Behavioural Aspects of Parasite Transmission

Symposium arranged with the British Society
for Parasitology and the British Society of
Protozoologists held in July 1971 and to be
published as a supplement to the
Zoological Journal of the Linnean Society

The Phylogeny and Classification
of the Filicopsida

Symposium arranged with the British Pteridological
Society to be held in April 1972

The Relationships of Fishes

Symposium to be held in June 1972

Published quarterly:

Biological Journal of the Linnean Society
Botanical Journal of the Linnean Society
Zoological Journal of the Linnean Society

The

BIOLOGY

and

CHEMISTRY

of the

UMBELLIFERAE

Edited by

V. H. Heywood

Department of Botany
The University, Reading, England

Supplement 1 to the Botanical Journal
of the Linnean Society   Volume 64 1971

*Published for the Linnean Society of London
by Academic Press*

ACADEMIC PRESS INC. (LONDON) LIMITED
24–28 Oval Road
London, NW1 7DX

U.S. Edition published by
ACADEMIC PRESS INC.
111 Fifth Avenue
New York, New York 10003

Library of Congress Catalog Card Number: 70–172364
ISBN: 0 12 346940 6

Made and printed in Great Britain by
William Clowes & Sons, Limited, London, Beccles and Colchester

List of contributors

BELL, C. RITCHIE. *Department of Botany, University of North Carolina, Chapel Hill, N. Carolina 27514, U.S.A.* (p. 93)

BOHLMANN, F. *Organisch-Chemisches Institut der Technischen Universität Berlin, 1 Berlin 12, Germany* (p. 279)

CARBONNIER, J. *Laboratoire de chimie du Muséum National d'Histoire Naturelle, 63 rue Buffon, Paris 5ème, France* (p. 337)

CAUWET, A.-M. *Laboratoire de Botanique, Centre Universitaire de Perpignan, Avenue de Villeneuve, 66-Perpignan, France* (p. 257)

CERCEAU-LARRIVAL, M.-Th. *Muséum National d'Histoire Naturelle, Laboratoire de Palynologie de l'E.P.H.E., 61 rue Buffon, Paris 5ème et Laboratoire de Biologie Végétale Appliquée, 91-Brunoy, France* (p. 109)

CONSTANCE, LINCOLN. *Department of Botany, University of California, Berkeley, California 94720, U.S.A.* (p. 1)

DAKSHINI, K. M. M. *Department of Botany, University of Delhi, India* (p. 217)

DAWSON, J. W. *Botany Department, University of Wellington, P. O. Box 196, Wellington, New Zealand* (p. 43)

FAIRBAIRN, J. W. *The School of Pharmacy, University of London, London, W.C.1, England* (p. 361)

FAIRBROTHERS, D. E. *Botany Department, Rutgers University, New Brunswick, New Jersey 08903, U.S.A.* (p. 315)

FRENCH, DAVID H. *Department of Anthropology, Reed College, Portland, Oregon 97202, U.S.A.* (p. 385)

FROEBE, HANS A. *Botanisches Institut der R.W.T.H., 51 Aachen, Hainbuchenstrasse 20, Germany* (p. 157)

GUYOT, M. *Laboratoire de Biologie Cellulaire, Faculté des Sciences, 21-Dijon, France* (p. 199)

HARBORNE, J. B. *Phytochemical Unit, Department of Botany, University of Reading, London Road, Reading, England* (p. 293)

HEGNAUER, R. *Laboratorium voor Experimentele Plantensystematiek van de Rijksuniversiteit te Leiden, 5e Binnenvestgracht 8, Leiden, Netherlands* (p. 267)

HEYWOOD, V. H. *Department of Botany, University of Reading, London Road, Reading, England* (pp. 31 & 217)

HILLER, K. *Sektion Chemie, Humboldt-Universität zu Berlin, Bereich Pharmazie, Goethe-Strasse 112 Berlin, Germany* (p. 369)

Jarreau, M.-C. *Laboratoire de chimie du Muséum National d'Histoire Naturelle, 63 rue Buffon, Paris 5ème, France* (p. 337)

Jössang, P. *Laboratoire de chimie du Muséum National d'Histoire Naturelle, 63 rue Buffon, Paris 5ème, France* (p. 337)

Mathias, Mildred, E. *Department of Botany, University of California, Los Angeles, California 90024, U.S.A.* (p. 13)

Molho, D. *Laboratoire de chimie du Muséum National d'Histoire Naturelle, 63 rue Buffon, Paris 5ème, France* (p. 337)

Moore, D. M. *Department of Botany, University of Reading, London Road, Reading, England* (p. 233)

Nielsen, B. Eichstedt. *The Royal Danish School of Pharmacy, Chemical Laboratory B, 2100 Copenhagen, Denmark* (p. 325)

*Pickering, Jerry L. *Botany Department, Rutgers University, New Brunswick, New Jersey, U.S.A.* (p. 315)

Rodríguez, Rafael L. *Department of Biology, University of Costa Rica, San José, Costa Rica, C.A.* (p. 63)

†Theobald, William L. *Biology Department, Occidental College, Los Angeles, California 90041, U.S.A.* (p. 179)

*Present Address: *Commonwealth of Pennsylvania, Indiana University of Pennsylvania, Indiana, Pennsylvania 15701, U.S.A.*

†Present Address: *Department of Botany, Plant Science Building, 3190 Maile Way, Honolulu, Hawaii 96822, U.S.A.*

Preface

This volume is based on papers presented at an international symposium on the Biology and Chemistry of the Umbelliferae held at the University of Reading on September 21–24, 1970, under the auspices of the Linnean Society in association with the Phytochemical Society.

The Umbelliferae is a large and widely distributed family and was probably the first to be recognized by taxonomists, because of its characteristic inflorescence and fruits. A great deal of research on the family is in progress in laboratories in various parts of the world. This research ranges from morphology and anatomy to electron microscopy, cytology and phytochemistry. Yet acute difficulties are experienced by taxonomists in arriving at satisfactory classifications of various parts of the family and at the same time very little is known about the floral biology or breeding systems operative. It is also one of the few families where sufficient data have accumulated to allow us to talk of its chemical profile. From an economic and medicinal point of view the family is of great interest.

It is against this background that it was decided to organize a symposium at which specialists in various aspects of biology and chemistry of the family could come together and outline the progress of their research and how it related to the systematics and classification of the family as a whole. Most of the world's leading umbellifer experts were able to participate and the meeting was generally agreed to be highly successful.

This resulting volume should be useful as a major source of information about the Umbelliferae although it is in no sense a systematic account.

The papers fall into several groups. The first, with papers by Constance, Mathias, Heywood, Dawson and Rodríguez, consists of surveys of our present knowledge of the classification and relationships of the family. In this group, points worth emphasizing are the complete bibliography of systematic papers on South American umbellifers, and post-1945 work on North American umbellifers in Mathias's paper, and Rodriguéz's wide-ranging review of relationships which can only be described as a *tour de force*.

The second set of papers, by Bell, Cerceau-Larrival, Froebe, Theobald, Guyot, Heywood and Dakshini, Moore and Cauwet deals with particular aspects of the family such as floral biology, pollen morphology, anatomy, stomata, inflorescences and chromosomes. Deserving of special mention are Cerceau-Larrival's extensive survey of pollen morphology, beautifully illustrated by scanning electron micrographs, and Moore's detailed analysis of chromosome numbers within the family. Bell's paper is a salutary reminder of just how little our knowledge of the floral biology and breeding systems of the Umbelliferae has advanced during the past hundred years.

The third series of papers, by Hegnauer, Bohlmann, Harborne, Fairbrothers and Pickering, Molho and collaborators, Nielsen, Fairbairn and Hiller covers the distribution of various classes of chemical constituents and their importance in detecting relationships. Hegnauer's contribution is a valuable introduction to the chemosystematics of the family and Harborne's outstanding analysis of flavonoid and phenylpropanoid patterns is an example of the value of detailed studies in our understanding of the chemistry and biology of these plants. The final chapter by French is a fascinating ethnobotanical study of the family which will be a valuable source of reference for many biologists.

It is clear on reading through these papers that despite all this impressive body of research on the Umbelliferae, a vast amount of new information and reappraisal is needed before a satisfactory systematic account of the family can be attempted. At least we can say that a hopeful beginning has been made.

About ninety participants from nine countries attended the meeting. Many people contributed to its success. In particular I would like to acknowledge the invaluable assistance given by Dr D. M. Moore and other members of the Department of Botany staff at Reading in making the arrangements for the meeting. Thanks are also due to the University of Reading for its hospitality and for the reception offered for the participants on Tuesday 22 September. The Royal Society generously provided a grant to assist several of the overseas speakers with their travel expenses.

I am most indebted to my colleague Dr J. B. Harborne for his assistance in editing this volume, especially the chemosystematic chapters. The production department of Academic Press has afforded its customary understanding and guidance in preparing the book for the press. Finally I wish to acknowledge the kind cooperation of the Linnean Society in permitting the volume to be published as a Supplement to its Botanical Journal.

V. H. HEYWOOD

October 1971

Contents

History of the classification of Umbelliferae (*Apiaceae*)

LINCOLN CONSTANCE, F.M.L.S.

Department of Botany, University of California, Berkeley, California, U.S.A.

After nearly three and a quarter centuries of work on the Umbelliferae, the first family of flowering plants to achieve general recognition, there is still disagreement as to its proper de- limitation and uncertainty as to its natural subdivisions and the criteria on which they should be erected. This historical survey outlines the development of an understanding and classification of the family from the first reference to a recognizable member (*Coriandrum*) by the Myceneans up to the present day. A series of portraits is provided of people who, through the ages, con- tributed notably to knowledge of the family.

CONTENTS

Systema Umbelliferarum me judice longe recedit a perfectione.

H. G. REICHENBACH, 1867

HISTORICAL SURVEY

In his *Landmarks of Botanical History* (1909), Edward Lee Greene remarks that, 'Botany did not begin with the first books of botany, nor with the men that indicted them. . . . The most remote and primitive of botanical writers, of whatever country or language, found a more or less extensive vocabulary of elementary botany in the colloquial speech of all.' Thus a utilitarian knowledge of the names and uses of local plants is a basic feature of all primitive cultures. Because of their distinctive chemi- stry, reflected in odour, flavour, esculence, or toxicity, members of Umbelliferae were familiar prehistorically to many peoples.

The Greek name for *Coriandrum* was one of the earliest words recognized by Michael Ventris in his brilliant deciphering of Linear B, the ancient Mycenean language of Crete in the fifteenth to seventeenth centuries B.C. (Chadwick, 1958). The Chinese classic materia medica, *Pen Ts'ao Chin*, compiled in the late Han Dynasty around the second and third century B.C., but apparently based upon an earlier oral tradition, includes at least nine Umbelliferae. Several Umbelliferae are known by Sanskrit names, but it is difficult to fix their identity and antiquity. Rodríguez (1957) has noted that long before the coming of the *conquistadores* to the New World, the Indians of Mexico had developed a crude but utilitarian botanical classification that included some apioid Umbelliferae.

Theophrastus of Eresus, according to Greene (1909), recognized Umbelliferae, under the name of *Narthekodes*, as one among the several natural plant families

1

with which that Aristotelian disciple was well acquainted and which he precisely defined. The Greek word *Narthex* became translated into the Latin *Ferula* for a dried stalk of *Ferula* or *Foeniculum*, and *Narthekodes* into *Ferulacea*. In Greek art, Dionysius is frequently identifiable by the fact that he is depicted holding a *Ferula* or ferule in his hand (Sichtermann, 1969). Greene's version is doubtless an exaggeration of the Greek classificatory achievement, but Rodríguez (1957) notes that Theophrastus did characterize such familiar plants as dill, coriander, anise, cumin, and fennel by their naked seeds and herbaceous habit (Theophrastus, 1916), and Sprengel (1817–18) listed more than a dozen presumptive Umbelliferae which can be found scattered through at least three books of the *Historia Plantarum*.

The *Greek Herbal* of Dioscorides lists over four times this many Umbelliferae in its five books, and most of them are placed rather closely together under the general heading of 'Herbs' (Gunther, 1959). Dioscorides' successive Islamic and European translators made no substantial improvement, although they frequently provided and sometimes transposed illustrations of varying quality and accuracy.

The published works of the sixteenth-century Herbalists reveal a gradual improvement in the grouping of umbelliferous as of other plants, largely by vegetative resemblance, but there are substantial confusions of names, descriptions, and illustrations with such extraneous elements as Papaveraceae, Saxifragaceae, Rosaceae, Compositae, Leguminosae, Cruciferae, Labiatae, Valerianaceae (not surprisingly), and even with *Asparagus*.

Cesalpino appears to have proposed the first over-all grouping in 1583, under the designation 'universum genus Ferulaceum', to embrace some 60 listed herbs. Such terms as 'plantae Umbelliferae' also began to come into general use at about the same time. Thus, Dodoëns (1583) utilized the designation 'De Umbelliferis Herbis', but since he followed the Dioscorean example of scattering umbelliferous species over at least two 'pemptades' and six 'books', this can scarcely be considered the establishment of a family. The latter achievement appears actually to have been accomplished by Dalechamps, who in his *Historia generalis plantarum* of 1586, dubbed the sixth book, 'In quo describuntur & depinguntur plantae Umbelliferae', and aggregated some four dozen Umbelliferae and a number of contaminants under it. De l'Écluse (1601) and Kaspar Bauhin (1623) both had at least part of Umbelliferae under a book or chapter so designated, but both admitted some foreign elements while excluding at least *Eryngium*.

The pioneer monograph by Robert Morison in 1672, the earliest systematic study of *any* group of plants, is astonishingly 'modern'. The author stressed seed characters (fruit and seed were poorly distinguished even at that time), and grouped all known Umbelliferae into nine 'genera' or classes. Vines & Druce observed: 'This arrangement of umbelliferous plants, and still more the eight illustrative diagrams, betray a remarkable sense of the relationship of the plants constituting the group; it is probably the first instance in botanical literature of anything of this kind' (1914: xli).

Tournefort (1694) brought all Umbelliferae together for the first time. His Classe VII, 'Suite des herbes á fleur en rose, savoir des fleurs en parasol ou en umbelle', is divided into nine sections on the bases of inflorescence, calyx, and fruit morphology. The last of these—Section IX—contains *Sanicula*, *Eryngium*, and *Hydrocotyle*, the first time that *Eryngium*, at least, had been removed from the company of thistles to that of carrots.

The persistent Theophrastian idea that Umbelliferae are characterized by naked seeds, although contested by Vaillant (1718), Micheli (1729), and Gaertner (1788–1791), persisted on into the nineteenth century (Persoon, 1805–07). Baillon states (1867–95) that de Jussieu, who used Umbelliferae as one of his models for delimiting families, separated Umbelliferae from Araliaceae in the belief that the former had naked seeds, whereas the latter had them enclosed within a pericarp.

Ray (1686–1704, 1703), Magnol (1720), Boerhaave (1727), van Royen (1740), von Haller (1753, 1768), and others each advanced varying arrangements of umbelliferous genera on differing combinations of floral, carpological, and foliar characters, but none of these classifications represents a significant advance over the formulations of Tournefort or Morison.

Linnaeus' classification of Umbellatae, first proposed in 1735 and repeated in the *Species plantarum* (1753), was actually the work of his colleague and friend, the 'unfortunate Artedius'. This comprised some 45 genera (including both *Eryngium* and *Hydrocotyle*) and emphasized presence or absence of involucre and involucel. Artedius (1962), who was also the 'Father of Ichthyology', apparently left no portrait of himself, but was commemorated by the following verse:

Here lies poor Artedi, in foreign land pyxed
Not a man nor a fish, but something betwixt,
Not a man, for his life among fishes he past,
Not a fish, for he perished by water at last.

G. SHAW, 1751–1813

This Linnean system was widely accepted and was apparently last employed by Don in 1845. However, the emphasis on involucral features came under heavy fire from various botanists, including Crantz (1766, 1767), who reduced the Linnean genera to 30 and grouped them into six sections based upon habit and fruit. Crantz scathingly criticized Linnaeus not only for including *Eryngium* in his Umbellatae, but also for asserting that there are five stamens and a bifid pistil in Umbelliferae!

Adanson (1763) was the first consciously to combine Umbelliferae (Umbellatae) with Araliaceae, and he predictably advocated the use of multiple characters to achieve natural subdivisions of the combined family. Necker, a quarter of a century later (1790) proposed the 'genera' *Gitonophytum* and *Sciadophytum*, the former containing a mixture of Umbelliferae and Araliaceae, and the latter Umbelliferae only.

In the eyes of many subsequent authors, the most perspicacious student of Umbelliferae in the eighteenth century was Pierre Cusson of Montpellier. He devised one system based on petals, and six alternative ones founded on fruit and seed characteristics, including the form of endosperm. His ideas unfortunately never reached publication except for a brief summary included by de Jussieu (1783) in an obituary of this French botanist-physician. Although de Jussieu (1789) could not bring himself to abandon the Linnean classification in favour of that of Cusson, the

ideas of the latter author continued to be rediscovered by such later writers as La
Gasca, Cavanilles and Sprengel.

The views of the Spaniard, La Gasca, were ostensibly first announced orally in
1806, then were written down in the thesis of his student, Estaban Vela, in 1815,
but were not published until 1821, and were then revised in 1826. La Gasca strongly
advocated abandoning involucral characteristics, and emphasized that umbel
taxonomy should consider fruit and flower alone for major divisions. Kurt Sprengel
(1813, 1820, 1825–28) also gave primacy to the fruit, but his nine tribes made use of
involucre and pubescence, as well. 'In spite of the defects indicated . . . the work of
Sprengel is, without any dispute, of a merit superior to any compilation that has been
published previously', in the opinion of the critical La Gasca (1826).

Hoffmann (1814, 1816), who was contemporary with La Gasca and Sprengel,
analysed all parts of the fructification with Teutonic throughness—including corolla,
stylopodium, commissure and carpophore—and was the first clearly to emphasize
and utilize the oil tubes or vittae of the fruit. La Gasca accused him of unreasonable
multiplication of genera, of which he recognized 60, although neither *Eryngium* nor
Hydrocotyle was included. The work of Hoffmann, emanating from Moscow, and
that of La Gasca, from Madrid, probably had less influence than might have been
the case had these two authors been geographically more central to the mainstream
of European science.

The nature of the seed face or endosperm, which had been alluded to by Cusson,
was promoted to a major criterion of classification by Koch (1824), who also stressed
fruit compression and the relative proportions of the dorsal and commissural surfaces, the number of mericarp ribs, and the dorsal vittae. De Candolle found Koch's
ideas so compatible with his own that he used a slightly modified version in his later
publications (1829, 1830). In the *Prodromus* (1830) all 107 genera of Umbelliferae
fall into the three familiar suborders Orthospermae, Campylospermae and Coelospermae. Lindley (1836), who incidentally offered the alternative name of Apiaceae for the family, and Endlicher (1836–40) followed the Koch–Candollean model.
Endlicher accounted for a total of 195 genera in his *Genera Plantarum*. Tausch (1834)
pointed out the variability and serious inadequacy of the endospermal criterion, and
regarded its nearly exclusive use as placing too heavy a dependence 'on a subordinate
part'. His own scheme divided the twelve tribes between only two suborders,
Mericarpae and Monocarpae, depending upon whether two carpels or only one
developed to maturity. Almost casually, Burnett in 1834 and 1835 rechristened
Umbellatae as Angelicinae and spawned the segregate family names Angelicaceae,
Smyrniaceae, Coriandraceae, and Umbellaceae, the first three as substitutes for
Orthospermae, Campylospermae and Coelospermae, respectively; the last was
arrived at independently some years later also by Dulac (1867).

Concurrently, the older Reichenbach (1828) created a highly original classification of his own. In this, Umbelliferae were expanded to embrace also the families
Araliaceae and Vitaceae. Thus subfamily B of Umbelliferae was made to include
all those genera that were later to be referred to subfamilies Saniculoideae and
Hydrocotyloideae, as well as Araliaceae, proper. In a similar vein, Baillon (1867–95)
harked back to Adanson in constituting Aralieae as a sixth tribe of Umbelliferae, and

Calestani (1905) regarded Apiaceae as comprising four subfamilies, of which the first is Aralineae, the others Eryngineae, Lagoecineae and Ferulineae, respectively.

In the *Genera Plantarum* (1867), Bentham produced a novel division of the family into the three Series Heterosciadiae, Haplozygiae, and Diplozygiae, founded on the nature of the inflorescence, the presence or absence of oil tubes, and the presence or absence of secondary ribs. Of the nine tribes, Hydrocotyleae, Mulineae, and Saniculeae fall under Heterosciadiae, with usually simple umbels and without vallecular oil tubes. The apioid Umbelliferae are allotted to Haplozygiae and Diplozygiae depending upon whether the fruits lack or possess secondary ribs. The tribes established by Koch and de Candolle are considerably rearranged, and a conservative view is taken of genera, which were reduced to 153.

The American monographers, Coulter & Rose (1888, 1895, 1900*a*, *b*), professed dissatisfaction with the Benthamian tripartite division and resorted to presence or absence of secondary ribs and compression of the fruit in contructing their artificial keys, but did not attempt any general revision of the family. The hydrocotyloid and saniculoid genera were unsatisfactorily scattered among the apioid. An alternative family name, Ammiaceae, was proposed by Britton & Brown (1896–98), borrowing a tribal designation from Presl & Presl (1822); this was accepted by Small (1903).

A segregation of European Umbelliferae into nine tribes, five of them containing a single genus each, with a primary emphasis on the nature of the inflorescence, was offered by Caruel (1892–97).

A geminal paper by Rompel (1895), completed in Wettstein's laboratory, investigated intensively the occurrence of calcium-oxalate crystals in the pericarp and its possible taxonomic value. Criteria of presence or absence and distribution of crystals led him to the recognition of a *Hydrocotyle*-Type, a *Sanicula*-Type, and a *Scandix*-Type.

The system developed by Drude (1898) for *Die Pflanzenfamilien* marked a rejection or subordination of the endospermal categories of Koch and de Candolle, the inflorescence groups of Bentham, the drastic union of families, tribes and genera by Baillon, and the apposition of certain genera by Caruel and by Coulter & Rose. In essence, Drude returned to the tribes established by Koch and de Candolle, emphasized the findings of Rompel, and divided Umbelliferae into the three subfamilies Hydrocotyloideae, Saniculoideae and Apioideae. After nearly three-quarters of a century, this remains the predominant system. The most prolific German worker on Umbelliferae in this century was, of course, Hermann Wolff (1910, 1913, 1927).

From an intensive survey of the vegetative organs of Umbelliferae, Domin concluded: 'Die Umbelliferen sind mit den Araliaceen so nahe verwandt, dass sie von streng systematischem Standpunkte aus als Unterfamilien einer und derselben Familie vereinigt werden sollten. Nur aus *praktischen* Rücksichten lassen wir sie als selbständige Familien bestehen, obzwar zwischen ihnen in *keinem* Merkmale eine scharfe Grenze existiert' (1908; 89).

In 1916 Koso-Poljansky again returned to the findings of Rompel, which he employed as a basis for dividing the family into the two very unequal subfamilies

Hydrocotyloideae and Ligusticoideae, and the latter into five 'legions' based upon distribution of crystals, vittae, and sclerenchyma and aerenchyma in the fruit walls.

Although Hutchinson in 1926–34 placed both Araliaceae and Umbelliferae under the single order Umbelliflorae, he suggested that the woody members and the herbaceous ones might have had different derivations. In 1959 and again in 1969 he separates the two families into two separate orders in different habital divisions, Araliales (Lignosae) and Umbellales (Herbaceae). 'He prefers to derive *Araliaceae* from the woody Cunoniales and the *Apiaceae* from the herbaceous Saxifragaceous stock, no doubt "heresy" to many botanists' (1969: 573).

Arguing that in the possession of a woody endocarp Hydrocotyloideae are essentially equidistant between Araliaceae and Umbelliferae, Hylander (1945) has proposed elevation of the subfamily to family status as Hydrocotylaceae. This view corresponds closely to that reached by Baumann in his penetrating study of the New Caledonian genus *Myodocarpus*, that '*Les Ombellifères* représentent une tribu différenciée des Araliacées; elles descendent des *Pro-Araliacées* tropicales, mais c'est dans les régions tempérées et fraiches qu'elles se sont développées le plus intensivement en évoluant vers un type particulier de fleur et de fruit selon les principes de l'evolution différentielle' (1946: 108). The evidence provided by Baumann from araliaceous fruits combined with that from Rodríguez's excellent monograph on the anatomy of woody Umbellales (1957), has recently induced Thorne (1968) to take the giant step of again combining Araliaceae and Umbelliferae (Apiaceae), following the examples of Adanson, Reichenbach, Baillon and Calestani. In 1949 Dostál coined the family Daucaceae.

Cerceau-Larrival (1962), from her study of the correlations between pollen morphology and the type of cotyledons, supported by evidence from adult vegetative morphology, inflorescence and fruit, proposes a very original division of Umbelliferae into the five subfamilies Bupleuroideae, Endressioideae, Azorelloideae, Eryngioideae, and Apioideae. Guyot (1966) finds that distribution of stomatal types confirms this arrangement.

Tamamschian (1964) has questioned the Baumann thesis, and is unable to visualize derivation of the often robust Apioideae from Araliaceae by way of the frequently diminutive, reduced and specialized Hydrocotyloideae. She concludes that, 'Considering as many characters as possible, one may conclude that there is no successiveness from Hydrocotyloideae in the subfamilies Saniculoideae and Apioideae' (p. 78, translation by Peter Rubtzoff).

Cronquist agrees that 'the two families are generally admitted to be intimately related, with the Araliaceae being the more primitive' (1968: 277) but prefers to keep them distinct, as does Takhtajan (1969).

Thus, although Umbelliferae were the first family of flowering plants to achieve general recognition, after nearly three and a quarter centuries of successive and multi-national effort, considerable disagreement still exists as to the proper delimitation of the family and even more uncertainty prevails as to its natural subdivisions and the criteria on which they should be erected. Clearly continued acquisition of new information and re-examination, refinement, and re-evaluation of accumulated evidence are urgently to be welcomed.

ACKNOWLEDGEMENTS

The writer wishes to express his gratitude for generous assistance in attempting to obtain information and illustrative material for this paper to his colleagues in the University of California, Professors M. B. Emeneau, Roger Hahn, Johannes Proskauer, J. B. de C. M. Saunders, and H. R. W. Smith and Mr Peter Rubtzoff; to Dr Hui-Lin Li of the Morris Arboretum, University of Pennsylvania; to Drs Christian Bénézech and Louis Dulieu, and M. G. Guillou and Mlle. Monique Durruty of Montpellier; Dr M.-Th. Cerceau-Larrival of Paris; to Dr Sophia Tamamschian of Moscow; to Dr R. E. G. Pichi-Sermolli of Genoa; to Dr Hans Froebe of Aachen; to Drs K.-H. Rechinger and H. Riedl of Vienna; to Dr Ivan Klášteřsky of Prague; and to the Arnold Arboretum-Gray Herbarium Library of Harvard University and the Hunt Botanical Library of Carnegie-Mellon University.

REFERENCES

ADANSON, M., 1763. *Familles des plantes*. 2 vols. Paris: Vincent.

ARTEDIUS, P., 1962. Ichthyologia. With introd. by A. C. Wheeler. *Hist. Natur. Classica*, **15**: 554.

BAILLON, H. E., 1867–1895. *Histoire des plantes*. 13 vols. Paris & London: Hachette.

BAUHIN, K., 1623. *Pinax theatri botanici*. 522 pp. Basel.

BAUMANN, M. G., 1946. *Myodocarpus* und die Phylogenie der Umbelliferen-Frucht. *Mitt. Bot. Mus. Univ. Zürich*, **177**: 13–112.

BENTHAM, G., 1867. Umbelliferae. In Bentham & Hooker, *Genera plantarum*, **1**: 859–931.

BOERHAAVE, H., 1727. *Historia plantarum, quae in Horto academico Lugduni-Batavorum crescent*. 2 vols. Rome.

BRITTON, N. L. & BROWN, A., 1896–1898. *Illustrated Flora of the Northern United States and Canada*. 3 vols. New York: Scribners.

BURNETT, J. F., 1834. Stephenson & Churchill, *Medical Botany*. 2nd ed. 2 vols. London.

BURNETT, J. F., 1835. *Outlines of Botany*. 2 vols. London.

CALESTANI, V., 1905. Contributo alla systematica dell ombrellifere d'europa. *Webbia*, **1**: 89–280.

CARUEL, T., 1892–1897. *Epitome florae europae*. Fasc. I–III. 384 pp. Florence.

CERCEAU-LARRIVAL, M.-Th., 1962. Plantules et pollens d'Ombellifères. *Mém. Mus. Hist. Nat. Paris*, II. ser. B., **14**: 164 pp.

CESALPINO, A., 1583. *De plantis libri xvi*. 621 pp. Florence.

CHADWICK, J., 1958. *The Decipherment of Linear B*. 159 pp. Pelican Book.

COULTER, J. M. & ROSE, J. N., 1888. *Revision of North American Umbelliferae*. 144 pp. Crawfordsville.

COULTER, J. M. & ROSE, J. N., 1895. Report on Mexican Umbelliferae, etc. *Contr. U.S. Nat. Herb.*, **3** (5): 289–323.

COULTER, J. M. & ROSE, J. N., 1900a. Monograph of the North American Umbelliferae. *Contr. U.S. Nat. Herb.*, **7** (1): 256.

COULTER, J. M. & ROSE, J. N., 1900b. A synopsis of Mexican and Central American Umbelliferae. *Proc. Wash. Acad.*, **1**: 111–159.

CRANTZ, H., 1766. *Institutiones rei herbariae*. 2 vols.

CRANTZ, H., 1767. *Classis Umbelliferarum*. 125 pp. Leipzig.

CRONQUIST, A., 1968. *The Evolution and Classification of Flowering Plants*. Boston: Houghton Mifflin. 396 pp.

DALECHAMPS, J., 1586. *Historia generalis plantarum*. 2 vols. Leiden.

DE CANDOLLE, A. P., 1829. *Collection de mémoires pour servir à l'histoire du régne végétal*, etc. V. Ombellifères. 84 pp.

DE CANDOLLE, A. P., 1830. Umbelliferae. In de Candolle, *Prodromus systematis naturalis regni vegetabilis*, **4**: 55–250.

DE L'ÉCLUSE, C., 1601. *Rariorum plantarum historia*. 364 pp. Antwerp.

DE JUSSIEU, A. L., 1783. Eloge de M. Cusson. *Hist. Soc. Roy. Méd.*

DE JUSSIEU, A. L., 1789. *Genera plantarum*. 498 pp. Paris.

DODOËNS, R., 1583. *Stirpium historiae pemptades sex sive Libri XXX*. 860 pp. Antwerp.

DOMIN, K., 1908. Morphologische und phylogenetische Studien über die Familie der Umbelliferen. *Bull. Internat. Acad. Bohême.* 109 pp. (Reprint.)

DON, P. N., 1845. *Donn's Hortus Cantabrigiensis*. 13th ed. 772 pp. London.

DOSTÁL, J., 1948–1950. *Květena ČSR*. Praha.

DRUDE, C. G. O., 1898. Umbelliferae. In Engler & Prantl, *Die natürlichen Pflanzenfamilien*, **3** (8): 63–250.

DULAC, J., 1867. *Flore du département des Hautes-Pyrénées*. 641 pp. Paris.

ENDLICHER, S. L., 1836–1840. *Genera plantarum secundum ordines naturales disposita*. 1483 pp. Vienna.

GAERTNER, J., 1788–1791. *De fructibus et seminibus plantarum*. 2 vols.

GREENE, E. L., 1909. Landmarks of botanical history. *Smithsonian Misc. Coll.* 329 pp.

GUNTHER, R. T., 1959. *The Greek Herbal of Dioscorides*. 701 pp. New York: Hafner.

GUYOT, M., 1966. Les stomates des Ombellifères. *Bull. Soc. Bot. France*, **113**: 244–273.

HOFFMANN, G. F., 1814. *Genera plantarum umbelliferarum*. 181 pp. Moscow.

HOFFMANN, G. F., 1816. *Plantarum umbelliferarum genera*. 222 pp. Moscow.

HUTCHINSON, J., 1926–1934. *The Families of Flowering Plants*. 2 vols. London: Macmillan.

HUTCHINSON, J., 1959. *The Families of Flowering Plants*. 2nd ed. 2 vols. Oxford: Clarendon Press.

HUTCHINSON, J., 1969. *Evolution and Phylogeny of Flowering Plants*. 717 pp. London & New York: Academic Press.

HYLANDER, N., 1945. Nomenklatorische und systematische Studien über nordische Gefässpflanzen. *Uppsala Univ. Årsskr.*, 1945: **7**: 5–337.

KOCH, W. D. J., 1824. Generum tribuumque umbelliferarum nova dispositio. *Nova Acta Acad. Leop. Carol.*, **12**: 55–156.

KOSO-POLJANSKY, B. M., 1916. Sciadophytorum systematis lineamenta. *Bull. Soc. Imp. Naturalistes Moscou*, II. **29**: 93–221.

LA GASCA, M., 1821. Dispositio umbelliferarum carpologica. *Amen. Nat. Españas*, **1** (2): 87–111.

LA GASCA, M., 1826. *Observaciones sobre la Familia Natural de las Plantas Aparasoladas (Umbelliferae)*. 43 pp. London.

LINDLEY, J., 1836. *A Natural System of Botany*. 2nd ed. 2526 pp. London.

LINNAEUS, C., 1735. *Systema naturae*. Leiden.

LINNAEUS, C., 1753. *Species plantarum*. 2 vols. Stockholm.

MAGNOL, P., 1720. *Novus caracter plantarum*. 327 pp. Montpellier.

MICHELI, P. A., 1729. *Nova plantarum genera*. 234 pp. Florence.

MORISON, R., 1672. *Plantarum umbelliferarum distributio nova*. 91 pp. Oxford.

NECKER, N. J., 1790. *Elementa botanica*. 3 vols. Neuwied.

PERSOON, C. H., 1805–1807. *Synopsis plantarum seu encharidium botanicum*. 2 vols. Paris.

PRESL, J. S. & PRESL, C. B., 1822. *Deliciae pragenses, historiam naturalem spectantes*. 244 pp. Praha.

RAY, J., 1686–1704. *Historia plantarum*. 3 vols. London.

RAY, J., 1703. *Methodus plantarum*. 202 pp. London: Smith & Walford.

REICHENBACH, H. G. L., 1828. *Conspectus regni vegetabilis*. 294 pp. Leipzig.

RODRÍGUEZ, R. L., 1957. Systematic anatomical studies on *Myrrhidendron* and other woody Umbellales. *Univ. Calif. Publ. Bot.*, **29** (2): 145–318.

ROMPEL, J., 1895. Krystalle von Calcium oxalat in der Fruchtwandt der Umbelliferen und ihre Verwerthung für die Systematik. *Sitzungsber. Akad. Wiss. Wien*, **104**: 417–476.

SICHTERMANN, H., 1969. *Griechische Vasen in Unteritalien*. 80 pp., 176 plates. Tübingen: Wasmuth.

SMALL, J. K., 1903. *Flora of the Southeastern United States*. 1370 pp. New York.

SPRENGEL, K., 1813. *Plantarum umbelliferarum denuo disponendarum prodromus*. 42 pp. Halle.

SPRENGEL, K., 1817–1818. *Geschichte der Botanik*. 2 vols. Altenburg & Leipzig: Brockhaus.

SPRENGEL, K., 1820. Umbelliferae. In Römer & Schultes, *Systema vegetabilium*, **6**: 315–628.

SPRENGEL, K., 1825–1828. *Caroli Linnaei . . . Systema vegetabilium*. 16th ed. 5 vols. Göttingen.

TAKHTAJAN, A., 1969. *Flowering Plants; Origin and Dispersal*. 310 pp. Washington: Smithsonian Inst.

TAMAMSCHIAN, S. G., 1964. Experiment of constructing a phylogenetic system of Dicots on the example of Umbellales and related orders. *2nd Sympos. Plant Phylogeny, Moscow*, pp. 77–80. [In Russian.]

TAUSCH, J. F., 1834. Das System der Doldengewächse. *Flora*, **17**: 337–348, 353–357.

THEOPHRASTUS, 1916. *Enquiry into Plants*. With English transl. by Sir A. Hort. London.

THORNE, R. F., 1968. Synopsis of a putatively phylogenetic classification of the flowering plants. *Aliso*, **6** (4): 57–66.

TOURNEFORT, J. P., 1694. *Élémens de Botanique*. 3 vols. Paris.

VAILLANT, S., 1718. *Discours sur la structure des fleurs*. 55 pp. Leiden.

VELA, S. E., 1821. Disertacion sobre la familia natural de las plantas *Aparasoladas*. *Amen. Nat. Españas*, **1** (2): 1–46.

VINES, S. H. & DRUCE, G. C., 1914. *An Account of the Morisonian Herbarium in the Possession of the University of Oxford*. 350 pp. Oxford: Clarendon.

VAN ROYEN, A., 1740. *Florae leydensis prodromus*. 538 pp. Leiden.

VON HALLER, A., 1753. *Enumeratio plantarum Hortii Regii et Agri Gottingensis*. 424 pp. Göttingen.

VON HALLER, A., 1768. *Historia stirpium indigenarum Helvetiae inchoata*. 3 vols. Bern.

WOLFF, H., 1910. Umbelliferae-Apioideae-Bupleurum, Trinia et reliquae Ammineae heteroclitae. In Engler, *Das Pflanzenreich*, IV, **43**: 1–214.

WOLFF, H., 1913. Umbelliferae-Saniculoideae. In Engler, *Das Pflanzenreich*, IV, **61**: 1–305.

WOLFF, H., 1927. Umbelliferae-Apioideae-Ammineae-Carinae, Ammineae novemjugatae et genuinae. In Engler, *Das Pflanzenreich*, IV, **90**: 1–398.

EXPLANATION OF PLATES

PLATES 1 and 2. Portraits of some major contributors to the classification of the Umbelliferae

PLATE 1

A.   A. Cesalpino
B.   R. Morison
C.   J. P. Tournefort
D.   M. Adanson
E.   P. Cusson
F.   M. La Gasca

PLATE 2

A.   K. Sprengel
B.   G. F. Hoffmann
C.   W. D. J. Koch
D.   J. Rompel
E.   C. G. O. Drude
F.   B. M. Koso-Poljansky

PLATE 1

PLATE 2

Systematic survey of New World Umbelliferae

MILDRED E. MATHIAS

Department of Botany, University of California, Los Angeles, California, U.S.A.

The taxonomy of the Umbelliferae has been developed in Europe based primarily on studies of European species. Plant collections received from the western hemisphere were often erroneously identified as belonging to European genera and it was not until the end of the nineteenth century that many of the American taxa were recognized as unique.

With the accumulation of collections and information from field studies it has been possible to prepare a revision of the family for North America. However, a revision of the entire family for South America is still in preparation. These taxonomic revisions should stimulate experimental studies which will augment our knowledge of the biology of the family and eventually lead to an improved taxonomy.

A tentative interpretation of geographical relations within the family has been proposed. The Apioideae and Saniculoideae, with a few holarctic genera such as *Angelica* and *Sanicula*, are well represented in the western hemisphere. Secondary centres of radiation have occurred in western North America and a number of genera such as *Cymopterus, Lomatium, Priono-sciadium* and *Tauschia* are endemic to that area.

Although both the Apioideae and Saniculoideae occur in South America the family is represented there primarily by the subfamily Hydrocotyloideae, a predominantly southern hemisphere group. In addition to such widespread genera as *Hydrocotyle* and *Azorella* there are a number of smaller endemic genera native primarily to temperate mountain areas.

Our knowledge of the distribution of western hemisphere Umbelliferae is still incomplete and continued collections and field studies are needed.

The basic taxonomy of the cosmopolitan plant family Umbelliferae with its three subfamilies and several tribes and sections was developed almost entirely from knowledge of Old World, and particularly Eurasian, taxa. Robert Morison (1672) in the first systematic treatment of the family described some 165 species, including from the New World only three now placed in the family Umbelliferae. One of these was *Angelica lucida*, one of two Umbelliferae illustrated and described by Cornuti (1635) in the first Canadian flora. Surprisingly Morison ignored the second species of *Angelica* recognized by Cornuti, *A. atropurpurea*. Knowledge of New World Umbelliferae had still not increased significantly by 1753 with the publication of Linnaeus, *Species Plantarum*. Of the 180 species included in the family by Linnaeus, only 19 were natives of the western hemisphere. There was only one reference to a South American collection, that of Piso (1648) and Marggraf (1648) for *Hydrocotyle umbellata*, a widespread aquatic weed. Likewise only one reference was made to a Mexican taxon, which Linnaeus identified as the ubiquitous neotropical weed, *Eryngium foetidum*. Our information on New World Umbelliferae, when compared to knowledge of European and near eastern representatives of the family, is of relatively recent origin, much of it dating from the twentieth century.

The last half of the eighteenth century and the first quarter of the nineteenth saw

13

increasing field activity in the Americas. In South America there were the noteworthy plant collections of Commerson, Humboldt and Bonpland, Ruíz & Pavón, Dombey, Aublet, Bertero, Poeppig, Pohl, Martius and Sainte-Hilaire. New information on the plants of the Caribbean, Central America and Mexico was obtained from the collections of Sessé and Mociño, Jacquin, Swartz and Browne. Collections were made not only along the coast but inland to the high Andes of South America and the mountains of Mexico and Central America, regions rich in Umbelliferae. In North America collections were being made in the west as well as in the eastern and central parts of the continent. Of particular note were those of Haenke, Elliott, Lewis and Clark, Pursh, Nuttall, Bradbury, the Bartrams, the Michauxs, Richardson, Drummond, Menzies and Chamisso.

The increased knowledge of the family, not only world-wide but particularly for the western hemisphere, was evidenced in de Candolle's (1829a, 1830) treatment for his *Mémoire* in 1829 and in the *Prodromus* in 1830. The *Prodromus* revision included 999 species, with 218 of western hemisphere origin. This comprehensive treatment also indicated the uniqueness of many umbels in the Americas, with the recognition of such distinctive American genera as *Erigenia* Nutt., *Micropleura* Lag., *Bowlesia* R. & P., *Mulinum* Pers., *Spananthe* Jacq., *Asteriscium* C. & S., *Zizia* Koch, *Ottoa* HBK., *Cynosciadium* DC., *Thaspium* Nutt., *Polytaenia* DC., *Cymopterus* Raf., *Osmorhiza* Raf., and *Arracacia* Bancroft.

Since the *Prodromus* revision of 1830 no author has treated the family on a world-wide basis at the species level, although Hermann Wolff (1910b, 1913, 1927) initiated a species revision for *Das Pflanzenreich*. Generic treatments for the entire family were presented by Bentham (1867) and Drude (1898). However, regional Floras have been published for many areas in the western hemisphere. Among the early Floras three stand out as landmarks with respect to additions to our knowledge of the Umbelliferae, Hooker (1840a), *Flora boreali-Americana*, Torrey & Gray (1840), *Flora of North America*, and Urban's (1879) revision for Martius, *Flora brasiliensis*.

The Floras of Hooker and Torrey & Gray synthesized much of the information from the early western expeditions. They were the standard references for the Umbelliferae until 1888 when Coulter & Rose (1888) published their revision, in which they recognized 59 genera and 233 species north of Mexico. Fifty-two of the genera were native but only 22 considered strictly North American. They continued to refer many American species to such Old World genera as *Selinum* and *Peucedanum* but at the same time described such endemic American genera as *Harbouria*, *Aletes*, *Museniopsis* (= *Tauschia*), and *Pseudocymopterus* and recognized *Cymopterus* and *Oreoxis* among others. For the first time a semblance of order was attained in the taxonomy of the Umbelliferae for North America. A beginning was made in the clarification of the chaotic synonymy since many species had been described more than once and under different generic names. The most remarkable case was *Aletes acaulis*, the type of the new genus *Aletes*, a species which had been referred to six genera and listed under three of them simultaneously. The Coulter & Rose revision undoubtedly encouraged exploration especially in the western United States and Mexico. The presence of specialists able to name the collections and to describe the novelties resulted in many specimens of Umbelliferae arriving in Washington, D.C. where Rose was located.

The year 1900 was a landmark year in the taxonomy of the family in the western hemisphere. In January Coulter & Rose (1900a) published *A synopsis of Mexican and Central American Umbelliferae*. The only earlier treatment of the family for this region had been by Hemsley (1880–81) in *Biologia Centrali-americana*. Hemsley's list of 25 genera and 76 native species was expanded by Coulter & Rose to 39 genera and 156 native species, a remarkable increase due largely to the superb collections of Nelson, Goldman, Pringle, Palmer and Rose himself. At the end of the same year in December 1900 there appeared the Coulter & Rose (1900b) *Monograph of the North American Umbelliferae*. Whereas the revision had included 52 native genera with 217 species, the monograph described 332 native species in 62 genera, an increase of over a third more species in the twelve year period. Arrangement of genera in the earlier publications had been largely artificial or according to the then current European treatment. The Coulter & Rose monograph was no exception and followed Drude's (1898) classification of the family. However, they deviated significantly from Drude's delimitation of genera and, for the first time, *Peucedanum* and *Selinum* were removed from the American flora. Coulter & Rose emphasized the diagnostic value of fruit characters to the almost total exclusion of floral and vegetative morphology. In these two treatments published in 1900 the total genera for the continent from Panama northward numbered 95, native and introduced, with 518 species. A previously poorly known plant family had finally received a complete revision of the North American taxa.

In the first quarter of the twentieth century subsequent to the publication of the Coulter & Rose monograph there were few publications on the family in North America. Bush (1902) studied the North American species of *Chaerophyllum*; Jepson (1923–29) studied the family extensively in the preparation of a flora of California; Jones (1902–35) published many notes on western species; MacBride (1918–19) and Nelson (1901, 1912a, b) published on Rocky Mountain taxa; Piper (1902–16) investigated the Umbelliferae of the northwest, especially of Washington; Rydberg (1900–32) studied the family in the preparation of his floras of the Rocky Mountains and prairies; Small (1903, 1933) prepared treatments of the family for his floras of the southeastern United States. However no one attempted to study the entire family and the Coulter & Rose monograph remained the standard reference.

In the southern half of the hemisphere there had been little progress in the study of the Umbelliferae. In addition to the noteworthy revision by Urban (1879) for *Flora brasiliensis* there were treatments of the family by Weddell (1860) in *Chloris Andina*, by Clos (1847) in Gay's *Flora chilena* and Reiche (1902a) in *Flora de Chile*. Hooker (1830) had discussed the Umbelliferae collected by Gillies; Wolff (1908a) had studied the Weberbauer collections from Peru; Johnston (1929) and Macbride (1930, 1931, 1934a, b) had described taxa from Peru and Chile; and Pérez-Moreau (1933, 1935, 1936, 1937, 1938, 1940) had published on Umbelliferae, primarily from Argentina.

Beginning in 1928 Mathias and later Constance initiated studies of the North

American Umbelliferae, reducing many of the segregate genera and re-evaluating the relationships of the species. As a result only 92 genera, including introductions, were recognized in their 1944–1945 revision for the North American Flora and the species total for North America, north of Panama and including the West Indies and Bahamas, was now 509. This represented a reduction in both species and genera from the 1900 total. Many species originally described from single or few collections were found to be variant and the appropriate reductions were made. While the importance of fruit characters was recognized, Mathias and Constance also described floral and vegetative characters and pointed out their usefulness in the taxonomy. The genera were arranged in essentially the order of Drude except to place *Eryngium* at the end of the family, removing it from its relatives in the Saniculoideae. This somewhat arbitrary placement has long since been abandoned and *Eryngium* returned to the Saniculoideae in subsequent publications.

Mathias, Constance, and their students have continued investigations of North American genera. As a result a number of changes has been made in the taxonomy since the publication of the revision in 1944–1945. Six species have been reduced to synonymy but 24 new species have been described by Mathias, Constance and others and two genera added to the flora, one of them a range extension northward from the Andes (*Niphogeton;* Mathias & Constance, 1962a), the other a new genus for the family (*Mathiasella* Constance & Hitchcock, 1954).

A number of problem genera has been re-examined and the taxonomies revised as a result of extensive field studies, chromosome counts, and detailed examination of general morphology and anatomy. Bell's (1954) investigation of the *Sanicula crassicaulis* complex is an example of the kind of study needed to give us a better understanding of the nature of variability in problem groups. This study of a polymorphic polyploid group demonstrated that 'variation ascribable to polyploidy *per se* is of no taxonomic value in the *S. crassicaulis* complex' (p. 205). Theobald's (1966) work on a closely related group of taxa in the large genus *Lomatium* provided a new taxonomy as a result of extensive studies of field populations and general morphology. The recent study of the genus *Perideridia* by Chuang & Constance (1969) includes a revision of the taxonomy based on extensive field studies, detailed morphological and anatomical investigations of vegetative and reproductive parts of the plants including pollen grain morphology, and chromosome counts. This genus has been particularly difficult because of the several sympatric species with wide morphological variability as well as the discrepancy between morphological variation and chromosome number. In the genus uniquely the polyploid taxa 'are mostly quite distinct and readily definable, while the diploid populations show essentially continuous variation' (p. 21). Rodríguez's (1957a) masterly study of the woody Umbellales has been of particular value in interpreting phylogenetic relationships within the family.

With the publication of the revision of the Umbelliferae for North America, Mathias and Constance extended their revisionary studies to South America. Mathias (1936) had previously published a revision of the genus *Hydrocotyle* in northern South America and Constance (1949) had prepared a revision of *Arracacia*. Their interest in South American Umbelliferae was a natural extension since many

North American genera were represented in the southern flora and the genera had to be studied in their entirety in order to arrive at a satisfactory taxonomy.

Three major distribution patterns connected the South American taxa with those of North America: (1) widespread genera such as *Eryngium* and *Hydrocotyle* were well represented in both continents; (2) genera such as *Arracacia*, *Oreomyrrhis* and *Niphogeton* ranged from the mountains of Mexico and Central America to the Andes and southward; and (3) there were north–south disjunct distributions such as shown in *Sanicula* and *Osmorhiza*. Consequently among the first genera studied were those with particularly interesting distribution patterns. The Constance & Shan (1948) publication on the genus *Osmorhiza* initiated the series with a taxonomy of the entire genus, including the one Asiatic species, and identifying the north–south disjunctions which occur in *O. mexicana*, *O. chilensis*, and *O. obtusa* (= *O. depauperata*). Constance and Shan postulated migration routes to explain the present distribution of the genus. Shan & Constance (1951) published a similar study of *Sanicula*, a genus well represented in the western hemisphere but subcosmopolitan with species in Eurasia and Africa. *Sanicula liberta* extends from Mexico to Bolivia and *S. crassicaulis* and *S. graveolens* show the north–south disjunct pattern between California and Chile. A third publication with particular distributional interest was that by Mathias & Constance (1955*a*) on *Oreomyrrhis*, an apioid genus widespread in the southern hemisphere and centred on the Pacific basin with one species relatively common in the high Andes of South America and three outlying local endemics in the high mountains of Mexico and Guatemala.

In connection with the preparation of a series of floristic treatments of the Umbelliferae for local South American Floras, namely *Flora of Peru* (Mathias & Constance, 1962*c*), *Flora of Venezuela* (Mathias & Constance, in press), *Flora Patagonia* (Mathias & Constance, in press), *Flora of Ecuador* (in preparation), and *Flora Ilustrada Catarinense* (in press), Mathias and Constance have completed taxonomic revisions of a number of unique southern hemisphere genera such as *Bowlesia* and *Homalocarpus* (Mathias & Constance, 1965), *Asteriscium*, *Pozoa*, *Eremocharis*, *Domeykoa*, and *Gymnophyton* (Mathias & Constance, 1962*b*), *Huanaca* (Mathias & Constance, in press) and *Niphogeton* (Mathias & Constance, 1951*d*, 1962*a*). They are extending their knowledge of such difficult genera as *Eryngium*, *Mulinum* and *Azorella*. Both Mathias and Constance have conducted field studies and made collections in South America during the past twenty years and have encouraged co-operation of their Latin American colleagues. As a result of increased field work and revisions three new genera have been recognized in the South American Umbelliferae and many new species described. However, our knowledge of the South American Umbelliferae is still uneven and no monographic studies have been completed. Mathias and students (Tseng, 1967) have made some preliminary investigations of generic relationships in the primarily southern hemisphere Hydrocotyloideae with studies of pollen morphology and fruit anatomy.

It may be seen from this brief review of the taxonomy of the Umbelliferae in the western hemisphere that our knowledge of this family is still in the alpha state. For the southern half of the hemisphere there is as yet no comprehensive treatment of the family even at the generic level. For the somewhat better known northern half much of the taxonomy is based primarily on herbarium material. Extensive field studies as well as experimental investigations are needed, including investigations of breeding structure and population variability. Chromosome numbers have been determined for less than half the taxa and often for only a single collection of a taxon (Bell & Constance, 1957, 1960, 1966). Pollen morphology has been studied for only a few species (Cerceau-Larrival, 1968a,b; Ting, 1961; Ting, Tseng, & Mathias, 1964). Chemotaxonomic investigations have been minimal (Fairbrothers & Boulette, 1960; Pickering, 1969; Pickering & Fairbrothers, 1970).

There is in addition to taxonomic studies a need for more information on distribution patterns. The family is cosmopolitan in its distribution, although in tropical latitudes, it is, except for certain weedy species, largely confined to temperate elevations. The three subfamilies show characteristic distributions, the largest, the Apioideae, being bipolar with major development in the northern hemisphere (Mathias, 1965). A number of North American species in this subfamily belong to genera well represented in the Eurasian flora and it is possible that additional investigations may lead to subspecific status for some North American taxa in such genera as *Chaerophyllum*, *Ligusticum*, *Heracleum*, and *Angelica*. Attention should be paid to *Bifora*, with two Mediterranean species and one in Texas, and *Bupleurum*, another large Mediterranean genus with one species in the northern Rocky Mountains. Mathias has pointed out patterns of radiation from the Mexican highlands, as in *Prionosciadium*, *Tauschia* and *Arracacia*, and an apparent centre of speciation and high endemism in western North America. Both of these patterns are secondary and doubtless represent speciation in response to changes in the environment since the beginning of the Tertiary. There has been restriction of distributions as well as expansion and this restriction is exemplified by the several local endemic species of *Tauschia* in the western United States, *Podistera*, and a number of local endemic species of *Cymopterus*.

The subfamily Saniculoideae is likewise bipolar but proportionately better represented in the southern hemisphere than the Apioideae. The subfamily Hydrocotyloideae is primarily a southern hemisphere group.

With respect to the occurrence of the family and subfamilies in the western hemisphere it is evident that the number of species is about what one might predict for a subcosmopolitan plant family with a long history of differentiation. Of the estimated 2500 species in the family a little less than one-third are native to the western hemisphere, a figure approximating the proportional land mass. However, the distribution of the subfamilies is somewhat different, certainly reflecting a long history of independent evolution. Only about 20% of the Apioideae are native to the western hemisphere while 60% of the Hydrocotyloideae occur in that hemisphere with almost 90% of these in South America where the subfamily is a prominent and interesting part of the south temperate flora. Fifty per cent of the subfamily Saniculoideae are in the western hemisphere, a figure resulting primarily from the many species of the genus *Eryngium*.

What is needed is a systematic revision of generic groups on a world-wide basis, rather than the piece-meal treatment of individual genera or of arbitrarily delimited geographical or political areas. Investigations are needed to determine, if possible, the phylogenetic relationships within such widely distributed genera as *Eryngium*, *Hydrocotyle* and *Ligusticum*. A distributional study based on poorly known taxonomy is of little value. Studies on pollen morphology, inflorescence structure, floral and fruit anatomy, cytogenetics, biochemistry, etc. will give additional data for evaluating generic relationships within the family and arriving at a better taxonomy. The sections proposed by Drude should be re-evaluated on the basis of our greatly expanded knowledge of the family, particularly in the western hemisphere. Hopefully the interest displayed in this symposium is the beginning of a new era.

As a postscript a recent contribution for the western hemisphere should be mentioned, the conclusion of Thorne (1968) that the Umbelliferae should not be given independent family status. His system proposes the Araliaceae with four subfamilies, Aralioideae, Hydrocotyloideae, Saniculoideae and Apioideae. Perhaps this symposium has been mistitled.

REFERENCES AND BIBLIOGRAPHY

Rickett in 1945 (*North American Flora* 28B: 317–374) included the Umbelliferae in his bibliography for the North American Flora. The following bibliography contains some publications cited by Rickett which are referred to specifically in the text of this paper. However, it has been prepared in an attempt to cover the taxonomic literature on North American Umbelliferae published since 1945 as well as the taxonomic publications on the Umbelliferae of South America.

ALBOFF, N., 1896. Umbelliferae. In Contributions à la Flore de la Terre de Feu. II. Enumération des plantes du canal de Beagle. *Revta Mus. La Plata*, **7**: 371–372.
ALLARD, H. A., 1944. The status of *Oxypolis rigidior* var. *ambigua* (Nutt.) Robinson. *Castanea*, **9**: 109–110.
ANDERSON, J. P., 1942. Papers on the Flora of Alaska. I. The genus Cicuta. *Torreya*, **42**: 176–178.
ARECHAVALETA, J., 1902–1905. *Flora Uruguaya* (*An. Mus. Hist. Nat. Montevideo*, **5**: 302–364.)
ASTRADA, I., 1915. Contribución al estudio de los *Mulinum spinosum* Pers. y *Mulinum ulicinum* Gill., pp. 1–18.
BAILLON, H. E., 1879. Ombellifères. In *Histoire des plantes*, **7**: 84–256.
BALL, J., 1885. Contributions to the flora of the Peruvian Andes, with remarks on the history and origin of the Andean flora. *J. Linn. Soc., Bot.*, **22**: 1–64.
BAUMANN, M. G., 1946. Myodocarpus und die Phylogenie der Umbelliferen-Frucht. *Mitt. bot. Mus. Univ. Zürich*, **177**: 13–112.
BEAMAN, J. H., DE JONG, D. C. D. & STOUTAMIRE, W. P., 1962. Chromosome studies in the alpine and subalpine floras of Mexico and Guatemala. *Am. J. Bot.*, **49**: 41–50.
BELL, C. R., 1954. The *Sanicula crassicaulis* complex (Umbelliferae). *Univ. Calif. Publs. Bot.*, **27**: 133–230.
BELL, C. R., 1957. *Hydrocotyle americana* L. in South Carolina. *J. Elisha Mitchell Sci. Soc.*, **73**: 446–447.
BELL, C. R., 1960. Chromosome numbers in *Eryngium* species of the southern United States. *ASB Bull.* **7**: 22.
BELL, C. R., 1964a. Cytomixis in *Tauschia nudicaulis* Schlecht. *Cytologia*, **29**: 396–398.
BELL, C. R., 1964b. Incidence of polyploidy correlated with ecological gradients. *Evolution*, **18**: 510–511.
BELL, C. R. & CONSTANCE, L., 1957. Chromosome numbers in the Umbelliferae. *Am. J. Bot.*, **40**: 565–572.
BELL, C. R. & CONSTANCE, L., 1960. Chromosome numbers in the Umbelliferae. II. *Am. J. Bot.*, **47**: 24–32.
BELL, C. R. & CONSTANCE, L., 1966. Chromosome numbers in Umbelliferae. III. *Am. J. Bot.*, **53**: 512–520.
BENTHAM, G., 1839–1857. *Plantae Hartwegianae*, pp. 1–393.
BENTHAM, G., 1867. Umbelliferae. In Bentham, G. & Hooker, J. D. *Genera Plantarum*, **1**: 859–931.
BERLIOZ, J., 1917. Contribution à l'ètude anatomique du fruit des Ombellifères (tribu des Hydrocotylées et des Saniculées), pp. 1–98.

BRITTON, N. L., 1891. Umbelliferae. In An enumeration of the plants collected by Dr H. H. Rusby in South America, 1885–1886. *Bull. Torrey Bot. Club*, **18**: 35–38.

BUSH, B. F., 1902. The North American species of *Chaerophyllum. Trans. Acad. Sci. St. Louis*, **12**: 57–63.

CABRERA, A. L. & DAWSON, G., 1942–44. Umbelíferae in La Selva Marginal de Punta Lara. *Revta Mus. La Plata, Secc. Bot.*, **5**: 348–350.

CALL, T. G. & FISCHER, E. B., 1957. A note on the volatile oil from the roots of *Pteryxia terebinthina* (Hook.) Coult. & Rose var. *terebinthina. J. Am. pharm. Ass. Sci. Ed.*, **46**: 704.

CALL, T. G. & FISCHER, E. B., 1958. Some pharmacological effects of the roots of *Pteryxia terebinthina* (Hook.) Coult. & Rose var. *terebinthina*, and of pteryxin, a substance isolated from the roots. *Northwest Sci.*, **32**: 96–100.

CALL, T. G. & FISCHER, E. B., 1961. Extractive studies of the roots of *Pteryxia terebinthina* var. *terebinthina* and the isolation of pteryxin. *Econ. Bot.*, **15**: 104–106.

CALL, T. G. & GREEN, J., 1956. Spasmolytics from plants. I. Suksdorfin A and Columbianin. *Proc. Montana Acad. Sci.*, **16**: 49–51.

CAVANILLES, A. J., 1791–1801. *Icones et descriptiones plantarum.* 6 vols.

CAVANILLES, A. J., 1800. Umbelliferae in Descripción de algunas plantas nuevas. *An. Hist. Nat.*, **2**: 115–119.

CERCEAU-LARRIVAL, M.-TH., 1962. Plantules et pollens d'Ombellifères leur intérêt systématique et phylogénique. *Mém. Mus. natn. Hist. nat., Sér. B., Bot.*, **4**: 1–166.

CERCEAU-LARRIVAL, M.-TH., 1964. Mise au point taxonomique concernant *Cyclospermum leptophyllum* (Persoon) Sprague. *Bull. Soc. bot. Fr.*, **111**: 93–96.

CERCEAU-LARRIVAL, M.-TH., 1965. Involucre et involucelle chez les Ombellifères. *Bull. Soc. bot. Fr.*, **112**: 255–267.

CERCEAU-LARRIVAL, M.-TH., 1968a. Contribution palynologique à l'étude du genre andine *Niphogeton* Schl. In *Biologie de l'Amérique Australe*, pp. 113–129.

CERCEAU-LARRIVAL, M.-TH., 1968b. Contribution palynologique à l'étude d'*Azorella* Lam. (genre presque exclusivement austral). In *Biologie de l'Amérique Australe*, pp. 131–160.

CHAMISSO, A. DE, 1833. Spicilegium plantarum e familiis jam prius recensitis praesertim Brasiliensium serius a Sellowio missarum. *Linnaea*, **8**: 323–332.

CHAMISSO, A. DE & SCHLECHTENDAL, D. F. L., 1826. De plantis in expeditione speculatoria Romanzoffiana observatis. *Linnaea*, **1**: 333 ('233')–401.

CHODAT, R., 1899. Umbelliferae. In Plantae Hasslerianae. *Bull. Herb. Boissier*, **7**, App. 1: 76–77.

CHODAT, R., 1920. Ombellifères in Chodat, R. (& Vischer, W.), La Vegetation du Paraguay. *Bull. Soc. bot. Genève*, II, **12**: 25–54.

CHODAT, R. & WILCZEK, E., 1902. Ombellifères. In Contributions à la flore de la République Argentine. *Bull. Herb. Boissier*, II, **2**: 525–528.

CHUANG, T.-I., 1970. A systematic anatomical study of the genus *Perideridia* (Umbelliferae-Apioideae). *Am. J. Bot.*, **57**: 495–503.

CHUANG, T.-I. & CONSTANCE, L., 1969. A systematic study of *Perideridia* (Umbelliferae-Apioideae). *Univ. Calif. Publs Bot.*, **55**: 1–74.

CLOS, D., 1847. Umbelíferas. In C. Gay, *Flora chilena*, **3**: 61–145.

COLLA, A., 1834. Umbelliferae in Plantae rariores in regionibus chilensibus a clarissimo M. D. Bertero nuper detectae. *Mem. Accad. Sci. (Torino)*, **37**: 80–85.

CONSTANCE, L., 1949. The South American species of *Arracacia* (Umbelliferae) and some related genera. *Bull. Torrey Bot. Club*, **76**: 30–52.

CONSTANCE, L., 1962. Umbelliferae. In Gould, F. W., *Texas plants, a checklist and ecological summary*, pp. 66–68.

CONSTANCE, L., 1965. Some subtractions from the Umbelliferae in South America. *Ann. Mo. Bot. Gdn.*, **52**: 274–280.

CONSTANCE, L., 1969. Umbelliferae. In Gould, F. W., *Texas plants, a checklist and ecological summary*. Rev. ed., pp. 68–70.

CONSTANCE, L., in press. Patterns in the distribution of Japanese-American Umbelliferae.

CONSTANCE, L. & HITCHCOCK, C. L., 1954. *Mathiasella*, a new genus of North American Umbelliferae. *Am. J. Bot.*, **41**: 56–58.

CONSTANCE, L. & SHAN, R. H., 1948. The genus *Osmorhiza* (Umbelliferae). *Univ. Calif. Publs Bot.*, **23**: 111–156.

CORE, E. L., 1952. Ranges of some plants of the Appalachian shale barrens. *Castanea*, **17**: 105–116.

CORNUTI, J. P., 1635. *Canadensium Plantarum Historia*, p. 196, *t. 197*, p. 198, *t. 199*.

COULTER, J. M. & ROSE, J. N., 1888. *Revision of North American Umbelliferae*, pp. 1–144.

COULTER, J. M. & ROSE, J. N., 1900a. A synopsis of Mexican and Central American Umbelliferae. *Proc. Wash. Acad. Sci.*, **1**: 111–159.

COULTER, J. M. & ROSE, J. N., 1900b. Monograph of the North American Umbelliferae. *Contr. U.S. natn. Herb.*, **7**: 1–256.

COVAS, G. & SCHNACK, B., 1946. Número de cromosomas en antofitas de la región de Cuyo (República Argentina). *Rev. Agr. Agron.*, **13**: 153–166.

Cox, G. E., 1863. Viaje a las regiones septentrionales de la Patagonia, 1862–1863. *An. Univ. Chile*, **23**: 1–103, 151–238, 437–509.

Crawford, D. J., 1970. The Umbelliferae of Iowa. *Stud. Nat. Hist. Iowa Univ.*, **21** (4): 1–37.

Cronquist, A., 1961. Umbelliferae. In Hitchcock, C. L. *et al.*, *Vascular Plants of the Pacific Northwest*, **3**: 506–586.

Decaisne, J., 1853. Description des plantes vasculaires. In Dumont d'Urville, J. S. C., *Voyage au Pôle sud et dans l'Océanie sur les corvettes l'Astrolabe et la Zelée. Botanique.*

Decaisne, J., 1873. Remarques sur les espèces du genre *Eryngium*, a feuilles parallélinerves. *Bull. Soc. bot. Fr.*, **20**: 19–28.

de Candolle, A. P., 1829a. Mémoire sur la famille des ombellifères. *Coll. Mém.*, **5**: 1–84.

de Candolle, A. P., 1829b. Notice sur l'Arracacha et quelques autres racines légumières de la famille des ombellifères. *Biblioth. Universelle Sci., Sci. Arts*, **40**: 74–82.

de Candolle, A. P., 1830. Umbelliferae. In *Prodromus Systematis Naturalis Regni Vegetabilis*, **4**: 55–250.

de Jussieu, A. L., 1789. Umbelliferae. In *Genera plantarum*, pp. 218–227.

Delaroche, F., 1808. *Eryngiorum nec non generis novi Alepideae historia*, pp. 1–70.

Domin, K., 1907. Zwei neue *Azorella*-arten aus Südamerika. *Repert. Spec. Nov. Regni Veg.*, **4**: 296–298.

Domin, K., 1908a. Ueber eine neue austral-antarktische Umbelliferengattung. *Bot. Jahrb. Syst.*, **40**: 573–585.

Domin, K., 1908b. Monographische Uebersicht der Gattung *Centella* L. *Bot. Jahrb. Syst.*, **41**: 148–169.

Domin, K., 1908–1909. Morphologische und phylogenetische Studien über die Familie der Umbelliferen. *Bull. Internat. Acad. Sci. Bohême (Česká Akad.)*, **13**: 108–153; **14**: 1–59 (reprint, pp. 1–109).

Drude, C. G. O., 1898. Umbelliferae. In Engler, A. & Prantl, K., *Die natürlichen Pflanzenfamilien*, **3** (8): 63–250.

Dumont d'Urville, J. S. C., 1825–1826. Flore des Îles Malouines. *Mém. Soc. Linn. Paris*, **4**: 572–621 (pp. 1–56 as a separate).

Dusén, P., 1905a. Umbelliferae. In Beiträge zur Flora von Ostpatagonien. *Svensk. Exped. Magell.*, **3**: 254.

Dusén, P., 1905b. Die Pflanzenvereine der Magellansländer nebst einem Beiträge zur Okologie der Magellanischen Vegetation. *Svensk. Exped. Magell.*, **3**: 485–486.

Dusén, P., 1908. Neue und seltene Gefässpflanzen aus Ost-und Südpatagonien. *Ark. Bot.*, **7**: 1–62.

Dusén, P., 1911. Ein neues eigentümliches Eryngium. *Ark. Bot.*, **10**: 1–5.

Easterly, N. W., 1957. A morphological study of *Ptilimnium*. *Brittonia*, **9**: 136–145.

Eliasson, U., 1970. Studies in Galapagos Plants IX. *Bot. Not.*, **123**: 346–357.

Endlicher, S. L., 1839. Umbelliferae. In *Genera plantarum*, pp. 762–793.

Espinosa, R., 1933. Umbelliferae in Oekologische Studien über Kordillerenpflanzen. *Bot. Jahrb. Syst.*, **65**: 148–153.

Fairbrothers, D. E. & Boulette, R., 1960. Some phytoserological relationships within the Umbelliferae. *A.I.B.S. Bull.*, **10**: 45.

Fassett, N. C., 1941. Wisconsin plant ranges. No. 1. Umbelliferae, pp. 1–10 (Mimeographed).

Fernald, M. L., 1924. *Polystichum mohrioides* and some other subantarctic or Andean plants in the northern hemisphere. *Contr. Gray Herb.*, **72**: 89–95.

Fernald, M. L., 1950. Umbelliferae. In Gray's *Manual of Botany*. 8th edition, pp. 1078–1105.

Fielding, H. B. & Gardner, G., 1844. *Sertum Plantarum*. 75 pl.

Foster, R. C., 1958. A catalogue of the ferns and flowering plants of Bolivia. *Contr. Gray Herb.*, **184**: 1–223.

Franchet, A., 1889. Umbelliferae. In Phanerogamie, in Hariot, P. *et al.*, *Mission scientifique du Cap Horn (1882–83)*, **5**: 337–339.

Froebe, H. A., 1964. Die Blütenstände der saniculoideen (Umbelliferae). *Beitr. Biol. Pflanzen*, **40**: 325–388.

Gaertner, J., 1788. Umbelliferae. In *De fructibus et seminibus plantarum*, **1**: 77–109.

Gandoger, M. 1912. Manipulus plantarum novarum praecipue Americae australioris. *Bull. Soc. bot. Fr.*, **59**: 704–710.

Gandoger, M., 1918. Sertum plantarum novarum. Pars prima. *Bull. Soc. bot. Fr.*, **65**: 24–69.

Gandoger, M., 1925. La flore des îles Kerguelen. *Bull. Soc. bot. Fr.*, **72**: 177–180.

Gardé, A. & Malheiros-Gardé, N., 1949. Contribuçao para o estudo cariológico da familia Umbelliferae. I. *Agron. Lusit.*, **11**: 91–140.

Gardé, A. & Malheiros-Gardé, N., 1954. Contribution to the karyological study of the family Umbelliferae. III. *Broteria*, **23**: 5–35.

Gaudichaud, C., 1826. In Freycinet, L. de, *Voyage autour du monde ... sur les corvettes de S. M. l'Oranie et la Physicienne pendant les années 1817, 1818, 1819 et 1820.*, **5**: 135–136.

Gay, J., 1848. Eryngiorum novarum vel minus cognitorum heptas. *Ann. Sci. Nat. Bot.*, III, **9**: 148–184.

Goebel, K., 1891. Die Vegetation der venezolanischen Paramos. *Pflanzenbiologische Schilderungen*, **2** (1): 3–50.

GOROVOY, P. G., 1966. *Eontichnya (sem. Umbelliferae Moris.) primorya i priamurya*, pp. 1–294. [In Russian.]

GRAY, A., 1854. Phanerogamia in Botany of the Wilkes Expedition in *U.S. expl. Exped.*, **15** (1): 692–713.

GRISEBACH, A., 1854. Systematische Bemerkungen über die beiden ersten Pflanzensammlungen Philippi's und Lechler's im südlichen Chile und an der Magellaens-Strasse, pp. 1–50. (*Abh. Königl. Ges. Wiss. Göttingen*, **6**: 89–138, 1856.)

GRISEBACH, A., 1874. Umbelliferae. In Plantae Lorentzianae. *Abh. Königl. Ges. Wiss. Göttingen*, **19**: 153–156.

GRISEBACH, A., 1879. Umbelliferae in *Symbolae ad floram Argentinam*, pp. 144–148.

HÅKANSSON, A., 1927. Der sechzehnkernige Embryosack von *Azorella trifurcata* (Gaertn.) Hook. *Ber. dtsch. Bot. Ges.*, **45**: 654–664.

HÅKANSSON, A., 1952. Seed development in *Bowlesia tenera*. *Bot. Not.*, **1952**: 33–45.

HÅKANSSON, A., 1953. Some chromosome numbers in Umbelliferae. *Bot. Not.*, **1953**: 301–307.

HAUMAN, L., 1919. Notes sur les espèces argentines des genres *Azorella* et *Bolax*. *Physis (Buenos Aires)*, **4**: 468–500.

HEDWIG, R. A., 1806. Umbelliferae. In *Genera plantarum*, pp. 190–204.

HEMSLEY, W. B., 1880–1881. Umbelliferae. In Godman, F. D. & Salvin, O., *Biologia Centrali-americana. Botany*, **1**: 557–571.

HICKEN, C. M., 1909. Una nueva especie de *Eryngium*. *Apuntes Hist. Nat.*, **1** (4): 52–53.

HICKEN, C. M., 1923. Umbelliferae. In Sertularium andinum. *Darwiniana*, **1**: 61–62.

HIERONYMUS, G., 1879. Umbelliferae in Sertum patagonicum. *Bol. Acad. Nac. Ci.*, **3**: 350–351, 384.

HIERONYMUS, G., 1895. Plantae Lehmannianae. *Bot. Jahrb. Syst.*, **20**. Beibl. **49**: 1–72.

HILL, A. W., 1904. Some high Andine and Antarctic Umbelliferae. *Proc. Camb. Phil. Soc.*, **12** (5): 362.

HILL, A. W., 1927. The genus Lilaeopsis: a study in geographical distribution. *J. Linn. Soc., Bot.*, **47**: 525–551.

HIROE, M., 1962. Supplementary notes on the genus *Glehnia* (Umbelliferae). *Acta Phytotax. Geobot.*, **19**: 39–44.

HIROE, M. & CONSTANCE, L., 1958. Umbelliferae of Japan. *Univ. Calif. Publs Bot.*, **30**: 1–144.

HODGE, W. H., 1954. The edible Arracacha—a little-known root crop of the Andes. *Econ. Bot.*, **8**: 195–221.

HODGE, W. H., 1960. Yareta—fuel Umbellifer of the Andean puna. *Econ. Bot.*, **14**: 112–118.

HOFFMANN, G. F., 1814a. *Syllabus plantarum umbelliferarum*, pp. 1–20.

HOFFMANN, G. F., 1814b. *Genera plantarum umbelliferarum*, pp. 1–182.

HOFFMANN, G. F., 1816. *Plantarum Umbelliferarum genera.* 2nd ed., pp. 1–222.

HOOKER, J. D., 1847. *Flora antarctica.* The botany of the antarctic voyage, **2**: 209–395.

HOOKER, W. J., 1830. On the plants of the natural order Umbelliferae. *Bot. Misc.*, **1**: 323–335.

HOOKER, W. J., 1840a. Umbelliferae in *Flora boreali-americana*, **1**: 257–272.

HOOKER, W. J., 1840b. *Eryngium humile* var. *caulescens. Hooker's Icon. Pl.*, **3**: *pl. 216.*

HOOKER, W. J., 1842. *Bolax glebaria* Comm. *Hooker's Icon. Pl.*, **5**: *pl. 492.*

HOOKER, W. J., 1843a. *Azorella filamentosa* Lam. *Hooker's Icon. Pl.*, **6**: *pl. 541.*

HOOKER, W. J., 1843b. *Azorella trifurcata* (Gaertn.) *Hooker's Icon. Pl.* **6**: *pl. 539.*

HOOKER, W. J., 1852. *Pozopsis* and *P. cordifolia. Hooker's Icon Pl.*, **9**: *pl. 859.*

HOOKER, W. J., 1856. Balsam-bog (*Bolax glebaria* Com.) *J. Bot. (Hooker)*, **8**: 74–80.

HOOKER, W. J. & Arnott, G. A. W., 1833. Contributions towards a flora of South America and the islands of the Pacific. *Bot. Misc.*, **3**: 129–212, 302–367.

HOOKER, W. J. & ARNOTT, G. A. W., 1830–1841. *The botany of Captain Beechey's Voyage*, pp. 1–485.

HOWELL, J. T., 1962. Five days to Reno: a botanical motorlogue. *Leafl. W. Bot.*, **9**: 233–242.

JACKSON, G., 1933. A study of the carpophore of the Umbelliferae. *Am. J. Bot.*, **20**: 121–144.

JEPSON, W. L., 1893a. Studies in the Californian Umbelliferae. I. *Erythea*, **1**: 8–10.

JEPSON, W. L., 1893b. Studies in Californian Umbelliferae. II. *Erythea*, **1**: 62–63.

JEPSON, W. L., 1923–1929. A revision of Californian Umbelliferae. *Madroño*, **1**: 101a–114; 117–130; 133–146; 149–162; 281–285.

JOHNSTON, I. M., 1929. I. Papers on the flora of northern Chile. II. Some undescribed species from Peru. *Contr. Gray Herb.*, **85**: 1–180.

JOHNSTON, I. M., 1938. Some undescribed species from Mexico and Guatemala. *J. Arnold Arbor.*, **19**: 117–128.

JOHOW, F., 1896. Umbelliferae. In *Estudios sobre la flora de las islas de Juan Fernández*, pp. 100–103.

JONES, M. E., 1883. New plants from California and Nevada, etc. II. *Am. Naturalist*, **17**: 973–974.

JONES, M. E., 1891a. New plants from Arizona, Utah and Nevada. *Zoe*, **2**: 12–17.

JONES, M. E., 1891b. New species and notes of Utah plants. *Zoe*, **2**: 236–252.

JONES, M. E., 1893a. Contributions to western botany. No. 3. *Zoe*, **3**: 283–309.

JONES, M. E., 1893b. Contributions to western botany. No. 4. *Zoe*, **4**: 22–54.

JONES, M. E., 1893c. Contributions to western botany. No. 5. *Zoe*, **4**: 254–282.

JONES, M. E., 1895. Contributions to western botany. No. VII. *Proc. Calif. Acad. Sci.* II. **5**: 611–733.

JONES, M. E., 1898. *Contr. W. Bot.*, **8**: 1–43.

JONES, M. E., 1902. *Contr. W. Bot.*, **10**: 1–90.

JONES, M. E., 1903. *Contr. W. Bot.*, **11**: 1–22.

JONES, M. E., 1908. *Contr. W. Bot.*, **12**: 1–100.

JONES, M. E., 1910a. Montana botany notes. *Bull. Montana State Univ., Biol. Ser.*, **15**: 1–75.

JONES, M. E., 1910b. *Contr. W. Bot.*, **13**: 1–87.

JONES, M. E., 1912. *Contr. W. Bot.*, **14**: 1–52.

JONES, M. E., 1929. *Contr. W. Bot.*, **15**: 1–163.

JONES, M. E., 1930a. *Contr. W. Bot.*, **16**: 1–53.

JONES, M. E., 1930b. *Contr. W. Bot.*, **17**: 1–31.

JONES, M. E., 1933. *Contr. W. Bot.*, **18**: 1–85.

JONES, M. E., 1935. *Contr. W. Bot.*, **18**: 86–157.

KNUTH, R., 1927. Umbelliferae in Initia Florae venezuelensis. *Repert. Spec. Nov. Regni Veg.*, Beih., **43**: 545–547.

KOSO-POLJANSKY, B. M., 1916. Sciadophytorum systematis lineamenta. *Bull. Soc. Imp. Nat. Moscou*, n.s., **29**: 93–222.

KOSO-POLJANSKY, B. M., 1917. Sciadophytorum systematis lineamenta. Mantissa prior. *Bull. Soc. Imp. Nat. Moscou*, n.s., **30**: 277–290.

KOSO-POLJANSKY, B. M., 1924. Hydrocotyloidearum revisio, I. *Not. Syst. Horti Petropol.*, V, **2**: 1–8.

KUNTH, C. S., 1821. Umbelliferae in Humboldt, F. H. A. von, Bonpland, A. J. A. & Kunth, C. S. *Nova Genera et species plantarum*, **5**: 12–35.

KUNTZE, O., 1891–1893. Umbelliferae. In *Rev. Gen. Plant.*, **1**: 264–270; **3**: 110–115.

KURTZ, F., 1893. Dos viajes botánicos al Río Salado superior. *Bol. Acad. Nac. Ci.*, **13**: 171–210.

LA GASCA, M., 1816. Umbelliferae in *Genera et species plantarum*, pp. 12–13.

LA GASCA, M., 1821a. Dispositio umbelliferarum carpologica. *Amenidades naturales de la Españas*, **1** (2): 87–111.

LA GASCA, M., 1821b. Prologo: a la disertación sobre la familia natural de las plantas Aparasoladas de su discípulo S. E. Vela. *Amenidades naturales de las Españas*, **1** (2): 47–60.

LA GASCA, M., 1826. *Observaciones sobre la familia natural de las plantas Aparasoladas*, pp. 1–43.

LAMARCK, J. B. DE, 1783–1817. *Encyclopédie méthodique. Botanique.* 13 vols.

LAMARCK, J. B. DE, 1791–1823. *Tableau encyclopédique et méthodique.* 6 vols.

LARRAÑAGA, D. A., 1923. *Escritos Larrañaga*, **2**: 108–117.

LATHROP, E., 1952. A key to the flowering plant genus Lomatium (Family Umbelliferae) of the Walla Walla Valley and adjoining regions. *Walla Walla Coll. Publ. Dept. Biol. Sci.*, **2**: 13–22.

LINNAEUS, C., 1753. Umbelliferae. In *Species plantarum*, **1**: 232–265.

LORENTZ, P. G. & NIEDERLEIN, G., 1881. Umbelliferae. In *Expedición al Río Negro. II. Botánica*, pp. 221–224.

MACBRIDE, J. F., 1918a. New or otherwise interesting plants, mostly North American Liliaceae and Chenopodiaceae. *Contr. Gray Herb.*, **53**: 1–22.

MACBRIDE, J. F., 1918b. Certain North American Umbelliferae. *Contr. Gray Herb.*, **56**: 28–35.

MACBRIDE, J. F., 1918c. Various American spermatophytes, new or transferred. *Contr. Gray Herb.*, **56**: 32–61.

MACBRIDE, J. F., 1919. Reclassified or new spermatophytes, chiefly North American. *Contr. Gray Herb.*, **59**: 28–39.

MACBRIDE, J. F., 1930. Spermatophytes, mostly Peruvian. II. *Field Mus. nat. Hist., Bot. Ser.*, **8**: 75–130.

MACBRIDE, J. F., 1931. Spermatophytes, mostly Peruvian. III. *Field Mus. nat. Hist., Bot. Ser.*, **11**: 1–35.

MACBRIDE, J. F., 1934a. New or renamed spermatophytes mostly Peruvian. *Candollea*, **5**: 346–402.

MACBRIDE, J. F., 1934b. New or renamed spermatophytes mostly Peruvian II. *Candollea*, **6**: 1–19.

MACLOSKIE, G., 1896–1899. Umbelliferae. In *Reports Princeton Exped. Patagonia*, **8** (2): 619–643.

MALHEIROS-GARDÉ, N. & GARDÉ, A., 1951. Contribuçao para o estudo cariológica da familia *Umbelliferae*. II. *Genét. Ibér.* **3**: 23–36.

MALME, G. O. A., 1904. Die Umbelliferen der zweiten Regnell'schen Reise. *Ark. Bot.*, **3** (13): 1–22.

MANGANARO, A., 1916. Breves notas sobre diantromorfismo y discarpomorfismo. *Physis (Buenos Aires)*, **2**: 244–245.

MARGGRAF, G., 1648. Historiae Rerum Naturalium Brasilieae. 27. In Piso, G., *Historia Naturalis Brasiliae.*

MATHIAS, M. E., 1928. Studies in the Umbelliferae. I. *Ann. Missouri Bot. Gard.*, **15**: 91–108.

MATHIAS, M. E., 1936. The genus *Hydrocotyle* in northern South America. *Brittonia*, **2**: 201–237.

MATHIAS, M. E., 1965. Distribution patterns of certain Umbelliferae. *Ann. Mo. Bot. Gdn.*, **52**: 387–398.

MATHIAS, M. E. & CONSTANCE, L., 1941a. New combinations and new names in the Umbelliferae. *Bull. Torrey Bot. Club*, **68**: 121–124.

MATHIAS, M. E. & CONSTANCE, L., 1941b. Limnosciadium, a new genus of Umbelliferae. *Am. J. Bot.*, **28**: 162–163.

MATHIAS, M. E. & CONSTANCE, L., 1941c. A synopsis of the North American species of Eryngium. *Am. Midl. Nat.*, **25**: 361–387.

MATHIAS, M. E. & CONSTANCE, L., 1941d. Three new species of Mexican Umbelliferae. *Bull. Torrey Bot. Club*, **68**: 254–256.

MATHIAS, M. E. & CONSTANCE, L., 1942a. A synopsis of the American species of Cicuta. *Madroño*, **6**: 145–151.

MATHIAS, M. E. & CONSTANCE., L., 1942b. New North American Umbelliferae. *Bull Torrey Bot. Club*, **69**: 151–155.

MATHIAS, M. E. & CONSTANCE, L., 1942c. New combinations and new names in the Umbelliferae. II. *Bull. Torrey Bot. Club*, **69**: 244–248.

MATHIAS, M. E. & CONSTANCE, L., 1943a. A new *Tauschia* from the State of Washington. *Madroño*, **7**: 65–67.

MATHIAS, M. E. & CONSTANCE, L., 1943b. New North American Umbelliferae. II. *Bull. Torrey Bot. Club*, **70**: 58–61.

MATHIAS, M. E. & CONSTANCE, L., 1944–1945. Umbelliferae in *North American Flora*, **28**B: 43–295.

MATHIAS, M. E. & CONSTANCE, L., 1950a. A second species of Eurytaenia. *Contr. Texas Res. Found., Bot. Stud.*, **1**: 2–3.

MATHIAS, M. E. & CONSTANCE, L., 1950b. Four new American Umbelliferae. *Bull. Torrey Bot. Club*, **77**: 133–139.

MATHIAS, M. E. & CONSTANCE, L., 1951a. Umbelliferae. In Kearney, T. H. and Peebles, R. H., *Arizona Flora*, pp. 606–624.

MATHIAS, M. E. & CONSTANCE, L., 1951b. Umbelliferae. In Lundell, C. L., *Flora of Texas*, **3**: 263–330.

MATHIAS, M. E. & CONSTANCE, L., 1951c. Supplementary notes on South American Hydrocotyle. *Bull. Torrey Bot. Club*, **78**: 300–309.

MATHIAS, M. E. & CONSTANCE, L., 1951d. A revision of the Andean Genus Niphogeton (Umbelliferae). *Univ. Calif. Publs Bot.*, **23**: 405–426.

MATHIAS, M. E. & CONSTANCE, L., 1951e. Umbelliferae. In Clokey, I. W., Flora of the Charleston Mountains, Clark County, Nevada. *Univ. Calif. Publs Bot.*, **24**: 162–166.

MATHIAS, M. E. & CONSTANCE, L., 1951f. Umbelliferae. In Abrams, L. R., *Ill. Fl. Pacific States*, **3**: 215–283.

MATHIAS, M. E. & CONSTANCE, L., 1952a. Umbelliferae. In Steyermark, J. A., Contributions to the Flora of Venezuela. *Fieldiana, Bot.*, **28**: 445–447.

MATHIAS, M. E. & CONSTANCE, L., 1952b. New South American Umbelliferae. *Bull. Torrey Bot. Club*, **79**: 359–370.

MATHIAS, M. E. & CONSTANCE, L., 1952c. Supplementary notes on the genus Tauschia (Umbelliferae). *Am. J. Bot.*, **39**: 652–655.

MATHIAS, M. E. & CONSTANCE, L., 1954. A new species of Eryngium (Umbelliferae) from southern Brazil. *Bull. Torrey Bot. Club*, **81**: 215–217.

MATHIAS, M. E. & CONSTANCE, L., 1955a. The genus Oreomyrrhis (Umbelliferae). *Univ. Calif. Publs Bot.*, **27**: 347–416.

MATHIAS, M. E. & CONSTANCE, L., 1955b. *Lomatium inyoense*. In Munz, P. A. & Roos, J. C., California Miscellany III. *Aliso*, **3**: 120–122.

MATHIAS, M. E. & CONSTANCE, L., 1955c. Umbelliferae. In Plants collected in Ecuador by W. H. Camp. *Mem. N.Y. bot. Gdn.*, **2**: 171–174.

MATHIAS, M. E. & CONSTANCE, L., 1957a. Umbelliferae. In Steyermark, J. A., Contributions to the Flora of Venezuela. *Fieldiana, Bot.*, **28**: 1045–1047.

MATHIAS, M. E. & CONSTANCE, L., 1957b. Umbelliferae of Nevada. In *Contributions toward a flora of Nevada*, **44**: 1–60.

MATHIAS, M. E. & CONSTANCE, L., 1957c. Four notable Umbelliferae from Peru. *Bull. Torrey Bot. Club*, **84**: 189–198.

MATHIAS, M. E. & CONSTANCE, L., 1958. Two new Eryngia (Umbelliferae) from Santa Catarina, South Brazil. *Bull. Torrey Bot. Club*, **85**: 255–259.

MATHIAS, M. E. & CONSTANCE, L., 1959a. Flora of Panama: Umbelliferae. *Ann. Mo. Bot. Gdn.*, **46**: 242–254.

MATHIAS, M. E. & CONSTANCE, L., 1959b. New North American Umbelliferae-III. *Bull. Torrey Bot. Club*, **86**: 374–382.

MATHIAS, M. E. & CONSTANCE, L., 1960. Umbelliferae. In Supplement to Kearney, T. H. & Peebles, R. H., *Arizona Flora*, p. 1062.

MATHIAS, M. E. & CONSTANCE, L., 1962a. The Andean genus Niphogeton (Umbelliferae) revisited. *Brittonia*, **14**: 148–155.

MATHIAS, M. E. & CONSTANCE, L., 1962b. A revision of Asteriscium and some related Hydrocotyloid Umbelliferae. *Univ. Calif. Publs Bot.*, **33**: 99–184.

MATHIAS, M. E. & CONSTANCE, L., 1962c. Umbelliferae. In Flora of Peru. *Field Mus. Nat. Hist., Bot. Ser.*, **13** (5A, no. 1): 1–97.

MATHIAS, M. E. & CONSTANCE, L., 1962d. Four new or renamed South American Umbelliferae. *Bull. Torrey Bot. Club*, **89**: 371–380.

MATHIAS, M. E. & CONSTANCE, L., 1964. Umbelliferae. In Shreve, F. & Wiggins, I. L., *Flora of the Sonoran Desert*, **2**: 1066–1075.

MATHIAS, M. E. & CONSTANCE, L., 1965. A revision of Bowlesia Ruiz & Pav. (Umbelliferae-Hydrocotyloideae) and its relatives. *Univ. Calif. Publs Bot.*, **38**: 1–73.

MATHIAS, M. E. & CONSTANCE, L., 1967. Some Umbelliferae of the Andean Paramos of South America. *Brittonia*, **19**: 212–226.

MATHIAS, M. E. & CONSTANCE, L., 1968. Two new Apioid Umbelliferae from southern Mexico. *Collect. Bot. (Barcelona)*, **7**: 759–766.

MATHIAS, M. E. & CONSTANCE, L., 1970. Umbelliferae. In Correll, D. S., *Manual of Texas Flora*, pp. 1139–1169.

MATHIAS, M. E. & CONSTANCE, L., 1971. Umbelliferae. In Wiggins, I. L., *Flora of the Galápagos Islands*, pp. 763–769.

MATHIAS, M. E. & CONSTANCE, L., in press. Umbelliferae. In Correa, N., *Flora Patagonia*.

MATHIAS, M. E. & CONSTANCE, L., in press. Umbelliferae. In *Flora of Venezuela*.

MATHIAS, M. E. & CONSTANCE, L., in press. A first revision of Huanaca Cav. (Umbelliferae-Hydrocotyloideae.) *Kurtziana*.

MATHIAS, M. E. & CONSTANCE, L., in press. Umbelliferae. In Reitz, P., *Flora Ilustrada Catarinense*.

MATHIAS, M. E., CONSTANCE, L. & SPARRE, B., 1968. Umbelliferae. In Böcher, T. W., Hjerting, J. P. & Rahn, K., Botanical studies in the Atuel Valley Area, Mendoza Province, Argentina. *Dansk Bot. Ark.*, **22**: 168–171.

MATHIAS, M. E., CONSTANCE, L. & THEOBALD, W. L., 1970. Two new species of Umbelliferae from the southwestern United States. *Madroño*, **20**: 214–219.

MATUDA, E., 1958. *Las Umbelíferas del Estado de México*, pp. 1–53.

MEYEN, F. J. F., 1834–1835. *Reise um die Erde ausgeführt auf dem königlich preussischen Seehandlungs-Schiffe, Prinzess Louise*, **1**: 1–493; **2**: 1–411.

MIRBEL, C. F., 1825. Umbelliferae. In Gaudichaud, C., Rapport sur la Flore des Îles Malouines. *Ann. Nat. (Paris)*, **5**: 104–105.

MORIS, J., 1835. Umbelliferae. In Plantae chilenses novae. *Mem. Accad. Sci. (Torino)*, **38**: 45–46.

MORISON, R., 1672. *Plantarum Umbelliferarum distributio nova*, pp. 1–91.

MORONG, T. & BRITTON, N. L., 1892. An enumeration of the plants collected by Dr Th. Morong in Paraguay, 1888–1890. *Ann. N. Y. Acad. Sci.*, **7**: 45–280.

MUEHLENBACH, V., 1969. Adventive plants new to the Missouri flora (III). *Ann. Missouri Bot. Gard.*, **56**: 163–171.

MUÑOZ PIZARRO, C., 1959. *Sinopsis de la flora Chilena*, pp. 1–840.

MURLEY, M. R., 1946. Fruit key to the Umbelliferae in Iowa, with plant distribution records. *Iowa State Coll. J. Sci.*, **20**: 349–364.

NANNFELDT, J. A., 1924. Revision der Verwandtschaftskreises von *Centella asiatica* (L.) Urb. *Svensk. Bot. Tidskr.*, **18**: 397–426.

NEGER, F., 1905. *Eryngium chubutense* n. sp. in Dusen, P., Beiträge zur Flora von Ostpatagonien. *Svensk. Exped. Magell.*, **3**: 254.

NELSON, A., 1898. New Plants from Wyoming. III. *Bull. Torrey Bot. Club*, **25**: 373–381.

NELSON, A., 1899a. New plants from Wyoming. VI. *Bull. Torrey Bot. Club*, **26**: 122–134.

NELSON, A., 1899b. New plants from Wyoming. VII. *Bull. Torrey Bot. Club*, **26**: 236–250.

NELSON, A., 1901. New plants from Wyoming. XIII. *Bull. Torrey Bot. Club*, **28**: 223–235.

NELSON, A., 1912a. New plants from Idaho. Contributions from the Rocky Mountain Herbarium. X. *Bot. Gaz. (Crawfordsville)*, **53**: 219–228.

NELSON, A., 1912b. Contributions from the Rocky Mountain Herbarium. XI. New plants from Idaho. *Bot. Gaz. (Crawfordsville)*, **54**: 136–151.

NELSON, A. & MACBRIDE, J. F., 1916. Western plant studies. III. *Bot. Gaz. (Crawfordsville)*, **61**: 30–47.

PARODI, L. R., 1927. Los géneros *Ammi* y *Falcaria* en la Argentina. *Physis (Buenos Aires)*, **8**: 585–587.

PÉREZ MOREAU, R. A., 1933. *Hydrocotyle* platenses. *Physis (Buenos Aires)*, **11**: 332–345.

PÉREZ MOREAU, R. A., 1935. Nuevas Umbelíferas del género *Lilaeopsis*. *Physis (Buenos Aires)*, **11**: 478–481.

PÉREZ MOREAU, R. A., 1936. Umbelíferas sudamericanas nuevas o interesantes. *Physis (Buenos Aires)*, **12**: 85–95.

PÉREZ MOREAU, R. A., 1937. Sinopsis de las Umbelíferas argentinas del género *Lilaeopsis*. *Lilloa*, **1**: 283–306.

PÉREZ MOREAU, R. A., 1938. Revisión de las *Hydrocotyle* argentinas. *Lilloa*, **2**: 413–463.

PÉREZ MOREAU, R. A., 1940. Una nueva especie de 'Umbelliferae'. *Lilloa*, **5**: 31–34.

PERSOON, C. H., 1805. Umbelliferae. In *Synopsis plantarum*, **1**: 298–324.

PFITZER, E., 1883. Zur Morphologie und Anatomie der Monokotylen-ähnlichen Eryngien. *Ber. dtsch. Bot. Ges.*, **1**: 133–137.

PHILIPPI, F., 1881. Catalogues plantarum vascularium chilensium adhuc descriptarum, pp. 1–377 (*An. Univ. Chile*, **59**: I-VIII, 49–422).

PHILIPPI, R. A., 1858. Umbelliferae in Plantarum novarum chilensium. Centuria prima. *Linnaea*, **28**: 651–655; Centuria altera, **28**: 695–696.

PHILIPPI, R. A., 1859. Centuriae sextae continuatio. *Linnaea*, **30**: 189–190.

PHILIPPI, R. A., 1860. *Florula atacamensis*, pp. 1–62.

PHILIPPI, R. A., 1861. Observaciones botánicas sobre algunas plantas recojidas in Chile por los señores don Ricardo Pearce y don Jerman Volckmann. *An. Univ. Chile*, **18**: 43–69.

PHILIPPI, R. A., 1864. Umbelliferae in Plantarum novarum chilensium. Centuriae inclusis quibusdam Mendocinis et Patagonicis. *Linnaea*, **33**: 88–97.

PHILIPPI, R. A., 1872. Descripción de las plantas nuevas incorporadas últimamente en el herbario Chileno. *An. Univ. Chile*, **41**: 663–746.

PHILIPPI, R. A., 1890. Umbelliferae in Verzeichniss der von d. Francisco Vidal Gormaz an den Küsten des nördlichen Chiles gesammelten Gefässpflanzen. *Verh. dtsch. Wiss. Vereins (Santiago, Chile)*, **2**: 107.

PHILIPPI, R. A., 1891. Catalogus praevius plantarum in itinere ad Tarapaca a Friderico Philippi lectarum. *An. Mus. Nac. Chile*, **2**, Secc. Bot. (no. 8): 1–96.

PHILIPPI, R. A., 1894. Umbelliferae in Plantas nuevas chilenas (continuación). *An. Univ. Chile*, **85**: 507–514, 699–726.

PICKERING, J. L., 1969. *A chemotaxonomic investigation of the Umbelliferae*. Ph.D. thesis, Rutgers University.

PICKERING, J. L. & FAIRBROTHERS, D. E., 1970. A serological comparison of Umbelliferae subfamilies. *Am. J. Bot.*, **57**: 988–992.

PIMENOV, M. G., 1965. De speciebus sectionis *Coelopleurum* (Ledeb.) M. Pimen. generis *Angelica* L. *Nov. Syst. Plant. Vasc.*, pp. 195–206.

PIMENOV, M. G., 1968a. Systematic grouping of species of *Angelica* L. occurring in the USSR, on the basis of coefficients of similarity. *Bjull. Moskovsk Obšč. Isp. Prir., Otd. Biol.*, **83**: 124–139.

PIMENOV, M. G., 1968b. The analysis of the distribution [of] species of *Angelica* L. occurring in the Soviet Far East. *Bot. Žurn (Moscow & Leningrad)*, **53**: 932–946.

PIMENOV, M. G. & YARYGINA, S. A., 1967. Chromosome numbers of the Far-Eastern species of *Angelica* L. *Bot. Žurn (Moscow & Leningrad)*, **52**: 356–359.

PIPER, C. V., 1898. New species of Washington plants. *Erythea*, **6**: 29–32.

PIPER, C. V., 1902. New and noteworthy Northwestern plants. VI. *Bull. Torrey Bot. Club*, **29**: 221–226.

PIPER, C. V., 1906. Flora of the State of Washington. *Contr. U.S. natn Herb.*, **11**: 1–637.

PIPER, C. V., 1916. New plants from Oregon. *Proc. biol. Soc. Wash.*, **29**: 99–101.

PISO, G., 1648. *Historia naturalis Brasiliae*, p. 90.

PITTIER, H., 1926. *Manual de las Plantas Usuales de Venezuela*, pp. 1–458.

PITTIER, H. *et al.*, 1947. *Catálogo de la Flora Venezolana*.

RAHN, K., 1960. Some chromosome numbers in South American angiosperms. *Bot. Tidsskr.*, **56**: 117–127.

RAMBO, B., 1957. O genero *Eryngium* no Rio Grande do Sur. *Sellowia*, **9**: 299–353.

RAUH, W., 1943. Über die Blattbildung von Discopleura capillacea (Michx.) DC. *Bot. Arch.*, **44**: 8–27.

RAVEN, P. & MATHIAS, M. E., 1960. Sanicula deserticola, an endemic of Baja California. *Madroño*, **15**: 193–197.

REICHE, C. F., 1899a. Zur Kenntnis einiger chilenischer Umbelliferen-Gattungen. *Bot. Jahrb. Syst.*, **28**: 1–17.

REICHE, C. F., 1899b. Estudios críticos sobre la flora de chile. *An. Univ. Chile*, **104**: 767–842.

REICHE, C. F., 1901. (continuación) *Anales Univ. Chile*, **109**: 586–587.

REICHE, C. F., 1902a. Umbelliferae in Reiche, C. F. & Philippi, F., *Flora de Chile*, **3**: 46–121.

REICHE, C. F., 1902b. Erwiderung. *Bot. Jahrb. Syst.*, **30**, Beibl. 67: 21–23.

REICHENBACH, H. TH. L., 1828. Umbelliferae. In *Conspectus regni vegetabilis*, pp. 141–145.

RENDLE, A. B., 1904. Mr Hesketh Prichard's Patagonian plants. *J. Bot.*, **42**: 321–334, 367–378.

RICARDI, M. & MARTICORENA, C., 1966. Umbelliferae in Plantas interesantes o nuevas para Chile. *Gayana, Bot.*, **14**: 16–19.

RICHARD, A., 1820. Monographie du genre *Hydrocotyle*. *Ann. Gen. Sci. Phys. Brux.*, **4**: 145–224.

RODGERS, C. L., 1950. The Umbelliferae of North Carolina and their distribution in the southeast. *J. Elisha Mitchell Sci. Soc.*, **66**: 145–266.

RODRÍGUEZ, R. L., 1957a. Systematic anatomical studies on Myrrhidendron and other woody Umbellales. *Univ. Calif. Publs Bot.*, **29**: 145–318.

RODRÍGUEZ, R. L., 1957b. Anotaciones a la anatomía comparada de las Umbelíferas. *Revta Biol. Trop.*, **5**: 157–171.

RODRÍGUEZ, R. L., 1960. Un híbrido natural de *Hydrocotyle* (Umbelliferae). *Revta Biol. Trop.*, **8**: 69–92.

ROMPEL, J., 1895. Krystalle von Calciumoxalat in der Fruchtwand der Umbelliferen und ihre Verwerthung für die Systematik. *Sitzungsber. Kaiserl. Akad. Wiss. Math.-Naturwiss. Cl. Abt. 1.*, **104**: 417–476.

ROSENGURTT, B., 1945. Adiciones a la flora Uruguaya. *Com. Bot. Mus. Hist. nat. Montevidéo*, 1: 1–9.

RUÍZ, H. & PAVÓN, J. A., 1794. *Florae peruvianae et chilensis prodromus*, pp. 1–153.

RUÍZ, H. & PAVÓN, J. A., 1798. Umbelliferae. In *Flora Peruviana et Chilensis*, 1: 75–79.

RUSBY, H. H., 1932. Llareta, a strange fuel. *Jl. N. Y. bot. Gard.*, 33: 54–57.

RYDBERG, P. A., 1896. Flora of the Black Hills of South Dakota. *Contr. U. S. natn Herb.*, 3: 463–536.

RYDBERG, P. A., 1900. Catalogue of the flora of Montana and the Yellowstone National Park. *Mem. N. Y. bot. Gdn*, 1: 1–492.

RYDBERG, P. A., 1904. Studies on the Rocky Mountain flora. XII. *Bull. Torrey Bot. Club*, 31: 555–575.

RYDBERG, P. A., 1906. Studies on Rocky Mountain flora. XVI. *Bull. Torrey Bot. Club*, 33: 137–161.

RYDBERG, P. A., 1913. Studies on the Rocky Mountain flora. XXVIII. *Bull. Torrey Bot. Club*, 40: 43–74.

RYDBERG, P. A., 1917. Ammiaceae. In *Flora of the Rocky Mountains and adjacent plains*.

RYDBERG, P. A., 1922. Ammiaceae. In *Flora of the Rocky Mountains and adjacent plains*. 2nd ed., pp. 606–633.

RYDBERG, P. A., 1931. Taxonomic notes on the flora of the prairies and plains of central North America. *Brittonia*, 1: 79–104.

RYDBERG, P. A., 1932. Ammiaceae. In *Flora of the prairies and plains of central North America*, pp. 585–604.

SCHEELE, A., 1843. Umbelliferae in Botanische Beiträge. *Linnaea*, 17: 339.

SCHEIDWEILER, M. J., 1842. Beschreibung einiger neuen Pflanzen. *Allg. Gartenzeitung*, 10: 285–286.

SCHELLENBURG, G., SCHINZ, H. & THELLUNG, A., 1914. Flora von Kolumbien und Westindien. *Mem. Soc. Sci. nat. Neuchâtel*, 5: 342–431.

SCHLECHTENDAL, D. F. L., 1857. Umbelliferae. In Plantae Lechlerianae. *Linnaea*, 28: 476–483, 546.

SCHUMANN, K., 1900. Neue Arten der Siphonogamen 1898. *Just. Bot. Jahresber.*, 26: 367–368.

SHAN, R. H. & CONSTANCE, L., 1951. The genus Sanicula (Umbelliferae) in the old world and the new. *Univ. Calif. Publs Bot.*, 25: 1–78.

SHINNERS, L. H., 1967. Bupleurum lancifolium (B. subovatum) (Umbelliferae) in Texas. *Sida*, 3: 185.

SKOTTSBERG, C., 1913. Die Gattung *Bolax* Commerson. *Bot. Jahrb. Syst.*, 48. Beibl., 107: 1–6.

SKOTTSBERG, C., 1916. Umbelliferae in Botanische Ergebnisse der Schwedischen Expedition nach Patagonien und dem Feuerlande 1907–1909. Die Vegetationsverhältnisse längs der Cordillera de los Andes S. von 41°S. Br. *Kongl. Svenska Vetenskapsakad. Handl.*, 56 (5): 274–281.

SMALL, J. K., 1903. Ammiaceae. In *Flora of the southeastern United States*, pp. 856–876.

SMALL, J. K., 1933. Ammiaceae. In *Manual of the southeastern flora*, pp. 960–986.

SPEGAZZINI, C., 1883. Umbelliferae in Plantae novae nonnullae Americae Australis (Decas I) *An. Soc. Ci. Argent*, 15: 106–107.

SPEGAZZINI, C., 1896. Umbelliferae in Plantae per Fuegiam in anno 1882 collectae. *An. Mus. nac. Hist. nat. Buenos Aires*, 5: 57–60.

SPEGAZZINI, C., 1897. Plantae Patagonicae australis. *Revta Fac. Agron. Univ. Nac. La Plata*, 3: 485–589.

SPEGAZZINI, C., 1899. Umbelliferae in Nova addenda ad floram patagonicam. *An. Soc. Ci. Argent.*, 48: 53–59.

SPEGAZZINI, C., 1902. Nova addenda ad Floram Patagonicam. IV. *An. Mus. Nac. Hist. nat. Buenos Aires*, 7: 135–315.

SPEGAZZINI, C., 1924. Interesante Umbelácea bonaerense. *Com. Mus. Cien. nat. Buenos Aires.*, 2: 79–86.

SPRENGEL, K., 1813. *Plantarum Umbelliferarum . . . prodromus*, pp. 1–42.

SPRENGEL, K., 1818. *Species Umbelliferarum*, pp. 1–154.

SPRENGEL, K., 1820. Umbelliferae. In Roemer, J. J. & Schultes, J. A., *Syst. Veg.*, 6: 395–628.

SPRENGEL, K., 1824. Umbelliferae. In *Systema vegetabilium*, 1: 868–919.

STOMPS, TH. J., 1929. Over *Bowlesia tenera* Spreng., B. incana R. & P. var. β. tenera (Spreng.) Urb. *Nederlandsch. Kruidk. Archief*, pp. 583–585.

STOUTAMIRE, W. P. & BEAMAN, J. H., 1960. Chromosome studies of Mexican alpine plants. *Brittonia*, 12: 226–229.

STRALEY, G. B., 1968. Bupleurum fontanessii (Umbelliferae) from Virginia. *Va. J. Sci.*, 19: 241.

SUESSENGUTH, K. & LAUNERT, E., 1955. *Azorella vareschii* spec. nov. *Mitt. Bot. Staats. München*, 2: 82–83.

TERNETZ, CH., 1902. Morphologie und Anatomie der *Azorella Selago* Hook. fil. *Bot. Zeit.*, 2. Abt. 60: 1–20.

THEOBALD, W. L., 1966. The Lomatium dasycarpum—mohavense—foeniculaceum complex (Umbelliferae). *Brittonia*, 18: 1–18.

THEOBALD, W. L., 1967. Venation pattern and fruit development in *Lomatium dasycarpum* (Umbelliferae). *Ann. Bot. (London)*, 31: 255–262.

THEOBALD, W. L., TSENG, C. C. & MATHIAS, M. E., 1964. A revision of Aletes and Neoparrya (Umbelliferae). *Brittonia*, 16: 296–315.

THORNE, R. F., 1968. Synopsis of a putatively phylogenetic classification of the flowering plants. *Aliso*, 6: 57–66.

TING, W. S., 1961. On some pollen of Californian Umbelliferae. *Pollen Spores*, **3**: 189–199.

TING, W. S., TSENG, C. C. & MATHIAS, M. E., 1964. A survey of pollen morphology of Hydrocotyloideae (Umbelliferae). *Pollen Spores*, **6**: 479–514.

TORREY, J. & GRAY, A., 1840. Umbelliferae. In *A flora of North America*, **1**: 598–645.

TSENG, C. C., 1967. Anatomical studies of flower and fruit in the Hydrocotyloideae (Umbelliferae). *Univ. Calif. Publs Bot.*, **42**: 1–79.

TURCZANINOW, N., 1847. Umbelliferae in Decas tertia generum adhuc non descriptorum adjectis descriptionibus nonullarum specierum ... Umbelliferarum imperfectarum. *Bull. Soc. Imp. nat. Moscou*, **20** (1): 169–173.

TURMEL, J. M., 1949. Répartition Géographique des Eryngium. II.—Nouveau Monde. *Bull. Mus. Hist. nat. (Paris)*, **21**: 120–131.

URBAN, I., 1879. Umbelliferae. In Martius, C. F., *Flora brasiliensis*, **11** (1): 261–354.

URBAN, I., 1882. Umbelliferae. In Zur Flora Südamerikas, besonders Brasiliens. *Linnaea*, **43**: 287–304.

URBAN, I., 1898. Plantae novae americanae imprimis Glaziovianae. II. *Bot. Jahrb. Syst.*, **25** Beibl. **60**: 1–57.

URBAN, I., 1901. Ueber einige südamerkanische Umbelliferen-Gattungen. *Bot. Jahrb. Syst.*, **20** Beibl. **65**: 1–2.

URBAN, I., 1902. Bemerkungen zu vorstehender Erwiderung. *Bot. Jahrb. Syst.*, **30** Beibl. **67**: 24–26.

URBAN, I., 1903. Umbelliferae. In Chodat, R. & Hassler, E., Plantae Hasslerianae. *Bull. Herb. Boissier*, II, **3**: 1121–1125.

URBAN, I. & MOEBIUS, M., 1884. Ueber *Schlechtendalia luzulifolia* Lees, eine monocotylenähnliche Compositae, und *Eryngium eriophorum* Cham., eine grasblättrige Umbelliferae. *Ber. dtsch. Bot. Gesell.*, **2**: 100–107.

URIBE-URIBE, L., 1948. Sertula Florae Colombiae, I. *Caldasia*, **5**: 77–83.

VELA, S. E., 1821. Disertación sobre la familia natural de las plantas Aparasoladas in Lagasca, M., *Amenidades Naturales de Españas*, **1** (2): 61–86.

VELLOZO, J. M., 1825. Umbelliferae. In *Florae fluminensis*, pp. 123–126.

WALPERS, G. G., 1843. Umbelliferae. In *Repert. Bot. Syst.*, **2**: 381–428, 937–939.

WALPERS, G. G., 1845–1846. *Repert. Bot. Syst.*, **5**: 838–924.

WEBER, W. A., 1958. Rediscovery of the genus Neoparrya Mathias (Umbelliferae). *Rhodora*, **60**: 265–271.

WEDDELL, H. A., 1860. Umbelliferae. In *Chloris Andina*, **2**: 186–208.

WERTH, E., 1907. Die Pflanzenwelt der Antarktis nach den Ergebnissen der deutschen Südpolar-Expedition. *Naturwiss. Wochenschr. N.F.*, **6** (24): 368–373.

WIENS, D. & HALLECK, D. K., 1962. Chromosome numbers in Rocky Mountain plants I. *Bot. Not.*, **115**: 455–464.

WILDEMAN, E. DE, 1904. *Eryngium serra* Cham. *Icon. Select. hort. Thenen.*, **5**: 25–28.

WILLIAMS, L. O., 1964. Umbelliferae in Tropical American plants. VI. *Fieldiana, Bot.*, **31**: 46–48.

WILLIAMS, L. O., 1966. Umbelliferae. In Standley, P. C. & Williams, L. O., Flora of Guatemala. *Fieldiana, Bot.*, **24** (8): 21–86.

WOLFF, H., 1908*a*. Umbelliferae austro-americanae. In Urban, I., Plantae novae andinae imprimis Weberbauerianae. III. *Bot. Jahrb. Syst.*, **40**: 281–306.

WOLFF, H., 1908*b*. Umbelliferae. In Aloysius Sodiro, S. J.: Plantae ecuadoroenses. V. *Bot. Jahrb. Syst.*, **40** Beibl. **91**: 48–51.

WOLFF, H., 1908*c*. *Eryngium Buchtienii* Wolff nov. spec. *Repert. Spec. Nov. Regni Veg.*, **6**: 24.

WOLFF, H., 1909. Species novae generis *Eryngii* Americae Centralis et australis. *Repert. Spec. Nov. Regni Veg.*, **7**: 274–279.

WOLFF, H., 1910*a*. *Eryngia* nova americana duo. *Repert. Spec. Nov. Regni Veg.*, **8**: 414–415.

WOLFF, H., 1910*b*. Umbelliferae Apioideae-Bupleurum, Trinia et reliquae Ammineae heteroclitae. In Engler, A., *Das Pflanzenreich*, IV, **43**: 1–214.

WOLFF, H., 1913. Umbelliferae-Saniculoideae. In Engler, A., *Das Pflanzenreich*, IV, **61**: 1–305.

WOLFF, H., 1921*a*. Umbelliferarum nov. gen. *Paraselinum* Peruvianum. *Repert. Spec. Nov. Regni Veg.*, **17**: 174.

WOLFF, H., 1921*b*. *Apium Weberbaueri, A. Kalbreyeri, A. Sprucei* species novae Austroamericanae. *Repert. Spec. Nov. Regni Veg.*, **17**: 175–176.

WOLFF, H., 1921*c*. *Spananthe paniculata* var. *peruviana* var. nov. Peruana. *Repert. Spec. Nov. Regni Veg.*, **17**: 176.

WOLFF, H., 1921*d*. *Azorella Dusenii* Patagonica et *A. Mutisiana* Colombiana species novae. *Repert. Spec. Nov. Regni Veg.*, **17**: 266.

WOLFF, H., 1921*e*. *Asteriscium polycephalum* Heiron. msc. aus Argentinien. *Repert. Spec. Nov. Regni Veg.*, **17**: 439.

WOLFF, H., 1921*f*. *Mulinum famatinense* et *M. Reichei* spec. nov. Austro-americanae. *Repert. Spec. Nov. Regni Veg.*, **17**: 441–442.

WOLFF, H., 1924. *Azorellopsis*, genus novum Umbelliferarum Bolivianum. *Repert. Spec. Nov. Regni Veg.*, **19**: 312.

WOLFF, H., 1927. Umbelliferae-Apioideae-Ammineae-Carinae, Ammineae novemjugatae et genuinae. In Engler, A., *Das Pflanzenreich*, IV, **90**: 1–398.

WOLFF, H., 1928. *Eryngia* nova americana. *Repert. Spec. Nov. Regni Veg.*, **24**: 224.

WRIGHT, C. H., 1911. Flora of the Falkland Islands. *J. Linn. Soc., Bot.*, **39**: 319–320.

Systematic survey of Old World Umbelliferae

V. H. HEYWOOD, F.L.S.

Department of Botany, University of Reading, England

The general outlines of classification of the Umbelliferae were established on the basis of Old World studies but no detailed modern survey of the family is available and few revisions or monographs of genera have been published in the last fifty years. On the other hand many new genera and species have been described from the Old World during this period and an attempt is made in this paper to survey the family with regard to centres of concentration, general patterns of distribution and degrees of endemism. It has been found that most tribes comprise a small number of large genera (one to four) which represent, in terms of species numbers, the greater part of the group, plus a large number of small genera, many of them with one or two species only. The taxonomic and evolutionary implications of this pattern are discussed. Particular attention is paid to the composition of the umbelliferous floras of the Atlantic and Mediterranean islands. The need for a detailed assessment of the status of genera described from poorly known areas such as C. and S.W. Asia is stressed.

CONTENTS

INTRODUCTION

It is difficult to obtain a realistic idea of the state of our systematic knowledge of any large plant family from the normal handbooks, apart from general notions as to the total numbers of species, genera, and tribal or higher groupings, their distribution and outline classification. This is especially true of the Umbelliferae which because of its very size has not, in common with most other large families, been the subject of a modern taxonomic treatment or monograph. Although the general classification of the family has been largely based on Old World studies, as Mathias

(1971) points out, it should not be assumed that our understanding of the Umbelliferae of this region is anywhere near satisfactory.

Few revisions, monographs or detailed treatments of genera of Umbelliferae have been published since the series included in the *Pflanzenreich* by Wolff (1910, 1913, 1927) and yet in the last fifty years very large numbers of new species and even genera have been described from the Old World, especially from S.W. Asia and the Mediterranean region.

In this paper I have analysed the Umbelliferous floras of various regions of the Old World—Macaronesia, the Mediterranean, North Africa, Mediterranean Islands, the Middle East, Europe, the U.S.S.R., W. and E. Africa, Asia and Japan. This survey is necessarily incomplete and somewhat inaccurate due to the lack of recent (or, indeed, any) treatments of the family in some of the areas concerned. This is particularly true of S.W. Asia (Anatolia, Afghanistan, Iran, etc.) which are known to be extremely rich in Umbelliferae but for which no recent Flora is available. Enough has emerged, however, from the survey to give us a reasonable idea as to the centres of concentration of the family, tribes, genera or species, general distributional patterns, degrees of endemism, etc.

SURVEY OF THE SUBFAMILIES

The general classification of Drude (1897–98) is adopted in this survey with some modifications. Notes are given on the generic pattern, distribution, degrees of endemism and taxonomy of the various groups.

Hydrocotyloideae

The Hydrocotyloideae is poorly represented in the Old World. There are only four genera, *Hydrocotyle* with the widespread *H. vulgaris* and *H. sibthorpioides* and a few other species, plus several introduced from the tropics, N. and S. America, and New Zealand, which are naturalized in Europe; *Centella* in the U.S.S.R. (1 species), Asia (1 species) and Angola (1 species); *Drusa glandulosa* endemic to the Canary Islands (although recorded, apparently erroneously, from Morocco); *Didiscus* (1 species in Borneo); *Dickinsia*, a monotypic genus from S.W. China and the recently discovered *Naufraga balearica* from Mallorca in the Balearic Islands (Constance & Cannon, 1967). The relatively rich representation of this subfamily in West Africa–Angola (six species) is in contrast with the poor distribution of the other subfamilies there.

Saniculoideae

The Saniculoideae has a larger representation in the Old World than the Hydrocotyloideae but is still small in comparison with the Apioideae. There are eight genera: the subcosmopolitan *Sanicula* with 10–12 species in the Old World (nine in Asia), *Astrantia*, with about 10 species, restricted to the Old World (Europe–Asia Minor, Caucasus), *Actinolema*, an E. Mediterranean genus with one or two species, *Alepidea* with 40 tropical and S. African species, *Eryngium* with *ca.* 50 species (out of 230 distributed in tropical and temperate regions of the world but not in South or Tropical Africa), showing concentrations in N. Africa (19 species in Morocco, 6 of them endemic), Iran (9 species), Syria and Lebanon (10 species), Europe (26 species, including 9 S. European-Mediterranean endemics), and U.S.S.R. (14 species of which 5 are endemic); two monotypic European genera *Hacquetia* from C. Europe and *Petagnia* endemic to Sicily; and the monotypic Mediterranean *Lagoecia*.

Apioideae

The Apioideae represents the major part of the family in the Old World, greatly outnumbering in genera and species the other two subfamilies. It is concentrated in temperate zones and is poorly represented in tropical Africa. Because of its size it is considered here tribe by tribe.

Echinophoreae

This is a small tribe restricted to the Mediterranean and Near East. Few of the genera have more than a handful of species—*Echinophora* with 10 species (Mediterranean-Iranian) and *Pycnocycla* (with 10 species from tropical Africa to N.W. India). There are a few monotypic or ditypic genera endemic to S.W. Asia, e.g. *Thecocarpus*, an Iranian endemic which possesses the most bizarre fruits in the family, and *Dicyclophora*, also endemic to Iran, and *Anisosciadium* with two species from S.W. Asia.

Scandiceae

This tribe is divided by Drude into two subtribes, the Scandicinae and Caucalinae but many of the genera in the latter subtribe show strong affinity with those included in Drude's tribe Dauceae (Crowden *et al.*, 1969; Heywood, 1971). I have preferred here to follow Boissier (1872) whose Caucalideae embraced both groups. Here only Scandicinae will be considered; it contains:

Scandix	European-Mediterranean with 15–20 species
Chaerophyllum	N. Temperate with 21 species (7 endemic) in the U.S.S.R. and 12 in Europe (5 endemic)
Anthriscus	European-temperate Asia with 20 species, 12 of them in the U.S.S.R. and 7 in Europe.
Grammosciadium	E. Mediterranean, 6 species
Osmorhiza	Japan to China, Himalayas, Manchuria, Siberia, 1 species
Rhabdosciadium	Europe-W. Asia, 2 species
Huetia	Mediterranean, 5 species
Myrrhoides	Mediterranean, 1 species
Balansea	Spain-N. Africa, 2 species
Scandicium	Mediterranean, 1 species
Krasnovia	C. Asia, 1 species
Albertia (*Kozlovia*)	U.S.S.R., 1 species

Myrrhis	Europe, W. Asia, 25 species
Molopospermum	W. Mediterranean, 1 species
Tinguarra	Canary Islands, 1 species
Sphallerocarpus	S. Asia, 1 species
Chaerophyllopsis	W. China, 1 species

Dauceae

This group is concentrated largely in Europe, the Mediterranean region and C. and W. Asia, with a very few species in *Daucus*, *Torilis* and *Caucalis* occurring outside these areas. It contains 18 genera and 80–100 species. The large and important genera are *Torilis* and *Daucus*, both 'successful' groups including many weed species, some of which have spread to the New World (e.g. *Torilis arvensis*, *Daucus carota*). Both these genera are taxonomically complex and contain subgroups sometimes treated at generic level.

Six of the genera are monotypic and two ditypic: *Ammiopsis*, *Ammodaucus*, *Artedia*, *Chaetosciadium*, *Exoacantha* (2 spp), *Pseudorlaya* (2 spp.), *Turgenia* and *Turgeniopsis*. The genus *Artedia* is unusual in having winged, not spiny, mericarps.

Coriandreae

This is a small tribe in the New World, with six genera distributed in the Mediterranean, Caucasus and C. Asia: *Schrenkia* (7 spp. in C. Asia), *Coriandrum* (2 spp., W. Mediterranean), *Bifora* (2 spp., Mediterranean-C. Asia), *Schtschurouskia* (2 spp., C. Asia), *Kosopoljanskia* (1 sp., C. Asia), *Fuernrohria* (1 sp., Caucasus-Armenia).

Smyrnieae

This tribe comprises about 25 genera in the New World. The largest are *Cachrys sensu lato* (incl. *Prangos*) with about 50 species, and *Scaligeria* with about 22 species, both distributed in the Mediterranean to C. Asia like most of the other genera; and *Trachydium*, with 10–40 species in C. Asia, Iran and W. China. Other important genera are *Pleurospermum* with 25–80 species in temperate Eurasia, and *Malabaila* with 10 species from the E. Mediterranean to Iran and C. Asia, and *Hymenolaema* with 10 species from the Himalayas to C. Asia. There are seven or eight mono- or ditypic genera such as *Lecokia*, *Haplosciadium*, *Magydaris*, *Eleutherospermum* (2 spp.), *Astoma*, *Nothosmyrnium*, *Astomatopsis*, *Eremodaucus* and *Smyrniopsis* (cf. Tamamschian, 1968).

Apieae (*Ammieae, Hohenackerieae*)

This tribe is well represented in the Old World with about 40 genera in Europe and 50 in the U.S.S.R.

(a) *Apiinae*. The major genera are *Bupleurum* and *Pimpinella*. *Bupleurum* is a remarkable genus with about 100–150 species found in Eurasia, North Africa and the Canary Islands with one species in Arctic N. America (*B. americanum*) and another in S. Africa (*B. mundtii*). It is morphologically unusual in having entire leaves with often parallel venation, frequently resembling those of Monocotyledons. It is clearly a successful genus—'the umbelliferous grasses'—with large concentrations of endemic species in N.W. Africa (7 in Morocco, 5 in Algeria), 12 in the U.S.S.R. and 14 in Europe (mainly Mediterranean); there are two endemic Canary Island and one Madeiran species.

Pimpinella has again about 150 species in Eurasia and Africa. The New World species previously referred to it are now placed in other genera (*Donnellsmithia, Ligusticum, Perideridia* and *Taenidia*—cf. Hiroe & Constance, 1958). There are 12 species endemic to the U.S.S.R., 7 to Europe, 15 in Asia, including 5 confined to Japan-Korea-China; all 5 representatives of the genus in the Canary Islands are endemic. Other important genera are *Carum* with about 20 Old World species including 5 endemic to the U.S.S.R., 4 to S. Europe and several in N. Africa; and *Bunium*, a taxonomically difficult genus with 30–40 species, including 8 endemic to the U.S.S.R. (out of 18). The related genus *Conopodium* is also taxonomically difficult. It has 20 species in Eurasia and N. Africa, six of the seven European species are endemic, mainly in the Iberian peninsula.

(b) *Seseliinae*. This subtribe is smaller than the Apiinae. The largest genus is *Seseli* itself with 50–80 European to C. Asiatic species. As Constance (1965) notes, one obscure taxon, *Seseli pencanum* has been described from Chile, but its origin and identity are uncertain. Indeed the genus is one of exceptional taxonomic difficulty and many rare, local species have been described from the Old World, several of which may not belong in the genus at all! Eighteen of the 34 European species are endemic—mainly in S. Europe—and 18 of the 47 U.S.S.R. species are endemic. There are five Asiatic species.

Oenanthe is the next largest genus with 35–40 species distributed in temperate Eurasia, the mountains of tropical Africa and with some species in the Pacific area. Half the 14 European species are endemic; *Ligusticum* is also an important genus with 20–25 species with a circumboreal distribution. Its exact size is difficult to determine because of disagreements about the delimitation of the genus. As Hiroe & Constance (1958) note, the New Zealand species are probably referable to *Anisotome* (cf. Dawson, 1968), while the South American species probably belong to *Apium*. Asiatic species are sometimes placed in *Angelica, Carum, Dystaemia, Pimpinella, Seseli* and *Tilingia*! There are 25 Asiatic species of which 21 are endemic (3 to Japan), 12 in the U.S.S.R. (5 endemic) and 7 in Europe, of which 5 are endemic.

In the tribe as a whole there are about 25 genera endemic to the Old World, seven of them in Europe (*Endressia, Grafia, Hladnickia, Portenschlagiella, Thorella, Trochiscanthes, Xatardia*, all of them monotypic except *Endressia* which is ditypic); 1 genus endemic to the Canary Islands—*Todaroa* with 2 species; *Chamaele* and *Apodicarpum*, both monotypic and endemic to Japan; *Baumiella*, monotypic and endemic to Angola; *Pterygopleurum*, monotypic and endemic to S. Japan and Korea; *Haplosphaera, Melanosciadium* and *Carlesia*, monotypic and endemic to China; *Phellolophium* and *Anisopoda*, monotypic and endemic to Madagascar; *Korshinskia*, 2 species in C. Asia; *Cenolophium*, 1 Eurasiatic species; *Polyzygus*, monotypic and endemic to S. India, *Cortia*, monotypic and endemic to the Himalayas; *Schultzia*, with 2 C. Asiatic and 2 W. Indian species; *Diplolophium* with 5 and *Physotrichia* with 10 tropical African species. The remaining genera are found in Asia Minor or S.W. Asia—*Froriepia*, monotypic in the Caucasus-Iran; *Buniotrinia*, *Pichleria* and *Schlerochorton* with 1 or 2 species, endemic to Iran; *Oliveria*—monotypic and endemic to Syria and Iran; *Szovitsia*, monotypic and restricted to Caucasus-Armenia-Iran; *Chamaesciadium*, monotypic in Caucasus-Iran-Asia Minor; and *Grammosciadium* in S.W. Asia.

Peucedaneae

This tribe is widely represented in the Old World. It is divided into three subtribes:

(a) *Angelicinae*. The largest genus is *Angelica* itself with about 80 species in the Northern Hemisphere. The largest concentration of species is in Japan where there are 23 species, of which 9 are endemic; there are 16 species in the U.S.S.R. (2 endemic) and 8 in Europe. Several genera such as *Ostericum*, *Coelopleurum* and *Archangelica* are sometimes kept separate from *Angelica*, sometimes included in it.

(b) *Peucedaninae*. The largest genus, *Ferula*, has 130 species confined to the Old World, from the Mediterranean region to C. Asia. The highest concentration of species is in the U.S.S.R. (nearly 100 species of which about 60 are endemic) and adjacent regions. There are over 20 species in Iran. Almost as large is *Peucedanum*, with about 120 species; there are 40 in the U.S.S.R. (11 of them endemic) and 30 in Europe (20 of which are endemic).

(c) *Tordyliinae*. This subtribe is dominated by *Heracleum*, a circumboreal genus which has about 60–70 species, many of which occur in the Old World. There are nearly 40 species in the U.S.S.R. (22 endemic), 9 in Europe, and 10 in Asia (7 endemic).

Apart from the major Old World genera there are in the *Apieae* many small genera, about 25 of them with only one or two species, found mainly in the Near East, S.W. and C. Asia.

Laserpitieae

This is a small tribe found mainly in the Old World. The largest genus is *Laserpitium* with 35 species, 13 of them in Europe (11 endemic). *Siler* contains 5 species confined to Europe. *Melanoselinum* is interesting in that its 7 species are restricted to Macaronesia—Madeira, Azores and the Cape Verdes. *Guillonea* is a monotypic genus found in S. Spain, and *Rouya* is monotypic, occurring in Corsica, Sardinia and N. Africa.

DISCUSSION

Systematic structure

It is a characteristic of each tribe or subtribe, especially in the subfamily *Apioideae*, that it contains a small number (1–4) of large genera which comprise the greater part of the group in terms of numbers of species, plus a large number of small 'satellite' genera, many of them with one or two species only.

How far this is an evolutionary pattern of the family and how far it is simply a reflection of taxonomic practice is not quite clear. As in most other 'natural' families such as the Labiatae, Compositae, Cruciferae and Fabaceae, the uniformity in inflorescence, floral and fruit structure imposed by the family characters tends to make recognition of tribes and genera difficult. For tribal and generic separation, recourse has to be made to very detailed or small scale features—so called 'trivial' characters—and there is considerable debate amongst taxonomists as to which should be used. If a conservative treatment is adopted, many of the small genera are absorbed into the 'dominant' genera of each tribe; if a more liberal attitude is followed, the number of small genera recognized can be greatly increased. In the search for new characters evidence in support of these small genera is often found. Even so, it is largely a matter of taxonomic taste whether one wishes to recognize few or many genera.

On the other hand, although some of the small satellite genera are of dubious value, many of them seem to be quite distinct and taxonomically isolated. I am inclined, therefore, to believe that in the Old World at least the family has evolved a limited number of successful character combinations—the large genera of each tribe—while the small genera are in part relict, even ancestral, groups and in part recently evolved variations on the basic themes of the large genera.

At the same time it has to be admitted that several of the large genera may be unnatural in the sense that species have been included in them on the basis of superficial similarity in conspicuous characters. As we have already noted above, *Seseli*, *Ligusticum*, *Pimpinella*, *Angelica*, *Daucus*, etc. are such examples.

The use of new lines of evidence such as pollen morphology, fruit structure as revealed by scanning electron microscopy, chemical constituents, etc. often indicates the degree to which some of the major genera are heterogeneous. Within the tribe *Caucalideae* we have been able to reallocate species in several genera such as *Torilis*, *Caucalis*, *Turgenia*, *Daucus*, etc. (see Heywood & Dakshini, p. 217) following the application of such new techniques. What is encouraging is that the results can often be confirmed by careful morphological study. In other words, basic morphological-taxonomic knowledge of many groups is simply inadequate.

In answer to the general question, how well do we know the Old World Umbelliferae, the conclusion must be a lot less than one might imagine. At the level of basic descriptive taxonomy a great deal of exploration and detailed study remains to be done at the generic and specific level. As so often happens in the Old World, the richest areas floristically are the least studied: the main areas of concentration and diversification are in regions such as the Mediterranean, S.W. and C. Asia and the Middle East where floristic/taxonomic knowledge is still relatively poor. Fortunately active research is in progress—at least in some of these areas.

Very little experimental or biosystematic research has been carried out on Old World Umbellifers. Part of the reason for this is, no doubt, the technical difficulties that the umbels present from the point of view of hybridization studies. Indeed, as Ritchie Bell indicates elsewhere in this volume (p. 93) little work has been carried out on the breeding systems in the Umbelliferae since the classical studies of last century. Even in commercial breeding, techniques are not very sophisticated.

That so little should be known about so important a family which contains such a large number of economically or pharmaceutically interesting plants is paradoxical. It is encouraging, however, that the growing interest in the family shown by chemists and phytochemists is acting as a stimulus to taxonomic studies.

GEOGRAPHICAL PATTERNS

Of the regions that have been covered by recent Floras, the richest Umbel flora is that of the U.S.S.R. with 142 genera (25 of them endemic) and 743 species. Many of them are from the Caucasus and C. Asiatic Russia and it has to be admitted that a proper assessment has yet to be made of a considerable number. On the basis of *Flora Europaea*, Europe has 110 genera (12 endemic), 417 species plus 91 subspecies with a further 39 species whose status has yet to be decided for lack of material or other evidence. It is the third largest family in Europe. Of the Russian species 214 are endemic while of the European species 168 are endemic plus many subspecies which in *Flora SSSR* might be treated as species so that the number of endemics is very similar in the two areas. As in other families, the European endemics are mainly found in the south and in the Mediterranean region, some of them being relict mountain species, others recently evolved species of the lowlands.

Asia, as judged by Hiroe's (1958) study, has 82 genera and 283 species (132 endemic). There is a high concentration of umbellifers, about 200 species, in the Nearer East [(Syria, Palestine, Jordan). Anatolia (with 90 genera according to Hedge & Lamond (1964))] and Afghanistan are also major centres but accurate estimates are difficult to make in our present stage of knowlege. Much active exploration and study of these areas is in progress and undoubtedly many new species and some genera remain to be described. N.W. Africa also has a rich umbel flora—Morocco with 138 species (28 endemic) and Algeria with 117 (24 endemic). Other areas of Africa (except the South) have poor umbel representations; the Sudan has only 26 species, Angola 32 (of which 8 are endemic!), Ethiopia with about 40 species, W. Tropical Africa with 18, etc.

THE ISLAND FLORAS

Two groups of island floras have been analysed in detail—the Atlantic islands (Macaronesia) comprising the Canary islands, Madeira, the Azores and the Cape Verdes, and the Mediterranean islands—the Balearics, Corsica, Sardinia, Sicily and Crete. The results can be seen in the Tables 1–3.

The Mediterranean islands all have similarly small umbel floras. Sicily is richest in genera and species (46/91), followed by Corsica (43/76), Sardinia (41/72), Crete (39/65) and the Balearics (29/41). All have a handful of endemic species:

Naufraga balearica	a monotypic genus in the Balearics
Eryngium ternatum	Crete
Petagnia saniculifolia	~~Crete~~ Sicily

Table 1. Generic summary of the Umbelliferae of the Atlantic and Mediterranean islands

	EUROPE						MACARONESIA				
	Bl	Co	Cr	Sa	Si	Total	Az	Ca	Cv	Ma	Total
HYDROCOTYLOIDEAE											
Hydrocotyle	—	1	—	—	2	2 (0)	1	—	—	—	1 (0)
*Naufraga	1 (1)	—	—	—	—	1 (1)	—	—	—	—	—
*Drusa	—	—	—	—	—	—	—	1	—	1	1 (1)
SANICULOIDEAE											
Sanicula	—	1	—	1	1		1 (1)	—	—	—	1 (1)
Eryngium	2	3	5	7	5 (1)	10 (1)	—	—	—	—	—
Lagoecia	—	—	1	—	—	1 (0)	—	—	—	—	—
Petagnia	—	—	1 (1)	—	—	1 (1)	—	—	—	—	—
APIOIDEAE											
Echinophora	1	1	1	1	1	2 (0)	—	—	—	—	—
Myrrhoides	—	1	—	1	1	1	—	—	—	—	—
Anthriscus	1	1	—	—	—	1 (0)	—	—	—	2	2 (0)
Huetia	—	—	1 (1)	—	—	1 (1)	—	—	—	—	—
Scandix	1	1	—	1	2	2 (0)	—	2	—	1	2 (0)
*Tinguarra	—	—	—	—	—	—	—	1 (1)	—	—	1 (1)
Chaerophyllum	—	1	1 (1)	1	—	2 (1)	1 (1)	—	—	—	1 (1)
Torilis	4	4	3	2	2	4 (0)	1	3	—	2	3 (0)
Caucalis	—	1	—	—	—	1 (0)	—	—	—	—	—
Turgenia	—	—	1	1	—	1 (0)	—	—	—	—	—
Orlaya	—	1	2	1	1	2 (0)	—	—	—	—	—
Daucus	1	2	4	2	3	6 (0)	1	2	1	1	2 (0)
Ammodaucus	—	—	—	—	—	—	—	1	—	—	1 (0)
Pseudorlaya	1	1	2	1	1	2 (0)	—	—	—	—	—
Coriandrum	—	—	[1]	—	[1]	[1]	1	—	1	1	1 (0)
Bifora	2	1	1	1	2	2 (0)	1	1	—	—	1(0)
Smyrnium	1	2	4	3	3	4 (0)	1	1	—	—	1 (0)
Scaligeria	—	—	1	—	—	1 (0)	—	—	—	—	—
Physospermum	—	1	—	—	1	2 (0)	—	—	—	—	—
Conium	1	1	1	1	1	1 (0)	1	1	—	—	1 (0)
Lecokia	—	—	1	—	—	1 (0)	—	—	—	—	—
Cachrys	—	—	1	—	4	5 (0)	—	—	—	—	—
Magydaris	1	—	—	1	1	2 (0)	—	—	—	—	—
Ruthea	—	—	—	—	—	—	—	1 (1)	—	—	1 (1)
Bupleurum	4 (1)	9	4	8	11 (2)	18 (3)	—	5 (2)	—	2 (1)	6 (3)
Trinia	—	?1	—	—	—	?1	—	—	—	—	—
Apium	2	3	3	3	4	5 (0)	2	3	—	3	3 (0)
Petroselinum	—	2	1	1	1	2 (0)	1	1	1	1	1 (0)
Ridolfia	1	1	—	1	1	1 (0)	—	1	—	—	1 (0)
Sison	1	1	—	1	1	—	—	—	—	—	—
Cryptotaenia	—	—	—	—	—	—	—	1 (1)	—	—	1 (1)
Ammi	2	2	1	2	3	3 (0)	4	3	—	3	5 (3)
Ptychotis	—	1	—	2 (1)	—	2 (1)	—	—	—	—	—
Ammoides	—	1	—	1	1	1 (0)	—	—	—	—	—
Carum	—	?1	1	—	—	2 (0)	—	—	—	—	—
Bunium	2	2	1	2	2	4 (0)	—	—	—	1 (1)	1 (1)
Conopodium	—	1	—	—	2	2 (0)	—	—	—	—	—
Pimpinella	2 (1)	2	3	1	4	6 (1)	1	5 (5)	—	—	6 (5)
Berula	1	1	1	1	1	1 (0)	—	—	—	—	—
Aegopodium	—	?1	—	—	—	1 (0)	—	—	—	—	—
Crithmum	1	1	1	1	1	1 (0)	1	—	—	1	1 (0)
Seseli	—	2	1	2	2	3 (0)	—	1 (1)	—	—	1 (1)
Oenanthe	2	6	2	7 (1)	6	8 (1)	—	—	—	1 (1)	1 (1)
Aethusa	—	1	—	—	1	1 (0)	—	—	—	—	—
Athamanta	—	—	—	—	1	1 (0)	—	—	—	—	—
*Todaroa	—	—	—	—	—	—	—	2 (2)	—	—	2 (2)
Foeniculum	—	1	1	1	1	1 (0)	1	1	1	1	1 (0)
Anethum	—	—	—	—	—	—	—	1	1	1	1 (0)
Kundmannia	—	1	1	1	1	1 (0)	—	—	—	—	—
Cnidium	—	—	1	—	1	1 (0)	—	—	—	—	—
Ligusticum	1 (1)	1 (1)	—	—	—	2 (2)	—	—	—	—	—
Bonannia	—	—	?1	—	1	1 (0)	—	—	—	—	—
Capnophyllum	—	—	—	1	1	1 (0)	—	1	1	1	1 (0)
*Astydamia	—	—	—	—	—	—	—	1	—	1	1 (1)
Ferula	1	1	1	1	1	1 (0)	—	2 (2)	—	—	2 (2)
Ferulago	—	—	3 (1)	—	2	4 (1)	—	—	—	—	—
Opopanax	—	—	—	1	2	2 (0)	—	—	—	—	—
Peucedanum	—	2	1 (1)	1	—	3 (2)	—	—	—	1 (1)	1 (1)
Pastinaca	1 (1)	2 (1)	—	1	?1	3 (2)	—	—	—	—	—
Heracleum	—	—	—	—	1	1 (0)	—	—	—	—	—
Tordylium	1	2	3	2	2	4 ( )	—	—	—	—	—
Elaeoselinum	1	—	—	1	1	1 (0)	—	—	—	—	—
Laserpitium	1	2	—	1	—	2 (0)	—	—	—	—	—
*Melanoselinum	—	—	—	—	—	—	1	—	5 (5)	2 (1)	7 (7)
Thapsia	1	—	1	1	1	1 (0)	—	—	—	—	—
Rouya	—	1	—	1	—	1 (0)	—	—	—	—	—

Bl = Balearic islands; Co = Corsica; Cr = Crete; Sa = Sardinia; Si = Sicily; Az = Azores; Ca = Canaries; Cv = Cape Verdes; Ma = Madeira.

The first figure in each column is the number of species followed, in round brackets, by the number of those which are endemic.

Numbers in square brackets refer to introduced species. * indicates an endemic genus.

Chaerophyllum creticum	Crete
Huetia cretica	Crete
Pimpinella bicknellii	Balearics
Oenanthe lisae	Sardinia
Bupleurum barceloi	Balearics
B. elatum	Sicily
B. dianthifolium	Sicily
Ptychotis morisiana	Sardinia
Ligusticum corsicum	Corsica
L. lucidum subsp. *huteri*	Balearics
Ferulago thyrsiflora	Crete
Peucedanum paniculatum	Corsica, Sardinia
P. alpinum	Crete
Pastinaca latifolia	Corsica
P. lucida	Balearics

Table 2. Summary of the Umbelliferae of the Mediterranean islands

	Co	Sa	Si	Cr	Bl
Hydrocotyloideae	1/1 (0)	1/1 (0)	1/1 (0)	—	1/1 (1)
Saniculoideae	2/4 (0)	2/6 (0)	2/8 (0)	3/7 (2)	1/2 (0)
Apioideae	40/71 (3)	38/65 (3)	43/82 (2)	36/58 (4)	27/38 (4)

Co = Corsica; Sa = Sardinia; Si = Sicily; Cr = Crete; Bl = Balearic islands.
The first figure is the number of genera, the second, after the oblique is the number of species and the figure in brackets, the number of endemic species.

Table 3. Summary of the Umbelliferae of the Atlantic islands

	Az	Ca	Cv	Ma
Hydrocotyloideae	1/1 (0)	1/1 (1)	—	1/1 (1)
Saniculoideae	1/1 (1)	—	—	—
Apioideae	13/17 (3)	24/42 (16)	7/11 (5)	18/24 (8)

Az = Azores; Ca = Canaries; Cv = Cape Verdes; Ma = Madeira.
The first figure is the number of genera, followed after the oblique by the number of species, with the number of endemic species in brackets.

The Atlantic islands have also a small umbel flora, with 34 genera of which 5 are endemic and 63 species of which 33 are endemic, about half of them to the Canary Islands. This is in line with the generally high degree of endemism found in these islands.

REFERENCES

BOISSIER, E., 1872. Umbelliferae. In *Flora Orientalis*, **2**. Genève & Basel.
CONSTANCE, L. & CANNON, J. M. F., 1967. Naufraga—a new genus of Umbelliferae from Mallorca. *Feddes Repert*, **74**: 1–4.
CROWDEN, R. K., HARBORNE, J. B. & HEYWOOD, V. H., 1969. Chemosystematics of the Umbelliferae—a general survey. *Phytochemistry*, **8**: 1963–1984.

DAWSON, J. W., 1968. New Zealand Umbelliferae. A leaf comparison of *Aciphylla* and *Anisotome*. *N.Z. Jl Bot.*, **6**: 450–458.

DRUDE, C. G. O., 1897–1898. Umbelliferae. In Engler, A. & Prantl, K. *Die natürlichen Pflanzenfamilien*, **3** (8): 63–250. Leipzig: Engelmann.

HEDGE, I. C. & LAMOND, J. M., 1964. A guide to the Turkish genera of Umbelliferae. *Notes R. Bot.Gdn Edinb.*, **25**: 2.

HEYWOOD, V. H., 1971. Chemosystematic studies in *Daucus* and allied genera. *Boissiera*, **19**: 289–295.

HIROE, M. & CONSTANCE, L., 1958. Umbelliferae of Japan. *Univ. Calif. Publs Bot.*, **30** (1): 1–144.

HIROE, M., 1958. *Umbelliferae of Asia (excluding Japan)*, No. 1. Tokyo: Maruzen Company Limited.

MATHIAS, M. E., 1971. Systematic survey of New World Umbelliferae. In Heywood, V. H. (ed.), *Biology and Chemistry of the Umbelliferae (Bot. J. Linn. Soc. suppl. 2)*.

TAMAMSCHIAN, S. G., 1968. On some relationships in the floras of Transcaucasia, Anatolia and Iran. *Notes R. Bot. Gdn Edinb.*, **28**: 201–208.

WOLFF, H., 1910. Umbelliferae—Apioideae—Bupleurum, Trinia et reliquae Amminae heteroclitae. In Engler, A. (ed.), *Das Pflanzenreich*, IV, **43**: 1–214.

WOLFF, H., 1913. Umbelliferae—Saniculoideae. In Engler, A. (ed.), *Das Pflanzenreich*, IV, **61**: 1–305.

WOLFF, H., 1927. Umbelliferae—Apioideae—Ammineae—Carinae, Amminae novemjugatae et genuinae. In Engler, A., *Das Pflanzenreich*, IV, **90**: 1–398.

Relationships of the New Zealand Umbelliferae

J. W. DAWSON

Botany Department, University of Wellington, New Zealand

The New Zealand genera are considered under the following headings—(a) Predominantly alpine, dioecious or gynodioecious genera of probable New Zealand origin. (b) Predominantly alpine hermaphrodite genera widely distributed outside New Zealand. (c) Predominantly lowland, hermaphrodite genera widely distributed outside New Zealand.

All genera of the first group belong to the Apioideae. *Scandia*, *Gingidia* and *Lignocarpa* share gynodioecism and rudimentary staminodes. The *Scandia* species are subshrubby and semi-climbing with the larger leaved forms occupying mild coastal sites in the north. It is suggested that *Scandia* could have existed under warm Tertiary conditions, later giving rise to the truly herbaceous higher altitude *Gingidia* and *Lignocarpa*.

Aciphylla and *Anisotome* share dioecism and differentiated staminodes and may have originated in the relatively cool Oligocene period on former land areas in the Chatham and Subantarctic Islands regions respectively, with later diversification on the mainland mountains.

The unusual features of *Aciphylla* are described, i.e. 'stipules', unifacial leaf segments and in some species spininess and narrow inflorescences.

It is suggested that the genera of the two other categories, many of which are represented by only one or a few species, could have reached New Zealand by overseas dispersal.

If the Gondwanaland concept is valid then the poor representation of Hydrocotyloideae in New Zealand and southern Africa may be due to the separation of these areas from the southern continent before the subfamily became widespread there. The predominance of the Apioideae is difficult to explain but it seems clear that the subfamily in New Zealand must have undergone extensive speciation and diversification when alpine conditions developed.

CONTENTS

INTRODUCTION

There are 95 indigenous species of Umbelliferae currently recognized in New

Zealand, of which 72 species (76%) in 9 genera (*Scandia* Dawson, *Gingidia* Dawson,* *Lignocarpa* Dawson, *Aciphylla* J.R. & G. Forst., *Anisotome* Hook, f., *Oreomyrrhis* Endl., *Apium* L., *Lilaeopsis* Greene, *Daucus* L.) belong to the subfamily Apioideae. (Some or all of the species of the first five genera have in earlier times been placed in one or more of the holarctic genera *Angelica* L., *Peucedanum* L. and *Ligusticum* L. Subsequent study has shown that the latter genera are not represented in New Zealand (Dawson, 1961; Moar 1966.) Also 22 species (23%) in 5 genera (*Schizeilema* Dom., *Hydrocotyle* L., *Centella* L., *Actinotus* de la Billard., *Azorella* Lam.) belong to the Hydrocotyloideae, and only 1 species (1%) belongs to the Saniculoideae (*Eryngium* L.).

The New Zealand Umbelliferae are predominantly plants of higher altitudes. About 75% of the species are upland to alpine in distribution and 25% lowland to coastal. Within the subfamilies the respective percentages are: Apioideae, 82%, 18%; Hydrocotyloideae, 55%, 45%; Saniculoideae—the one species of *Eryngium* is mostly coastal. In view of the evidence—(a) that New Zealand was a low-lying land area until late in the Tertiary, with climates probably warmer than those of the present; (b) that at the time when the mountains were elevated at the end of the Tertiary New Zealand was probably separated as now by more than 1,000 miles of ocean from other land areas—the derivation of the New Zealand alpine flora as a whole has long been regarded as a puzzle.

Some rocky lowland and alpine habitats are ecologically similar and Cockayne (1928) suggested that some alpine species of the Cretaceous mountains could have survived on 'rocky faces' during the Tertiary and later provided a nucleus for the present alpine flora. A second suggestion has been put forward by Wardle (1968). He recognizes two general types of soil occupied by alpine species in New Zealand: (1) cool, wet, infertile, old soils often on level terrain, and (2) steeper, younger, better drained soils. The latter would not have become common until the present mountains were elevated late in the Tertiary, so the many alpine species occupying them would have mostly evolved during the Quaternary; the former and the relatively few alpine species occupying them could have existed throughout the Tertiary as soils of this type with an alpine flora occur as low as 600 metres above sea level in Hawaii today.

These two theories will be considered in the following review in which the New Zealand genera of Umbelliferae are grouped according to altitude and geographical distribution.

* **Gingidia** Dawson, **nom. nov.** Type species: **Gingidia montana** (J.R. & G. Forst.) Dawson, **comb. nov.**

The first published name applied to this genus, *Gingidium* J.R. & G. Forst. (1776), was antedated by *Gingidium* Hill (1756). The latter, which appeared in a rare Herbal now regarded as a taxonomically valid publication, was a synonym for *Ammi* L.

The following new combinations are necessary:

Gingidia decipiens (Hook. f.) Dawson, **comb. nov.** Syn. *Angelica decipiens* Hook. f., *Handbk. N. Zeal. Fl.*, 98 (1864).

Gingidia trifoliolata (Hook. f.) Dawson, **comb. nov.** Syn. *Ligusticum trifoliolatum* Hook. f. *Handbk. N. Zeal. Fl.*, 97 (1864).

Gingidia enysii (Kirk) Dawson, **comb. nov.** Syn. *Ligusticum ensyii* Kirk, *Trans. N. Zeal. Inst.* **9**: 548 (1877).

Gingidia flabellata (Kirk) Dawson, **comb. nov.** Syn. *Ligusticum flabellatum* Kirk, *Stud. Fl. N. Zeal.*, 205 (1899).

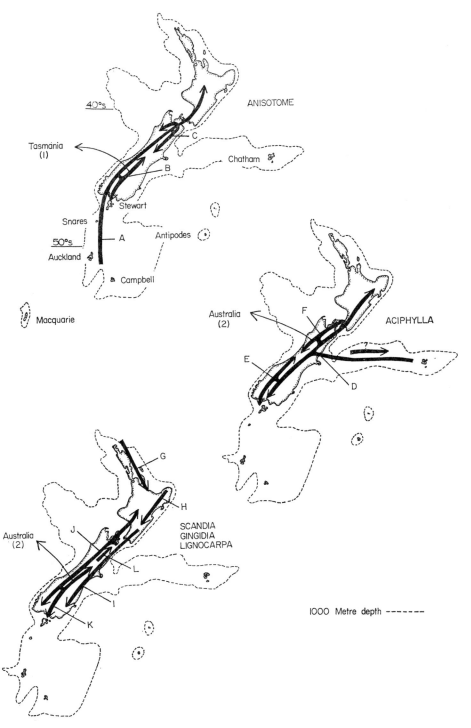

FIGURE 1. Maps showing possible migration patterns of *Anisotome*; *Aciphylla*; *Scandia*, *Gingidia*, *Lignocarpa*. A. long petioles; B. short petioles; C. *Anisotome filifolia* and *A. deltoidea*; D. short stipules, narrow inflorescences; E. long stipules; F. short stipules, broad inflorescences; G. *Scandia rosaefolia*, broad leaflets; H. *S. rosaefolia*, narrow leaflets; I. *S. geniculata*; J. *Gingidia*, winged mericarps; K. *Gingidia*, unwinged mercarps; L. *Lignocarpa*.

PREDOMINANTLY ALPINE, DIOECIOUS OR GYNODIOECIOUS GENERA OF PROBABLE NEW ZEALAND ORIGIN (Fig. 1)

Scandia, Gingidia, Lignocarpa

These genera are related by their gynodioecism; lack of bristles or spines from the leaflet teeth; rudimentary staminodes in the female flowers (Fig. 2A, B); and consistently minute oil tubes in the mericarp ribs.

Scandia (Dawson, 1967*b*) is a genus of two species distinguished by terminal inflorescences, mericarps with winged lateral ribs, and extended perennial, semi-climbing vegetative stems, which become quite woody at the base.

Scandia rosaefolia (Hook. f.) Dawson is restricted to the central and northern North Island and appears to have two forms, which may warrant formal status as varieties. A form with broad leaflets is restricted to rocky coastal sites on or near the North Auckland peninsula. It often occurs in coastal shrubbery where its stems gain some support from the associated shrubs. The other form (Plate 1A) has mostly narrower leaflets and is found in central to north-eastern parts of the North Island at coastal and inland sites mostly below 3,000 feet.

Scandia geniculata (G. Forst.) Dawson (Plate 1B) occurs in coastal and mostly lower elevation inland sites in the south of the North Island and in the east of the South Island. The weak stems of this species are usually supported by shrubs. It differs strikingly from *S. rosaefolia* in the leaves, which have small generally simple laminae. Such a leaf contrast, however, is found in several other woody New Zealand genera where a group of species with very small leaves tends to have a more southerly and more elevated distribution than their larger leaved relatives (Rattenbury, 1962).

Gingidia, with five New Zealand species (Dawson, 1967*a*), chiefly differs from *Scandia* by its rosulate, herbaceous habit and axillary inflorescences (Fig. 3C). The species can be separated into a group of three with mericarps with winged lateral ribs and a group of two with unwinged mericarps. Two species of the winged mericarp group, *G. montanum* (J. R. & G. Forst.) Dawson and *G. decipiens* (Hook. f.) Dawson, have a similar range throughout the mountains mostly on the wetter western side of the South Island, although the former also extends to the North Island. The third species, *G. trifoliolatum* (Hook. f.) Dawson, is restricted to swampy montane sites in the northern South Island. In the unwinged mericarp group varieties of *G. enysii* (Kirk) Dawson occur in central to southern montane sites on the drier eastern side of the South Island, although there is a very disjunct occurrence of one of the varieties at the north-western tip of the island. The other species in the group, *G. flabellatum* (Kirk) Dawson, occurs in sandy coastal to montane sites in southern Stewart Island. There appears to be some geographical separation of the two groups as a line joining the north-eastern and south-western corners of the South Island would roughly separate them.

Lignocarpa (Plate 1C) (Dawson, 1967*b*) has two species, which are distinctive in several respects. They agree with *Gingidia* in their rosulate, herbaceous habit, axillary inflorescences and, with one group of *Gingidia*, in their unwinged mericarps, but chiefly differ in being very fleshy, having minute petal- as well as staminode-rudiments in the female flowers (Fig. 2A), and heavily lignified mericarp endocarps

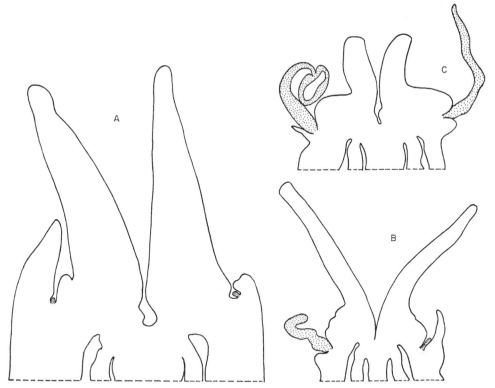

FIGURE 2. L.S. female flowers. (a) *Lignocarpa*. Staminode stippled on left, rudimentary petal on right; (b) *Gingidia, Scandia*. Staminode stippled on right, petal on left; (c) *Aciphylla, Anisotome*. Staminode stippled on left, petal on right.

(Plate 1D). The last feature is particularly striking as it is generally regarded as exclusive to the subfamily Hydrocotyloideae. However, there is no doubt on other grounds that *Lignocarpa* belongs to the Apioideae, and in this case the woody endocarp might be interpreted as an adaptation to the unusual habitat of the species. They occur only in extensive, steeply inclined shingle slips on mountains mostly east of the divide in the northern half of the South Island, so the hard mericarps may prevent mechanical damage from movements of the shingle, which is usually poised at the angle of rest.

Aciphylla *and* Anisotome

Both genera have terminal inflorescences (Fig. 3A, B) and differ from the *Scandia* group in being dioecious, having the staminodes in the female flowers differentiated into filaments and anthers (Fig. 2C), usually having the leaflet teeth produced into bristles or spines, and often having prominent oil tubes in the mericarp ribs.

Of the two genera, *Aciphylla,* with about 37 New Zealand species, is the more unusual as many species have rigid leaf- and bract-segments tipped by needle-sharp spines which fully justify such specific epithets as *horrida* and *ferox*. Many of the

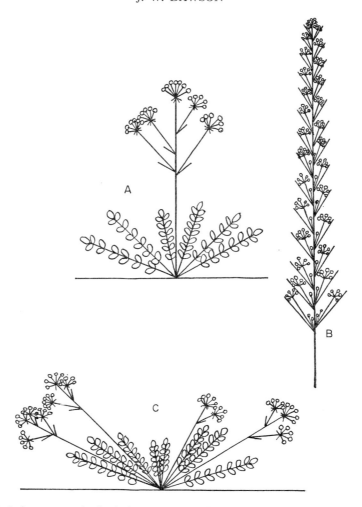

FIGURE 3. Inflorescences (each circle represents a simple umbel). A. Broad, terminal as in *Anisotome*, some Aciphyllas and *Scandia* (last however caulescent not rosulate). B. Narrow, terminal as in most Aciphyllas. C. Axillary as in *Gingidia* and *Lignocarpa*.

species also have an unusually large number of reduced compound umbels aggregated into narrow, elongate inflorescences (Fig. 3B; Plate 2A, B), sometimes 12 feet high in one species, which contrast with the more usual open arrangement of a smaller number of longer peduncled compound umbels (Fig. 3A) in most Apioideae.

However, as presently defined the genus includes species that are not spinescent and/or do not have narrow, elongate inflorescences. The distinctive characteristics of *Aciphylla* (Dawson, 1968) are both foliar: (a) All leaves are without petioles, consequently the proximal pair of leaf divisions arise from the top of the sheath and are in fact continuous with it (Plate 2C–E, Plate 3A–C). (In species where these divisions are reduced they have been regarded as stipules. Perhaps the mode of origin of 'stipules' in *Aciphylla* could lead us to a better understanding of stipules in general); (b) both surfaces of the flattened lamina segments are morphologically abaxial with the exception of a narrow longitudinal groove representing the reduced adaxial surface (Fig. 4).

The spinescent species readily draw blood on contact, so the habit would appear to be a defence against animals despite the fact that primitively New Zealand had no mammals other than bats. It has been suggested that the spines may have been a defence against moas, large browsing flightless birds now extinct. A second suggestion is that the spiny Aciphyllas are xerophytes and that the spines are a non-adaptive by-product of the extensive development of sclerenchyma characteristic of many xerophytes (Oliver, 1956). This view, however, must be questioned as most *Aciphylla* species grow in moist or even saturated soils. Of the two species that do grow in drier habitats on the eastern side of the South Island, *A. aurea* Oliver and *A. subflabellata* Oliver, the former has the stomata sunken in grooves, an undoubted xerophytic modification.

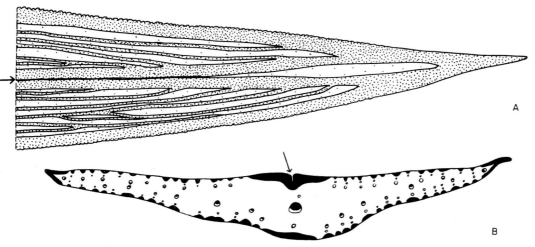

FIGURE 4. *Aciphylla colensoi*. A. Leaf segment tip. Sclerenchyma stippled. Adaxial groove indicated by arrow (× 4). B. T.S. leaf segment. Sclerenchyma and xylem black. Adaxial groove indicated by arrow (× 10).

As with *Gingidia* two groups of *Aciphylla* species can be recognized which appear to have different geographical centres. The first group comprises eleven rather small species centred at higher altitudes in the southern third of the South Island. The group is distinguished by leaves with a basically ternate-pinnate pattern in which the 'stipules' are as long, or almost as long as the median portion of the leaf (Plate 3A–C) even in species with reduced leaves. Six of the species in the group have broad, open inflorescences and occur in rocky habitats. The remaining five species have narrow, condensed inflorescences and occur in alpine grassland.

The second, larger group of about 25 species in *Aciphylla* is characterized by probably basically ternately compound leaves exhibiting a reduction trend involving great shortening of the 'stipules' relative to the rest of the leaf (Plate 2C–E). Again a further subdivision can be made on the basis of inflorescence form: (a) Six species have broad, open inflorescences. They are small plants of the main islands where they favour higher altitude grassland—one in the southern North Island; two in the northern, one in the central and two in the central and southern South Island; (b) 20 species have narrow, elongate inflorescences* and mostly favour subalpine shrubland or grassland—eight in the northern South Island and/or North Island; three ranging throughout the South Island; one in central, four in central and southern and two in southern South Island; and two in the Chatham Islands.

The short-stipuled species of *Aciphylla* are not so clearly centred geographically as is the long-stipuled group. However 15 of the 26 species are restricted to more northern areas (central and northern South Island, North Island, Chatham Islands) and of the remaining eleven species only four are restricted to the southern South Island, so it seems reasonable to postulate a central to northern South Island centre for the group on the main islands.

Anisotome is more in conformity with the general apioid growth habit than *Aciphylla* although a few higher alpine species are greatly reduced mat or cushion plants. The genus comprises more or less soft-textured plants with pinnately compound petiolate leaves (Plate 3E, F) lacking the extreme reduction of the abaxial leaflet surfaces exhibited by *Aciphylla* and with broad open inflorescences.

As with *Aciphylla* there appears to be a group of species in *Anisotome* centred at higher altitudes in the southern South Island, which includes the reduced cushion and mat forms already mentioned. *A. lanuginosa* (Kirk) Dawson and *A. imbricata* Hook. f. var. *imbricata* Dawson are restricted to the southern South Island; *A. flexuosa* Dawson extends from the south into the central South Island, but becomes less common in the northern part of its range, and *A. imbricata* var. *prostrata* Dawson apparently replaces the type variety in the central and northern South Island. The group is distinguished by leaves with very short to obsolete petioles; male and female inflorescences either both sessile or the male much shorter than the female; short and broad fruits with low ribs.

The other *Anisotome* group is characterized by well-defined petioles; male and female inflorescences never sessile and about the same height; fruits narrow with prominent ribs. It may be possible to distinguish two subgroups here. One comprises four rather large species growing at or near sea level—two in the Auckland and Campbell Islands south of New Zealand, of which one extends to Antipodes Island; one on the Snares Islands and the fourth, comprising a number of not yet clearly defined forms, in Stewart Island and the south and south-west coasts of the South Island. This subgroup is clearly centred in the subantarctic zone. The other subgroup comprises six smaller species in mostly alpine habitats in Stewart Island and through the South Island, with one species extending to the North Island. The geographical centre of this subgroup is not clear—one species extends throughout the South Island and into the North Island, two species extend throughout the South Island and three species are restricted to the southern South Island. If anything this suggests a southern South Island centre.

---

* The two Chatham Island species, *A. dieffenbachii* (Muell.) Kirk and *A. traversii* (Muell.) Hook. f., and *A. inermis* Oliver near Mt Cook in the central South Island, have inflorescences more or less intermediate between narrow and broad. However, other features of the first two species suggest that they belong with the narrow inflorescence group, e.g. mericarps with some ribs obsolete and more than one oil-tube per interval. Female plants of *A. inermis* have not yet been seen, but the habit and habitat of the species allow a tentative assignment to the same group.

The taxonomic placing of two other species in the *Aciphylla-Anisotome* group is uncertain. The species are *Anisotome filifolia* (Hook, f.) Ckn. & Laing and *A. deltoidea* Cheesem. As a result of a misinterpretation of their inflorescence position Dawson (1961) transferred them from *Anisotome* to *Gingidia*. However their terminal inflorescences and dioecious sexual pattern separate them from the latter genus and indicate a relationship with *Aciphylla* and *Anisotome*. The distinct petioles and unreduced adaxial leaflet surfaces of the two species suggests a greater affinity with *Anisotome*, although they differ from that genus in their ternate or ternate-pinnate leaf pattern, lack of hairs or bristles at the tips of the leaflet teeth, very broad carpophores in the fruit and obscure rib oil tubes. In this case pollen evidence does not help. Moar (1966) states that *A. filifolia* has the same pollen type as *Aciphylla* and *Anisotome*, while the pollen of *A. deltoidea* is similar to that of *Scandia*. On morphological grounds *A. deltoidea* is related to *A. filifolia* and not to *Scandia*.

Perhaps it would be best in the meantime to return these two species to *Anisotome* as a distinct section. They occur in montane to alpine grassland and herbfield and appear to be centred in the northern South Island. *A. deltoidea* is restricted to that region and *A. filifolia* extends into the central South Island.

Discussion of the New Zealand species

The genera considered in this section all belong to the Apioideae and comprise almost two-thirds of the species of Umbelliferae native to New Zealand and all the species having some form of unisexuality (dioecious—*Aciphylla*, *Anisotome*; gynodioecious—*Scandia*, *Gingidia*, *Lignocarpa*).

It is postulated that the ancestral stock of *Scandia*, *Gingidia* and *Lignocarpa* could have existed under quite warm climatic conditions during the Tertiary just as the larger leaved form of *S. rosaefolia* does on the northern New Zealand coasts today. It follows that *Scandia* would be the most primitive genus in the group and its semiwoody habit would suggest that its ancestors may have been small trees perhaps similar in habit to the present-day montane tropical *Myrrhidendron* Coulter & Rose of Central America, and *Heteromorpha* Cham. & Schecht., *Diplolophium* Turez. and *Steganotaenia* Hochst. of Africa. With the development of the mountains and colder conditions in the late Tertiary the smaller-leaved forms of *Scandia* would have evolved and moved south into higher latitudes but mostly in the lowlands, while the more cold-tolerant *Gingidia* and *Lignocarpa*, perhaps derived directly from *Scandia*, would have become established at higher altitudes. The group of *Gingidia* species with winged mericarps and a northern and western South Island centre come closest to *Scandia* and from this group may have been derived the southern and eastern South Island-centred group with unwinged mericarps and the north-eastern South Island scree genus *Lignocarpa* (Fig. 1).

The ancestors of *Aciphylla* and *Anisotome*, unlike those of the preceding genera, probably required cool climatic conditions.

It is tempting to suggest the Oligocene as the time of origin of the two genera. The Oligocene saw the first appearance of many herbaceous families in the fossil record and, according to Fleming (1962) and others, there is evidence that it was a relatively cool period in New Zealand and a time when most of the region occupied by the present main islands was submerged. Land is thought to have existed in the positions of the present Chatham Islands and Subantarctic Islands; in the latter case possibly extending to the position of the present southern South Island. Climatic conditions could have been suitable for the ancestral stock on these two island areas and in time the isolation of the two populations could have resulted in a divergence to *Aciphylla* in the Chathams area and to *Anisotome* in the subantarctic-southern South Island area.

When the mountains were raised and the main islands emerged alpine species of *Anisotome* would have evolved, migrated northwards and at some stage given rise to the generally higher altitude, southern South Island centred, short-petioled group of species and possibly to the *A. deltoidea*, *A. filifolia* group in the northern South Island (Fig. 1).

Present distribution patterns suggest that *Aciphylla* may have established first in the central to northern South Island, migrated north and south while diversifying and at some stage gave rise to the higher altitude, long-stipuled, southern South Island centred species group (Fig. 1).

The above interpretation is clearly only one of several possibilities. It might be argued, for instance, that *Aciphylla* and *Anisotome* originated on mainland New Zealand and later migrated to the Chatham and Subantarctic Islands; however if this were the case, it is rather surprising that only *Aciphylla* reached the former and only *Anisotome* the latter. It is possible also that the genera concerned originated on a warmer Antarctica and migrated independently to Australia and New Zealand late in the Tertiary.

In view of the suggestions of Cockayne and Wardle that present alpine species or their ancestors could have existed during the Tertiary on rocky cliffs or cool poorly drained infertile sites respectively, it is interesting to note that the species of *Aciphylla*, *Anisotome* and *Scandia* in the postulated regions of origin of these genera mostly grow in such sites—the large-leaved form of *Scandia rosaefolia* inhabits coastal cliffs in the north of the North Island; in the Chatham Islands *Aciphylla dieffenbachii* inhabits coastal cliffs and *A. traversii* mostly lowland peaty sites; in the Foveaux Strait-Subantarctic Island region *Anisotome latifolia* Hook. f. grows mostly in lowland swamps in the Auckland and Campbell Islands, *A. antipoda* Hook. f. grows in rocky coastal cliff sites or higher hill outcrops in the same islands, but in swampy sites on Antipodes Island, and *A. acutifolia* Kirk in the Snares Islands and *A. lyallii* Hook. f. in Stewart Island and the south to south west of the South Island mostly grow on coastal cliffs.

Why these genera that have probably had a long history in New Zealand should be either dioecious or gynodioecious is not clear. Isolated islands in general tend to have a significantly higher percentage of unisexual species than continental areas and Dawson (1964) suggests that this may be because island isolation gives exclusively or predominantly outcrossing, and hence variable species a great selective advantage. When environmental conditions change drastically on isolated islands the chances for survival by migration are limited and in these circumstances variable, outcrossing species have the best chance of surviving and taking advantage of the new habitats. It has been suggested that many of the genera in New Zealand that survived the late

Tertiary topographic and climatic changes speciated and became morphologically and ecologically diverse quite rapidly. This is the impression one gets from a consideration of the genera in this section. In *Aciphylla*, for instance, the smallest species have inflorescences only a few inches high, while those of the largest may be 12 feet high or more and there is a similarly wide range in other features. In view of such wide morphological variability in this and many other New Zealand genera it is surprising to find that natural hybridism is quite common, sometimes between species of very different form. On this point Wardle (1963) says, 'The widespread hybridism also points to recent and rapid evolution of the mountain flora. The numerous interspecific hybrids indicate recent differentiation and continuing evolution, while the reported occurrence of several intergeneric and intersubgeneric hybrids suggests that intense selection pressures, operating under conditions of rapid mountain-building and cooling climates, led to morphological evolution outstripping the evolution of genetical barriers'.

Australian representatives

One species of *Anisotome* occurs in alpine sites in Tasmania. At present it is known as *Aciphylla procumbens* Muell. It belongs to the southern South Island centred, short-petioled species group.

Two species of *Aciphylla*, *A. glacialis* (Muell.) and *A. simplicifolia* (Muell.) occur in the Australian Alps in short alpine grassland. They are small plants with broad, open inflorescences and, in the case of *A. glacialis*, short stipules. *A. simplicifolia* has reduced simple leaves with no stipules. These species can probably be referred to the broad inflorescence subgroup of the short-stipuled group in New Zealand, although none of the subgroup in New Zealand has simple leaves nor the thick almost fleshy texture of the Australian species.

Two species which should probably be referred to *Gingidia* grow in moist to swampy sites in the Australian Alps. They would belong to the southern and eastern South Island species group with unwinged mericarps, and are at present known as *Seseli algens* Muell. and *S. harveyanum* Muell.

The Australian species of *Anisotome* and *Aciphylla* are dioecious, but insufficient material of the Seselis has been seen to determine whether or not they are gynodioecious.

Although dioecism would seem to reduce the chances of establishment after migration the three genera may have reached Australia from New Zealand by overseas dispersal, although not too recently, as none of the Australian species is conspecific nor closely related to any in New Zealand.

Alternatively, the genera may have established in Australia when, in terms of the Gondwanaland theory, Australia and New Zealand were closer together.

PREDOMINANTLY ALPINE HERMAPHRODITE GENERA WIDELY DISTRIBUTED OUTSIDE NEW ZEALAND

Oreomyrrhis

This genus belongs to the Apioideae, but is quite distinct from any of the genera in the preceding section by virtue of its being pubescent, having mostly simple umbels and obsolete sepals. In addition those species of *Oreomyrrhis* whose chromosomes have been counted have $2n = 12$ or 14, while all chromosome numbers determined in the other genera are $2n = 22$.

Oreomyrrhis, comprising 23 species, has a very wide range from Central America, via South America to New Zealand, Tasmania, Australia, New Guinea, Borneo and Taiwan (Mathias & Constance, 1955). The twelve species in Tasmania, Australia and New Guinea exhibit a wider range of habit, including cushion species, than the species in other areas.

The three New Zealand species occur mostly at middle altitudes, two throughout the South Island and one through both main islands and in the Chatham Islands.

It would be difficult to argue that *Oreomyrrhis* originated in the New Zealand region and the wide range of the genus suggests that it may be capable of wide overseas dispersal, despite the lack of any obvious dispersal mechanism, and may have reached New Zealand in the Quaternary, perhaps from Australia.

The remaining genera in this section all belong to the Hydrocotyloideae.

Schizeilema

This genus of small stoloniferous herbs is best represented in New Zealand with eleven species, there being one other species in Victoria and another in Tierra del Fuego and the Falkland Islands. However, the distinctions between this genus and *Huanaca* Cav. in Chile and *Diplaspis* Hook. f. in Tasmania are not clear (L. Constance, personal communication).

The genus appears to have undergone some diversification in New Zealand, three of the species occurring in very wet swampy situations from the lowlands to middle altitudes, five in damp sites in montane grassland and shrubland and three in rocky subalpine habitats. There is no clear geographical pattern in the distribution of the species—one is restricted to the Subantarctic Islands, two to the southern South Island, two to the northern South Island and two to the north-eastern North Island. One species ranges through both islands and two through the South Island and into the southern North Island.

In view of the minor representation of the Hydrocotyloideae in New Zealand it seems unlikely that *Schizeilema* originated there. The subfamily is strongly represented in Australia and particularly South America, and Constance (personal communication) suggests that the fact that only the South American species of *Schizeilema* has a carpophore might indicate that it is primitive and that South America is the home of the genus.

It is well known that the chances for long distance dispersal of marsh and water plants are relatively high, probably as a result of transport by migratory birds, with the result that some species in these habitats are almost cosmopolitan. As three of the New Zealand species of *Schizeilema* occur in very wet habitats they or their ancestors may have reached New Zealand by overseas dispersal and later given rise to species suited to drier conditions.

Presence in New Zealand as a result of overseas dispersal is even more likely in the cases of the other two genera in this section.

Actinotus

The only species of this Australian genus in New Zealand also occurs in Tasmania, although Allan (1961) recognizes an endemic New Zealand variety. The latter occurs throughout the South Island and Stewart Island in boggy subalpine sites and is probably derived from an immigrant from Tasmania.

Azorella

Of this large South American genus only one species (*A. selago* Hook. f.) occurs in the New Zealand region and there only on Macquarie Island. The same species is found in Tierra Del Fuego and other widely separated islands in comparable latitudes. As Macquarie Island is thought to have been entirely devegetated during the last glaciation *Azorella selago* must have reached there overseas since that time, probably by the agency of some of the many migratory birds in those latitudes.

PREDOMINANTLY LOWLAND HERMAPHRODITE GENERA WIDELY DISTRIBUTED OUTSIDE NEW ZEALAND

All but one of the six genera in this section are represented in New Zealand by only one or a few species. Four genera belonging to the Apioideae (*Apium, Daucus, Lilaeopsis*) and Saniculoideae (*Eryngium*) probably originated in the Northern Hemisphere and two genera belonging to the Hydrocotyloideae (*Hydrocotyle, Centella*) in the Southern Hemisphere, although probably not in the New Zealand region.

The widely disjunct distributions of the genera and, in some cases, species in this section suggests that they are all capable of dispersal over quite wide ocean gaps. The first three genera considered below have at least some species occurring in very wet habitats which, as already mentioned, appear to provide favourable conditions for long distance dispersal.

Hydrocotyle

The eight New Zealand species appear to spread and establish very readily in moist lowland sites and all of them range throughout the main islands and in some cases to the Subantarctic, Chatham and Kermadec Islands. Of the three species favouring very wet sites two are said also to occur in Australia and Tasmania and a third species is said to range throughout North and South America.

The mixture of endemic and non-endemic species suggests migration to New Zealand on more than one occasion and possibly from more than one source.

Centella

The majority of the species of this genus are South African.

The one New Zealand species (*C. uniflora* (Col.) Nannf. is common throughout New Zealand and the Chatham Islands in moist to wet sites. It was formerly referred to the widespread *C. asiatica* Urban and is probably derived from that species.

Lilaeopsis

About 15 species of North and South America to Australia and New Zealand.

The three New Zealand species are regarded as endemic, but they are not well known. They all occur in very wet situations at lower elevations.

Apium

About 50 species widespread in both hemispheres.

The two New Zealand species occur in coastal habitats throughout and forms similar to them are widespread throughout the southern hemisphere.

Daucus

About 60 species mostly of the northern hemisphere. The single New Zealand species *D. glochidiatus* Fisch. is found throughout the main islands and in the Chatham Islands. It also occurs in Australia and Tasmania.

Eryngium

An almost cosmopolitan genus of about 200 species.

The sole New Zealand species, *E. vesiculosum* Labill. grows in coastal sites through the main islands and is also a native of Australia and Tasmania.

GENERAL DISCUSSION

In view of the fact that the subfamily Apioideae is thought to have originated in the northern and the subfamily Hydrocotyloideae in the southern hemisphere, perhaps the most puzzling feature of the New Zealand Umbelliferae is that the former subfamily is much more strongly represented than the latter. This situation is in contrast to that obtaining in Australia and South America where the Hydrocotyloideae are predominant. Australia has about 177 species of Umbelliferae of which only 20 (11%) belong to the Apioideae, 151 (85%) to the Hydrocotyloideae and 6 (4%) to the Saniculoideae. South America has about 273 species of which 35 (13%) belong to the Apioideae, 170 (62%) to the Hydrocotyloideae and 68 (25%) to the Saniculoideae.

The proportions of the subfamily in southern Africa are similar to those of New Zealand—of about 200 species 150 (75%) belong to the Apioideae, 30 (15%) to the Hydrocotyloideae and 20 (10%) to the Saniculoideae. In the case of Africa it might be hypothesized that the reason for that continent's poor representation of the Hydrocotyloideae might be that it separated from Gondwanaland before the subfamily became widespread in the remaining southern land areas and that its relatively strong representation of Apioideae might have resulted from its later connection with Eurasia.

A similar hypothesis for New Zealand would seem much less plausible. Conceivably the poor representation of the Hydrocotyloideae in New Zealand might also be explained by an early separation from Gondwanaland, but unlike Africa there is no connection with the north temperate regions to provide a possible explanation for the predominance of Apioideae. Considering the Apioideae alone there seem to be several possibilities with regard to the ultimate origin of the genera which appear to have had a long history in New Zealand and perhaps Australia. These genera may have had north temperate ancestors which reached New Zealand in the Tertiary either by migration from North America via South America and Antarctica or directly by long distance dispersal. The former is made less likely by the fact that neither the New Zealand genera concerned, nor apparently any genera related to them, occur in South America.

If, as seems likely, the herbaceous Apioideae evolved from montane tropical woody apioid ancestors of at least shrub to small tree dimensions, then the evolution of herbaceous forms could have taken place in both north and south hemispheres. If this were the case then the endemic southern hemisphere genera of the Apioideae are not necessarily directly related to genera originating in the northern hemisphere.

Whatever their origin it seems clear that the genera of Umbelliferae with a probable long history in New Zealand owe their present numbers and diversity of species to the development of extensive alpine habitats during the late Tertiary and Quaternary. If the genera of this group occurring in Australia have had an equally long history there then the small representation of species may reflect the more limited and less diverse alpine habitats of south-eastern Australia and Tasmania.

ACKNOWLEDGEMENTS

I am grateful to Dr Lincoln Constance for his helpful comments on the manuscript, to Mr M. D. King for most of the photographs, and to the *New Zealand Journal of Botany* for permission to reprint them.

REFERENCES

ALLAN, H. H., 1961. *Flora of New Zealand.* Vol. I. Wellington: Government Printer.

COCKAYNE, L., 1928. *The Vegetation of New Zealand.* 2nd ed.—*Die Vegetation der Erde.* XIV. Leipzig.

DAWSON, J. W., 1961. A Revision of the Genus *Anisotome. Univ. Calif. Publs Bot.*, **33**: 1–98.

DAWSON, J. W., 1964. Unisexuality in the New Zealand Umbelliferae. *Tuatara*, **12**: 67–68.

DAWSON, J. W., 1967a. The New Zealand Species of *Gingidium* (Umbelliferae). *N.Z. Jl Bot.*, **5**: 84–116.

DAWSON, J. W., 1967b. New Zealand Umbelliferae. *Lignocarpa* gen. nov. and *Scandia* gen. nov. *N.Z. Jl Bot.*, **5**: 400–417.

DAWSON, J. W., 1968. New Zealand Umbelliferae—A Leaf Comparison of *Aciphylla* and *Anisotome. N.Z. Jl Bot.*, **6**: 450–458.

FLEMING, C. A., 1962. New Zealand Biogeography. A Paleontologist's Approach. *Tuatara*, **10**: 53–108.

FORSTER, J. R. and G., 1776. *Characteres Generum Plantarum.* . . . London.

HILL, J., 1756. *The British Herbal.* London.

MATHIAS, M. E. & CONSTANCE, L., 1955. The Genus *Oreomyrrhis* (Umbelliferae). *Univ. Calif. Publs Bot.*, **27**: 347–416.

MOAR, N. T., 1966. Studies in Pollen Morphology. 3. The Genus *Gingidium* J. R. and G. Forst. in New Zealand. *N.Z. Jl Bot.*, **4**: 322–332.

OLIVER, W. R. B., 1956. The Genus *Aciphylla. Trans. R. Soc. N.Z.*, **84**: 1–18.

RATTENBURY, J. A., 1962. Cyclic Hybridization as a Survival Mechanism in the New Zealand Forest Flora. *Evolution*, **16**: 348–363.

WARDLE, P., 1963. Evolution and Distribution of the New Zealand Flora as Affected by Quaternary Climates. *N.Z. Jl Bot.*, **1**: 3–17.

WARDLE, P., 1968. Evidence for an Indigenous pre-Quaternary Element in the Mountain Flora of New Zealand. *N.Z. Jl Bot.*, **6**: 120–125.

EXPLANATION OF PLATES

PLATE 1
A. *Scandia rosaefolia* (narrow-leaflet form). Hermaphrodite ($\times 0.25$).
B. *Scandia geniculata*. Tips of climbing stems ($\times 0.5$).
C. *Lignocarpa carnosula*. Inflorescence with some surrounding stones removed to show attachment to rootstock ($\times 0.5$).
D. *Lignocarpa carnosula*. T.S. mericarp. The woody endocarp appears black ($\times 30$).

PLATE 2
A. *Aciphylla aurea*. Female plant with narrow, spiny infructescence ($\times 0.1$).
B. *Aciphylla colensoi*. Portion of infructescence showing short axillary compound umbels and spiny bracts ($\times 0.3$).
C–E. *Aciphylla*. Leaves of three species of the short-stipule group illustrating reduction trend of stipules.
C, *A. subflabellata* ($\times 0.2$); D, *A. sp.* ($\times 0.12$); E, *A. colensoi* ($\times 0.12$).

PLATE 3
A–D. *Aciphylla*. Leaves of 4 species of the long-stipule group.
A. *A. pinnatifida* ($\times 0.9$); B, *A. crosby-smithii* ($\times 0.5$); C, *A. dobsonii* ($\times 0.5$); D, *A. simplex* ($\times 0.5$).
E–F. *Anisotome*. Leaves of two species. Top of sheath indicated by arrows. E, *A. haastii* ($\times 0.4$); F, *A. aromatica* ($\times 0.4$).

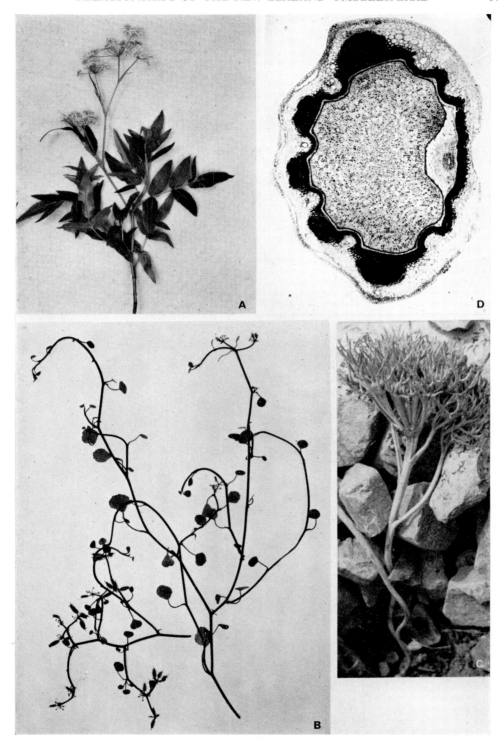

PLATE 1

Plate 2

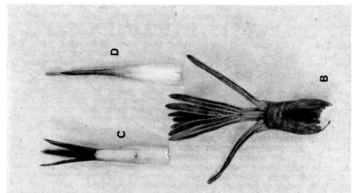

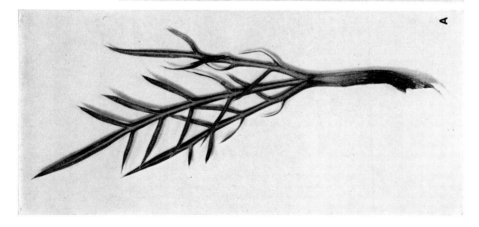

PLATE 3

The relationships of the Umbellales

RAFAEL L. RODRÍGUEZ C.

Department of Biology, University of Costa Rica, Costa Rica, C.A.

The Umbelliferae as usually defined are closely connected with the mostly tropical and woody Araliaceae, and often united with them into a single family. With them, or separate and close to them, is placed the Cornalean alliance of some 15–20 woody genera, variously interpreted as containing from one to seven families, and including the Garryaceae, a unigeneric family of apetalous anemophiles. The group as a whole has been held to derive from Hamamelidales, Saxifragales, Myrtales or Rhamnales; recently, separate relationship has been postulated, the Cornales with the Escalloniaceae, the Umbellales s. str. with the Sapindales.

Wood anatomy has provided several scales by which phylogenetic relationship may be thought probable or improbable. Application of such criteria to the Umbellalean group, in correlation with recent morphological, palynological, phytochemical and serological techniques, points to the two large alliances with their peripheral families forming a flabellate cluster of advanced taxa originating from a common area near Escalloniaceae, encompassing the Rhizophoraceae and relating in some degree with Rutaceae-Sapindaceae, Caprifoliaceae, Pittosporaceae and Compositae. Advanced features in flower, fruit or inflorescence may accompany relatively primitive xylem within this assemblage. The author argues for a reappraisal of inflorescence characters indicating relative degrees of functional organization.

CONTENTS

INTRODUCTION

The apioid Umbelliferae of the European scene offered such a picture of recognizable characters that they served to lead the popular mind and the early botanists towards the very concept of taxonomic relationship. As the search for a coherent system continued, authors free from a Theophrastean tree/shrub/herb bias perceived some degree of similarity between the Umbelliferae they knew and plants mostly of quite different habit—*Hedera* L., *Aralia* [Tourn.] L., *Sambucus* [Tourn.] L., *Vitis* [Tourn.] L. (cf. Adanson, 1763; De Jussieu, 1789; Endlicher, 1841). The nineteenth century brought about fuller knowledge of the corresponding families, and the affinity of the Araliaceae and the Cornaceae with the Umbelliferae was repeatedly noted, giving rise to the concept of Umbelliflorae or Umbellales. Phylogenetic thinking readily postulated a sequence in them, usually culminating in the Umbelliferae (Roederer, 1930; Takhtajan, 1959) or, in many versions, leading on further towards sympetalous, epigynous groups—Caprifoliaceae, Rubiaceae, Compositae (cf. Bessey, 1915; Soó, 1961). The order as usually delimited comprises the two large families, Araliaceae and Umbelliferae, with some 70 and 300 genera respectively and together totalling some 3750 species, and a cluster of genera— *Alangium* Lam., *Aucuba* Thunb., *Camptotheca* Dcne., *Cornus* [Tourn.] L., *Corokia* A. Cunn., *Curtisia* Ait., *Davidia* Baill., *Garrya* Dougl. ex Lindl., *Griselinia* Forst. f., *Helwingia* Willd., *Kaliphora* Hook. f., *Lautea* F. Brown, *Mastixia* Blume, *Melanophylla* Bak., *Nyssa* Gronov. and *Torricellia* DC., encompassing in all some 140 species and variously treated as forming from one (Cornaceae: Harms, 1898) to seven families. The order is characterized by mostly pentamerous or tetramerous flowers with a reduced calyx, free petals and stamens, inferior ovaries mostly with a pulviniform disk or a stylopodium supporting one or more styles, tending to 5, 4, 2, or 1 locules with one pendent, anatropous functional ovule per locule; by drupaceous or schizocarpous fruits (a few baccate), and seed with abundant endosperm and small, straight embryos; by occasional trends to unisexuality and apetaly; and by usually involucrate, cymose, umbellate or capitate inflorescences.

The association of this latter group with the umbello-aralian alliance is accepted by numerous authors (Bartling, 1830; Endlicher, 1841; Brongniart, 1843; Bentham & Hooker, 1862; Harms, 1898; Hallier, 1905, 1912; Bessey, 1915; Lotsy, 1911; Johnson, 1931; Engler & Diels, 1936; Wettstein, 1935; Pulle, 1952; Soó, 1961; Emberger, 1960, with reservations; Melchior, 1964; and Thorne, 1968). Others see them as a separate order, in sequence with the Umbellales s. str. or parallel with them (De Jussieu, 1789; De Candolle, 1830; Novák, 1954; Benson, 1957; Takhtajan, 1959*). Hutchinson (1926, 1969) associates them with the Araliaceae, maintaining his view of the separate origin of the Umbelliferae. The close relationship between the two alliances has been challenged more than once—by Hoar (1915), Mittal (1961), Cronquist (1965, 1968), Eyde (1967) and Hegnauer (1969).

Taxonomic treatments were initially based on morphological criteria; anatomical characters were brought into consideration about the turn of the century and have continued to carry weight in the discussion (cf. Géneau de Lamarlière, 1893;

---

* Later Takhtajan, *Flowering Plants. Origin and Dispersal*, Edinburgh: Oliver and Boyd (1969), adopted a broad order Cornales including the Cornaceae, Araliaceae and Apiaceae.

Van Noenen, 1895; Drude, 1897; Nestel, 1905; Viguier, 1906, 1909; Hoar, 1915; Mittal, 1961). Beginning about 1917 with Jeffrey's work, the next twenty-five years saw the development of wood anatomy as an additional, specialized method of identification and of phylogenetic research. The secondary xylem, produced by a different meristem from that giving rise to the reproductive organs and evolving under different environmental demands, was found to exhibit a one-way sequence from a largely undifferentiated pattern to one of highly differentiated conducting and mechanical elements; the evolutionary process being in effect a decrease in randomness and an increase in functional effectiveness of the tissue and its components. Critical summaries of the basic findings and criteria have been published by Bailey (1951, 1953), Tippo (1946), Metcalfe (1946, 1968), Metcalfe & Chalk (1950), and Carlquist (1961), among others; and summaries of the accepted criteria are usually included in studies of particular groups or problems. Various such studies of umbellalean families have been made (Adams, 1949; Titman, 1949; Li & Chao, 1954; Moseley & Beeks, 1955; Rodríguez, 1957a, b), all the families except the Umbelliferae being predominantly arborescent and the Umbels themselves having some species of perennial woody habit and secondary xylem developing in a number of shrubby and herbaceous species.

Among the various characters considered in such studies, I have argued (Rodríguez, 1957a, b) for greater attention to be given to certain features of the vessel element end-wall which, as part of the assembled information, seem to summarize the relative advancement of the species examined. These features are the details of the perforation plate and the end-wall angle (see Figs 1–5), expressed not only as an average figure but as the frequency curve of the angles observed in a sample of 200— in accordance with the recommendation of Rendle & Clark (1934) that 100 vessel elements be measured. This is feasible by recording the quotient of the height of the end-wall along the element's long axis divided by the width at the point where the end-wall ends, i.e. the value of the cotangent of the end-wall angle. This can be done very rapidly in a sample of macerated material, in whatever position the vessel elements are observed, with any type of ocular micrometer; two decimals are sufficient for a breakdown in intervals of ten degrees.

The further resources of present day taxonomy—cytology, phytochemistry, serology, palynology (cf. Davis & Heywood, 1963; Heywood, 1968b)—have also been utilized; and several workers, like Philipson and Eyde, have made important contributions by careful reinvestigation of apparently well-known floral and fruit characters.

In the discussion of the various problems found in this interesting group, there is still another criterion, relating to the inflorescence, that should be considered. The families included in the Umbellales have a diversity of inflorescence-types in which rather elaborate arrangements are repeatedly achieved, indicating a history of cumulative modifications. Cerceau-Larrival (1962) explored briefly the degree of organization in the umbelliferan inflorescence, following an interesting thought of Gaussen (1947) which has largely gone unheeded, perhaps because in publication it was tied to the less acceptable concept of 'surévolution'. I have been preparing for publication a different view, which may be briefly summarized here. In Leppik's (1957)

FIGURES 1–3. Vessel element end-wall angle frequency curves in families included in the Umbellales *s. lat.*, or considered related to them, drawn according to the percentage scale shown in Fig. 1.

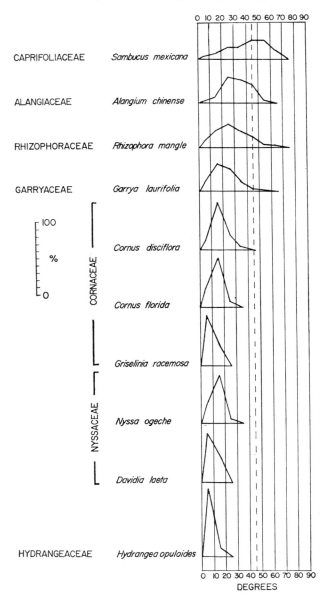

FIGURE 1. Curves from a sampling of species in the Hydrangeaceae, Nyssaceae, Cornaceae, Garryaceae, Rhizophoraceae, Alangiaceae and Caprifoliaceae (Sambucaceae?).

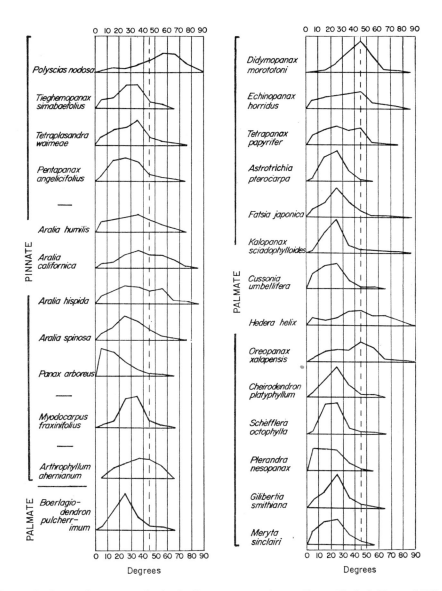

FIGURE 2. Curves from genera in the Araliaceae, arranged according to Eyde & Tseng (1970). The pinnate-leaved series comprises members of four divergent lines. Note curves indicating greater advance in xylem characters in *Polyscias* and *Didymopanax*, *Hedera*, the herbaceous species of *Aralia*, *Oreopanax*, and the unicarpellate *Arthrophyllum*.

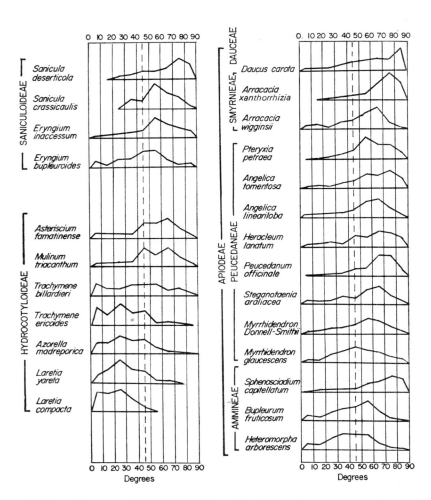

FIGURE 3. Curves from genera in the Umbelliferae. Note independent sequences of progression in all three subfamilies. The species shown of *Eryngium, Trachymene, Steganotaenia, Myrrhidendron, Bupleurum* and *Heteromorpha* are woody and shrubby or arborescent.

FIGURES 4–5. Patterns of vessel element perforation plates found in a sampling of the families included in the Umbellales *sensu lato*, or thought to be related to them.

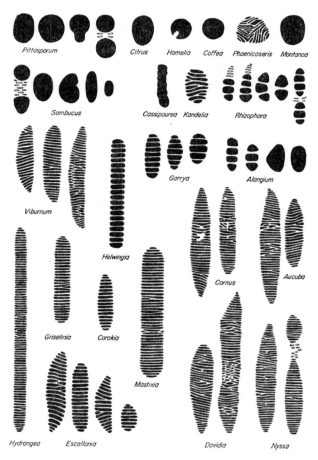

FIGURE 4. Perforation plates characteristic of diverse families. Note in *Hydrangea* (Hydrangeaceae) very long plates with numerous bars; in *Escallonia* (Escalloniaceae) shorter plates with many bars and irregular or reticular patterns. In the cornalean alliance, the same tendencies reappear in *Davidia*, *Nyssa* (note double perforation plate), *Mastixia*, *Cornus* and *Aucuba*. In the problem genera *Griselinia* and *Corokia*, scalariform plates with reduced size and number of bars; in *Helwingia* (Helwingiaceae), a long perforation plate with bars widely spaced. *Garrya* (Garryaceae) has few-barred scalariform plates; in Alangiaceae, sect. Conostigma has few-barred plates (after Eyde, 1968) and *A. chinense* the usual simple perforations. In Rhizophoraceae, a long, simple perforation of *Cassipourea* and a scalariform plate of *Kandelia* (after Marco, 1935) are shown, and few-barred plates of *Rhizophora* with occasional double perforation plates. In *Pittosporum* (Pittosporaceae), simple perforations with occurrence of double perforations and occasional vestigial bars. In Caprifoliaceae, the scalariform perforation plates of *Viburnum* contrast with the simple and occasional double perforations of *Sambucus*. Wide, simple perforations of *Citrus* (Rutaceae) and smaller ones of *Hamelia* and *Coffea* (Rubiaceae) represent the norm of their respective families, as well as *Montanoa* for the Compositae. *Phoenicoseris* (Compositae: Cichorieae) contrasts, with its reticulate plates (after Carlquist, 1961).

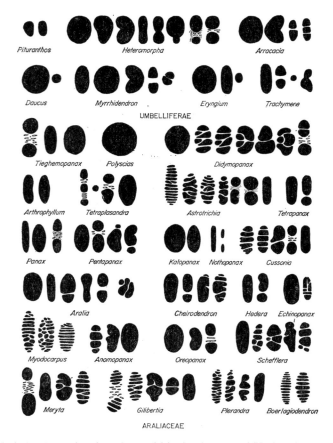

FIGURE 5. Variation in perforation plates within Araliaceae and Umbelliferae. The species of Araliaceae are arranged roughly according to Eyde & Tseng (1970). The pinnate-leaved group (left) comprises representatives of four divergent lines. Note the broad scope of the family from purely scalariform and reticulate plates (*Boerlagiodendron*, *Mydocarpus*) through many graded combinations of simple and scalariform plates with the frequent occurrence of double perforations, vestigial and free bars and some reticulate patterns, to exclusively simple perforations (*Polyscias*, *Kalopanax*). The Umbelliferae have predominantly simple perforations with rare double perforations or vestigial bars, except in *Heteromorpha* in which the latter features are fairly frequent.

sequence of flower types from an 'amorphic' model through the ranalean 'haplomorphic' to 'actinomorphic', 'stereomorphic' and 'zygomorphic' types, the appearance of the amorphic model and the transition to the haplomorphic represent the culmination of one line of progress implying the subordination of a number of independently produced organs into a unit, so co-ordinated that our ancestors—and most people even today—would perceive it as a *part of the plant*, comparable to leaf or stem—in fact, a functional unit, structurally so much so that we speak of a floral meristem. The further stages, successive animal-oriented pollination adaptations, or the comparable steps in simplification in anemophilous flowers (*vide* Stebbins, 1951, on the four general adaptive trends in floral evolution), constitute an additional sequence of changes in the information determining the behaviour of the floral meristem, a series of possibilities opened up by the achievement of the haplo-morphic model. Meanwhile, a separate step of refinement in the information acting on meristematic cells but involving a different meristem takes place in the change from randomly associated flowering apices to describable cymose or racemose structures, to those in which the organization of the inflorescence, or its symmetry, becomes meaningful for the reproductive function, on to those in which the inflorescence *is* the functional unit and individual flowers assume the role of stamens, pistils or petals, or, lacking the latter, there may appear a second-order 'perianth' of bracts of some sort: by then a second cycle of organization has been completed and we are faced by an integrated structure, the daisy or the Gerbera, seen as a flower until we learned to call it a capitulum. We should call to mind here Gaussen's (1947) felicitous term, 'péricyathe' for the ring of petaloid bracts in a cyathium such as that of *Euphorbia fulgens*, which practically duplicates the picture of an actinomorphic peach flower. From here possibilities open up for further progress—capitula or cyathia in loose association, functioning singly, on to neatly defined third-order inflorescences (*Pedilanthus* Neck.), until the capitula, cyathia or umbels take on the function of stamens or pistils in a third-order 'flower'—the Poinsettia, now at the amorphic-haplomorphic stage with a third-order 'perianth'. Gaussen (1947), calling this an 'incyathescence', saw this as a pseudo-cyclic phenomenon. I would rather suggest a succession of cycles, not in the sense of returning, or seeming to return, to a given starting point, but in the sense of the 'cycles' in semilogarithmic graph paper, the culmination of one becoming the starting point of the next (cf. Stebbins, 1970, on transference of function in dispersal). We could thus assign either qualitative or conventional ordinal relative values to the types of inflorescence found in the Umbellales.

UMBELLIFERAE

The Umbelliferae, our central topic, are characterized by a little-varying floral pattern comprising an inferior bicarpellate ovary, a much reduced calyx, five free petals and stamens and a stylopodium supporting two styles; by the basic uniformity and infinite variation of the fruit with two one-seeded, five-ribbed mericarps; by trinucleate (Brewbaker, 1967), tricolporate pollen grains; by inflorescences based on a simple or compound umbel or a capitulum; and by a definite range of leaf form and division. Anatomically they also present characteristic features like the development of collenchyma support, the presence of secretory ducts in spatial relation to the vascular bundles, and the multilacunar nodes. The family is divided into three subfamilies, well differentiated by the structure of the fruit. In all three there occur independently similar phenomena—different degrees of dissection of the leaf blade; different degrees of petal infolding and lobing of the apex; comparable modifications of the inflorescence; presence of woody, shrubby or arborescent species. Such woody species show similar general characteristics; pores diffuse, scanty vasicentric parenchyma, Heterogeneous IIB rays, vessel elements with almost exclusively simple perforations and mostly wide angles (Figs 3, 5) and, in some cases, further modifications like helical ('spiral') thickenings.

Chemical affinities of the Umbelliferae with the Hydrangeaceae, Rutaceae, Simaroubaceae and Compositae are mentioned by Paris (1963), Shorland (1963) and Sørensen (1963). Ehrlich & Raven (1967) and Hegnauer (1969) stress the chemical nexus with the Rutaceae as indicative of relationship.

Hydrocotyloideae

Hylander's (1945) proposal of a separate family Hydrocotylaceae has not been accepted generally, the links with the other groups being too evident; but a long independent history is indicated by the basic chromosome numbers (Darlington & Wylie, 1955; Bell & Constance, 1957–66), by the chemical dissimilarity noted by Ehrlich & Raven (1965) and by the predominantly Southern Hemisphere pattern of distribution and differentiation (Mathias, 1965). The subfamily is usually considered more primitive, implying that it is nearer the Araliaceae, than to the other two. The structure of the fruit is one reason, since, through *Hydrocotyle* [Tourn.] L. and *Myodocarpus* Brongn. & Gris. (Baumann, 1946) a convincing typological sequence bridges the gap between both families. Tseng (1967) points out other details of the anatomy of *Hydrocotyle* which are also araliad-like. Cerceau-Larrival (1962) contests the assumption that the laterally compressed fruit of *Hydrocotyle* and other related genera is the primitive form, arguing in favour of one like that of *Azorella* Lam., not compressed in either direction; Tseng (1967) concurs in regarding the *Hydrocotyle* type as one of several forms of functional specialization of the bicarpellate schizocarp, one not necessitating the production of a free carpophore. He also describes the vascular system of the ovary and fruit of the Hydrocotyloideae, showing the absence of ventral bundles in most species of *Hydrocotyle* and in *Bowlesia* Ruiz & Pav., a condition considered by Jackson (1933) as more advanced than the presence of four centrally placed ventral strands.

In spite of such indications of a primitive nature, the members of the Hydrocotyloideae offer many others of a high level of advancement—the creeping, herbaceous habit of *Hydrocotyle*; the orbicular, peltate leaves of some of its species, with unifacial petioles capable of great elongation (up to 1·20 m); the extreme reduction of habit of *Naufraga* Constance & Cannon; or the sympodial pseudodichotomy of *Spananthe* Jacq. No tall forms are included; *Asteriscium* Cham. & Schlechtd., *Gymnophyton* Clos ex Gay, *Mulinum* Pers. and *Trachymene* Rudge are small perennials (Mathias & Constance, 1962) with some development of secondary xylem which reflects the adaptive habit modifications of the plants (vide Hooker, 1834) in the marked shortening of the vessel elements (Rodríguez, 1957a). Vestigial bars and irregular perforations (Fig. 5) occur here more frequently than in the other subfamilies. The cushion plant species of *Azorella* and *Laretia* Gill. & Hook. present extreme morphological and anatomical adaptations, those of the xylem (Ternetz, 1902; Rodríguez, 1957a) strongly indicative of a paedomorphic process (Carlquist, 1962).

Saniculoideae

Many features of this group indicate a much-evolved position and a separate evolutionary development from the other two. Basic chromosome numbers (Darlington & Wylie, 1955; Bell & Constance, 1957–1966) are largely restricted to 7 and

8, in contrast with the greater diversity in the other subfamilies. In none of the genera are ordinary flat petals found; nearly all show advanced modification of the habit, mostly toward rosette plants with thick roots or rootstocks, including in the array the American species of *Eryngium* [Tourn.] L. with Bromeliad-like habit. The tree-like species of *Eryngium*, *E. bupleuroides* Hook. & Arn. (1833), *E. sarcophyllum* Hook. & Arn. (1833) and *E. inaccessum* Skottsberg (*vide* Bertero, 1830; Skottsberg, 1922, 1945) of the Juan Fernández Islands develop a woody trunk, whose xylem is not at all primitive for the family (Figs 3, 5; *vide* Rodríguez, 1957*a*) and which may be one more case of the island gigantism discussed by Carlquist (1965).

The degree of organization of the inflorescence is one of the most noteworthy features of the group (Cerceau-Larrival, 1960): umbels or capitula with perianth-like involucres or involucels (*Astrantia* [Tourn.] L., *Eryngium*, *Hacquetia* Neck.); third-order umbels or capitula reduced to second- or prime-order appearance (*Eryngium*); umbels or capitula with functionally unisexual flowers taking on the role of stamens or pistils (*Astrantia*, *Petagnia* Guss., *Sanicula* [Tourn.] L.); umbels or capitula themselves taking on the role of stamens or pistils in a more complex inflorescence (*Astrantia*); inflorescences constituting a single dispersal instrument (*Petagnia*, *Thecocarpus* Boiss.), the latter even more complete an example of sub-ordination into a functional unit than Zohary (1950) found in the Compositae.

Ehrlich & Raven (1965) note the difference in chemical content among the sub-families of Umbelliferae, which again indicates a long history of independent evolution; but mention should be made of the remarkable convergence in aromatic compounds shown by *Eryngium foetidum* L. and *Coriandrum sativum* L. (Apioideae) bridging this gap.

Apioideae

The classic umbellifers, with a long history of advancement of their own written in every organ, have exploited the compound umbel to great advantage, usually carrying it to a sympodial succession of such units or to a dichasial or pleochasial arrangement of them. Further degrees of organization and of subordination of the flower to the higher unit are seen in genera like *Coriandrum*, in which the peripheral flowers are zygomorphic in relation to the radial planes of the main umbel; in cases of unisexuality or of specialization of a terminal flower, as in *Daucus* [Tourn.] L.; in species of *Bupleurum* [Tourn.] L. in which the involucel becomes functionally showy; or in the Mexican *Mathiasella bupleuroides* Const. & Hitchc. (1954), in which a showy involucre and involucels recalling a malvaceous corolla set off mono-ecious umbellets of petalled staminate and achlamydeous pistillate flowers—a truly second-order haplomorph 'flower'!

Many species of this so consistently herbaceous group do develop secondary xy-lem; but truly woody, arborescent or shrubby species are found especially in two groups, combining in each case some primitive features with an over-all high level of advancement.

Peucedaneae-Ferulinae

Conspicuous here are the high-montane Central and South American genus *Myrrhidendron* Coulter & Rose (1894, 1927) and the African *Steganotaenia* Hochst., both showing scalariform bordered side-wall pitting (rather primitive) and (advanced) exclusively simple perforations (one double perforation in *M. donnell-smithii* Coulter & Rose in several thousand elements examined). Although the isolated populations of *Myrrhidendron* on mountain summits above the 3000 m level offer the temptation to see its woodiness and tall habit as a case of gigantism related to insularity ('islands of the upper air'; Carlquist, 1965)—and so it may be, like *Rumex costaricensis* Rechinger—it has none of the 'rosette' foliage type, and the structure of the xylem is that of normal dicotyledon wood, with no indication of secondary derivation (Rodríguez, 1957a).

Ammineae-Carinae

In this group there are several shrubby species of *Bupleurum* and the remarkable *Heteromorpha arborescens* (Thunb.) Cham. & Schlechtd., with (advanced) opposite to alternate pitting and helical ('spiral') thickenings and (relatively primitive) vestigial bars in the simple perforations and as much as 7% double perforations in the material examined. The small African xerophytic shrub *Pituranthos aphylla* (Cham. & Schlechtd.) Schinz (*vide* Messeri, 1938; Rodríguez, 1957a) presents a case of diminution of the xylem components paralleling the phenomena described by Carlquist (1958, 1961) in certain Compositae.

The Apioideae show a wider range of chromosome base numbers (6–12) than either the other subfamilies or the Araliaceae (Darlington & Wylie, 1955; Bell & Constance, 1957–1966).

ARALIACEAE

The Araliaceae, an assemblage of mostly arborescent, mostly tropical species, have been recognized as a separate family (Linnaeus, 1764; De Jussieu, 1789; Necker, 1790; De Candolle, 1830; Bartling, 1830; Endlicher, 1841; Brongniart, 1843; Bentham & Hooker, 1862; Harms, 1908; Bessey, 1915; Johnson, 1931; Wettstein, 1935; Rendle, 1938; Pulle, 1952; Cronquist, 1957, 1968; Takhtajan, 1959; Emberger, 1960; Melchior, 1964) closely related to the Umbelliferae, and by numerous other authors as forming a single family with them (Adanson, 1763; Crantz, 1767; Seeman, 1864; Baillon, 1880; Calestani, 1905; Hallier, 1905, 1912; Thorne, 1967) while Hutchinson (1926, 1929, 1969) holds the two families to converge from separate stocks. The distinction is not very important except from the latter viewpoint, as even those who recognize the two families agree that no clear dividing line can be drawn between them (cf. Harms, 1898; Domin, 1908). Nearly every vegetative or floral feature typical of the Umbelliferae occurs somewhere within the Araliaceae (cf. Philipson, 1951; Baumann, 1946; Baumann-Bodenheim, 1955); both groups are also linked by chemical (Hegnauer, 1969) and palynological (Brewbaker, 1967) similarities. The Araliaceae, however, present such a broad spectrum of characters (Philipson, 1970) that they exceed the role usually attributed to them of 'leading' to the Umbelliferae. The latter are evidently a derived group, with a narrower genetic repertoire, later enriched to exploit to the utmost its possibilities; but the Araliaceae, apart from their proximity to them, and starting, as Eyde (1970) argues (in opposition to Cronquist's view, 1968) from a plerandrous, pluricarpellate stock, show not only a trend towards the Umbelliferous pattern indicated by the reduction of stamens (to five) and carpels (to five and to two: Baumann (1946) and to one: Baumann-Bodenheim, (1955)), but other trends such as secondary increase of stamens and of carpels (to hundreds), secondary hypogyny (Eyde & Tseng, 1969), unisexuality and sympetaly. Philipson (1970) points out the frequency of foliar dimorphism, and, like Eyde & Tseng (1970), distinguished two tendencies in leaf-form, one of pinnately compound, the other of palmately compound or palmately lobed leaves. The Araliaceae also show a broad range of inflorescence patterns, including typical simple and compound umbels, umbels associated in racemes and panicles, and also umbels modified to compact heads, some functioning very much like units, and organized in spikes, racemes or panicles (*Oreopanax* Dcne. & Planch.). In some species, as in *O. oerstedianus* March, crimson-tinted bracts enveloping the young inflorescence suggest the trend towards a second-cycle 'perianth' such as both the Umbelliferae and the Cornaceae have developed.

The Araliaceae show, in contrast to the Apioideae and the Hydrocotyloideae, considerable consistency in a basic chromosome number of $x = 12$ (Darlington & Wylie, 1955).

The wood anatomy of the Araliaceae is quite varied in comparison with that of the Umbelliferae. Some species have wood and vessel-element characteristics much like those of arborescent Umbelliferae—*Oreopanax xalapensis* (HBK) Dcne. & Planch. in comparison with the sympatric *Myrrhidendron donnell-smithii*; on the other hand, within the family there is also found a succession of grades in perforation plates, including scalariform types of from very few to many bars—up to 24 in my observations and still longer plates as shown by Soper (1957)—and many instances of wood with simple perforations and a proportion of elements with one bar and vestiges of bars and branching hairs (a tendency early recognized by Brown, 1918); few-barred plates with reticulate patterns are also frequent. Double perforations, noted in *Heteromorpha* and occasionally elsewhere among the Umbelliferae, are found in many Araliaceae, varying in proportion from 1 to 35% of the vessel elements studied. Longer vessel-elements, and end-wall angles which are slightly to much sharper than in the Umbelliferae are usual, but the Aralieae, with shrubby and even herbaceous species, and *Hedera* [Tourn.] L. with climbing stems, present xylem features linking up with those of the more woody umbellifers to form an unbroken series (Rodríguez, 1957a: 242–243). *Myodocarpus*, carpologically intermediate towards the Umbelliferae (Baumann, 1946), has vessel-element characters poorly suited for that role but perhaps more acceptable in an archaic umbellifer connecting with the common trunk of both families. It is this image of a cluster of divergent groups—within the Araliaceae proper and the three subfamilies of Umbelliferae separately—that leads Thorne (personal communication) to consider the four groups as of equal rank within a single family.

The interpretation offered by Eyde & Tseng (1970: Fig. 5) of the intrafamilial relationships seems more satisfactory than those of Viguier (1906) or Harms (1908) in relation to the data of wood anatomy (Rodríguez, 1957a). In Figs 2 and 5 a sampling of end-wall angle frequency curves and perforation plate patterns is shown, arranged in accordance with their scheme. In both the pinnate-leaved and palmate-leaved halves, relatively advanced xylem features are shown by the species with herbaceous (*Aralia* Tourn.) or climbing habit (*Hedera*), bicarpellate fruit or capitate inflorescences (*Oreopanax*). *Myodocarpus* and *Boerlagiodendron* Harms, however, with some conspicuously advanced feature of fruit or flower, are examples of wood specialization having gone at a markedly slower rate. In *Polyscias* Forst. the compressed bilocular ovary and the rather atypical wood equally suit the position assigned it near the end of a branch; the placing of *Pentapanax* Seem. and *Tetraplasandra* A. Gray on the same branch, and of *Panax* L. and *Aralia* upon the imbricate-petalled branch also agrees with the evidence from wood anatomy. The numerous species within the palmate-leaved half of the family for which data are available form a coherent succession of variations on a single theme.

NYSSACEAE

Nyssa, *Davidia* and *Camptotheca* are usually considered to form a separate family (Wangerin, 1910*b*) and to be among the least advanced of the whole alliance; Engler assigned the family a place among the Myrtales in the *Syllabus* from 1909 to 1936, followed by Wettstein (1935) with reservations. The primitive condition is substantiated by the floral organization (cf. Eyde, 1963) and by the wood anatomy (Titman, 1949; Li & Chao, 1954), most details of which are indeed of a primitive character, including the size of the components, the thin-walled angular vessel-elements, and the many-barred scalariform perforation plates. In *Nyssa* double perforation plates occur frequently (Rodríguez, 1957*a*).

Still more primitive in detail is the wood of *Davidia* (Figs. 1, 4), which, together with the numerous stamens, 6–8 carpels and several histological details (Eyde, 1963), points to a position near the base of the stem of the group, extending down to link with the Saxifragales; Horne (1909) and Takhtajan (1959) recognize also some affinity with *Alangium*. The unisexual apochlamydeous flowers, however, suggest considerable advance, as does the degree of organization of the inflorescence, with two or three white bracts subtending a head of staminate flowers with showy purple stamens out of which a single perfect flower stands out, corresponding to a second, reduced inflorescence and playing the role of a gynoecium—a second-cycle haplomorph reproductive unit. Takhtajan (1954 cited in 1959) and Li (1954) follow Titman's lead and cite further differences to propose familial rank for *Davidia*, already considered by Wangerin (1910*b*) and accepted by Melchior (1964) and Cronquist (1968). Markgraf (1963) also accepts it, but argues in favour of placing it next to and in common descent with the Actinidiaceae, a view rejected on several points by Eyde (1967).

Nyssa and *Camptotheca*, closely related, have a slightly higher evolutionary level, as shown by their xylem characters (Figs 2, 4; cf. Titman, 1949; Li & Chao, 1954), their perianth, present but with a tendency to reduction, fewer stamens (becoming a stable 10 in *Camptotheca*), and one (rarely two) carpels, and by the fruit structure (Eyde, 1963). The inflorescence, again, shows an advanced degree of organization. The species of *Nyssa* are polygamo-dioecious or dioecious; the male flowers are produced in racemose to umbelliform or capitate inflorescences while the perfect (female) flowers are single to umbellate or capitate; *Camptotheca* has polygamous branching systems of capitula. Eyde (1967) finds the floral vascular pattern similar to that of *Cornus* and rejects other differences which have been adduced to keep the Nyssaceae separate, casting doubts on the convenience of maintaining the family. Johnson & Fairbrothers (1961) obtained serological cross-reactions between *Cornus* and *Nyssa* (Fairbrothers, 1968), which Ferguson (1966b) says 'may be interpreted to support the separation of Nyssaceae from Cornaceae'. The relationship of *Davidia*, *Nyssa* and *Camptotheca* to each other and to *Cornus* is further supported by chemical investigation (Hegnauer, 1965, 1969), as is their connection with the Hydrangeaceae-Escalloniaceae.

CORNACEAE

As delimited by Wangerin (1910d) the family comprises some 90 species belonging to 10 (or 15) genera, encompassing rather primitive palaeotropic species like those of *Mastixia* to highly specialized ones like the circumboreal dwarfed species of *Cornus*. Being mostly advanced taxa in one aspect or another—vegetative structure, inflorescence, or flower and fruit—they offer a picture of divergent lines rather than a sequence, and several problems of relationship have arisen in regard to them. The xylem is mostly of primitive character, with Heterogeneous I or IIA rays and moderately long components, the vessel elements with scalariform perforation plates (in most cases with numerous bars: Fig. 4) and sharp end-wall angles (Adams, 1949), agreeing closely with that of the Nyssaceae, and supports the relationship with the Hydrangeaceae-Escalloniaceae (Fig. 1), often suggested on morphological grounds and on chemical affinities (Hegnauer, 1969). The floral anatomy of *Cornus* has been investigated by Horne (1914), Martel (1908), Wilkinson (1944) and Eyde (1967), revealing a peculiar pattern of vasculature, in which no strands run centrally in the ovary. Eyde (1963) opposes Wilkinson's (1944) interpretation of this feature as indicating a placental nature of the ovarian septum and (1967) points out the occurrence of the same vascular pattern in *Nyssa*, *Torricellia* and *Alangium*, but not in *Corokia*, *Curtisia*, *Helwingia*, *Kaliphora* or *Melanophylla*, for which reason he proposes the exclusion of the latter genera from the family. The absence of this feature in the Hydrangeaceae is also adduced by him to question the affinity of the Cornaceae with that group.

Cornus *and its segregates*

Wangerin (1910d) separated the 50 or so species of *Cornus* into 7 subgenera. Nakai (1909, 1927, cited by Hara, 1948), Hutchinson (1942) and Hara (1948) consider some of them distinct enough to be separate genera, and limit the concept of *Cornus* to the numerous species with an open cymose inflorescence without involucral bracts. Hutchinson (1942) accepts the separation of *Mesocarpium* Nakai (1909) for the umbellate, herbaceous-bracteate species (*C. mas* L., *C. officinalis* Sieb. & Zucc.); adopts *Chamaepericlymenum* Graeb. for the segregate *Arctocrania* Nakai, comprising the herbaceous, rhizomatous, uniloculate, petaloid-involucrate *C.*

suecica L. and *C. canadensis* L.; limits *Cynoxylon* Raf. to the capitate, involucrate species with separate fruit like *C. florida* L. and *C. disciflora* Moc. & Sessé, proposing *Dendrobenthamia* Hutch. for those with coalescent fruit and *Afrocrania* Hutch. for the isolated East African dioecious species *C. volkensii* Harms. *Cynoxylon* and *Dendrobenthamia* had been united by Nakai as *Benthamia* (1909) and under *Cynoxylon* (1927); Hara (1948) maintains the group as *Benthamidia* Spach, disregarding the difference in fruiting behaviour. Ferguson (1966*a*) reviews fully the nomenclatural vicissitudes of the group, arguing for the retention of the whole of it in *Cornus*. Adams's (1949) xylological data appear to support the separation of *Chamaepericlymenum*, the xylem of *C. canadensis* being definitely more advanced than the others' in *Cornus*. He indicated separate origins for the subgenera *Benthamia* (= *Cynoxylon*) and *Benthamidia* (= *Dendrobenthamia*), thus apparently supporting Hutchinson's treatment of them as two genera. The strong serological correspondence found by Johnson and Fairbrothers (1961) between *C. florida* and *C. kousa* Buerg. ex Miq. (= *D. japonica* (Sieb. & Zucc.) Hutch.), greater than that between either and *C. racemosa*, seems to support Hara's viewpoint; further support for the latter and for separation of *Chamaepericlymenum* is found in the BP serological correspondence curves shown by Fairbrothers (1968) in which three species corresponding to *Benthamidia*, but representing both of Hutchinson's genera, give essentially similar reactions to the antigen of *C. racemosa* (*C. florida* 51%, *C. kousa* 49%, *C. nuttallii* 45%), and *C. canadensis* and *C. suecica* also coincide in their reactions to the same antigen (24% and 23% respectively). In terms of the scale of inflorescence organization values suggested above, the segregation of these genera appears justified, the types shown by Hutchinson (1942) representing successively higher stages along the second cycle of organization, like the stipitate, half-coherent and coherent-carpellate genera of the Annonaceae along the first cycle.

Mastixia

Of the other genera included in the Cornaceae, *Mastixia* is usually regarded as the most primitive in several aspects: less definite phyllotaxy (*vide* Eyde, 1963), complete, bisexual flowers, bracteate, paniculate inflorescences, and detailed wood anatomy (Fig. 4; Adams, 1949; Li & Chao, 1954). The pseudomonomerous ovary alone appears as a derived feature, in which the vascular pattern is difficult to compare. Eyde (1963) expressed doubt as to the close relationship of *Mastixia* to the Nyssaceae, but in 1967 cited palaeobotanical evidence that the original condition of the ovary was as in *Cornus*. Takhtajan (1959) supports the establishment of a separate family, Mastixiaceae Van Tieghem, 1906. Philipson (1967), on the other hand, considers the vascular pattern of *Mastixia* similar to that of the unilocular araliad *Arthrophyllum* Blume, and calls it (1970) a 'satellite genus' of the Araliaceae. Significant in this respect are two other Aralian features of *Mastixia*, the possession of secretory canals, alone among the cornalean alliance, and of vasicentric xylem parenchyma. Wangerin (1910*d*) includes among the generic characters, petals with inflexed apices, a characteristic feature among Umbelliferae. Hegnauer (1969) records chemical affinity between *Mastixia, Cornus, Corokia* and the Nyssaceae, and dissimilarities between that group and *Aucuba, Garrya, Griselinia* and *Helwingia*.

Corokia *and Lautea*

On the basis of floral vascular pattern, Eyde (1966) and Philipson (1967) support the return of *Corokia* to the Saxifragaceae-Escallonioideae (= Escalloniaceae)-Argyrophylleae as proposed by Engler (1930). The xylem, which as Adams shows (1949), is of about the same grade of advancement as *Cornus* (Fig. 4), 'is especially close to that of the family Saxifragaceae' (Li & Chao, 1954). The change is indirectly supported by Fairbrothers's (1966) report of but slight immunological correspondence with other taxa within the Cornaceae and Nyssaceae and still less with the Garryaceae. *Lautea*, closely related to *Corokia* and morphologically less advanced, is also transferred to the Escallonioideae. The chemical affinity with *Cornus*, *Nyssa* and *Mastixia* must, however, be kept in mind as indicative of a further nexus between the two families; Takhtajan (1959) and Cronquist (1968) respectively consider and suggest *Corokia* as a link between Cornaceae and Escalloniaceae (in Cronquist, Grossulariaceae), retaining the genus in the Cornaceae.

Kaliphora, Melanophylla, Curtisia

The separation of the Madagascan genera *Kaliphora* and *Melanophylla* from a narrowly-defined Cornaceae is not difficult to accept, to judge from Adams's (1949) comments and anatomical data. *Melanophylla*, with loose inflorescences of bisexual flowers and 2- or 3-locular ovaries minus the distinctive *Cornus* vascularization (Eyde, 1967), has vessel elements with about 20% simple perforations and the rest averaging 15 bars per plate—on the whole an advanced xylem level for the Cornaceae but comparable to an intermediate grade in the peri-Aralian group to which it might be moved.

Kaliphora madagascarensis Hook. f., the sole species, with paniculate inflorescence, tetramerous, dioecious flowers, and bilocular ovary which also lacks the *Cornus* pattern of vascularization, and whose fruit separates into one-seeded nutlets, has wood with several advanced features for the Cornaceae—short xylem components, simple perforations, low L:W ratio, fairly wide end-wall angles (Adams, 1949), adding up to a level familiar in the Araliaceae. Adams notes the elongate, basifixed anthers; these recall the general type found in *Alangium* and in the Rubiaceae. I know of no definite proposal for the transfer of *Kaliphora*.

The monotypic *Curtisia*, placed in a separate subfamily, is similarly considered by Eyde (1966, 1967) and Philipson (1967). Its tetramerous, perfect, 4-locular flowers have axial ventral bundles, thus approaching either the saxifragalean or the Araliaceous pattern rather than that of *Cornus*. Its terminal panicles are of a relatively low level of organization. Its wood characters give it, in Adams's (1949) opinion, 'an equivocal position' within the Cornaceae, with both advanced and primitive features, the latter appearing to prevail—long vessel elements, high L:W ratio, Heterogeneous I rays, etc.

Torricellia

A different problem is presented by *Torricellia*, a group of three Himalayan species of dioecious trees. Its apetalous pistillate flowers and palmately-veined leaves recall *Davidia*'s (Eyde, 1967) or some Araliaceae; the vascular system of its plurilocular ovary links it clearly to the Cornaceae (Eyde, *loc. cit.*) while its alternate phyllotaxy, long petioles and cortical parenchyma, and particularly a number of xylem features —simple porous perforations, end-wall angles averaging 40°, Heterogeneous IIA rays, low L:W ratio and short vessel elements with alternate side-wall pitting and helical (spiral) thickenings (Adams, 1949; Li & Chao, 1954)—point toward a relation with the Araliaceae, among which the wood characteristics would be fairly advanced. The staminate flowers have concave petals with an inward-pointing tip recalling the infolded apices of many Umbelliferae. Other than the dioecious condition, its lax paniculate inflorescences show no advancement comparable to that of *Davidia* or *Benthamidia*. Hu (1934) and Takhtajan (1954, cited in 1959) propose its separation as a family, with support from Chao (1954) on pollen morphology and from Li & Chao (1954) on the wood anatomy.

Helwingia

The combination of characters found in *Helwingia* likewise does not fit well in the Cornaceae—stipulate, dentate leaves; epiphyllous umbellate inflorescences; drupes dividing into 3 or 4 one-seeded nutlets; xylem components with several araliaceous characters such as scalariform side-wall pitting and long, 20-26-barred perforation plates (Fig. 4) in which the openings are wider than the bars and, as in *Cornus*, *Nyssa* and *Myodocarpus*, fully bordered. Hegnauer (1966) finds it chemically little related to the cornacean group. A position in or near the Araliaceae, where it was placed by Bentham and Hooker (1867), is suggested by Eyde (1966) and by Philipson (1967, 1970) while Chao (1954) and Li & Chao (1954) offer as an alternative the reinstatement of Helwingiaceae of Endlicher. The high chromosome numbers recorded (Darlington and Wylie, 1955), contrasting with those of the rest of the Cornaceae and apparently based on the frequent $x = 12$ of the Araliaceae, seem to support both the latter course and a peri-Aralian position.

No phylogenetic significance is attributed by Adams (1949) to the epiphyllous inflorescence; but in view of the saxifragalean connection of the whole alliance, the suggestion comes to mind that *Helwingia* may have repeated, in that respect, the genetic-morphologic pathway of *Phyllonoma* Willd. ex Schult.

Aucuba

The position of *Aucuba* in the Cornaceae remains undecided by Eyde's criterion, due to the unilocular ovary, interpreted as pluricarpellate (Horne, 1914; Eckardt, 1937, who saw in the pseudomonomery of *Aucuba* a highly advanced condition; Kubitzki, 1963) or unicarpellate (Philipson, 1967). Its three Oriental species have dichotomously branching inflorescences whose articulated pedicels relate it to *Torricellia* and *Griselinia*, and the dioecious, tetramerous flowers have inflexed, acuminate petals like *Torricellia*'s and *Mastixia*'s recalling a character frequent in the Umbelliferae. The wood (Fig. 4) has a number of typically cornaceous features (Adams, 1949; Li & Chao, 1954); it resembles that of *Corokia* in the large size of its Heterogeneous I or IIA rays, and appears closer to *Torricellia* and *Griselinia* again in other details like the occurrence of helical thickenings in the vessel element walls. Chemically it has little affinity with either genus or with the main cornaceous group, and some only with *Garrya* (Lebas, 1909; Herissey & Lebas, 1910; Paris, 1963; Hegnauer, 1969).

Griselinia

The southern hemisphere genus *Griselinia* of mostly climbing epiphytes combines paniculate inflorescences of a moderate degree of organization with specialized characters like dioecism and a unilocular, uniovulate ovary which, as in *Aucuba*, precludes the application of Eyde's (1967) criterion. Philipson (1967) found the vasculature of *Griselinia* to match neither the typical cornaceous nor the araliaceous or escalloniaceous patterns but to approach rather that of *Arthrophyllum*, *Melanophylla* and *Mastixia*, with an independent vascular supply to each of the three styles; it shows a dorsal ovular trace, as in the Cornaceae and some Escalloniaceae; no special bundles supply the disk, as in Cornaceae or Araliaceae. Chemically unrelated to the main *Cornus-Mastixia-Davidia-Nyssa* group (Hegnauer, 1969), *Griselinia* shares a baccate fruit with *Aucuba*, and, with *Aucuba*, approaches *Garrya* most of the cornaceous genera, so that Eyde (1964) is led to postulate a common origin within the Cornaceae for the three genera. The wood anatomy is of a moderately advanced cornaceous type (Fig. 4; Adams, 1949; Li & Chao, 1954) but could also be regarded as of a low-araliaceous type (Philipson, 1967). As drawn by the latter, the sum of characters would give it a position bridging the distance between Araliaceae and Cornaceae, as an advanced member of the Escalloniaceae in affinity with *Corokia* and *Melanophylla*, or perhaps as a somewhat modified remnant of the common cornaceo-aralian ancestral stock. The cornaceous origin of the *Aucuba-Griselinia-Garrya* line suggested by Eyde (1964) might thus be thought to arise from a lower, Escalloniaceous source and to parallel the true cornaceous line.

GARRYACEAE

The position and relationships of the Garryaceae, comprising some sixteen species of the one genus *Garrya*, have been long-persistent systematic problems. On the one hand, their dioecious, anemophilous, all-but achlamydeous flowers in ament-like racemes seemed to place them among the Amentiferae of the Englerian school (*vide* also Benson, 1957); on the other, floral, fruit and seed characters pointed to an affinity with the Cornaceae (cf. Brongniart, 1843; Bentham & Hooker, 1867; or Baillon, 1880). There was marked disagreement on the interpretation of the flower, particularly of the position of the ovary (cf. Baillon, 1880, and Hallock, 1930, *vs* Wangerin, 1910*a*, Horne, 1914, and Reeve, 1942). From either viewpoint, the group has been thought separable with ordinal rank (Johnson, 1931; Engler & Diels, 1936; Pulle, 1952; Novák, 1954; Benson, 1957; Cronquist, 1957 but not 1968; Emberger, 1960). Moseley & Beeks (1955) disagreed with the placing of the Garryaceae among the Amentiferae or their implied primitiveness, and found anatomical evidence in favour of its connection and possible derivation from the Cornaceae; Brewbaker (1967) found both families to have binucleate pollen grains. Chemical affinity links *Garrya* and *Aucuba* alone among the Cornaceae (Lebas, 1909; Herissey & Lebas, 1910; Paris, 1963; Jha, 1969; Hegnauer, 1969); Eyde (1964), reinvestigating the floral structure and anatomy, found *Garrya* to relate to *Aucuba* and particularly to *Griselinia*: the link with the Cornaceae thus depending on the position finally accorded these two genera. The xylem characters (Figs 1, 4) would allow a sequence *Aucuba-Griselinia-Garrya*, the latter being of a level comparable with that of intermediate Araliaceae.

ALANGIACEAE

The Alangiaceae are another monogeneric family customarily placed in the Umbellales or Cornales, where they stand near the Cornaceae-Nyssaceae appearing more primitive with their perfect, pentamerous, regular flowers, isomerous or secondarily pleiomerous stamens and corymbose or cymose, open inflorescences, and where their unilocular or bilocular ovary and their xylem—with, for instance, few-barred or (mostly) simple porous perforations (Figs 1, 4)—are of a medium or some-what advanced level, comparable to advanced Araliads but certainly different from the Cornaceae (Li & Chao, 1954). Takhtajan (1959) places them with the Cornales and close to the Nyssaceae but notes the difference from the rest of them in the nuclear endosperm. The binucleate pollen grains (Brewbaker, 1967) and chemical characters (Hegnauer, 1965, 1966) in turn would support the relationship with the Cornaceae but not with the Araliaceae. Eyde (1968) presents a phylogenetic inter-pretation of the family based mainly on Bloembergen's (1939) review, in which he casts doubt on the usual position of *Alangium* near the Cornaceae while negating other proposed affinities (Combretaceae, Rhizophoraceae, Olacaceae), and suggests that the final relationship of the Alangiaceae may be with the Rubiaceae. He stresses the occurrence in *Alangium* of several alkaloids peculiar to the Rubiaceae (emetine, cephaline, psychotrine: Hegnauer, 1965, 1966). He might have mentioned among the similarities between both families the elongate, valvate flower buds and the type of stamen, in both of which the Alangiaceae are closer to the Rubiaceae than to the Cornalean (except *Kaliphora*) or Aralian alliances. The simple inflorescences with little complexity of organization of *Alangium* are easily related to those of some rubiaceous genera (*Hamelia, Psychotria*); but the mention of emetine and cephaline recalls the fact that in *Cephaelis* we find a compact inflorescence subtended by a whorl of coloured bracts, functional in pollination and dispersal—on a level with, and suggestive of, *Benthamidia* if not of *Davidia*, and of the showy-involucrate Saniculoideae and Apioideae—i.e. somewhere in the 'second-cycle' flower sequence. The recorded occurrence (Darlington & Wylie, 1955) of 11 as a basic chromosome number in one species of *Alangium*, in *Nyssa, Benthamidia* and *Chamaepericlymenum*, and in many Rubiaceae including *Cephaelis, Psychotria* and *Coffea* may add some weight to this connection.

RHIZOPHORACEAE

The affinities of the Cornales (*s. str.*) are extended in Cronquist's (1968) classifica-tion by the inclusion therein of the Rhizophoraceae. They are further expanded in the broader Cornales of Thorne (1968) in which he retains the two main alliances as twin suborders and adds three more suborders to include the Rhizophoraceae, the Vitaceae and the Haloragaceae (including Gunneroideae, = Gunneraceae) and Hippuridaceae.

The Rhizophoraceae are brought in from the Myrtales, where they stood near the Alangiaceae and Nyssaceae in Engler & Diels's (1936) arrangement. The transfer brings these families into proximity again and satisfies systematists' doubts as to the myrtalean kinship of the Rhizophoraceae. Many features of the latter point to a cornalean relation (Cronquist, 1968; Thorne, personal communication), from the endospermous seeds, which argue for the family's exclusion from the Myrtales, to the 4- or 5-merous flowers, the occurrence of epigynous disks, and the xylem characteristics. No detailed comparison of the wood anatomy has been feasible, but the available information (Marco, 1935; Metcalfe & Chalk, 1950) and the material examined (Fig. 4) show the Rhizophoraceae to range in a parallel sequence to the Araliaceae, from their lowest to their advanced levels, in some cases touching also the cornalean level. Details familiar in umbellalean woods appear here again—double perforations, tendency to reticulate elaboration of few-barred scalariform patterns.

THE FRINGE RELATIONSHIPS

The similarities between the Cornaceae, or the Umbellales in general, and the Caprifoliaceae have been repeatedly noted (De Jussieu, 1789; Lamarck & De Candolle, 1815; Harms, 1898; Rendle, 1938; Baumann, 1946; Melchior, 1964) even though, as 'Metachlamydeae', the latter were placed in the Rubiales or the Dipsacales—Jurica alone (1922) suggesting that the Umbelliferae themselves belong among the Metachlamydeae rather than in the Archichlamydeae, and Gundersen (1950) joining Umbellales and Rubiales in a superorder Rubiflorae. The Cornaceae offer the closest link to the Caprifoliaceae (Wilkinson, 1949), yet the latter have trinucleate pollen grains matched not by the former but by the Araliaceae and Umbelliferae (Brewbaker, 1967), and Eyde (1967) cites evidence that the gynoecial vascularization is different in Cornaceae (i.e. *Cornus*) and Caprifoliaceae. Morphologically, the greatest resemblance to the Cornaceae is through *Sambucus*; yet the xylem of *Sambucus* is more like that of the Araliaceae (Figs 1, 4; cf. Metcalfe & Chalk, 1950) than of the Cornaceae. It is also markedly different from that of *Viburnum* L. (Fig. 4), whose secondary xylem vascular elements are of a strong cornaceous-escalloniaceous type. Chemical affinity links the Caprifoliaceae with the cornalean group (Hegnauer, 1969); serological affinity is so much greater with *Cornus* and the araliads than with the Rubiaceae that the transfer of the family to the Umbellales is suggested (Hillebrand & Fairbrothers, 1966, 1970) and Thorne (1968) moves the whole order Dipsacales to a superorder Corniflorae, next to his Cornales. *Cornus* and *Nyssa* show high serological correspondence with *Sambucus* and low with *Viburnum* (Hillebrand & Fairbrothers, 1970). Within the Caprifoliaceae, the Viburneae and Sambuceae are serologically (and cytologically: *vide* Darlington and Wylie, 1955) separate from each other and from the Loniceraceae-Linnaeae-Diervilleae, which form a close serological unit; a careful re-examination of the Caprifoliaceae as a group is needed, as Cronquist suggests (1965), with the possibility of separation of these tribes to conform with better understood affinities. Takhtajan (1959) retained the Sambucaceae Link of 1829 as a valid family, while Cronquist (1968) remains cautious about recent findings.

A rather surprising thing to most systematists was Hegnauer's (1969) indication of a chemical affinity between the umbello-aralian group and the Pittosporaceae. The obvious differences between both groups—position of the ovary, number of ovules, degree of perianth cohesion—would normally outweigh the resemblances—trinucleate pollen (Brewbaker, 1967), endosperm, embryo, to a certain degree the inflorescence; yet Schulz-Gaebel (1930) had postulated such an affinity on cytological observations (cf. Darlington & Wylie, 1955). A brief look at the xylem of *Pittosporum rhombifolium* and *P. mannii* revealed a striking resemblance to aralian material, including frequent double perforations in the latter species (Fig. 4) and left the impression that careful investigation of serological and anatomo-morphological relationships between the Pittosporaceae and the Umbellales in general should prove rewarding.

Thorne's (1968) inclusion of the Vitaceae in the order also responds to several similarities with the Cornales, from the minute embryo and abundant endosperm to the numerous small, actinomorphic flowers in cymose inflorescences, the reduced calyx, the disk, the 6- to 2-loculate and -carpellate ovary with two or one ovules in each locule, etc. The liana genera have marked anatomical adaptations including characteristically large pores; but those of upright habit (Leeoideae of Metcalfe & Chalk, 1950 and Thorne, 1968; Leeaceae of Suessenguth, maintained by Emberger, 1960, Melchior, 1964 and Cronquist, 1968) have xylem characters on a level with advanced Araliaceae; both groups present side-wall features and wood parenchyma (excepting some strongly modified types) compatible with that affinity (Metcalfe & Chalk, 1950). The usually accepted proximity of Vitaceae and Rhamnaceae, held significant by Cronquist (1968), is seen by Thorne (personal communication) as due to convergence rather than relationship.

Thorne's (1968) placing of the Haloragidinae (Haloragales of Takhtajan, 1959 and Cronquist, 1968) in his Cornales is again based on ovary, ovule, embryo and endosperm characters, the reduced calyx and androecial details, which together seem to fill in the distance between the Vitinae and Corninae. Schindler (1905) had already noted the similarity with Cornaceae as to endosperm, but doubted the relationship. *Gunnera* L., for one, gives an impression of umbellalean affinity in its gross morphology, and the association with the Umbellales has often been felt intuitively by many. The whole group is so strongly modified by adaptation to a hygrophilic or aquatic life, that comparison of anatomical details is difficult and of little help; the information presented by Metcalfe & Chalk (1950) attests to a long history of modification. Aucubin has been found in the Haloragaceae (Paris, 1963), providing at least a link with *Aucuba* and *Garrya*; and the concave, infolded, apiculate petals of *Gunnera* (cf. Weber & Mora, 1958) recall a similar trait richly developed in the Umbelliferae and found also in *Torricellia* and *Aucuba*. The meagre cytological information available (cf. Darlington & Wylie, 1955) seems compatible with the proposed transfer.

CONCLUDING REMARKS

In attempting to assess our present taxonomic understanding of the Umbellales we find, in the first place, a wealth of observations and data from both traditional and various subsidiary disciplines, yet it is fragmentary for our needs. Not even floral anatomy has been described in equal detail for all the genera concerned. Wood anatomy has been investigated in all the classic umbellalean families, yet a full, detailed treatment of each, allowing satisfactory comparison, is not yet available. In some cases, conclusions have been based on very few 'representative' species; in others, average figures are given for the genera, tribes or families, and the figures, and hence, the conclusions, will depend on which species are accepted as forming part of the taxon in question by the author. Serological data shed light (cf. Davis & Heywood, 1963; Fairbrothers, 1968; Cronquist, 1968), but only on those relationships deliberately tested by reason of previously established or suspected affinities: thus the Caprifoliaceae-Cornaceae link has been investigated, but not the possible relationships of, say, Araliaceae with Pittosporaceae or Haloragaceae; many proposed relationships remain as yet untested. The gradually accumulated store of phytochemical information should also continue to grow as the whole assemblage is screened for affinities and discrepancies.

The potentialities of the scanning electron microscope as a taxonomic tool have been proved considerable (Heywood, 1968a, c, 1969, 1971) but its actual use on the problems in question is as yet exceedingly small. When shall we be able to compare leaf-surface, pollen, seed, fruit-surface and trichome features in the manifold scales of detail that it can yield, for each of the genera in the broad umbellalean field? What fresh view will it afford of the xylem and its components?

Much cytological and embryological information is available, but it is not yet sufficient, in coverage or detail, for a single all-encompassing interpretation at the required level. The detailed knowledge of the cytology of Umbelliferae available contrasts with the scarcity of counts recorded for most of the cornalean genera. Patient study and evaluation of the levels of organization of the inflorescence, as suggested above, may add a further set of useful data; the eventual use of this concept cannot depend only on purely morphological or typological analysis: detailed knowledge of the actual reproductive biology of each of our groups, from development to pollination to seed dispersal, will be necessary.

The data accumulated attest to certain well-established associations—Nyssaceae-Cornaceae, Araliaceae-Umbelliferae—but also to a remarkable network of interrelations and similarities across the gap between the two main clusters; between either and the additional suborders of Thorne; back to Saxifragalean sources, the Cunoniales of Takhtajan; outward to the Pittosporaceae, the Rutaceae, the Sapindales, the Rubiaceae, the Dipsacales via Caprifoliaceae, the Compositae—many confirming each other, others complicating the picture (as the ovule characters shared by the Haloragales, *Davidia*, *Nyssa*, *Alangium* and the Araliaceae, but not by the core Cornaceae: Takhtajan, 1959); in some instances contradicting each other (as the discrepancy shown by serological agreement and vascularization differences between Cornaceae and Caprifoliaceae, or the trinucleate pollen grains in the Escalloniaceae: Brewbaker, 1967). Digesting the information, one has the feeling of having sat down to figure out 'who owns the Zebra', as in *Life*'s (1962) memorable puzzle, knowing that in this case not all the necessary clues are available to us.

The accumulated data are variously interpreted, and yield a broad spectrum of opinion. Melchior (1964) and Thorne (1968) favour a broad definition of a single order encompassing both the cornalean and umbello-aralian alliances, in the latter's view including other related lines as suborders and adding a twin order, Dipsacales, to form the superorder Corniflorae; Takhtajan (1959) makes the Umbellales and Cornales twin orders of the superorder Umbelliflorae, derived from the same general source (Cunoniales) as the Celastrales, Rutales, Sapindales and Myrtales-Haloragales (Myrtiflorae); Emberger (1960) also conceives twin orders, Ombelliflores, comprising both alliances, with Garryales separate, in common descent from an unspecified origin with the Terebinthales, Rubiales, Rhamnales-Celastrales-Ligustrales; Eyde (1968, 1970) and Cronquist (1965, 1968) consider the two alliances taxonomically and phyletically separate.

The phytochemical and anatomical gaps between the cornalean and umbello-aralian alliances have been emphasized by Cronquist (1965, 1968), Hegnauer (1969), Eyde (1967, 1970) and Philipson (1970). They are undeniably of great weight in the definition of the families and in interpreting their relationships; but the admonition, variously expressed by Vestal (1940), Davis & Heywood (1963), Metcalfe (1968), Heywood (1968c) or Sastri (1969) against the over-weighting of the newest source of data is once more timely.

In the present state of our knowledge of these plants, and taking into consideration the strong affinities and broad differences along with the many 'hydrogen-bond' cross links, it would appear that Thorne's solution, or Takhtajan's, is still the most satisfactory. In the first case, the subordinal gaps might be thought to do justice to the major differences between the cornalean and umbello-aralian groups. The presence of the Vitaceae, Rhizophoraceae and the haloragalean group within the order, with equal subordinal rank, would justify the same rank for the Cornineae and Aralineae. Takhtajan's two orders would again satisfy the division imposed by chemical and anatomo-morphological differences, while uniting them again in a superorder would, in turn, acknowledge the many lesser links that have been detected.

Eyde's (1967) restriction of the Cornaceae to the genera showing the distinctive gynoecial vascularization of *Cornus* leaves out a number which approach the aralian or escallonian condition and continue to fill intermediate positions and to provide links of one kind or another in spite of having been refused cornacean membership. Philipson's (1967) discussion of the problem (pp. 156–163) could profitably be quoted here in full, although his position apparently has varied somewhat (1970) as consideration of the second, functionally modified ovule in the aralian locule, lacking in the Cornaceae, leads him closer to Cronquist's view. Still, he points out an important fact, equally stressed by Moseley and Beeks (1955). The genera of the cornalean alliance in question are all, in one sense or another, well advanced taxa best understood as end-points of several related lines springing from the same general stock as the two main alliances. As a flabellate group of small families, perhaps reducible to a very few, they might form a separate small order between Cornales and Umbellales (as in Takhtajan's treatment), or a suborder between Corneae and Aralieae (as in Thorne's), or else fit in between Cornaceae and Araliaceae in flabellate arrangement branching from one or the other suborder. The

Incognitales of Swamy and Bailey that Philipson (1967) evokes are, for our needs, the very Umbelliflorae, Corniflorae or Umbellales broadly defined of recent treatments.

REFERENCES

ADAMS, J. E., 1949. Studies in the comparative anatomy of the Cornaceae. *J. Elisha Mitchell Soc.*, **65**: 218–244.

ADANSON, M., 1763. *Familles des Plantes*. 2 vols. Paris: Vincent.

BAILEY, I. W., 1951. The use and abuse of anatomical data in the study of phylogeny and classification. *Phytomorphology*, **1**: 67–69.

BAILEY, I. W., 1953. Evolution of the tracheary tissue of land plants. *Am. J. Bot.*, **40**: 4–8.

BAILLON, H. E., 1880. *Histoire des Plantes*. Paris: Hachette.

BARTLING, F. G., 1830. *Ordines Naturales Plantarum*. Gottingen.

BAUMANN, M. G., 1946. *Myodocarpus* und die Phylogenie der Umbelliferen-Fruchte. *Ber. Schweiz. Bot. Ges.*, **56**: 11–112.

BAUMANN-BODENHEIM, M. G., 1955. Ableitung und Bau bicarpellat-monospermer und pseudomono-carpellater Araliaceen- und Umbelliferen-Früchte. *Ber. Schweiz. Bot. Ges.*, **65**: 481–510.

BELL, C. R. & CONSTANCE, L., 1957. Chromosome numbers in Umbelliferae. I. *Am. J. Bot.*, **44**: 565–572.

BELL, C. R. & CONSTANCE, L., 1960. Chromosome numbers in Umbelliferae. II. *Am. J. Bot.*, **47**: 24–32.

BELL, C. R. & CONSTANCE, L., 1966. Chromosome numbers in Umbelliferae. III. *Am. J. Bot.*, **53**: 512–520.

BENSON, L., 1957. *Plant Classification*, 688 pp. Boston: D. C. Heath & Co.

BENTHAM, G. & HOOKER, J. D., 1867. *Genera Plantarum*, Vol. I. London.

BERTERO, M., 1830. Notice sur l'histoire naturelle de l'Ile Juan Fernández, extraite d'une lettre de M. Bertero. *Ann. Sci. Nat. (Paris)*, **21**: 344–351.

BESSEY, C. E., 1915. Phylogenetic taxonomy of flowering plants. *Ann. Mo. Bot. Gdn*, **2**: 109–164.

BLOEMBERGEN, S., 1939. A revision of the genus *Alangium. Bull. Jard. Bot. Buitenzorg*, III, **16**: 139–235.

BREWBAKER, J. L., 1967. The distribution and phylogenetic significance of binucleate and trinucleate pollen grains in the Angiosperms. *Am. J. Bot.*, **54**: 1069–1083.

BRONGNIART, A., 1843. *Enumération des Genres de Plantes cultivés au Muséum d'Histoire Naturelle de Paris*. Paris: Fortin, Masson & Cie.

BROWN, F. B. H., 1918. Scalariform pitting a primitive feature of angiospermous secondary wood. *Science*, n.s., **48**: 16–18.

CALESTANI, V., 1905. Contributo alla sistematica delle Ombrellifere d'Europa. *Webbia*, **1**: 89–280.

CARLQUIST, S., 1958. Wood anatomy of Heliantheae (Compositae). *Trop. Woods*, **108**: 1–30.

CARLQUIST, S., 1961. *Comparative Plant Anatomy*, 146 pp. New York: Holt, Rinehart & Winston.

CARLQUIST, S., 1962. A theory of paedomorphosis in dicotyledonous woods. *Phytomorphology*, **12**: 30–45.

CARLQUIST, S., 1965. *Island Life*. 451 pp. New York: Nat. Hist. Press.

CERCEAU-LARRIVAL, M.T., 1962. Plantules et pollens d'Ombellifères. *Mém. Mus. natl. Hist. nat., Sér. B, Bot.*, **14**: 1–164, 26 pl.

CHAO, C.-Y., 1954. Comparative pollen morphology of the Cornaceae and allies. *Taiwania*, **5**: 93–106.

CONSTANCE, L. & HITCHCOCK, C. L., 1954. *Mathiasella*, a new genus of North American Umbelliferae. *Am. J. Bot.*, **41**: 56–58.

COULTER, J. M. & ROSE, J. N., 1894. New genus of Umbelliferae. *Bot. Gaz. (Crawfordsville)*, **19**: 466.

COULTER, J. M. & ROSE, J. N., 1927. Revision of the genus *Myrrhidendron. J. Wash. Acad. Sci.*, **17**: 213–214.

CRANTZ, H. I. N., 1767. *Classis Umbelliferarum*. Leipzig: I. P. Kraus.

CRONQUIST, A., 1957. Outline of a new system of families and orders of Dicotyledons. *Bull. Jard. Bot. État*, **27**: 13–40.

CRONQUIST, A., 1965. The status of the general system of classification of flowering plants. *Ann. Mo. Bot. Gdn*, **52**: 281–303.

CRONQUIST, A., 1968. *The Evolution and Classification of Flowering Plants*, 396 pp. Boston: Houghton Mifflin.

DARLINGTON, C. D. & WYLIE, A. P., 1955. *Chromosome Atlas of Flowering Plants*. 2d. ed., 520 pp. George Allen & Unwin, Ltd.

DAVIS, P. H. & HEYWOOD, V. H., 1963. *Principles of Angiosperm Taxonomy*. 556 pp. Edinburgh, London: Oliver & Boyd.

DE CANDOLLE, A. P., 1830. *Prodromus Systematis Naturalis Regni Vegetabilis*. Part 4. Paris.

DOMIN, K., 1908. Morphologische und phylogenetische Studien über die Familie der Umbelliferen. I. *Bull. Inst. Acad. Prague*, **13**: 108–153.

DRUDE, C. G. O., 1897–1898. Umbelliferae. In Engler, A. & Prantl, K. (eds), *Die natürlichen Pflanzenfamilien*, **3**[8]: 63–128, 129–250. Leipzig.

ECKARDT, T., 1937. Untersuchungen über Morphologie, Entwicklungsgeschichte und systematische Bedeutung des pseudomonomeres Gynoeceums. *Nova Acta Leop.*, n. F., **5**: 1–112.

EHRLICH, P. R. & RAVEN, P., 1965. Butterflies and plants: a study in coevolution. *Evolution*, **18**: 586–608.

EHRLICH, P. R. & RAVEN, P. H., 1967. Butterflies and plants. *Scient. Am.*, **216** (6): 105–113.

EMBERGER, L., 1960. Les Végétaux vasculaires. In Chaudefaud, M. & Emberger, L. *Traité de Botanique Systématique*, **II**, 2, 1540 pp. Paris: Masson & Cie.

ENDLICHER, S. L., 1841. *Enchiridion Botanicum*. Leipzig: Engelmann.

ENGLER, A., 1930. Saxifragaceae. In Engler, A. & Prantl, K. (eds), *Die natürlichen Pflanzenfamilien*, 2nd. ed., **18a**: 74–226.

ENGLER, A. & DIELS, L., 1936. *Syllabus der Pflanzenfamilien*. 11th ed. Berlin.

EYDE, R. H., 1963. Morphological and palaeobotanical studies of the Nyssaceae. I. A survey of the modern species and their fruits. *J. Arnold Arbor.*, **44**: 1–54, pl. I–IV.

EYDE, R. H., 1964. Inferior ovary and generic affinities of *Garrya*. *Am. J. Bot.*, **51**: 1083–1092.

EYDE, R. H., 1966. Systematic anatomy of the flower of *Corokia*. *Am. J. Bot.*, **53**: 833–847.

EYDE, R. H., 1967. The peculiar gynoecial vasculature of Cornaceae and its systematic significance. *Phytomorphology*, **17**: 172–182.

EYDE, R. H., 1968. Flowers, fruits and phylogeny of the Alangiaceae. *J. Arnold Arbor.*, **49**: 167–192.

EYDE, R. H. & TSENG, C. C., 1969. Flower of *Tetraplasandra gymnocarpa*: hypogyny with epigynous ancestry. *Science, N.Y.*, **166**: 506–508.

EYDE, R. H. & TSENG, C. C., 1970. What is the primitive floral structure of Araliaceae? *J. Arnold Arbor.*, (in press).

FAIRBROTHERS, D. E., 1966. Serological correspondence of the genus *Corokia* with taxa of the Cornaceae, Nyssaceae and Garryaceae (Abstract). *Am. J. Bot.*, **53**: 638.

FAIRBROTHERS, D. E., 1968. Chemosystematics, with emphasis on systematic serology. In Heywood, V. H. (ed.), *Modern Methods in Plant Taxonomy*, pp. 141–174. London & New York: Academic Press.

FERGUSON, I. K., 1966a. Notes on the nomenclature of *Cornus*. *J. Arnold Arbor.*, **47**: 100–105.

FERGUSON, I. K., 1966b. The Cornaceae in the Southern United States. *J. Arnold Arbor.*, **47**: 106–116.

GAUSSEN, H., 1947. L'évolution pseudocyclique et la notion de surévolution. *Scientia*, **41**: 65–68.

GÉNEAU DE LAMARLIÈRE, L., 1893. *Recherches morphologiques sur la famille des Ombellifères*. Thèse, Fac. Sci. Paris, sér. A, **195**, 784, 200 pp. Lille: Le Bigot.

GUNDERSEN, A., 1950. *Families of Dicotyledons*. Waltham, Mass.

HALLIER, H., 1905. Provisional scheme of the natural (phylogenetic) system of flowering plants. *New Phytol.*, **4**: 151–162.

HALLIER, H., 1912. L'origine et le système phylétique des Angiospermes. *Arch. Néerl. Sci. Exact. Nat.*, III, B, **1**: 146–234.

HALLOCK, FRANCES A., 1930. The relationship of *Garrya*. *Ann. Bot.*, **44**: 771–812.

HARA, H., 1948. The nomenclature of the flowering dogwood and its allies. *J. Arnold Arb.*, **29**: 111–115.

HARMS, H., 1897. Araliaceae. In Engler, A. & Prantl, K. (eds), *Die natürlichen Pflanzenfamilien*, **3**[8]: 1–62. Leipzig.

HARMS, H., 1898. Cornaceae. In Engler A. & Prantl, K. (eds), *Die natürlichen Pflanzenfamilien*, **3**[8]: 251–270.

HEGNAUER, R., 1965. Chemismus und systematische Stellung der Cornaceae. In *Beiträge zur biochemie und Physiologie von Naturstoffen: Festschrift Kurt Mothes zum 65 Geburtstag*, pp. 235–246. Jena: G. Fischer.

HEGNAUER, R., 1966. Comparative phytochemistry of alkaloids. In Swain, T. (ed.,) *Comparative Phytochemistry*, pp. 211–230. London & New York: Academic Press.

HEGNAUER, R., 1969. Chemical evidence for the classification of some plant taxa. In Harborne, J. B. & Swain, T. (eds), *Perspectives in Phytochemistry*, pp. 121–138. London & New York: Academic Press.

HERISSEY, H. & LEBAS, C., 1910. Présence de l'aucubine dans plusieurs espèces du genre *Garrya*. *Bot. Zentralbl.*, **116**: 176.

HEYWOOD, V. H., 1968a. Scanning electron microscopy and microcharacters in the fruits of the Umbelliferae-Caucalidae. *Proc. Linn. Soc. London*, **179**: 287–289.

HEYWOOD, V. H., 1968b. Plant taxonomy today. In Heywood, V. H. (ed.), *Modern Methods in Plant Taxonomy*, pp. 3–12. London & New York: Academic Press.

HEYWOOD, V. H., 1968c. *Taxonomía Vegetal.*, 102 pp. Transl. E. Fernández-Galiano. Madrid: Alhambra, S. A.

HEYWOOD, V. H., 1969. Scanning electron microscopy in the study of plant materials. *Micron* **1**: 1–14.

HEYWOOD, V. H., 1971. The characteristics of the Scanning Electron Microscope and their importance in Biological Studies. In Heywood, V. H. (ed.), *Scanning Electron Microscopy. Systematic and Evolutionary Applications*, pp. 1–16. London & New York. Academic Press.

HILLEBRAND, G. R. & FAIRBROTHERS, D. E., 1966. Phytoserological systematic studies of selected genera of the Rubiales and Umbellales. *Am. J. Bot.*, **53**: 638 (Abstract).

HILLEBRAND, G. R. & FAIRBROTHERS, D. E., 1970. Serological investigation of the systematic position of the Caprifoliaceae. I. Correspondence with selected Rubiaceae and Cornaceae. *Am. J. Bot.*, **57**: 810–815.

HOAR, C. S., 1915. A comparison of the stem anatomy of the cohort Umbelliflorae. *Ann. Bot.*, **29**: 55–63.

HOOKER, W. J., 1834. *Trachymene lanceolata.* Lance-leaved Trachymene. *Bot. Mag.*, 1834, pl. 3334.

HOOKER, W. J. & ARNOTT, G. A. W., 1833. Contributions towards a flora of South America and the islands of the Pacific. *Bot. Misc.*, **3**: 302–367.

HORNE, A. S., 1909. The structure and affinities of *Davidia involucrata* Baill. *Trans. Linn. Soc. London, Bot.*, **7**: 303–326.

HORNE, A. S., 1914. A contribution to the study of the evolution of the flower, with special reference to the Hamamelidaceae, Caprifoliaceae and Cornaceae. *Trans. Linn. Soc. London, Bot.*, **8**: 239–309.

HU, H. H., 1934. Notula systematica ad floram sinensium. V. *Bull. Fan Mem. Inst. Biol.*, **5**: 305–318.

HUTCHINSON, J., 1926. *The Families of Flowering Plants. I. Dicotyledons.* London: McMillan & Co., Ltd.

HUTCHINSON, J., 1929. The phylogeny of flowering plants. *Proc. Int. Congr. Plant Sci., Ithaca*, **1**: 419–420.

HUTCHINSON, J., 1942. Neglected generic characters in the family Cornaceae. *Ann. Bot. (London)*, n.s., **6**: 83–93.

HUTCHINSON, J., 1969. *Evolution and Phylogeny of Flowering Plants.* 717 pp. London & New York: Academic Press.

HYLANDER, N., 1945. Nomenklatorische und systematische Studien über nordische Gefasspflanzen. *Uppsala Univ. Årsskr.*, **7**: 5–337.

JACKSON, G., 1933. A study of the carpophore of the Umbelliferae. *Am. J. Bot.*, **20**: 121–143.

JEFFREY, E. C., 1917. *The Anatomy of Woody Plants.* Univ. Chicago Press.

JHA, U. N., 1969. Chemotaxonomy of the 'Amentiferae'. *J. Indian Bot. Soc.*, **48**: 202–212.

JOHNSON, A. M., 1931. *Taxonomy of the Flowering Plants.* London: The Century Co.

JOHNSON, A. M. & FAIRBROTHERS, D. E., 1961. Serological correspondence in Cornaceae and Nyssaceae. *Am. J. Bot.*, **48**: 534 (Abstract).

JURICA, H. S., 1922. A morphological study of the Umbelliferae. *Bot. Gaz. (Crawfordsville)*, **74**: 292–309, pl. xiii–xiv.

JUSSIEU, A. L. DE, 1789. *Genera Plantarum.* Paris, Herissant.

KUBITZKI, K., 1963. Zur Kenntnis des unilokularen Cornaceen-Gynözeums (Cornaceen-Studien I). *Ber. dtsch. Bot. Ges.*, **76**: 33–39.

LAMARCK, J. B. DE & DE CANDOLLE, A. P., 1815. *Flore Française.* 3rd ed. Paris: Desray.

LEBAS, C., 1909. Sur la présence d'aucubine dans les diverses varietés d'*Aucuba japonica* L. *J. Pharm. Chim.*, 6e. sér., **30**: 390–392.

LEPPIK, E. E., 1957. A new system for classification of flower types. *Taxon*, **6** (3): 64–67.

LI, H.-L., 1954. *Davidia* as the type of a new family, Davidiaceae. *Lloydia*, **17**: 329–331.

LI, H.-L. & CHAO, C.-Y., 1954. Comparative anatomy of the woods of the Cornaceae and allies. *Q. Rev. Taiwan Mus.*, **7**: 119–136, pl. I–VIII.

LIFE INT., 1962. Who owns the Zebra? *Life International*, **33** (13): 95.

LINNAEUS, C., 1764. *Genera Plantarum* 6th ed. Stockholm.

LOTSY, J. P., 1911. *Vorträge über botanische Stammgeschichte.* Jena: G. Fischer.

MAEKAWA, F., 1965. *Aucuba* and its allies—the phylogenetic consideration on the Cornaceae. *J. Jap. Bot.*, **40**: 41–47.

MARCO, H. F., 1935. Systematic anatomy of the woods of the Rhizophoraceae. *Trop. Woods*, **44**: 1–20, pl. I–VI.

MARKGRAF, F., 1963. Die phylogenetische Stellung der Gattung *Davidia*. *Ber. dtsch. Bot. Ges.*, **76**: 63–69.

MARTEL, E., 1908. Contribuzione all'anatomia del fiore dell' *Hedera Helix*, dell'*Aralia Sieboldii* e del *Cornus sanguinea.* *Mem. Acad. Sci. Torino*, II, **58**: 561–579.

MATHIAS, M. E., 1965. Distribution patterns of certain Umbelliferae. *Ann. Mo. Bot. Gdn*, **52**: 387–398.

MATHIAS, M. E. & CONSTANCE, L., 1962. A revision of *Asteriscium* and some related Hydrocotyloid Umbelliferae. *Univ. Calif. Publs Bot.*, **33**: 99–184.

MELCHIOR, H.(ed.), 1964. *A. Engler's Syllabus der Pflanzenfamilien.* 12th ed., vol. 2, 666 pp. Berlin-Nikolassee: Geb. Borntraeger.

MESSERI, ALBINA, 1938. Studio anatomico-ecologico del legno secondario di alcune piante del Fezzan. *Nuovo Giorn. Bot. Ital.*, n.s., **45**: 267–356.

METCALFE, C. R., 1946. The systematic anatomy of the vegetative organs of the Angiosperms. *Biol. Rev. Camb. Phil. Soc.*, **21**: 159–172.

METCALFE, C. R., 1968. Current developments in systematic plant anatomy. In Heywood, V. H. (ed.), *Modern Methods in Plant Taxonomy*, pp. 45–57. London & New York: Academic Press.

METCALFE, C. R. & CHALK, L., 1950. *Anatomy of the Dicotyledons*. 2 vols, 1500 pp. Oxford: Clarendon Press.

MITTAL, S. P., 1961. Studies in the Umbellales, II. The vegetative anatomy. *J. Indian Bot. Soc.*, **40**: 424–433.

MOSELEY, M. F. JR & BEEKS, R. M., 1955. Studies of the Garryaceae. I. The comparative morphology and phylogeny. *Phytomorphology*, **5**: 314–346.

NAKAI, T., 1909. Cornaceae in Japan. *Bot. Mag. (Tokyo)*, **23**: 35–45.

NECKER, N. J., 1790. *Elementa Botanica*. 3 vols. Neuwied.

NESTEL, A., 1905. Beiträge zur Kenntnis der Stengel- und Blattanatomie der Umbelliferen. *Mitteil. Bot. Mus. Univ. Zürich*, **24**: 1–126.

NOVÁK, F. A., 1954. Systém Angiosperm. *Preslia*, **26**: 337–364.

PARIS, R., 1963. The distribution of plant glycosides. In Swain T. (ed.), *Chemical Plant Taxonomy*, pp. 337–358. London & New York: Academic Press.

PHILIPSON, W. R., 1951. Contributions to our knowledge of Old World Araliaceae. *Bull. Br. Mus. (Nat. Hist.), Bot.*, **1**: 3–20.

PHILIPSON, W. R., 1967. *Griselinia* Forst. fil.—anomaly or link. *N. Z. Jl Bot.*, **5**: 134–165.

PHILIPSON, W. R., 1970. Constant and variable features of the Araliaceae. *Bot. J. Linn. Soc. (London)*, Suppl. **1**: 87–100.

PULLE, A. A., 1952. *Compendium van de Terminologie, Nomenclatuur en Systematiek der Zaadplanten.* 3rd ed. Utrecht: Oosthoek's.

REEVE, R., 1942. Structure and growth of the vegetative shoot apex of *Garrya elliptica* Dougl. *Am. J. Bot.*, **29**: 697–711.

RENDLE, A. B., 1938. *The Classification of Flowering Plants*, Vol. 2. Dicotyledons. Cambridge: Univ. Press.

RENDLE, B. J. & CLARKE, S. H., 1934. The diagnostic value of measurements in wood anatomy. *Trop. Woods*, **40**: 27–37.

RODRÍGUEZ, R. L., 1957a. Systematic anatomical studies on *Myrrhidendron* and other woody Umbellales. *Univ. Calif. Publ. Bot.*, **29**: 145–318.

RODRÍGUEZ, R. L., 1957b. Anotaciones a la anatomía comparada de las Umbelíferas. *Revta. Biol. Trop.*, **5**: 157–171.

ROEDERER, H., 1930. Die Phylogenie des Rosales-Astes. *Bot. Arch.*, **29**: 330–436.

SASTRI, R. L. N., 1969. Comparative morphology and phylogeny of the Ranales. *Biol. Rev. Camb. Phil. Soc.*, **44**: 291–319.

SCHINDLER, A. K., 1905. Halorhagaceae. In Engler, A. (ed.), *Das Pflanzenreich*, **IV. 225**: 133 pp.

SCHULZ-GAEBEL, H. H., 1930. Entwicklungsgeschichtlich-zytologische Studien an der Umbelliferen-Unterfamilie der Apioideen. *Beitr. Biol. Pfl.*, **18**: 345–398.

SEEMAN, B., 1864. On the aestivation of *Crithmum maritimum*. *J. Bot.*, **11**: 5.

SHORLAND, F. B., 1963. The distribution of fatty acids in plant lipids. In Swain, T. (ed.), *Chemical Plant Taxonomy*, pp. 253–309. London & New York: Academic Press.

SKOTTSBERG, C., 1922. *The Natural History of Juan Fernández and Easter Island*. Vol. 2. Botany.

SKOTTSBERG, C., 1945. The Juan Fernández and Desventuradas Islands. In Verdoorn, F. (ed.), *Plants and Plant Science in Latin America*, pp. 150–153. Waltham: Chronica Botanica.

SØRENSEN, N. A., 1963. Chemical taxonomy of acetylenic compounds. In Swain, T. (ed.), *Chemical Plant Taxonomy*, pp. 219–252. London: Academic Press.

SOÓ, R., 1961. Present aspect of evolutionary history of Telomophyta. *Ann. Univ. Sci. Budapest Rolando Eötvös, Sect. Biol.*, **4**: 167–178.

SOPER, KATHLEEN, 1957. Comparative morphology of the New Zealand species of Pseudopanax and Nothopanax. *Trans. R. Soc. N. Z.*, **84**: 749–755, p. 47.

STEBBINS, G. L., 1951. Natural selection and the differentiation of angiosperm families. *Evolution*, **5**: 299–324.

STEBBINS, G. L., 1970. Transference of function as a factor in the evolution of seeds and their accessory structures. *Israel J. Bot.*, **19**: 59–70.

TAKHTAJAN, A., 1959. *Die Evolution der Angiospermen*. 344 pp. Jena: G. Fischer.

TERNETZ, C., 1902. Morphologie und Anatomie der *Azorella Selago* Hook. fil. *Bot. Zeit., 2. Abt.*, **60**: 1–20, Taf. 1.

THORNE, R. F., 1968. Synopsis of a putatively phylogenetic classification of the flowering plants. *Aliso*, **6**: 57–66.

TIPPO, O., 1946. The role of wood anatomy in phylogeny. *Am. Midl. Naturalist*, **36**: 362–372.

TITMAN, P. W., 1949. Studies in the wood anatomy of the family Nyssaceae. *J. Elisha Mitchell Soc.*, **65**: 245–261.

TSENG, C. C., 1967. Anatomical studies of flower and fruit in the Hydrocotyloideae (Umbelliferae). *Univ. Calif. Publs Bot.*, **42**: 1–79.

VAN NOENEN, F., 1895. *Die Anatomie der Umbelliferenachse in ihrer Beziehung zum System*. Inaug. Diss. F. A. Univ. Erlangen.

VESTAL, P. A., 1940. Wood anatomy as an aid to classification and phylogeny. *Chron. Bot.*, **6** (3): 53–54.

VIGUIER, R., 1906. Recherches anatomiques sur la classification des Araliacées. *Ann. Sci. nat. Bot.* *Sér. 9*, **4**: 1–209.

VIGUIER, R., 1909. Nouvelles recherches sur les Araliacées. *Ann. Sci. nat. Bot.*, Sér. 9, **9**: 305–405.

WANGERIN, W., 1910*a*. Garryaceae. In Engler, A. (ed.), *Das Pflanzenreich*, **IV**, **56**a, 17 pp.

WANGERIN, W., 1910*b*. Nyssaceae. In Engler, A. (ed.), *Das Pflanzenreich*, **IV**, **220**a, 20 pp.

WANGERIN, W., 1910*c*. Alangiaceae. In Engler, A. (ed.), *Das Pflanzenreich*, **IV**, **220**b, 24 pp.

WANGERIN, W., 1910*d*. Cornaceae. In Engler, A. (ed.), *Das Pflanzenreich*, **IV**, **229**, 110 pp.

WEBER, H. & MORA, L. E., 1958. Zur Kenntnis der Gattung *Gunnera* L. in Costa Rica. *Beitr. Biol. Pfl.*, **34**: 467–477.

WETTSTEIN, R. VON, 1935. *Handbuch der systematischen Botanik.* 4th ed. Leipzig and Vienna.

WILKINSON, ANTOINETTE M., 1944. Floral anatomy of some species of *Cornus. Bull. Torrey Bot. Club*, **71**: 276–301.

WILKINSON, ANTOINETTE M., 1949. Floral anatomy and morphology of *Triosteum* and of the Caprifoliaceae in general. *Am. J. Bot.*, **36**: 481–489.

ZOHARY, M., 1950. Evolutionary trends in the fruiting head of Compositae. *Evolution*, **4**: 103–109.

Breeding systems and floral biology of the Umbelliferae
or
Evidence for specialization in unspecialized flowers

C. RITCHIE BELL

Department of Botany, University of North Carolina, Chapel Hill, U.S.A.

The relatively high degree of floral uniformity found throughout the Umbelliferae may represent an ancient adaptive peak, or specialization, for pollination by a large number of unspecialized pollinators. Promiscuous pollination by many species of unspecialized insects removes what is for many plants an effective isolating mechanism, but also removes a possible limiting factor in wide geographic distribution. However, even the unspecialized flowers of umbels show a rather wide series of presumably adaptive variations in stylopodia shape, size, colour and nectar secretion as well as many more subtle but distinct morphological and physiological variations in other floral characters. Protandry, for example, is so widespread in the family that it might be expected to exist without marked variation from one genus to the next. However, between the extremes of self-pollination and obligate outcrossing protandry has produced a mosaic of adaptations that have variously altered the floral composition (i.e. the percentage of staminate flowers), and thus the reproductive biology of the umbels of many genera.

CONTENTS

INTRODUCTION

Shortly after the publication of Darwin's *Origin of Species* there was among the world's biologists an intense inquiry into the 'use', the 'purpose', or the 'survival value' of many characters of both plants and animals that might, in one way or another, represent specific adaptations. For a group as large, widespread, and well known as the Umbelliferae these plants were conspicuous by their absence in this series of detailed observations and studies. To this day, the biological importance of the various characters of flowers, inflorescence and fruit, (upon which we base our taxonomic and phylogenetic ideas), remains essentially unknown. Thus the term 'breeding systems' does not quite seem to fit when applied to the Umbelliferae which have 'unspecialized' flowers that are pollinated by unspecialized pollinators.

Plants with such unspecialized flowers have been termed 'promiscuous plants' (as opposed to the more specialized 'bee plants', 'bird plants' and so forth) by Verne Grant (1949) in his work on pollination in relation to floral structure and to taxonomy.

A search of the literature provided no material at all specifically on breeding systems in the Umbelliferae; and, except for Knuth's 1908 *Handbook of Flower Pollination*, there is practically nothing in the literature on the floral biology of the umbels. Drude (1898), Coulter & Rose (1900), and most recent workers remark in one way or another on the insignificant variation and the monotonous uniformity of umbel flowers. Although such comments are, of course, usually made in relation to the plants of a single genus or a small group of genera, the aspect of a relatively high degree of floral uniformity throughout the entire family is one of the accepted features of the Umbelliferae and is a positive mark, in such a large and widespread family, of unspecialized flowers.

In addition to their general morphological uniformity, individual umbel flowers are small and difficult to manipulate mechanically in experimental work; from the few indications in the literature (e.g. Darwin, 1891) and from my own observations (Bell, 1954), self-fertility is the rule and self-sterile plants appear to be the very rare exception; hybridization is almost unknown in the family; and, finally, genetic studies of the sort associated with 'breeding systems' are completely lacking for any uncultivated umbelliferous plant. Nowhere did I find any reference to 'floral biology' in the Umbelliferae and its associated concept of intricate pollinator-flower interactions and complex evolutionary pathways leading to co-adaptation between pollinators and flowers.

However, if one leaves the literature and the herbarium and makes even a casual, one-season survey of the living plants available in an area with a moderately diverse umbelliferous flora, it soon becomes apparent that there are many subtle floral differences, and presumably adaptive specializations, in the Umbelliferae despite their general appearance of uniformity. Thus in following more the subtitle of this paper I would like to mention and illustrate some of these specializations and comment briefly on, or question, their impact on the reproductive biology of certain umbels.

To establish some points for reference it is helpful to consider some of the general floral features shared by plants of many North Temperate genera of the Umbelliferae:

(1) a prominent stylopodium	(5) protandry
(2) exposed nectar	(6) actinomorphic corollas
(3) promiscuous pollination	(7) sexual reproduction
(4) perfect flowers	(8) semi-compact umbels

In those instances in which the plants of a genus do not share these traits in common with related genera, we may logically consider that differences in selective pressures have resulted in evolutionary changes, or modifications, from the more generalized, probably ancestral, condition.

STYLOPODIUM

The stylopodium—the swollen, often colourful, nectar-secreting style-base characteristic of the Umbelliferae has some rather striking differences from one genus to the next, and provides a good starting-point for a brief survey of flora specialization in the umbels. Although the stylopodium is evident in numerous published drawings of umbel flowers or fruits, it rarely so much as rates a label, and more rarely yet any discussion, by most of the anatomists, morphologists and taxonomists in whose work such figures appear. Thus, unfortunately, little is known of the actual origin, structure, or function of the stylopodium despite its rather apparent significance in the total reproductive biology of many umbels.

The nectar secretion of the stylopodium can be quite copious, as can be seen in fresh flowers of *Ptilimnium capillaceum* (Michaux) Raf. and *Conium maculatum* L. (Plate 1, A, B). In some species this secretion continues in an individual flower well after the stamens and petals are shed. Obviously a long period of nectar secretion is helpful if unspecialized pollinators are to be attracted to protandrous flowers with ripe anthers and then later back to the same flowers when their stigmas are finally receptive. Of course a long period of nectar flow also may be achieved by sequential nectar secretion by the many flowers of the inflorescence.

The stylopodia of staminate flowers are usually somewhat reduced in size, as illustrated in a comparison with the stylopodium of a perfect flower in *Zizia trifoliata* (Michaux) Fernald (Fig. 1) and *Heracleum lanatum* Michaux (Fig. 2).

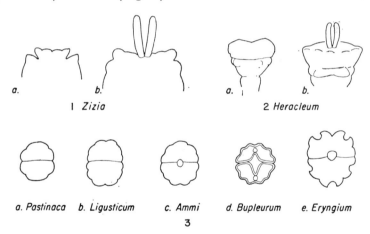

FIGURE 1. Longitudinal section through flowers (petals removed) showing differences in stylopodium size between a staminate flower (a) and a perfect flower (b) of *Zizia trifoliata* (*ca.* ×15).

FIGURE 2. Longitudinal section through flowers (petals removed) showing differences in stylopodium size between a staminate flower (a) and a perfect flower (b) of *Heracleum lanatum* (*ca.* ×7·5).

FIGURE 3. Variation in stylopodium shapes in plants of different genera as indicated (all drawings *ca.* ×15).

However, these reduced stylopodia apparently continue to function effectively in nectar secretion and thus assure the insect visits necessary for effective pollination among strongly protandrous or andromonoecious plants. The large and often brightly coloured stylopodia found in such genera as *Foeniculum, Cicuta* and *Daucus* may serve as further attractive devices for pollinators quite apart from their nectar secreting role, although the colour of the stylopodium may change with age, as in *Pastinaca sativa*. Stylopodium colour may contrast somewhat with the colour of the petals, as in the case of *Cicuta maculata* L. or the colour may be the same as that of the petals as in *Conium maculatum* and *Angelica triquinata* Michaux, thus intensifying the colour effect of the total inflorescence. No differentiation between petals and stylopodium occurred in any of the several flower samples tested under ultraviolet light.

Further enhancement of this visual attraction function may be brought about by differences in stylopodium shape (as seen from above) in some genera (Fig. 3). The pronounced lobing of the stylopodium of *Eryngium yuccifolium* is the result of the tubular form of these crowded flowers causing the stylopodium to grow around the filament bases. Furthermore, the form of the stylopodium of an *Eryngium* flower is more or less completely hidden by the infolded petals, thus there is little reason to ascribe attractive, or selective, value to stylopodium shape in this genus as might be done in some others.

The sticky surface of the stylopodium often has pollen adhering to it in varying quantity as was observed in *Heracleum lanatum, Ptilimnium capillaceum* and *Ligusticum canadense* (L.) Britton. Occasionally an entire anther would be stuck to the stylopodium in flowers of the last two species. There is a remote possibility that the stylopodium might function as a secondary stigmatic surface in some species (most likely annuals) or the stylopodium might serve as a 'pollen reservoir' in such plants as *Foeniculum* and *Bupleurum* in which the flowers are strongly protandrous and the stigmas are not developed until well after the anthers are shed. The developing stigma then grows from (or through) the smooth surface of the stylopodium and presumably through any remaining nectar film which might contain viable pollen.

Another function that the stylopodium may serve in some species is protective. The relatively large succulent tissue of the stylopodium is free of oil tubes (or apparently so in most species examined) and, in *Angelica triquinata*, is eaten by some of the visitors to the flowers. Rarely does the damage reach the ovule itself which, of course, is further protected not only by the oil tubes but to some degree by the presence of intracellular crystals and, perhaps, by the additional vascular tissue of the carpophore. It thus appears that the stylopodium may acquire, in some umbels, specialization beyond the basic role of nectar secretion.

Reduction in the size of the stylopodium in perfect flowers of some species constitutes another trend of specialization of this floral structure, and this specialization or modification may take two forms. In the first, the stylopodium is conical in shape and the total cross-sectional area of the stylopodium is greatly reduced along with a reduction in surface area. Such a condition can be observed in the perennial *Cryptotaenia canadensis* (L.) DC. and the annual *Chaerophyllum tainturieri* Hooker. In the second form of reduction, often associated with floral specialization toward protection of the nectar, the stylopodium is strongly flattened as well as somewhat reduced in surface area. This is illustrated by plants in the closely related apioid genera *Thaspium* and *Zizia*, both perennials of woodlands and woodland margins in the southeastern United States. *Sanicula*, in the Saniculoideae and another woodland perennial, also has a flattened stylopodium as do the two perennials *Hydrocotyle bonariensis* Lam. and *Lilaeopsis carolinensis* C. & R. in the Hydrocotyloideae.

Differences at the cellular level are an even stronger indication of modification of the stylopodium. The flattened stylopodium of *Zizia trifoliata* has a rather uniform and well-defined epidermal layer, as does the enlarged stylopodium of *Daucus carota* L. The stylopodium of *Conium maculatum* is smooth but has a definite subepidermal layer of presumably secretory cells. The large stylopodia of *Angelica venenosa* (Greenw.) Fern. and *Angelica triquinata* Michx. have a surface that appears pitted (Plate 1C). In sectioned material the cells in the area of the 'pits' hold more stain and also have more crystals than surrounding cells. The 'pits', which seem to be centres of nectar secretion, are always in association with a stomate. The greater density of crystals in the vicinity of these pits may represent either a build-up of metabolic by-products or a protective device, or both.

It is in *Eryngium*, however, that one finds the most interesting series of surface modifications of the stylopodia (Fig. 4). In the small flowers of *Eryngium prostratum*

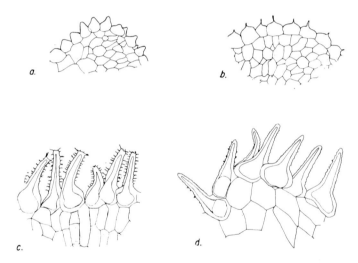

FIGURE 4. Longitudinal sections to show differences in the features of the surface cells of the stylopodia in *Eryngium*. (a) *E. prostratum*; (b) *E. aquaticum*; (c) *E. yuccifolium*; (d) *E. maritimum* (all drawings *ca.* × 25).

Nuttal the convex mass of secretory tissue has a papillose surface and the papillate cells each have a small apical tuft. In *Eryngium aquaticum* L. the cells are more nearly rectangular in section and have an uneven surface—either from hair-like appendages or the breakup of a surface layer, possibly of dried nectar. In *Eryngium yuccifolium* Michaux (and also *Eryngium maritimum* L. from preliminary observations) the surface cells of the stylopodium have elongate processes with apical tufts. These cells also have thicker walls than the subsurface cells of the stylopodium.

The different combinations of stylopodium shape, size, structure and colour certainly attest to differences in selective pressures on, and adaptive significance of, this relatively conservative floral organ. Unfortunately there have been no studies to determine what, if any, correlations exist between variation in the stylopodium and variation in pollinators or pollinator behaviour and effectiveness.

EXPOSED NECTAR

Exposure of the stylopodium, and thus the nectar, depends upon petal size, shape and position. In the more or less tightly closed flower buds characteristic of most umbels the stylopodium is covered. As anthesis occurs the induplicate petals spread and also may straighten, fully exposing the stylopodium and its secretions as in *Ptilimnium capillaceum* (Plate 1A), and *Hydrocotyle verticillata* Thunb. (Plate 1D.) Occasionally, as in *Foeniculum vulgare* Mill. (Plate 1E) the size and position of the petals in bud are such that they do not completely cover the stylopodium even at this early stage of floral development. This provides not only a longer exposure of the nectar-bearing stylopodia, but may serve also as a 'pollen reservoir'. Similar exposed stylopodia occur in the buds of *Pastinaca* and *Bupleurum*.

In the other direction there are several examples of umbel flowers with the nectar protected to varying degrees. As mentioned earlier, there seems to be a positive correlation in the few samples examined between protection of the nectar and a reduced, usually flattened, stylopodium.

In the Apioideae, for example, the erect, strongly induplicate petals of *Zizia* and *Thaspium* do not spread or straighten, but rather remain erect and form an effective 'corolla tube' 1 mm or more long, through which only the very centre of the stylopodium is exposed to pollinators. In addition, apical flaps (Fig. 5) on the tips of the

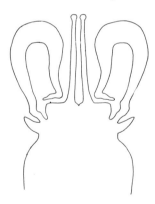

5 *Thaspium*

FIGURE 5. Diagrammatic section through a flower of *Thaspium barbinode* showing 'tubular' corolla formed by erect, unfolded petals. Note apical flaps on petals over stylopodium (*ca.* ×40).

petals further cover the stylopodium and prevent access to its surface until after the petals are shed—an event that may correlate with the maturation of the stigmas of these flowers. A correlation of this type could lead to a degree of pollinator specialization through selective forces related primarily to the staminate phase of a protandrous flower.

The greatest degree of protection of the nectar appears to be in plants of the genus *Eryngium*, in the subfamily Saniculoideae. Here a thin septum actually develops between the basal and apical portions of the infolded petal which not only prevents the petal from straightening (it cannot spread or reflex because of the compact arrangement of the flowers in the head), but with the septum of the adjacent petal, forms a cavity or chamber in which the anther fits tightly with the filament crooked up through the narrow space between the margins of the two petals. The long anthers thus effectively strengthen the 'corolla-tube' of *Eryngium* and help enforce a slight shift toward pollination by more specialized long-tongued insects. When the crooked filaments straighten and the anthers are pulled from their petaloid chambers the five chambers themselves then provide additional tubular pathways to the surface of the stylopodium for those long-tongued insects that can reach it. Because of considerable differences in flower size between some of the species of *Eryngium*, with concomitant differences in depth of the 'corolla-tube', the effectiveness of this particular floral specialization in regard to a shift to long-tongued insects probably varies from species to species. The previously mentioned specialized surface features of the lobed stylopodium of *Eryngium* may also be correlated with the slight shift in pollinators.

POLLINATION

In many families and genera of plants with more sophisticated pollination systems there is a considerable difference between an 'insect visitor' and a 'pollinator'. However, in the umbels, where each plant characteristically produces large numbers of small, closely spaced flowers with exposed nectar, each insect visitor to the inflorescence is a potential and probable pollinator. Therefore the published lists of insect visitors to the flowers of various species of umbels can be taken as a fair indication of the number and diversity of the actual pollinators in the species (and in the geographic areas) treated.

For most species of umbels treated by Knuth (1908) and Robertson (1928) the number of different kinds of pollinators is rather large, often between two and three hundred. If the published data of Knuth and Robertson are reworked to show the percentage of each group of pollinators to the whole pollination fauna for a species (Fig. 6), it is easy to see that the umbels are, indeed 'promiscuous' plants, pollinated by an array of insects. Equally obvious is the fact that most of the pollinators are Dipterans—flies, mosquitoes and gnats, or some of the more unspecialized bees, wasps and ants of the Hymenoptera. With few exceptions the more specialized bees, butterflies and moths make up only a small percentage of the pollinators. The Coleoptera and the Hemiptera, usually not considered to be specialized as pollinators, might be expected to occur in greater numbers. However, the oils found throughout most umbels might deter these chewing or sucking insects.

Even in the small sample illustrated, it appears that a few species of umbels may be developing a weakly specialized flower-pollinator interaction.

The strongest indication of specialization is obviously in *Sanicula marilandica* L. which has few species of insect visitors (mostly short-tongued bees) and usually sets abundant fruit. The relatively high percentage of bugs (Hemiptera) visiting *Sanicula* may represent the start of another line of specialization.

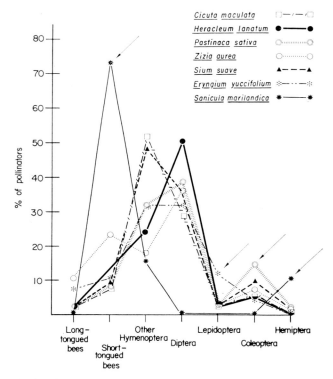

FIGURE 6. Graph showing percentage of various pollinators for seven different species (and genera) of Umbelliferae. Arrows indicate possible trend toward a more specialized pollinator-flower relationship.

In the case of *Eryngium yuccifolium* the higher percentage of visits by long-tongued Lepidoptera correlates strongly with the previously mentioned protected nectar and 'corolla-tube' modifications of these *Eryngium* flowers. A minor degree of specialization might also be indicated by the somewhat higher percentage of visits by Coleoptera to *Pastinaca sativa*. Once developed, specialization for pollinator-plant specificity will, like most adaptive peaks, be difficult to reverse.

It may be that specialization of many umbels for pollination by unspecified insects will be equally difficult to reverse or change and that most umbels will become more 'promiscuous' in their pollination rather than more specialized. This line of evolution is made even more likely by the fact that the umbels, as are many other plants, are often infested with thrips (see Plate 1B). These minute insects are so prevalent in umbel flowers that they serve somewhat as a 'universal pollinator', and self pollination by thrips reduces the selective effectiveness of morphological modifications that might otherwise lead to more specific pollinators.

PROTANDRY

The fact is well established that most umbels are indeed protandrous, though a few protogynous exceptions may exist in some genera (e.g. *Hydrocotyle, Sanicula* and *Erigenia*), and in a few other genera, notably annuals such as *Chaerophyllum* and *Ptilimnium*, protandry seems to be only weakly developed. In a few instances of apparent protogyny (e.g. *Eryngium*) the long styles are well exserted from the flower bud several days before the anthers are evident, but the stigmas of a given flower are not receptive until after the pollen has been shed from the anthers of that flower.

With such near universal occurrence of protandry in the family one might expect a rather uniform series of functional floral adaptations toward it. However, differences in the degree of dichogamy and the sequence of flowering within a plant can produce different pollination patterns, or potential patterns, from one genus to the next. If protandry is only weakly developed (Fig. 7), as was indicated previously for *Ptilimnium* and *Chaerophyllum*, self-pollination can easily occur, and this appears to be the

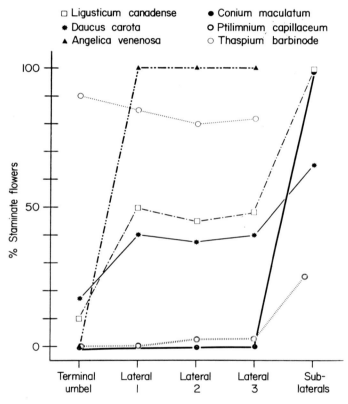

FIGURE 7. Different patterns in the changes in the sexual composition of umbels from the terminal (primary) umbel through the series of lateral (secondary, and tertiary, etc.) umbels in plants of six species.

case in both *Ptilimnium capillaceum* and *Chaerophyllum tainturieri*. If filament length is great enough, as in *Daucus, Cicuta, Heracleum, Conium* (Plate 1F) and others, weak protandry will permit geitonogamy. This pollination by the anthers of adjacent flowers in the umbel has no genetic advantage over self-pollination, but may be of selective advantage by ensuring pollination after a brief period of time in which outcrossing could occur. Both of the above types of pollinations can, and do, take place in the absence of insect pollinators. If protandry is more strongly developed it will enforce geitonogamy, here by insect vector (or possibly by gravity in some cases) or it may enforce actual outcrossing. The latter is mandatory only if the flowering sequence for an individual plant is so synchronized that all umbels flower at once and the male stage of all flowers is completed before the female stage begins, as reported for *Peucedanum lubimenkoanum* Kot. by Ponomarev (1960).

Between the extremes of self-pollination and obligate outcrossing protandry has produced a mosaic of adaptations that have variously altered the floral composition in terms of the percentage of staminate flowers in the sequence of umbels, from terminal (primary) to laterals (secondary) to sublateral (tertiary) in the genera surveyed.

The flowers of an umbel, and its component umbellets, open in sequence, of course, despite modification of the umbel, from the outer whorl to the centre. Pollen for the protandrous outer flowers is supplied by the protandrous inner flowers; pollen for the inner flowers is supplied by the outer flowers of a secondary umbel, and so on.

Under the continued selection of protandry the evolutionary development of staminate flowers is made more likely. Once staminate flowers are present their number and synchronization in the flowering cycle of a plant will doubtless change with any changes in the pollination cycle, and the evolutionary progression from a few staminate flowers per umbel to completely staminate-flowered umbels is assured under certain selection patterns. In such a plant the usual expectation would be a high percentage of perfect flowers in the primary umbels and a progressively lower percentage of perfect flowers in the successive umbels until the last umbels to flower are composed mostly or entirely of male flowers. In some species such as *Daucus carota* and *Ligusticum canadense* this is precisely what one finds in an analysis of the individual flowers from the various umbellets of the series of umbels. When graphed (Fig. 7) the data from these two species give rather similar curves characteristic of the usual protandrous condition. As the data for additional species are added to the graph it immediately becomes apparent that protandry varies in degree and in evolutionary results. Unfortunately, at this point there are few observations, and no experimental evidence, to give some clue as to the *reasons* for such diversity.

As can be seen from Fig. 7, the annual *Ptilimnium capillaceum* shows a quite different pattern from *Daucus carota*, perhaps because the *Ptilimnium* is more effective at self-pollination. The graph would indicate that the biennial *Conium maculatum*, which was cited by Knuth (1908) as a typical example of a plant with protandrous flowers, may be only weakly protandrous, or, more likely in this instance, it has evolved some unnoticed mechanism that ensures more effective pollination of the flowers in the secondary umbels, thus reversing the selection for additional staminate flowers at this point in the flowering cycle. Both *Ptilimnium* and *Conium* therefore represent specializations beyond the more typical condition expressed by the 'protandrous curve' as exemplified by *Daucus* and *Ligusticum*. Although each of these specializations would result in an increase in the potential number of seeds per plant, it appears that the results may have been obtained by different evolutionary pathways despite the apparently unspecialized nature of the flowers, inflorescences, and pollinators involved.

The effect of strong protandry in *Angelica venenosa* provides a striking contrast to *Conium* in this respect (Fig. 7). Usually all of the flowers of the terminal umbel of *Angelica venenosa* are perfect and all of the flowers of the lateral or secondary umbels are staminate. Depending upon the synchronization between the female stage of the flowers in the terminal umbel and the opening of the anthers in the flowers of the laterals, protandry could produce either facultative or obligate outcrossing. Here again, the difference in the graphs strongly indicates specialization beyond, or at least differing from, the protandrous pattern of plants such as *Daucus* or *Ligusticum*.

Interestingly enough, *Angelica triquinata* is equally as protandrous as *A. venenosa*, but all flowers of the terminal and lateral umbels are perfect. Thus within the genus *Angelica* we have another indication of specialization in unspecialized flowers leading to drastic differences in the sexual composition of the umbels. I would like to postulate that the lack of development of numerous male flowers in *Angelica triquinata* is due to a high degree of successful pollinations of flowers in all umbels of these plants brought about by an interesting feature of the copious nectar. Not only are numerous insects attracted by the large quantity of nectar produced by the many flowers of the large compound umbels, but the nectar is narcotic, especially to *Bombus* and similar Hymenoptera, and in effect provides the plant with numerous captive pollinators. The drugged insects scurry frantically over the assemblage of primary, secondary and tertiary umbels—all of which are conveniently on the same horizontal plane by the time the flowers of the latter umbels open. Soon the insects fall into a stupor and drop to the ground, where they remain immobile for approximately $1\frac{1}{2}$ minutes. After some movement is evident another 15–30 seconds are required before the insects are air-borne again. They usually weave back to an umbel to start the cycle over.

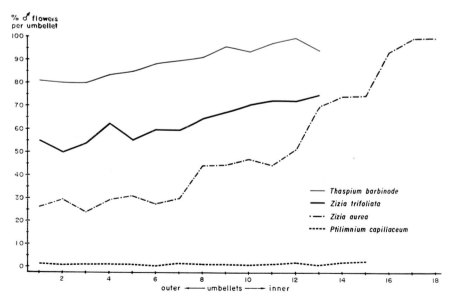

FIGURE 8. Different patterns in the changes in the sexual composition of umbellets (of all umbels) in plants of four species.

If the plants of a species produce small umbels or umbels few in numbers, and if the plants are solitary or are widely scattered, the accompanying changes in selection would be expected to produce some further modification of the 'protandrous curve'. One of the most obvious modifications would be changes in the number and placement of male flowers in the individual umbels since each umbel might now have to furnish entirely its own pollen source. Some preliminary sexual ratios obtained for the flowers of a number of individual umbellets of two species of *Zizia* and one of *Thaspium* show such a modification (Fig. 8). In *Zizia aurea* (L.) W. D. J. Koch the outer umbellets are composed of 25% male flowers. As the percentage of male flowers increases steadily toward the centre of the umbel, the central umbellets are usually composed only of staminate flowers. Surprisingly, the data for the closely related *Thaspium barbinode* (Michaux) Nutt., which is ecologically and morphologically much like *Zizia* in many respects, has a much lower initial percentage of perfect flowers yet still shows a similar decrease in the number of perfect flowers toward the centre of each umbellet and each umbel. The autogamous flowers of *Ptilimnium*, by contrast, are essentially all perfect. Perhaps some future comparative study of the pollination of these two woodland perennials will disclose the biological reasons for the interesting differences in their floral ratios.

FLOWERS REGULAR

Zygomorphic flowers are associated with very specialized pollinator-flower interaction in the plants of such families as the Orchidaceae, Scrophulariaceae and Lamiaceae. In the Asteraceae and the Apiaceae the function of the zygomorphic or irregular flowers, when present, is primarily to attract the generally unspecialized pollinators to the inflorescence. *Daucus carota*, *Heracleum lanatum*, *Coriandrum sativum* L. and *Caucalis latifolia* L. are all good examples of plants which produce some irregular or zygomorphic flowers—usually toward the outside of the umbel. In none of the above cases are the flowers with the zygomorphic corollas known to have pollinators different from the smaller actinomorphic flowers of the rest of the umbel.

Visual impact of an umbel may also be increased if there is an increase in the number and size of the umbellets and also by closer spacing of the individual flowers, and the individual umbellets, in the umbel. In those species with zygomorphic flowers larger, and also more compact, umbels are common. Where neither zygomorphic flowers nor larger umbels have evolved, the bracts subtending the inflorescence may be enlarged and also brightly coloured. *Eryngium maritimum* L. from Europe, *Eryngium proteaflorum* Delar. and *Eryngium carlinae* Delar. of Mexico and *Actinotus helianthi* Labillard. of Australia present an interesting comparison here of convergent evolution.

Of course specialization in umbel size can go in the opposite direction, as the reduced and compact umbels of *Sanicula*, *Torilis* and *Hydrocotyle* evidence. In *Hydrocotyle*, *Centella*, *Lilaeopsis* and some species of *Eryngium* (e.g. *E. prostratum*) and *Cicuta* (e.g. *C. bulbifera* L.) the smaller umbels and inconspicuous flowers correlate suspiciously well with very effective methods of asexual reproduction, but no quantitative studies exist to confirm these suspicions!

In the genus *Eryngium*, despite the compactness of the inflorescence in such species as *Eryngium prostratum*, the evolution of certain presumably protective features seems to be forcing a shift away from mass pollination and toward the more specific pollination of individual flowers. The protective shift, and the resulting increase in floral individuality, involves a wider spacing of the flowers in the head (as in *Eryngium aquaticum*), the hidden stylopodium or nectary, the 'tubular' corolla, and the separation of the individual flowers in the head by means of stout, elongate bracts that equal or exceed the length of the styles and thus reduce indiscriminate wandering over the surface of the inflorescence by the pollinators. In some species of *Ptilimnium* and *Oxypolis* there has been a considerable decrease in the compactness or density of the umbels in comparison with the umbels of such plants as *Conium* or *Daucus* and numerous other genera previously discussed. Although the wide spacing of the flowers in *Ptilimnium* might be taken to indicate a trend toward more individual pollinator attention (and perhaps, in time, more pollinator specificity), the open nature of these umbels may, in fact, be the result of the evolution of an effective system of self-pollination, as shown by Loveless (1970, unpublished) in her preliminary observations on pollination and reproduction in *Ptilimnium capillaceum*.

CONCLUSION

Considering the biotic nature of the natural selection involved in the evolution of the floral parts of entomophilous plants, the basic floral uniformity of the umbels may be the result of strong natural selection producing an ancient adaptive peak involving primitive, unspecialized or 'promiscuous' pollinators. The selective effectiveness of such a pollination system during extensive migrations could lead to 'fixation' of the characters involved. Once this happened the completeness of the adaptation to unspecialized pollinators would, in itself, minimize the effect of any subsequent more specialized selective forces. Thus any further morphological or physiological floral adaptations are represented by small modifications superimposed on the ancient reproductive patterns. More detailed studies of these relatively minor evolutionary changes that have taken place in the breeding systems of the Umbelliferae might thus represent more informative or interesting lines of investigation, with wider application to phylogenetic studies within the family, than similar investigations of more exotic plants with a high degree of floral variation and adaptation to their specific pollinators. After some 2500 years of alpha taxonomy such evolutionary studies, which might more closely relate form with function, are sorely needed in order to assess properly and correlate more effectively, the information we have with the information we are now getting with the aid of our advanced technology.

REFERENCES

BELL, C. R., 1954. The *Sanicula crassicaulis* complex (Umbelliferae). *Univ. Calif. Publs Bot.*, **27**: 133–230.

COULTER, J. M. & ROSE, J. N., 1900. Monograph of the North American Umbelliferae. *Contr. U.S. natn. Herb.*, **7**: 1–256.

DARWIN, C., 1859. *On the Origin of Species by means of Natural Selection.* London.

DARWIN, C., 1891. *The effects of Cross and Self Fertilization in the Vegetable Kingdom.* 3rd ed. London.

DRUDE, C. G. O., 1898. Umbelliferae. In Engler, A. & Prantl, K. (eds), *Die natürlichen Pflanzenfamilien,* **3** (8): 63–250.

GRANT, V., 1949. Pollination systems as isolating mechanisms in Angiosperms. *Evolution,* **3**: 82–97.

KNUTH, R., 1908. *Handbook of Flower Pollination.* Oxford.

LOVELESS, MARILYN D., 1970. Flowering sequence and reproductive biology of *Ptilimnium capillaceum* (Michx.) Raf. (unpublished N.S.F. research report.)

PONOMAREV, A. N., 1960. Concerning Protandry in Umbelliferae. *Dok. Akad. Nauk SSSR* **135** (3): 750–752. (Translated.)

ROBERTSON, C., 1928. *Flowers and Insects.* Carlinville, Illinois.

EXPLANATION OF PLATE

PLATE 1

A. Flower of *Ptilimnium capillaceum* with nectar droplets on the stylopodium and dehiscing anthers ($\times 20$). The stigmas of this flower were receptive when the photograph was taken.

B. Copious nectar of *Conium maculatum* after the petals have been shed (plant in water in laboratory) ($\times 20$). Note thrip caught in nectar on right.

C. Pitted surface of stylopodium of *Angelica triquinata* ($\times 20$).

D. Fully exposed stylopodium of *Hydrocotyle verticillata* with nectar droplets ($\times 20$).

E. Flower bud of *Foeniculum vulgare* with the central area of the stylopodium exposed ($\times 20$).

F. *Conium maculatum* flower with elongate filaments ($\times 10$).

PLATE 1

Morphologie pollinique et corrélations phylogénétiques chez les Ombellifères

M.-Th. CERCEAU-LARRIVAL

Muséum National d'Histoire Naturelle, Laboratoire de Palynologie de l'E.P.H.E., Laboratoire de Biologie Végétale Appliquée, Paris, et Laboratoire d'Ecologie Générale, Brunoy, France.

A palynological study of 1500 species in the Umbelliferae has revealed a great variety in the pollen which can be grouped around five basic types: subrhomboidal, subcircular, ovoid, subrectangular and equatorially constricted. These types are arranged in a phyletic series. The scanning electron microscope and ultrasonic fracturing of the pollen grains permits a better knowledge of the ultrastructure of the membranes and particularly of the exine.

A study of the seedlings, observations on leaf ontogeny, the adult vegetative body, the inflorescence and the fruit suggest that the general evolutionary development has been from (1) a perennial, small in stature, with simple entire leaves; seedling with very small cotyledons and primordial leaves always entire; pollen small, subrhomboidal with the exine thin, the tectal surface smooth or cerebroid, with the columellae very short, straight, with globular heads, unstructured to (2) an annual with more or less small stems, divided leaves (1–5 pinnatisect); large fruit, often spiny, seedling large with sizeable cotyledons and primordial leaves always dissected; pollen large, equatorially constricted, with the exine well developed, the tectal surface striate-reticulate or micro-reticulate, with large columellae and micro-columellae in the tectum which is distinct in relation to the feet of the underlying columellae.

The importance of palynology in the study of geographical distribution and historical plant geography is discussed.

Chez les Ombellifères, une étude palynologique portant sur 1500 espèces, met en évidence une grande variété de formes polliniques, que l'on peut grouper autour de 5 types fondamentaux: subrhomboïdal, subcirculaire, ovale, subrectangulaire, équatorialo-constricté.

Le microscope électronique à balayage et la fracture des grains de pollen au moyen des ultrasons permet de mieux connaître l'ultrastructure des membranes et plus particulièrement de l'exine.

Les 5 types polliniques ont été mis en série phylétique.

L'étude des plantules menée corrélativement, les observations faites sur l'Ontogénie foliaire, l'Appareil Végétatif adulte, l'Inflorescence et le Fruit permettent de constater que l'Evolution générale se fait:

— à partir d'une plante vivace, de petite taille, à feuilles simples, entières; à fruit petit, glabre; à petite plantule possédant de très petits cotylédons, à feuilles primordiales toujours entières; à pollen petit, subrhomboidal, à exine mince, à surface tectale lisse ou cérébroïde, avec des columelles très courtes, droites, à têtes globuleuses, non structurées.

— pour aboutir à une plante annuelle, de taille plus élevée, à feuilles simples, découpées, (1–5 fois pennatiséquées); à fruit gros, souvent hérissé d'aiguillons; à grande plantule possédant des cotylédons importants, à feuilles primordiales toujours découpées; à gros pollen équatorialo-constricté, à exine extrêmement développée, à surface tectale striato-réticulée ou micro-réticulée, avec des grandes columelles digitées et des micro-columelles propres au tectum qui acquiert une totale individualisation par rapport aux pieds des columelles sous-jacentes.

Dans le domaine de la Biogéographie, la Palynologie a également un rôle à jouer, notamment dans l'étude des répartitions géographiques actuelles, et dans l'histoire du peuplement végétal.

TABLE DES MATIÈRES

INTRODUCTION

Ce n'est que pendant ces dernières décennies que toute l'ampleur des applications offertes par l'étude des grains de pollen, ou palynologie, est apparue.

Ainsi, dans le domaine de la systématique et de la phylogénie, le pollen présente des caractères de première valeur, utilisés de plus en plus par les botanistes.

Nous allons voir ce que la Palynologie a pu apporter à la taxonomie des Ombellifères, et les corrélations qui ont pu être faites avec des caractères offerts par d'autres disciplines.

Une étude approfondie, portant sur près de 1500 espèces de cette famille, met en évidence une grande variété de formes polliniques, que l'on peut grouper autour de cinq types fondamentaux, parfaitement discriminables, et des tailles échelonnées entre 15 μm et 70 μm.

Des recherches récentes, faites au microscope électronique à balayage, ont permis de mieux interpréter les surfaces polliniques, mais encore grâce à une technique nouvelle, la fracture des grains de pollen au moyen des ultrasons, de connaître avec une plus grande précision l'ultrastructure des membranes (Cerceau-Larrival *et al.*, 1970).

En nous basant sur les résultats offerts par le microscope photonique à des grossissements × 1000 et, chaque fois que cela a été possible, par le microscope électronique à balayage à des grossissements pouvant atteindre × 50,000, nous allons examiner les cinq types principaux et voir les caractères qui ont présidé à leur établissement.

Ces observations sont faites sur des pollens vidés de leur contenu cytoplasmique, puisque la Palynologie repose sur l'étude du sporoderme et plus particulièrement de l'exine.

Principales caractéristiques des pollens d'Ombellifères

Un pollen d'Ombellifères possède: (1) un axe de symétrie généralement d'ordre 3 (quelques exceptions à symétrie d'ordre 2, 4, 5) et un plan de symétrie perpendiculaire à cet axe (pollen isopolaire). Il y a 3 systèmes aperturaux: 3 ectoapertures qui sont des sillons longitudinaux, 3 endoapertures qui sont formées par l'arrêt d'une des membranes polliniques et par òu peut sortir le tube pollinique. (2) c'est un pollen longiaxe, ou très rarement équiaxe: c'est-à-dire que la valeur du rapport P/E est supérieure à 1 (P = axe polaire; E = diamètre équatorial): 1 < P/E < 2·5. (3) l'exine comprend: (a) une ectexine infrastructurée formée: d'un tectum qui apparait comme lisse, continu au microscope photonique, laissant apparaître, en coupe optique, les columelles disposées en réseau (Le tectum s'est révélé au microscope électronique à balayage être plus ou moins structuré suivant le niveau évolutif du pollen); de columelles, le plus souvent droites, mais pouvant être, dans certains cas, digitées. (b) une endexine au sens large du terme, qui s'interrompt au niveau de l'endoaperture, et qui, au microscope électronique à balayage, se montre formée par la sole sur laquelle respose la base des columelles, et par l'endexine au sens restreint.

Différents types de pollens

La nomenclature des cinq types polliniques est établie d'après le contour interne de l'endexine et non d'après le contour général du pollen, donné par l'ectexine, qui peut subir de légères modifications à l'intérieur d'une même espèce, alors que le contour de l'endexine reste stable étant donné sa constitution beaucoup plus compacte (Cerceau-Larrival, 1959, 1962*b*).

Les cinq types polliniques sont (Cerceau-Larrival 1962*b*, 1967): le type subrhomboidal (Rh), le type subcirculaire (C), le type ovale (O), le type subrectangulaire (Rg), le type équatorialo-constricté (E).

Chez les Ombellifères, l'étude des plantules et des cotylédons a permis l'établissement de deux lignées cotylédonaires (Cerceau-Larrival, 1962*b*): la lignée cotylédonaire longue (L) où le limbe cotylédonaire s'atténue insensiblement en pétiole; la lignée cotylédonaire ronde (R) où le limbe cotylédonaire s'atténue brusquement en pétiole.

Les cinq types polliniques se trouvent tous représentés dans la lignée cotylédonaire ronde, alors que le type subcirculaire, jusqu'à présent, n'a pas été observé dans la lignée cotylédonaire longue; il est donc caractéristique de la lignée cotylédonaire ronde.

Nous allons suivre la structure et l'évolution du pollen, à travers les cinq types observés.

Provenance du matériel

Le matériel étudié provient soit de mes collections personnelles issues de cultures dans les serres de Brunoy (CB), soit des Grands Herbiers dont la liste suit: State Herbarium of South Australia, Adelaide, Australia (AD); Conservatoire et Jardin Botaniques, Genève, Suisse (G); The Herbarium, Royal Botanic Gardens, Kew, Great-Britain (K); Institut de Botanique, Montpellier, France (MPU); Muséum National d'Histoire Naturelle, Laboratoire de Phanérogamie, Paris, France (P); Herbarium of the S.N. Djanashia Georgian State Museum, Tbilisi, U.S.S.R. (TGM); Herbarium of the University of California, Berkeley, U.S.A. (UC).

MORPHOLOGIE POLLINIQUE

Type subrhomboidal (Rh)

Le type subrhomboidal est caractéristique des grains de pollen de très petite taille: les valeurs de l'axe polaire P se situent entre 15 μm et 30 μm avec un essor particulier entre 20 μm et 30 μm.

Ce type a été observé dans la tribu des *Mulineae* Drude (*Azorella* Lam.) et des *Ammineae* Drude (*Bupleurum* L.).

La valeur du rapport P/E est faible, comprise entre 1 et 1·5; la symétrie est d'ordre 3; l'ectoaperture est longue; l'endoaperture est très grande, rectangulaire-curviligne; l'exine, très mince, est sensiblement d'égale épaisseur sur tout le pourtour de grain.

Bupleurum *L.*

L'étude palynologique du genre *Bupleurum*, caractéristique de l'Hémisphère Nord, a été entreprise avec Dodin (en préparation). *Bupleurum* a été situé à l'origine des Ombellifères à cotylédons longs (Cerceau-Larrival, 1962b, 1967). Dodin s'est tracé comme but l'étude de plusieurs espèces dans chacun des sections établies par Tutin (1968), en corrélation avec le caryotype étudié par Cauwet (1970).

B. angulosum L. (CB), espèce spéciale aux Pyrénées et aux Corbières, a un pollen de 30 μm (Planche 1, E–H); la vue polaire est subcirculaire et la coupe optique équatoriale montre la proéminence des apertures (Planche 1, I, J).

Chez *B. angulosum*, le microscope électronique à balayage révèle une surface tectale bien cérébroïde, les têtes non structurées des columelles se soudant en portées très courtes et incurvées (Planche 1, L, N). L'électronique confirme la structure primitive de ce type de pollen.

B. ranunculoides L. (CB), espèce des montagnes du Centre et du Sud l'Europe, a un pollen qui, au microscope électronique à balayage, offre un tectum assez compact, très peu structuré, lisse ou légèrement cérébroïde, avec des perforations dues à des espacements entre les têtes lisses des columelles (Planche 1, K, O).

Les fractures dues aux ultrasons permettent d'apercevoir l'ultrastructure de l'exine formée par une endexine mince (au sens strict), une sole épaisse, des columelles très courtes avec des têtes globuleuses, non structurées; l'ensemble n'atteint pas 2 µm d'épaisseur (Planche 1, M).

Le genre *Bupleurum* renferme de nombreuses espèces, le plus souvent vivaces, à feuilles simples, toujours entières. La plantule est de très petite taille, avec des petits cotylédons linéaires, un hypocotyle court, des feuilles primordiales toujours entières. L'inflorescence est généralement une ombelle d'ordre 2 avec des bractées de l'involucre et de l'involucelle correspondant à des feuilles entières, sessiles (Cerceau-Larrival, 1965). Le fruit est petit glabre, sans côte ou avec des côtes peu développées, non comprimé.

Azorella *Lamk.*

L'étude palynologique du genre *Azorella* (genre presque exclusivement austral, renfermant de très nombreuses endémiques) a été entreprise au cours de recherches accomplies dans le cadre d'une étude biologique de l'Amérique Australe.

Les 23 espèces étudiées ont été procurées par le Professeur Constance et correspondent à des échantillons s'échelonnant depuis les Andes de Colombie en passant par les Andes de l'Equateur, du Pérou et du Chili et de la République Argentine, jusqu'en Patagonie avec des stations dans une des dernières îles de la Terre de Feu.

Toutes les espèces observées présentent le même type subrhomboïdal; elles peuvent se classer en fonction de la valeur du rapport P/E, et des corrélations ont été établies entre cette valeur et la Répartition Géographique (Cerceau-Larrival, 1968).

Le pollen de ce genre est tout à fait comparable à celui rencontré chez *Bupleurum* et présente les mêmes caractéristiques primitives.

A. trifoliata Clos (UC), espèce spéciale à la Cordillère chilienne, possède un pollen de 29 µm, fortement subrhomboïdal (Planche 1, A, B); la vue polaire est subcirculaire et la coupe optique équatoriale, comme chez *Bupleurum*, montre la proéminence des apertures (Planche 1, C, D).

Toutes les espèces sont vivaces, à feuilles simples entières ou peu divisées, souvent en rosettes; les inflorescences sont très primitives et formées d'ombelles simples à peu de fleurs; les bractées sont entières ou légèrement divisées, semblables aux feuilles stériles (Cerceau-Larrival, 1965*b*); les fruits, très rares, sont petits peu ou pas comprimés.

Pour l'ensemble de ces caractères, le genre *Azorella* a été considéré comme archaïque et certaines de ces espèces seraient même de véritables fossiles vivants (espèces des hautes terres équatoriales et des basses terres magellaniques) (Cerceau-Larrival, 1968).

Bupleurum et *Azorella* renferment de très nombreuses espèces endémiques et tout laisse supposer que nous nous trouvons en présence d'endémiques anciennes (paléoendémiques).

Type subcirculaire (*C*)

Ce type pollinique renferme des grains de pollen dont la taille se situe dans les mêmes limites que celles des grains subrhomboïdaux. Il a été observé uniquement chez des plantes appartenant à la lignée cotylédonaire ronde, et plus particulièrement, au groupe des *Hydrocotyleae* Drude (*Hydrocotyle*) et à celui des *Xanthosieae* Drude (*Xanthosia*).

La valeur du rapport P/E est voisine de E; le pollen est équiaxe. La symétrie peut être élevée: d'ordre 5, mais généralement d'ordre 3; l'ectoaperture est longue; l'endoaperture est très grande; l'exine, très mince, est sensiblement d'égale épaisseur sur tout le pourtour du grain.

Xanthosia *Rudge*

X. atkinsoniana F. Muell. (CB), endémique d'Australie, possède un pollen très arrondi, à exine très mince et caractérisé par une symétrie d'ordre 5 (Planche 2, C).

Hydrocotyle *L.*

H. vulgaris L. (CB), espèce des lieux humides d'Europe méridionale et centrale, a un pollen de 19 μm, présentant une grande endoaperture (Planche 2, E); la vue polaire est subtriangulaire (Planche 2, F).

H. laxiflora DC. (AD), espèce australienne, a un pollen de 26 μm, présentant un très léger épaississement de l'exine aux pôles (Planche 2, A, B).

Les observations faites au microscope électronique à balayage montrent une surface tectale moins lisse que chez *Bupleurum* et qui présente un début de rugulation; les têtes de columelles, toujours non structurées, se soudent entre elles en portées assez courtes (Planche 2, I, K).

Avec ce type subcirculaire, nous nous trouvons, également, devant une structure pollinique primitive. Les grains de pollens subrhomboïdaux et subcirculaires constituent environ 70% des grains de petites ou de très petites tailles (15 μm < P < 25 μm) rencontrés chez les Ombellifères. Il y a là une corrélation importante entre le type pollinique et la taille. (Cerceau-Larrival, 1967).

Hydrocotyle et *Xanthosia* renferment des espèces vivaces, à feuilles simples, palmées à palmatiséquées, ou peltées, ou cordiformes.

Ces plantes sont caractérisées: (1) par une plantule de très petite taille avec de minuscules cotylédons arrondis, et par des feuilles primordiales palmées; (2) par un fruit comprimé par le côté à 5 côtes filiformes (*Hydrocotyle*), à 9 côtes (côtes primaires dorsales proéminentes: *Xanthosia*; (3) par des bractées externes des ombellules bien développées et correspondant à des feuilles entières sessiles (*Xanthosia*).

L'inflorescence des *Hydrocotyle* est un cas particulier: l'ombellule centrale peut devenir sessile, les ombellules latérales peuvent disparaître à l'exception d'une seule et donner ainsi une fausse apparence de verticille. (Cerceau-Larrival, 1962*b*).

Type ovale (O)

Ce type pollinique est caractéristique des grains de pollen de petite taille; les valeurs de l'axe polaire P, avec un essor particulier entre 25 μm et 35 μm, peuvent atteindre 65 μm chez quelques formes géantes. Ce type, rencontré dans les deux lignées cotylédonaires, est surtout bien représenté dans la lignée ronde.

En voici quelques exemples choisis parmi des genres répartis dans différentes tribus: *Aciphylla* Forst. (tribu des *Ammineae* Drude), *Heracleum* L. (tribu des

Peucedaneae Drude), *Trachymene* Rudge (tribu des *Hydrocotyleae* Drude); ils appartiennent à la lignée ronde pour les deux derniers et à la lignée longue pour *Aciphylla*.

La valeur du rapport P/E est comprise entre 1·5 et 2; la symétrie est d'ordre 3; l'ectoaperture est longue; l'endoaperture plus petite que dans les 2 types précédents est ovale; l'exine devient plus épaisse généralement aux pôles.

Aciphylla *Forst.*

A. procumbens F. Muell (AD), espèce rencontrée en Tasmanie, possède un pollen de 27 μm, présentant toutes les caractéristiques précédentes (Planche, 2 D).

A. procumbens montre au microscope électronique à balayage une surface tectale cérébroïde, les têtes des columelles lisses, sont soudées en portées courtes et incurvées, assez similaires à celles observées chez *Bupleurum angulosum*. (Planche 2, H, J).

Ce matériel n'a pas été traité aux ultrasons.

La plante adulte est vivace de petite taille, à feuilles adultes stériles peu découpées, avec une plantule d'assez petite taille, à cotylédons linéaires peu importants, à feuilles primordiales entières.

Heracleum *L.*

Certaines espèces, qui présentent ce type ovale, peuvent avoir un pollen d'assez grande taille (60 μm) comme *Heracleum lanatum* Michx. espèce d'Amérique du Nord, de très grande taille (64 μm) comme *Heracleum mantegazzianum* Somm. & Lev., espèce originaire du Caucase, et acclimatée un peu partout dans le Bassin de la Méditerranée, et en France dans la Région Parisienne, notamment à Brunoy, dans le Parc du Laboratoire d'Ecologie Générale du Muséum.

H. lanatum Michx. (P) et *H. mantegazzianum* Somm. & Lev. (TGM) (Planche 3, A–D; Planche 4, A–F) ont ainsi un pollen ovale de taille importante, avec un épaississement marqué de l'exine aux pôles, dans la zone équatoriale; l'ectoaperture est difficilement visible du fait de l'épaisseur de l'exine; l'endoaperture est ovale, plate; les columelles sont grandes, espacées.

Les observations faites au microscope électronique à balayage ont montré pour:

(1) *H. lanatum* (Planche 3, E–H) un tectum rugulé, constitué par des têtes de columelles qui se soudent en portées plus ou moins longues (rugules) et qui s'enchevêtrent sans aucune direction préférentielle (Planche 3, E, G).

Les cassures dues aux ultrasons révèlent un emboîtement spectaculaire des têtes qui ne sont pas tout à fait soudées; la base des columelles est élargie (Planche 3, H). Une cassure longitudinale montre comment l'endexine se sépare de l'ectexine pour aller former l'endoaperture; l'endexine est lisse intérieurement (Planche 3, F).

(2) *H. mantegazzianum* (Planche 4, G–I, Planche 5, A–F) une surface tectale striato-rugulée, plus heurtée et enchevêtrée dans les zones aperturales, et à portées plus longues et plus organisées aux pôles (Planche 4, G, H, Planche 5, A, C).

Une cassure longitudinale, due aux ultrasons, permet de voir la surface interne lisse de l'endexine, et une endoaperture vue de l'intérieur du grain (Planche 4, I). Une cassure transversale montre: une endexine au sens large, fort épaisse, de très grandes columelles qui peuvent se digiter au niveau des mésocolpiums, avec des têtes très épaisses, sensiblement structurées et soudées en portées longues à ce niveau; au niveau de la zone aperturale, l'endexine au sens large est toujours très épaisse, mais les columelles sont plus courtes, même trappues, avec des têtes bien structurées et soudées en portées courtes et enchevêtrées (Planche 5, B, D, E, F).

Dans le microphylum des *Heracleae*, cette espèce serait une fin de série évolutive. Les autres caractères, tirés de la plantule et de l'appareil végétatif adulte, confirment cette hypothèse: *H. mantegazzianum* peut atteindre 3 mètres de haut; les feuilles adultes stériles sont immenses, peu découpées, palmées à palmatipartites; la plantule est très grande, à cotylédons géants; la première feuille primordiale est palmatilobée; les bractées très importantes sont entières et ne correspondent plus qu'à des gaines blanches, très spectaculaires, avec très rarement un peu de limbe terminal; les inflorescences sont des ombelles d'ordre 2 et de très grande taille; le fruit est gros, comprimé dorsalement.

Trachymene *Rudge*

T. glaucifolia F. Muell. (AD), espèce australienne, présente également un pollen ovale, de 48 µm, mais avec des épaississements d'exine dans les zones subpolaires. Ces épaississements sont dus à des columelles assez grandes, mais surtout à un tectum extrêmement épais, dont la structure est très difficilement visible au microscope photonique; les ectoapertures sont bordées de marges épaissies (Planche 6, A–F).

Dans ce cas, l'apport du microscope électronique à balayage est remarquable: les vues de surface révèlent un tectum rugulé à éléments très enchevêtrés et très épais, constitué par la superposition de 2 à 3 niveaux de têtes de columelles se soudant dans les 3 dimensions (Planche 6, G–I), comme le montrent les fractures obtenues après avoir cassé les grains au moyen des ultrasons (Planche 7, A–D, F).

L'ultrastructure, révélée par cette méthode, montre que l'endexine (au sens strict) n'est pas compacte, mais est constituée de 2 couches reliées entre elles par des trabécules (Planche 7, C). Les ultrasons provoquent également des arrasements, permettant de voir des columelles sectionnées à différents niveaux (Planche 7, B, E).

Le microscope électronique à balayage confirme une structure plus évoluée que dans les types précédents, subrhomboïdal et subcirculaire, autant dans les caractères propres au tectum, que dans ceux offerts par l'ensemble de l'exine.

Dans son ensemble, *T. glaucifolia* présente des caractères plus évolués que *Bupleurum* et *Azorella*: les feuilles adultes sont découpées, palmatiséquées; la plantule est de taille moyenne, à cotylédons ovales, à feuilles primordiales palmatilobées; les inflorescences sont des ombelles simples ou d'ordre 2; le fruit, assez petit, est fortement comprimé latéralement.

Type subrectangulaire (Rg)

Ce type a été observé dans les deux lignées cotylédonaires, mais beaucoup plus fréquemment dans la lignée longue.

Ce type pollinique est caractéristique des grains de pollens de taille moyenne: les valeurs de l'axe polaire P se situent, essentiellement entre 35 µm et 45 µm où nous assistons à un épanouissement remarquable de ce type, mais elles peuvent atteindre et dépasser, dans quelques cas, 50 μm. Il constitue le type pollinique le plus fréquemment observé chez les Ombellifères.

Ainsi, par exemple, la plus grande partie des genres de la tribu des *Scandicineae* Drude présente ce type (*Scandix* L., *Psammogeton* Edgew.) Tous les genres de la tribu des *Coriandreae* Drude possèdent ce type de pollen, ainsi qu'un grand nombre d'espèces de la tribu des *Smyrnieae* Drude (*Cachrys* L.), ainsi que celle des *Ammineae* Drude (*Diplolophium* Turcz.).

La valeur du rapport P/E est importante, généralement supérieure à 2; la symétrie est d'ordre 3; l'ectoaperture est généralement courte ou résiduelle; l'endoaperture est petite, rectangulaire ou carrée; l'exine est très importante, peut présenter ses épaississement soit aux pôles, soit dans les zones subpolaires, soit dans la zone équatoriale; le tectum est épais.

Scandix *L.*

Chez *S. pecten-veneris* L. (CB), espèce très répandue en Europe, en Asie occidentale et Afrique septentrionale, les premières constatations sont: d'une part, l'allongement du pollen: P = 43 μm et E = 20 μm; la valeur du rapport P/E est supérieure à 2; le grain prend une forme en osselet très nette, (2) d'autre part, la réduction des apertures (l'ectoaperture n'est plus longue, mais courte) et l'augmentation sensible de l'épaisseur de l'exine (columelles grosses et espacées) (Planche 8, M, N).

Cette plante, annuelle, possède des feuilles très découpées, bi-tripennatiséquées; une plantule de grande taille, à cotylédons importants, linéaires-lancéolées, à feuilles primordiales toujours découpées; les feuilles adultes fertiles sont moins découpées que les feuilles adultes stériles et les bractées entières sont réduites à la gaine, par disparition du limbe terminal; le fruit a un bec très allongé.

Psammogeton *Edgew.*

P. crinitum Boiss. (K), qui se rencontre en Iran et en Inde boréale occidentale, possède bien un pollen subrectangulaire en osselet de 34 μm, mais l'épaississement de l'exine dans les zones subpolaires et le rétrécissement à l'équateur, donnent un faux aspect d'équatorialo-constricté; l'ectoaperture difficilement visible, est discontinue; l'endoaperture est petite, carrée, fortement saillante; les columelles sont allongées, régulières, assez fines. (Planche 8, E, F).

Une vue polaire et une coupe optique équatoriale montrent les 3 importantes carènes d'exine dues au fort épaississement de l'exine dans les zones subpolaires (Planche 8, G, H).

Cachrys *L.*

C. alpina Bieb. (M), espèce typiquement méditerranéenne, a un pollen de 55 μm présentant un épaississement marqué de l'exine aux pôles, ce qui accentue son aspect en osselet; l'ectoaperture ne subsiste plus que sous la forme réduite d'un sillon vestigial au-dessus de l'endoaperture; les columelles sont grosses et parfois digitées; le tectum est fort épais (Planche 8, A–D).

C. goniocarpa Boiss. (G), a un pollen de 50 μm, également subrectangulaire en osselet, mais avec un épaississement plus marqué dans la zone équatoriale (Planches 9, A–C).

Le microscope électronique à balayage montre une surface tectale très heurtée, notamment dans les zones aperturales (Planche 9, E, H). Aux pôles, la surface a une apparence striato-rugulée assez comparable à celle observée par Nigaud (1970) chez certaines espèces de *Peucedanum* L.: les têtes structurées des columelles se soudent en portées assez longues qui peuvent s'orienter dans des directions privilégiées. Chaque portée est bien individualisée (Planche 9, E, I).

Une cassure transversale due aux ultrasons, dans une zone subpolaire, montre une endexine au sens strict épaisse, une sole également épaisse, des columelles grandes souvent digitées, avec des têtes soudées en surface en portées plus ou moins longues, mais présentant une certaine structuration visible en coupe, et indépendante des pieds. Nous assistons, ici, à une amorce d'individualisation des têtes des columelles par rapport à leurs pieds. L'endexine est lisse intérieurement (Planche 9, D, F, G).

Diplolophium *Turcz.*

L'espèce *D. africanum* Turcz. (P) du genre africain *Diplolophium*, récoltée en République Centre Africaine du Cameroun, possède un pollen subrectangulaire en osselet de 35 μm (Planche 8, I, J).

Au microscope électronique à balayage, ce pollen offre une surface tectale striato-rugulée, à organisation plus poussée que chez *Cachrys*, présentant des corps d'Ubisch: pollen jeune (Planche 8, K–O).

Une cassure transversale, dans la zone équatoriale, montre une endexine au sens strict assez importante, une sole épaisse sur laquelle reposent des columelles assez courtes et trappues et souvent digitées au sommet; les têtes ont une structuration très nette, indépendante du pied (Planche 8, P).

Le microscope électronique à balayage, chez *Cachrys* et *Diplolophium*, met en évidence des caractères évolués de l'ectexine et du tectum en particulier. *Cachrys* et *Diplolophium* sont des plantes caractérisées par des feuilles adultes stériles très découpées, souvent en lanières filiformes; les feuilles adultes fertiles, comme les bractées de l'involucre et de l'involucelle, reviennent au type entier par la gaine, après disparition du limbe terminal; la plantule de *Cachrys* est très grande, avec des cotylédons géants; les feuilles primordiales sont très découpées; le fruit est très gros.

L'ensemble de ces caractères situe ces plantes à un niveau évolutif élévé, en corrélation parfaite avec celui du type pollinique.

Jacques-Félix (1970) considère le genre africain *Diplolophium* comme allié au genre méditérranéen *Cachrys*, ce que la Palynologie confirme.

Type équatorialo-constricté (E)

Ce type pollinique est caractéristique des grains de pollen de grande taille: les valeurs de l'axe polaire P, les plus fréquemment rencontrées, sont comprises entre 45 μm et 70 μm. Ce type se rencontre aussi bien dans la lignée ronde que dans la lignée longue. Mais, jusqu'à présent, il n'a été observé que dans des groupements à répartition géographique essentiellement méditérranéenne: sous-tribu des *Tordy-*

linae Drude (tribu des *Peucedaneae* Drude); tribu des *Echinophoreae* Drude (*Echinophora* L., *Pycnocycla* Lindl.); sous-tribu des *Caucalinae* Drude (tribu des *Scandicineae* Drude) (*Orlaya* Hoffm., *Lisaea* Boiss., *Turgenia* Hoffm.).

Ces différents groupements ont fait l'objet de révisions systématiques d'après le type pollinique (Cerceau-Larrival, 1962*b*, 1963, 1965).

La valeur du rapport P/E est égale ou supérieure à 2; la symétrie est soit d'ordre 3, soit d'ordre 2; l'ectoaperture est très courte ou résiduelle; l'endoaperture est très petite, rectangulaire ou carrée; l'exine extrêmement importante constitue généralement des ailes épaisses sur chaque mésocolpium; les columelles sont fréquemment grandes et digitées; le tectum est très épais et souvent composé de petites columelles qui lui sont propres.

Echinophora *L.*

E. spinosa L. (CB), plante caractéristique des sables du littoral de la Méditerranée, possède un gros pollen de 48 μm présentant une symétrie bilatérale, caractéristique de toutes les espèces de la tribu des *Echinophoreae*, et à valeur du rapport P/E supérieure à 2; il est également très constricté dans la zone équatoriale, avec une réduction des apertures (ectoapertures très courtes); les columelles sont assez espacées (Planche 10, A–D, G).

Au microscope électronique à balayage, la surface tectale apparaît microréticulée ou striato-réticulée de façon très dense (Planche 10, E, F, H).

Une cassure longitudinale due aux ultrasons, révèle une endexine au sens large très importante, des columelles fines et rapprochées avec des têtes très bien structurées; cette structuration, qui leur est propre, forme en surface une microréticulation ou une striato-réticulation dense (Planche 10, H, I).

Pycnocycla *Lindl.*

P. ledermanii Wolff. (P), espèce qui se rencontre au Cameroun et qui est considérée par Jacques-Félix (1970) comme une vicariante de *P. glauca* Lindl. largement répandue en Inde, en Arabie et en Ethiopie, a une grand pollen de 50 μm présentant une symétrie bilatérale comme *Echinophora*; la vue polaire et la coupe optique équatoriale, ovales, sont tout à fait révélatrices, ainsi que la vue méridienne et la coupe optique méridienne du mésocolpium, de cette symétrie d'ordre 2; les apertures sont très réduites; les columelles sont très régulières; le tectum est assez épais (Planche 11, A–F).

Au microscope électronique à balayage, la symétrie bilatérale ressort de façon très spectaculaire (Planche 11, H, I, et Planche 12, A, C).

La surface tectale est striato-réticulée de façon très dense. Les enchevêtrements des têtes des columelles sont très ténus et les portées constituées par les têtes soudées sont courtes Planche 11, G, Planche 12, E). Les ectoapertures, courtes, ne sont bordées de zones épaissies qu'au niveau des endoapertures (Planche 11, H; Planche 12, C).

Les ultrasons ont provoquées soit des arrasements, soit des fractures transversales. Certains arrasements montrent des columelles entières, puis sectionnées à différents niveaux des pieds, qui reposent sur la sole au contact de l'endexine au sens strict

(Planche 12, B, F). Une des fractures transversales met bien en évidence la symétrie d'ordre 2, avec des épaississement de l'exine marqués sur les mésocolpiums qui se font face; ces épaississements sont, à la fois, formés par une endexine et une sole plus importantes, et par des columelles plus allongées dans leur totalité (pieds et têtes) (Planche 12, B).

A ce niveau, les columelles ont des pieds très fins, longs et rapprochés, et chaque tête, bien structurée (avec une structuration indépendante du pied qui la supporte) semble constituée de petits éléments en forme de champignons et soudés entre eux. L'endexine est toujours parfaitement lisse intérieurement (Planche 12, F).

Sur le plan palynologique, ce type a atteint un niveau évolutif élevé. Il en est de même pour tous les autres caractères fournis par la morphologie et l'ontogénie.

Echinophora et *Pycnocycla* ont un appareil végétatif charnu et spinescent, rarement inerme; les feuilles adultes stériles sont très divisées, deux à cinq fois pennatiséquées, découpées en lanières linéaires; la plantule est de grande taille, à cotylédons très importants, charnus, à gros hypocotyle; la première feuille primordiale est déjà bien découpée, et cette découpe s'accentue très rapidement au cours de l'apparition des feuilles primordiales successives. Les inflorescences sont formées par des ombelles d'ordre 2 groupées en cymes, ou groupées en ombelles terminales; on assiste à une spécialisation poussée des fleurs de l'ombellule: une ou deux à trois fleurs centrales de chaque ombellule sont seules fertiles; elles sont sessiles et entourées d'une couronne de fleurs mâles, à pétales extérieurs le plus souvent extrêmement développés (rayonnants) et donnant à l'ensemble de l'ombellule l'apparence d'une fleur unique. Les fruits sont gros à méricarpes à cinq côtes égales, déprimées, ondulées ou hérissées.

Ainsi, cette tribu des *Echinophoreae*, à répartition géographique essentiellement méditerranéenne, est très bien définie par des caractères facilement observables du pollen, et par une morphologie et une ontogénie qui lui sont bien particulières.

Les dernières espèces observées qui possèdent un pollen équatorialo-constricté, sont contenues dans la sous-tribu des *Caucalinae* Drude, sous-tribu caractérisée par des nombreux genres à distribution géographique orientale. Il est bien certain que, si la majorité des espèces est située sur le pourtour oriental de la Méditerranée (*Lisaea papyracea* Boiss., en Asie Mineure), des espèces peuvent également être rencontrées sur le pourtour occidental, aussi bien sur les côtes européennes qu'africaines. Certaines espèces même, peuvent remonter assez haut à l'intérieur de l'Europe, ou atteindre le littoral atlantique: *Orlaya grandiflora* (L.) Hoffm. et *Turgenia latifolia* (L.) Hoffm.

Orlaya *Hoffm.*

O. grandiflora (L.) Hoffm. (CB), espèce des lieux arides d'Europe médiane et méditerranéenne, du Caucase, ainsi que d'Afrique boréale, possède un pollen équatorialo-constricté de très grande taille (52 μm), à valeur du rapport P/E très élevé, proche de 2·5; l'exine est très épaisse à l'équateur et dans la zone subpolaire; l'ectoaperture est moyenne ou courte; l'endoaperture est ovale, étirée; les columelles, assez grosses, sont espacées, régulières; le tectum est épais (Planche 13, A–C).

Au microscope électronique à balayage, la surface tectale se révèle micro-réticulée ou densement striato-réticulée, assez comparable à celle observée chez *Echinophora spinosa* (Planche 13, D, F).

Une cassure transversale due aux ultrasons montre une endexine extrêmement épaisse, des columelles grosses et assez allongées, avec des têtes très importantes, bien structurées en éléments qui se soudent à leur sommet, donnant une surface tectale densément striato-réticulée ou micro-réticulée dont la structuration n'a rien à voir avec les pieds des columelles sous-jacentes (Planche 13, E–G).

O. grandiflora est une très jolie plante annuelle, à feuilles adultes stériles bien découpées tripennatiséquées, à feuilles adultes fertiles moins découpées tripennatiséquées, à feuilles adultes fertiles moins découpées pouvant revenir au type entier par la gaine qui est blanchâtre, scarieuse; à très grande plantule, à cotylédons importants très allongés, à hypocotyle très long, à feuilles primordiales découpées. Les bractées de l'involucre et de l'involucelle sont des gaines lancéolées, blanches-scarieuses au bord (le limbe terminal a complètement disparu). Dans chaque ombellule, les fleurs de la circonférence ont les pétales extérieurs très développés, et chaque ombellule donne l'apparence d'une seule fleur. Le fruit est gros, hérissé d'aiguilles et nettement comprimé par le dos.

Enfin, avec *Lisaea* (genre typiquement oriental) et *Turgenia* (qui peut avoir une aire plus occidentale et qui se rencontre également en Asie tempérée), nous atteignons la forme pollinique la plus grande, la plus structurée, la plus évoluée observée jusqu'à présent chez les Ombellifères.

Lisaea *Boiss.*

L. papyracea Boiss. (P), espèce du Proche et Moyen Orient, possède un très gros pollen de 64 μm, caractérisé par des ailes d'exine sur chaque mésocolpium, constituées essentiellement par des columelles très allongées, digitées et d'un tectum épais, composé lui-même de petites columelles bien visibles au microscope photonique (épaisseur de l'exine à l'équateur: 12 μm); l'ectoaperture, courte, est peu visible étant donné l'épaisseur de l'exine (Planche 14, A, D).

Turgenia *Hoffm.*

T. latifolia (L.) Hoffm. (CB), ombellifère du Proche-Orient, d'Europe médiane et méditerranéenne, d'Asie tempérée et d'Afrique boréale, possède un très gros pollen équatorialo-constricté, très voisin de celui de *Lisaea* (64 μm) avec les mêmes caractéristiques spectaculaires: un épaississement très important de l'exine à l'équateur (12 μm), en particulier sur chaque mésocolpium; l'ectoaperture est courte; l'endoaperture est ovale, rectangulaire, peu visible étant donné l'épaisseur de l'ectexine; comme chez *Lisaea*, les columelles sont très importantes, digitées; le tectum est très épais et composé de petites columelles; en vue polaire, ce pollen est subtriangulaire; et en coupe optique équatoriale, on aperçoit trois immenses carènes d'exine dues à l'extraordinaire développement de l'exine dans les régions subpolaires et équatoriales (Planche 14, B, C, E).

Mais, c'est chez ce pollen de *Turgenia* que le microscope électronique à balayage a apporté, sur le plan palynologique pur, une précision structurale fondamentale, et invisible au microscope photonique le mieux équipé (Cerceau-Larrival, 1970).

Au microscope électronique à balayage, la surface du tectum est micro-réticulée: elle montre des micro-perforations situées au milieu des micro-mailles formées par les micro-columelles du tectum (Planche 14, F, G, H; Planche 15, A, D, E).

Les ultrasons provoquent des cassures transversales, tout à fait révélatrices de la structure de l'exine (Planche 15, B, E). La fracture permet d'apprécier l'importance de l'exine sur chaque mésocolpium, due à de très grandes columelles digitées; et l'on aperçoit, également, l'épaississement de l'endexine avant de s'interrompre au niveau de l'endoaperture visible. Au milieu de chaque mésocolpium, les columelles digitées, atteignent leur plus grande taille, et l'endexine devient un mince feuillet alors que la sole est très épaisse. C'est ce même niveau qui révèle l'existence d'une lamelle continue située au sommet des columelles digitées et sur laquelle repose le tectum constitué, lui-même, par de petites columelles qui lui sont propres (Planche 15, B, C). La présence de cette membrane, séparant le tectum (qui a une totale individualisation) des pieds des columelles sous-jacentes, pose sous un jour nouveau, le problème de la formation de l'exine et de l'ectexine en particulier. Car, jusqu'à présent, la columelle était considérée comme un tout: tête et pied ayant vraisemblablement la même origine.

Des recherches sont actuellement menées dans les différents laboratoires de Palynologie afin de mieux connaître: (1) d'une part, la nature chimique de l'exine constituée de sporopollenine (polyterpène), (2) d'autre part, sa formation et son ontogénie. (Quel est l'apport dû au cytoplasme, et quel est l'apport dû à l'assise tapétale, par l'intermédiaire des corps d'Ubisch?)

Avec le pollen de *Lisaea* et *Turgenia*, nous avons la forme pollinique la plus évoluée observée jusqu'à ce jour chez les Ombellifères.

Le rapprochement entre *Turgenia* et *Lisaea* se trouve confirmé si l'on approfondit l'étude de l'Appareil Végétatif adulte, de l'inflorescence et du fruit: les feuilles adultes stériles sont pennatiséquées à segments dentés; l'inflorescence est caractérisée par le développement des pétales extérieurs des fleurs; le fruit est gros, hérissé d'aiguilles, non comprimé et a été étudié au microscope électronique à balayage par Heywood (1967, 1969; voir aussi p. 221, ce volume).

Seule la plantule de *Turgenia latifolia* est connue: elle est de grande taille, robuste, avec des cotylédons importants oblongs à nervation réticulée, à hypocotyle gros; la première feuille primordiale a déjà le type de la feuille adulte stérile: pennatiséquée.

L'ensemble des caractères offert par la Palynologie, la Morphologie de l'Adulte, la Plantule et l'Ontogénie foliaire, l'Inflorescence et le Fruit, indique, chez cette plante, un niveau évolutif très élevé.

CONCLUSIONS

Grâce aux observations précédentes, nous concluons de la façon suivante: (1) en premier lieu, les corrélations de caractères chez les grains de pollen d'Ombellifères (2) ensuite, ce que la Palynologie, liée à l'Ontogénie chaque fois que la chose est possible, a pu apporter à la Systématique et à la Phylogénie des Ombellifères; (3) les corrélations établies entre Pollens—Plantules—Appareil végétatif—Inflorescence et Fruit; (4) enfin, la contribution apportée par la Palynologie et l'Ontogénie pour une meilleure connaissance des différents problèmes offerts par la Biogéographie des Ombellifères.

Corrélation de caractères chez les grains de pollen d'Ombellifères
(Cerceau-Larrival, 1967)

(a) Le type pollinique subrhomboïdal ou subcirculaire est représentatif des grains de pollen de très petite taille: 15 μm < P < 25 μm (dans quelques cas, P peut atteindre 30 μm); la symétrie est parfois élevée (d'ordre 5); l'ectoaperture est longue; l'exine, très mince, est sensiblement d'égale épaisseur sur tout le pourtour du grain.

Le microscope électronique à balayage révèle une surface tectale très peu spectaculaire, presque lisse, légèrement cérébroïde avec, dans quelques cas, des perforations dues aux têtes non soudées des columelles.

Les ultrasons donnent des fractures qui montrent l'ultrastructure de l'exine constituée par une endexine mince, une sole épaisse, des columelles très courtes, droites, avec des têtes lisses pratiquement non structurées. L'ensemble de l'exine n'atteint pas 2 μm d'épaisseur (*Bupleurum, Azorella, Hydrocotyle, Xanthosia*).

(b) Le type pollinique ovale est représentatif des grains de pollen de petite taille: 25 μm < P < 35 μm; la symétrie est d'ordre 3, quelquefois d'ordre 4; l'ectoaperture est longue; l'exine mince, est légèrement plus épaisse à l'équateur. (Ce type peut être observé chez quelques formes géantes où P peut atteindre 65 μm.)

Le microscope électronique à balayage révèle une surface tectale assez structurée, rugulée, constituée par les têtes des columelles qui se soudent en portées plus ou moins longues (rugules) et qui s'enchevêtrent sans aucune direction préférentielle.

Les cassures aux ultrasons montrent: une endexine assez mince, une sole épaisse, des columelles assez courtes et trappues avec des têtes légèrement structurées et montrant un emboîtement des uns dans les autres assez spectaculaire. L'ensemble de l'exine peut atteindre 2 à 4 μm d'épaisseur (*Aciphylla, Heracleum, Trachymene*).

(c) Le type subrectangulaire est représentatif des pollens de taille moyenne: 35 μm < P < 45 μm; la symétrie est toujours d'ordre 3; l'ectoaperture est moyenne ou courte; l'exine est assez importante, devenant plus épaisse soit aux pôles, soit dans les zones subpolaires soit à l'équateur (P peut atteindre ou dépasser 50 μm dans quelques cas).

Le microscope électronique à balayage révèle une surface tectale très heurtée dans les zones aperturales; aux pôles, la surface tectale a une apparence striato-rugulée: les têtes structurées des columelles se soudent en portées assez longues qui peuvent s'orienter dans des directions privilégiées. Chaque portée est bien individualisée.

Les cassures aux ultrasons montrent: une endexine épaisse, une sole également épaisse, des columelles grandes, souvent digitées avec des têtes présentant une structuration visible en coupe et indépendante des pides. Nous assistons ici à une amorce d'individualisation des têtes de columelles par rapport à leurs pieds. L'ensemble de l'exine peut atteindre 6 à 8 μm (*Scandix, Psammogeton, Cachrys, Diplolophium*).

(d) Le type équatorialo-constricté est représentatif des grains de pollen de grande taille : P > 45 μm et pouvant atteindre 70 μm ; la symétrie est d'ordre 3, ou d'ordre 2 ; l'endoaperture est courte ou même réduite à un très petit sillon superposé à l'endoaperture ; l'exine prend de grandes proportions à l'équateur (columelles digitées, tectum composé).

Le microscope électronique à balayage révèle une surface tectale striato-réticulée (*Pycnocycla*) ou micro-réticulée (*Turgenia*) et, dans ce cas, elle montre des micro-perforations situées au milieu des micro-mailles formées par les micro-columelles propres au tectum.

Les cassures aux ultrasons permettent d'apprécier l'importance de l'exine sur chaque mésocolpium ; elles montrent : une endexine importante, une sole très épaisse, des columelles très grandes, digitées, une lamelle continue (qui n'avait jusqu'alors jamais été observée) située au sommet des digitations des columelles, et sur laquelle repose le tectum constitué lui-même par de micro-columelles qui lui sont propres. L'exine peut atteindre 12 μm d'épaisseur (*Lisaea*, *Turgenia*).

Apport de la Palynologie à la Systématique et à la Phylogénie des Ombellifères

Systématique

Nous avons vu que la nomenclature des formes des grains a été établie d'après le contour interne de l'endexine, et non d'après le contour général du pollen donné par le contour externe de l'ectexine. La forme du pollen, donnée par le contour interne de l'endexine, définit parfaitement un 'bon genre' : elle est constante pour toutes les espèces du même genre. Toutes les espèces d'un bon genre ont, non seulement le même type fondamental de pollen, mais souvent les mêmes nuances à l'intérieur du type fondamental. En effet, chaque catégorie, définie par un type fondamental de pollen, renferme des pollens dont le type oscille autour du type principal (Cerceau-Larrival, 1962b). La forme du pollen étant un excellent caractère de distinction générique a une grande valeur du point de vue systématique (Cerceau-Larrival, 1962a, 1962b, 1963, 1965, 1967, 1968).

Les tribus établies par Drude (1898) peuvent se classer en 5 catégories suivant les nombres des types polliniques qu'elles renferment :

Tribus à 1 seul type pollinique :
  Lagoecieae (Rg)
  Echinophoreae (E)
  Coriandreae (Rg)

Tribus à 2 types polliniques :
  Dauceae (Rh Rg)
  Hydrocotyleae (0 et C)
  Saniculeae (0 et Rg)
  Laserpitieae (0 et Rg)

Tribus à 3 types polliniques:
Mulineae (Rh, C, O)
Scandicineae (Rh, Rg, E)
Peucedaneae (O, Rg, E)

Tribus à 4 types polliniques:
Ammineae (Rh, C, O, Rg)
Smyrnieae (Rh, O, Rg, E)

Tribus renfermant les 5 types polliniques rencontrés chez les Ombellifères:
Aucune tribu

Le fait que certaines tribus de Drude ne renferment qu'un seul type de pollen, et possèdent des caractères très homogènes de la plantule, de l'appareil végétatif m'a incitée à réviser les tribus contenant plusieurs types polliniques. Et, chaque fois, ces tribus, hétérogènes sur le plan palynologique, se sont révélées également très hétérogènes sur le plan cotylédonaire, et sur le plan de l'ontogénie foliaire, de l'appareil végétatif, de l'inflorescence et du fruit.

C'est la raison pour laquelle il m'a semblé bon de considérer le niveau taxonomique des tribus valable quand il ne renfermait que des genres présentant le même type pollinique. Et cela m'a amenée à scinder certaines des tribus de Drude (Cerceau-Larrival, 1962*a*, 1963, 1965*a*). De nouvelles révisions sont en cours.

Phylogénie

Ces différents types polliniques ont été mis en série phylétique proposant les filiations suivantes: Pollen subrhomboïdal (pollen primitif) → pollen ovale (pollen moyennement évolué) → pollen subrectangulaire (pollen évolué) → pollen équatoria-lo-constricté (pollen très évolué).

Corrélation entre le pollen, la plantule, l'appareil végétatif, l'inflorescence et le fruit

L'étude des plantules menée corrélativement avec celle des pollens correspondants, les observations faites sur l'ontogénie foliaire, l'appareil végétatif adulte (feuille adulte stérile, feuille adulte fertile), l'inflorescence et le fruit, permettent de constater que, chez les Ombellifères, l'évolution générale se fait (Cerceau-Larrival, 1962*b*, 1967):

(i) à partir d'une plante vivace, de petit taille, à feuilles simples entières linéaires, à fruit petit glabre, sans côte, non comprimé, avec un méricarpe à cinq côtes, arrondi, dépourvu de canaux sécréteurs, ou en possédant peu; à bractées de l'involucre et de l'involucelle entières, à limbes linéaires ou lancéolées; à petite plantule possédant de petits cotylédons à trois nervures, glabres, à feuilles primordiales entières linéaires, à hypocotyle réduit à accélération basifuge faible et peu de canaux sécréteurs, à formations secondaires importantes; à pollen petit, subrhomboïdal, à grande endoaperture, à ectoaperture longue, à exine mine et d'égale épaisseur sur tout le pourtour du grain, et avec un rapport P/E faible compris entre 1 et 1·5 (le microscope électronique à balayage révèle une surface tectale très peu structurée, presque lisse ou légèrement cérébroïde avec des columelles très courtes, droites, à têtes globuleuses lisses, pratiquement non structurées, l'ensemble de l'exine n'atteignant pas 2 μm d'épaisseur).

(ii) pour aboutir à une plante annuelle, de taille plus élevée, à feuilles simples découpées (1 à 5-pennatiséquées); à fruit gros, non comprimé, ou comprimé par le dos, à méricarpes à neuf côtes, souvent hérissés d'aiguilles, à canaux sécréteurs nombreux et allongés; à bractées de l'involucre ou de l'involucelle souvent nulles, ou quand elles existent, entières et constituées uniquement par des gaines résiduelles; à pétales extérieurs des fleurs des ombellules périphériques rayonnants; à grande plantule possédant des cotylédons importants souvent à cinq nervures, velus dans quelques cas, à feuilles primordiales toujours découpées (la première feuille primordiale étant parfois aussi découpée que la feuille adulte stérile), à hypocotyle allongé à accélération basifuge forte, et peu ou pas de formation secondaire, à nombreux canaux sécréteurs souvent fusionnés; à gros pollen équatorialo-constricté, à petite endoaperture ovale, à ectoaperture très courte et à exine extrêmement développée formant des ailes importantes sur chaque mésocolpium et avec un rapport P/E élevé, supérieur à 2 et pouvant atteindre 2·5 (le microscope électronique à balayage révèle une surface tectale striato-réticulée, ou micro-réticulée, les micro-perforations sont situées au milieu des micro-mailles formées par les micro-columelles propres au tectum; les columelles digitées atteignent une taille élevée et au sommet des digitations se trouve une lamelle sur laquelle reposent les micro-columelles du tectum qui a acquis une totale individualisation par rapport aux pieds des columelles sous-jacentes; l'ensemble de l'exine peut atteindre 12 μm d'épaisseur).

Contribution apportée par la Palynologie et l'Ontogénie pour une meilleure connaissance des problèmes offerts par la Biogéographie des Ombellifères

Aucune discussion biogéographique ne peut ignorer les renseignements donnés par les fossiles, et la Palynologie s'est révélée être une source fort précieuse d'informations stratigraphiques et paléoclimatologiques (analyses polliniques des sédiments). Mais, dans l'étude des Répartitions géographiques actuelles, la Palynologie, a, également, un rôle à jouer.

Paléoendémisme

Ainsi, au cours de l'ensemble des recherches polliniques entreprises chez les Ombellifères, j'ai pu constater que les espèces endémiques anciennes (paléo-endémiques) se trouvant, comme l'écrit Ozenda (1964) 'pour des raisons géographiques passées,* dans des régions relativement isolées: les îles, les montagnes, les déserts', ne se rencontrent que dans des groupes possédant un type de pollen très primitif subrhomboïdal ou subcirculaire et présentant des caractères archaïques: *Azorella, Bupleurum, Xanthosia.*

Azorella. Azorella en fournit un exemple assez remarquable. Ce genre typiquement austral, à côté des nombreuses espèces endémiques andines, renferme également quelques espèces endémiques d'Australie, de Tasmanie, de Nouvelle-Zélande, des îles Kerguelen, et des îles Macquaries (avec une espèce, *A. selago* Hook, rencontrée dans une des dernières îles de la Terre de Feu, et dans les îles Kerguelen. Le type pollinique observé chez toutes ces endémiques est subrhomboïdal. Mais, à l'intérieur du genre *Azorella,* les espèces qui poussent dans les Andes équatoriales, à

---

* Certaines espèces ont déjà pu se différencier dès le Tertiaire (Ozenda, 1964).

des altitudes très élevées, voisines à 5000 m (comme *A. pedunculata*), et les espèces de la zone magellanique et antarctique (comme *A. selago*), en raison des conditions biogéographies extrêmes et pratiquement constantes dans lesquelles elles vivent depuis des temps très reculés, n'ont guère pu évoluer, et possèdent les caractères polliniques les plus primitifs (très petite taille, valeur du rapport P/E très faible, voisine de 1) et présentent un état archaïque dans toute leur morphologie. Les hautes terres équatoriales andines et les basses terres magellaniques et antarctiques constitueraient, vraisemblablement, de véritables réserves de reliques, de fossiles vivants par rapport à l'ensemble du groupe *Azorella*, et peut-être, également, par rapport à l'ensemble de la famille des Ombellifères.

Azorella, Ombellifère archaïque par l'ensemble de ses caractères, serait, peut-être une descendante des premières Umbellales qui, d'après Thomas (1936) sont apparues au Crétacé supérieur, et une survivante de la Géoflore antarctique tertiaire (Cerceau-Larrival, 1968). La répartition géographique actuelle des *Azorella* est très analogue à celle de la Géoflore antarctique donnée par Axelrod (1960) et qui a conquis ses aires de répartition entre le Crétacé et le début du Tertiaire.

Tout ceci laisse supposer: (i) d'une part, une dérive continentale (hypothèse très en faveur surtout depuis les recherches de Bullard *et al.* (1965) et les études sur l'expansion des fonds océaniques par Coulomb (1969), (ii) d'autre part, l'importance du rôle joué par le Continent Antarctique au Tertiaire 'à partir duquel des formes variées s'irradièrent jusqu'aux extrémités les plus au Sud de nos continents actuels' (extrait d'une lettre de Darwin à Hooker).

Bupleurum. Chez *Bupleurum*, autre genre caractérisé par un type pollinique subrhomboïdal, mais rencontré presque exclusivement dans l'Hémisphère Nord, des recherches sont en cours sur les espèces endémiques de la zone himalayenne (Dodin, en préparation) notamment dans les régions de forte altitude.

Les résultats polliniques seront confrontés avec ceux déjà connus se rapportant à certaines endémiques des hautes montagnes européennes: ainsi, *B. angulosum* L., espèce spéciale aux Pyrénées et aux Corbières et *B. stellatum* L., espèce des Alpes occidentales et méridionales, font partie, selon Favarger & Kupfer [(1967, 1968) (cf. Cauwet, 1970)] 'd'un ensemble de taxa schizoendémiques inclus dans une ancienne flore* orophile commune aux Pyrénées et aux Alpes occidentales et méridionales'.

Jusqu'à ce jour, à l'intérieur du genre *Bupleurum*, la forme pollinique la plus primitive a été observée chez *B. mundtii* Cham. & Schl., seule espèce connue dans l'Hémisphère Sud, et rencontrée en Afrique australe (Le Cap et Transvaal).

La disjonction observée en Afrique, pour le genre *Bupleurum* (bien représenté en Afrique du Nord, et ne se rencontrant pas en Afrique tropicale et équatoriale et possèdant en Afrique du Sud, une seule espèce, *B. mundtii*, à caractères très archaïques) ne peut s'expliquer que par une implantation fort ancienne de ce genre sur le continent africain, genre qui aurait disparu dans les zones tropicales et équatoriales. L'espèce *B. mundtii*, en Afrique australe, serait le vestige d'une im-

---

* flore antérieure au Tertiaire moyen qui est l'époque où les Alpes et les Pyrénées ont été séparées.

plantation vraisemblablement contemporaine de l'apparition des Ombellifères (fin du Crétacé ?).

Alors qu'en Afrique du Nord, et dans tout le Bassin de la Méditerranée, le genre *Bupleurum*, s'est fortement diversifié, en Afrique du Sud, la souche originelle subsisterait grace à *B. mundtii*, seule espèce existante.

Chez *Azorella* et *Bupleurum*, nous nous trouvons, pour les espèces les plus archaïques, en présence de paléoendémiques possédant toutes un pollen subrhomboïdal à caractères extrêmement primitifs.

Néoendémisme

Xatartia. Des plantes isolées plus récemment (ou néoendémiques) comme *Xatartia scabra* (Lap.) Meissn., endémique des Pyrénées orientales, dont l'isolation est dues aux vicissitudes quaternaires amenées par les périodes glaciaires et interglaciaires, présentent un type de pollen plus évolué (ovale et de grande taille, dans le cas de *Xatartia*) et un appareil végétatif caractérisé par des feuilles découpées.

Centre de différentiation et d'évolution pour les espèces actuelles

Enfin, les Ombellifères qui possèdent le type pollinique le plus évolué, équatorialoconstricté, sont, comme nous l'avons vu, des plantes annuelles à cycle végétatif très court et à répartition géographique liée au Bassin de la Méditerranée, en ce qui concerne l'Hémisphère Nord. Le Bassin de la Méditerranée peut être considéré comme un centre de différenciation pour les espèces actuelles puisque s'y rencontrent les Ombellifères les plus évoluées (*Echinophora, Orlaya, Lisaea, Turgenia*), aussi bien par les caractères offerts par le pollen que ceux offerts par l'ontogénie et la morphologie de l'appareil végétatif. La différenciation et l'expansion de la Famille dans ces régions, serait, apparemment, une réponse à des conditions progressivement plus sèches.

On voit ainsi apparaître un nouvel intérêt de la Palynologie, au sujet des problèmes posés par les phénomènes de la variation, de la diversification des taxa (aux différents niveaux) et de l'endémisme.

Dans le domaine de la Biogéographie, la Palynologie a donc un rôle à jouer, notamment dans l'étude des répartitions actuelles, et dans l'Histoire du peuplement végétal.

Enfin, une collaboration semble s'établir entre les Palynologues-Botanistes qui étudient les pollens des espèces actuelles, et les Palynologues-Géologues qui étudient les pollens fossiles. L'ensemble des recherches faites sur le matériel actuel et fossile pourrait permettre de reconstituer l'Histoire évolutive des groupes végétaux, retracé par les étapes palynologiques, à travers les temps géologiques.

REMERCIEMENTS

Je tiens à exprimer, particulièrement, ma reconnaissance à Monsieur le Professeur Laffitte ainsi qu'à Mademoiselle D. Noël qui m'ont permis l'accès au microscope électronique à balayage du Laboratoire de Géologie du Muséum National d'Histoire Naturelle de Paris.

J'adresse, également, tous mes remerciements à Mademoiselle L. Derouet et à Monsieur J. P. Bossy pour leur précieuse collaboration technique.

SUMMARY AND PRINCIPAL CONCLUSIONS

Introduction

It is only in the course of the last few decades that the extent of all the applications opened up by the study of pollen grains has become apparent. Thus in the fields of systematics and phylogeny, pollen grains offer characteristics of great importance and are widely used.

This paper discusses the contribution of palynology to the taxonomy of the Umbelliferae, and the correlations that can be noted with features drawn from other disciplines.

A detailed study of nearly 1500 species of the Umbelliferae has revealed a wide variety of pollen shapes which may be grouped in five basic types, clearly distinguishable, and ranging in size from 15 μm to 70 μm.

Recent research, carried out with the scanning electron microscope (SEM), has provided not only a better interpretation of the pollen surfaces, but also, thanks to a new technique—the splitting of pollen grains by ultrasonic vibrations—a greater knowledge of the ultrastructure of the membranes (Cerceau-Larrival et al., 1970).

These observations are made on pollen grains emptied of their cytoplasmic contents, since palynology depends primarily on the study of the sporoderm and more especially of the exine.

An umbelliferous pollen grain has:

(1) A polar axis (generally of third-order symmetry,* with a second-, fourth- or fifth- order symmetry occurring in a few cases) and a plane of symmetry which is perpendicular to it (isopolar pollen).

(2) There are three apertural systems: three ectoapertures which are the longitudinal colpi; and three endoapertures where the endexine is absent and through which the pollen tube escapes.

(3) It is longiaxial, or very rarely breviaxial, i.e. with a ratio of $P/E > 1$–2.5. (P = polar axis, E = equatorial diameter.)

(4) The exine consists of:

(a) an ectexine with a substructure of:

(i) a tectum which in cross-section appears smooth and continuous under the optical microscope, revealing the columellae arranged in a reticulum. Observed however through the SEM, the tectum is seen to have a more or less complex structure depending on the evolutionary level of the pollen;

(ii) columellae, which are usually straight, but which can, in some cases, be branched (Columellae digitatae);

(b) an endexine, in the wide sense of the word, which stops at the level of the

* In the crystallographic sense.

endoaperture and which, through the SEM, is seen to be formed by the foot layer, on which the base of the columellae lies, and by the endexine in a restricted sense.

The nomenclature of the five pollen-types is determined according to the internal contour of the endexine and not according to the general outline of the pollen given by the ectexine, which may undergo slight changes within the same species, whereas the contour of the endexine remains stable on account of its constitution which is far more compact.

The five pollen-types are: the subrhomboidal type (Rh); the subcircular type (C); the oval type (O); the subrectangular type (Rg); and the equatorially-constricted type (E). The study of seedlings and cotyledons in the Umbelliferae has made it possible to determine two categories of cotyledons:

(1) long (L) where the lamina of the cotyledon almost imperceptibly diminishes into a petiole;

(2) round (R) where the lamina of the cotyledon contracts abruptly into a petiole.

The five pollen-types are all represented in the round cotyledonary category, whereas the subcircular type has not been seen so far in the long cotyledonary category; it seems therefore to be characteristic of the round cotyledonary category.

Conclusions

Correlation of characters in pollen grains of Umbelliferae

(a) The subrhomboidal or subcircular pollen type has the following features: grains very small, 15 μm (< P ⩽ 25 μm) (a few cases where P may reach 30 μm) with a third- or a fifth-order symmetry; the ectoaperture is long, the exine very thin, with practically an even thickness all over the grain. (Plate 1, A–J; Plate 2, A, B, C, E, F).

The SEM shows a very unspectacular tectal surface, almost smooth, slightly cerebroid in some cases, with perforations due to non-fused heads of the baculae (Plate 1, K, L, N, O; Plate 2, G, I, K).

Ultrasonic vibrations produce fractures that show the ultrastructure of the exine, made up of a thin endexine, a thick foot layer, very short straight columellae with smooth heads, practically without structure (Plate 1, M).

The whole of the exine is less than 2 μm thick (*Bupleurum, Azorella, Hydrocotyle, Xanthosia*).

(b) The oval pollen type is characterized by: grains small (25 μm < P ⩽ 35 μm) with third-order symmetry; the ectoaperture is long; the exine thin, but slightly thicker at the equator (this latter type can be observed in a few giant forms where P may reach 65 μm) (Plate 2, D; Plate 3, A–D; Plate 4, A–F, Plate 6, A–F).

The SEM shows a fairly structured tectal surface, cerebroid or rugulose, made up of columellae heads fused in groups of different lengths (rugae) and which overlap in any direction. (Plate 2, H–J; Plate 3, E, F, G; Plate 4, H–I; Plate 5, A–C; Plate 6, G, H, I).

Fractures with ultrasonic vibrations reveal a rather thin endexine, a thick foot layer, rather short stumpy columellae with slightly structured heads and showing a somewhat spectacular interlocking. The whole of the exine may reach 2 to 4 μm in thickness (*Aciphylla, Heracleum, Trachymene*).

(c) The subrectangular type is characterized by medium-sized grains (35μm < P ⩽ 45 μm) with third-order symmetry; the ectoaperture is medium or short; the exine is very substantial, thickened either at the poles or in the subpolar zones, or at the equator (P may reach or exceed 50 μm in some cases (Plate 8, A–J, M, N; Plate 9, A–C).

The SEM shows a very contrasting tectal surface in the apertural zones; at the poles, the tectal surface has a striate-rugulose appearance; the structured heads of the bacula are fused in fairly long groups which may show orientation in certain directions. Each group is quite separable (Plate 8, L, O, P; Plate 9, E, H, I).

The fractures produced by ultrasonic vibrations show a thick endexine, an equally thick foot layer, large and frequently digitate columellae with heads presenting visible structuring in section and independent of the feet. We can see here the beginnings of separation of the columellae heads in relation to their feet. The whole of the exine may attain 6 to 8 μm. (*Scandix, Psammogeton, Cachrys, Diplolophium*) (Plate 9, D, F, G).

(d) The equatorially constricted type is characterized by: grains large (P > 45 μm) with second- or third-order symmetry; the endoaperture is short or even reduced to a very small colpus superposed on the endoaperture; the exine assumes considerable proportions at the equator (columellae digitatae, compound tectum) (Plate 10, A–G; Plate 11, A–F; Plate 13, A–C; Plate 14, A–E).

The SEM reveals a striato-reticulate tectal surface (*Pycnocycla*) or micro-reticulate (*Turgenia*) and, in this case, it shows micro-perforations situated in the middle of the micro-lumina formed by the little columellae belonging to the tectum (Plate 10, E, F, H; Plate 11, G–I; Plate 12, A, C, E; Plate 13, D, F; Plate 14, F–H; Plate 15, A, D, E). The fractures produced by ultrasonic vibrations allow one to appreciate the thickness of the exine on each mesocolpium, showing an endexine, a very thick foot layer, very large digitate columellae, a continuous lamella (which had so far remained unnoticed) on the top of the columellae digitations on which lies the tectum which itself is composed of micro-columellae belonging to the tectum. The exine may attain a thickness of 12 μm (*Echinophora, Pycnocycla, Orlaya, Lisaea, Turgenia*) (Plate 10, I; Plate 12, B, D, F; Plate 13, E, G; Plate 15, B, C).

Contribution of palynology to the systematics and phylogeny of the Umbelliferae

(a) *Systematics.* We have seen that the nomenclature of grain shapes was determined by the internal contour of the endexine and not by the general shape of the pollen produced by the external contour of the endexine.

The shape of the pollen given by the internal contour of the exine will clearly define a 'clear-cut' genus; it is constant for all species of the same genus. All the species of a clear-cut genus have not only the same basic pollen type, but often the same slight differences within the basic type. Indeed, each category, defined by a basic pollen type, includes pollen which represents a variation of the main type (Cerceau-Larrival, 1962*b*).

The shape of the pollen, being an excellent character for generic distinction, has great value from a systematic point of view (Cerceau-Larrival, 1962a, 1962b, 1963, 1965, 1967, 1968).

The tribes determined by Drude (1898) may be placed in five categories according to the number of pollen-types they include:

Tribes with one pollen type only:
  Lagoecieae (Rg)
  Echinophoreae (E)
  Coriandreae (Rg)

Tribes with two pollen types:
  Dauceae (Rh, Rg)
  Hydrocotyleae (O and C)
  Saniculeae (O and Rg)
  Laserpitieae (O and Rg)

Tribes with three pollen types:
  Mulineae (Rh, C, O)
  Scandicineae (Rh, Rg, E)
  Peucedaneae (O, Rg, E)

Tribes with four pollen types:
  Ammineae (Rh, C, O, Rg)
  Smyrnieae (Rh, O, Rg, E)

Tribes with all five pollen types found in the Umbelliferae:
  None

The fact that some of Drude's tribes have only one type of pollen and are uniform as regards their seedlings, leaf ontogeny and morphology of the adult plant, persuaded me to revise those tribes which were heterogeneous from a palynological point of view. These proved to be very heterogeneous also with regard to their cotyledons, leaf ontogeny, morphology of the adult plant, inflorescence and fruit. This is why it seemed to me desirable to consider the tribes to be valid only when they included genera with the same pollen type. In turn it has led me to split some of Drude's tribes (Cerceau-Larrival, 1962a, 1963, 1965a). Further revisions are under way.

(b) *Phylogeny.* The different pollen-types have been placed in a phyletic series with the following proposed sequence: subrhomboidal pollen (primitive pollen) → oval pollen (moderately developed pollen) → subrectangular pollen (developed pollen) → equatorially-constricted pollen (highly developed pollen).

(c) *Correlation between pollen, seedlings, vegetative system, inflorescence and fruit.* The study of seedlings, carried out in conjunction with that of the corresponding pollen, observations on the leaf ontogeny, the adult vegetative system (sterile adult leaf, fertile adult leaf), the inflorescence and the fruit enables one to note that, in the Umbelliferae, the general evolutionary pattern has been as follows (Cerceau-Larrival, 1962, 1967).
Beginning with a perennial, of small size with simple, entire, linear leaves; with

small glabrous fruit, without ribs, not compressed, with a five-ribbed, circular mericarp lacking secretory canals or with only a few; with entire involucral bracts and involucels, with linear or lanceolate laminas; with small seedlings with small cotyledons, with three ribs, glabrous, entire primordial linear leaves, reduced hypocotyl, with weak basifugal acceleration and few secretory canals, considerable secondary formation; with small subrhomboidal pollen with large endoaperture, with long ectoaperture, thin exine of equal thickness all around the grain and with a low P/E ratio of between 1 and 1·5 (the SEM showing a very slightly cerebroid surface with very short straight columellae having smooth almost non-structured heads, the total thickness of the exine being 2 μm),

Ending up with a taller annual plant with divided leaves (1- to 5-pinnate); with large dorsally compressed or uncompressed fruits, having nine-ribbed mericarps, often spiny, with numerous elongate secretory canals; with involucral bracts often absent, or when present entire and consisting entirely of residual sheaths; with radiating outer petals of the peripheral umbels; with large seedlings with large cotyledons, often with five nerves, having, in some cases, constantly denticulate primordial leaves (the first primordial leaf being sometimes as denticulate as the sterile adult leaf), with elongated hypocotyl having a strong basifugal acceleration and little or no secondary formation and numerous, frequently fused secretory canals; with large equatorially constricted pollen with a small oval endoaperture, very short ectoaperture and highly developed exine forming sizeable wings on each mesocolpium and with a high P/E ratio from more than 2 to as much as 2·5 (the SEM revealing a striato-reticulate or micro-reticulate tectal surface, the micro-perforations situated in the middle of the micro-laminae formed by the micro-columellae belonging to the tectum; the columellae digitatae reaching a considerable size, and at the top of the digitations with a lamella on which the micro-columellae of the tectum rests; the tectum having become completely separable in relation to the underlying columellae feet; the over all thickness of the exine up to 12 μm.

Contribution of palynology and ontogenesis to the biogeography of the Umbelliferae

No biogeographical discussion can leave aside the information provided from fossils, and palynology has proved to be a very valuable source of stratigraphic and paleoclimatological information (pollen analysis of sediments). But, in the study of present-day geographical distribution, palynology has also a part to play.

Thus during the course of my research into the pollen of the Umbelliferae, I have been able to note that the archaic endemic species (paleoendemics) found, as Ozenda writes (1964), 'for past geographical reasons, in relatively isolated regions: islands, mountains, deserts', are only found in groups having a very primitive subrhomboidal or subcircular pollen-type and presenting primitive characteristics: Azorella, Bupleurum, Niphogeton, Xanthosia.

Azorella, an archaic Umbellifer according to its general characteristics, is perhaps a descendant of the first Umbellales which, according to Thomas (1936), appeared in the upper Cretaceous, and a survivor of the Tertiary Antarctic Geoflora (Cerceau-Larrival, 1968).

Plants which have become isolated more recently (neoendemics), like Xatartia *scabra* (Lap.) Meissn., endemic to the Eastern Pyrenees, whose isolation is due to Quaternary changes brought about by the glacial and interglacial periods, present a more developed pollen-type (oval and large in the case of *Xatartia*) and denticulate leaves.

Finally, the Umbelliferae with the most developed pollen-type—equatorially-contricted—are, as we have seen, annual plants with a very short vegetative cycle and a geographical distribution limited, in the Northern Hemisphere, to the Mediterranean basin.

The Mediterranean basin may be considered as a centre of differentiation for present-day species since the most highly developed Umbelliferae (*Echinophora, Orlaya, Lisaea, Turgenia*) are found there. They are the most highly developed both in the characteristics of their pollen and in the features of their ontogeny and vegetative morphology. The differentiation and expansion of the family in these regions would seem to be a result of progressively drier conditions.

We can therefore note a new role for palynology, in the study of problems raised by the phenomena of variation and diversification of taxa (at different levels) and endemism. Palynology has its part to play in the field of biogeography, especially in the study of present-day distributions, and in the history of plant migrations.

BIBLIOGRAPHIE

AXELROD, D., 1960. The Evolution of Flowering Plants. In Sol Tax (ed.), *The evolution of Life*, vol. 1, *Evolution after Darwin*: 227–305. Chicago: University of Chicago Press.

BULLARD, E., EVERETT, J. E. & Smith, A. G., 1965. The fit of the continents around the Atlantic: 41–51. In A Symposium on Continental Drift, *Phil. Trans. R. Soc. London*.

CAUWET, A. M., 1970. Contribution à l'étude caryosystématique du genre *Bupleurum* (Tourn.) L. Thèse 3ème cycle, Montpellier. 161 pp. (ronéotypé).

CERCEAU-LARRIVAL, M.-TH., 1959. Clé de détermination d'Ombellifères de France et d'Afrique du Nord, d'après leurs grains de pollen. *Pollen et Spores*, 1: 149–190.

CERCEAU-LARRIVAL, M.-TH., 1962a. Le pollen d'Ombellifères méditerranéennes, 1. *Echinophoreae*. *Pollen et Spores*, 4: 95–104.

CERCEAU-LARRIVAL, M.-TH., 1962b. Plantules et Pollens d'Ombellifères. Leur intérêt systématique et phylogénique. Thèse. *Mém. Mus. natl Hist. nat.*, Sér. B, 14: 166 pp.

CERCEAU-LARRIVAL, M.-TH., 1963. Le pollen d'Ombellifères méditerranéennes, 2. *Tordylineae* Drude. *Pollen et Spores*, 5: 297–323.

CERCEAU-LARRIVAL, M.-TH., 1965a. Le pollen d'Ombellifères méditerranéennes, 3. *Scandicineae* Drude, 4. *Dauceae* Drude. *Pollen et Spores*, 7: 35–62.

CERCEAU-LARRIVAL, M.-TH., 1965b. Involucre et Involucelle chez les Ombellifères. *Bull. Soc. bot. Fr.*, 112: 252–267.

CERCEAU-LARRIVAL, M.-TH., 1967. Corrélations de caractères chez les grains de pollen d'Ombellifères. *Rev. Palaeobot. Palyn.*, 4: 311–324.

CERCEAU-LARRIVAL, M.-TH., 1968. Contribution palynologique et biogéographique à l'étude biologique de l'Amérique Australe. *Biol. Am. Austr.*, 4: 197 pp. Paris.

CERCEAU-LARRIVAL, M.-TH., HIDEUX, M., MARCEAU, L. & ROLAND, F., 1970. Cassure du pollen par les ultrasons pour l'étude structurale de l'exine au microscope électronique à balayage. *C. r. Acad. Sci., Paris*, 270: 66–69.

COULOMB, J., 1969. L'expansion des fonds océaniques et la dérive des Continents. 'La Science Vivante'. 222 pp. Paris: Presses Universitaires de France.

DODIN, R., en préparation. Contribution à l'étude palynologique du genre *Bupleurum* L. Thèse, Paris.

DRUDE, C. G. O., 1898. *Umbelliferae*. In Engler, A. & Prantl, K. (eds), *Die natürlichen Pflanzenfamilien*, 3 (8): 63–200, Leipzig.

HEYWOOD, V. H., 1967. Reprinted 1970. *Plant Taxonomy*. 60 pp. London & Beccles: Edward Arnold Ltd.

HEYWOOD, V. H., 1969. Scanning electron microscopy in the study of plant materials. *Micron*, 1: 1–14.

JACQUES-FÉLIX, H., 1970. Contribution à l'étude des Umbellifloreae du Cameroun. *Adansonia*, sér. 2, 10: 35–94.

Nigaud, M., 1970. Contribution à l'étude palynologique du genre *Peucedanum* L. Diplôme Etudes Supérieures. 170 pp. Paris. (ronéotypé)

Ozenda, P., 1964. Biogéographique végétale. 374 pp. Paris: Doin.

Thomas, H. H., 1936. Palaeobotany and the origin of the Angiosperms. *Bot. Rev.*, **2**: 397–418.

Tutin, T. G., 1968. *Umbelliferae*. In Tutin, T. G., Heywood, V. H., *et al.* (eds). *Flora Europaea*: 315–375. Cambridge: Cambridge University Press.

EXPLICATION DES PLANCHES

PLANCHE 1

A–D: *Azorella trifoliata* Clos

A. (×1000) pollen subrhomboïdal, vue méridienne de profil (contraste de phase).

B. (×1000) coupe optique méridienne de profil, exine mince sensiblement d'égale épaisseur sur tout le pourtour du grain (contraste de phase).

C. (×1000) vue polaire, subcirculaire.

D. (×1000) coupe optique équatoriale, montrant la proéminence des 3 endoapertures.

E–J, L, N: *Bupleurum angulosum* L.

E. (×1000) pollen subrhomboïdal, vue méridienne de profil.

F. (×1000) coupe optique méridienne de profil, exine mince, sensiblement d'égale épaisseur sur tout le pourtour du grain.

G. (×1000) vue méridienne de face, endoaperture grande, rectangulaire-curviligne.

H. (×1000) coupe optique méridienne, une aperture de face, et deux apertures de profil.

I. (×1000) vue polaire, subcirculaire.

J. (×1000) coupe optique équatoriale, montrant la proéminence des 3 endoapertures.

L. (×2100) mésocolpium vu de face.

N. (×10 500) surface tectale cérébroïde, les têtes des columelles lisses (non structurées) se soudent en portées très courtes et incurvées.

K, M, O: *Bupleurum ranunculoides* L.

K. (×2300) grain vu de 3/4, montrant la forme subrhomboïdale typique.

M. (×13 000) coupe aux ultrasons, révélant une endexine mince, une sole très mince sur laquelle reposent de petites columelles courtes avec des têtes lisses (non structurées) très largement soudées les unes aux autres.

O. (×11 500) surface tectale cérébroïde ou réticulée.

Clichés du Laboratoire de Géologie du Muséum National d'Histoire Naturelle de Paris.

PLANCHE 2

A, B, G, I, K: *Hydrocotyle laxiflora* DC.

A. (×1000) pollen subcirculaire à tendance subrhomboïdale, vue méridienne, ectoaperture longue, endoaperture saillante.

B. (×1000) coupe optique méridienne, exine mince, légèrement plus épaisse aux pôles.

G. (×2150) le M.E.B. fait ressortir la tendance subrhomboïdale de ce pollen.

I. (×8600) surface tectale peu structurée (zone polaire).

K. (×8500) surface tectale montrant les têtes des columelles soudées entre elles en portées assez courtes (mésocolpium): surface rugulée.

E, F: *Hydrocotyle vulgaris* L.

E. (×1000) vue méridienne de face montrant l'endoaperture rectangulaire curviligne.

F. (×1000) vue polaire triangulaire, laissant apercevoir les 3 endoapertures fortement saillantes.

C: *Xanthosia atkinsoniana* F. Muell

C. (×1000) pollen subcirculaire, coupe optique méridienne montrant la symétrie d'ordre 5.

D, H, J: *Aciphylla procumbens* F. Muell

D. (×1000) pollen ovale, coupe optique méridienne.

H. (×2200) grain de pollen au contact de la surface tapétale.

J. (×20 000) surface tectale cérébroïde; les têtes des columelles sont soudées en portées courtes et incurvées.

Clichés du Laboratoire de Géologie du Muséum National d'Histoire Naturelle de Paris.

PLANCHE 3

A–H: *Heracleum lanatum* Michx.

A. (×1000) pollen ovale, vue méridienne de face, apertures peu visibles, ectoaperture moyenne, épaississement de l'exine dans la zone équatoriale.

B, C, D. (×1000) coupes optiques méridiennes successives, traversant le tectum (B), traversant, l'ectexine dans sa totalité (C, D), endoaperture ovale-rectangulaire.

E. (× 2000) le M.E.B. montre une surface tectale beaucoup plus enchevêtrée et heurtée dans les zones aperturales.

F. (× 5000) cassure longitudinale due aux ultrasons, montrant la façon dont l'endexine se sépare de l'ectexine pour venir former l'endoaperture équatoriale; elle met aussi en évidence la continuité de l'ectexine au-dessus de l'endoaperture.

G. (× 10 000) surface tectale polaire, les têtes des columelles se soudent en portées assez longues et enchevêtrées: surface rugulée.

H. (× 20 000) cassure due aux ultrasons, montrant les columelles, grandes et trappues, avec des têtes légèrement structurées qui s'emboîtent les unes dans les autres, et qui se soudent entre elles de façon plus ou moins continue.

Clichés du Laboratorie de Géologie du Muséum National d'Histoire Naturelle de Paris.

PLANCHE 4

A–I: *Heracleum mantegazzianum* Somm. & Lev.

A. (× 1000) pollen ovale, vue méridienne de face, apertures peu visibles, ectoaperture moyenne, épaississement de l'exine à l'équateur et aux pôles.

B, C, D. (× 1000) coupes optiques méridiennes, de face, successives traversant le tectum (B), traversant une partie de l'ectexine (C), puis traversant l'ectexine dans sa totalité (D), endoaperture ovale-rectangulaire.

E. (× 1000) coupe optique méridienne d'un mésocolpium, columelles importantes et épaississement très net de l'ectexine dans la zone équatoriale.

F. (× 1000) vue méridienne d'un mésocolpium.

G. (× 10 000) surface tectale polaire, les têtes des columelles sont soudées en portées assez longues: surface striato-rugulée.

H. (× 5000) surface tectale dans une zone aperturale, à structure plus heurtée que la précédente et beaucoup plus enchevêtrée.

I. (× 2000) cassure longitudinale due aux ultrasons, révélant une endexine parfaitement lisse intérieurement, et montrant la forme de l'endoaperture.

Clichés du Laboratoire de Géologie du Muséum National d'Histoire Naturelle de Paris.

PLANCHE 5

A–F: *Heracleum mantegazzianum* Somm. & Lev.

A. (× 2000) aspect d'ensemble du grain vu au M.E.B.

B. (× 10 000) surface tectale aux pôles avec une structure moins heurtée et enchevêtrée que la C, et cassure due aux ultrasons révélant une endexine (au sens strict) épaisse, une sole assez mince, de grandes columelles digitées avec des têtes épaisses légérement structurées et se soudant, à ce niveau là, en portées assez longues: surface striato-rugulée.

C. (× 10 000) surface tectale dans une zone aperturale: heurtée et enchevêtrée.

D. (× 20 000) détail de B, au niveau des grandes columelles digitées.

E. (× 2000) cassure d'une calotte polaire due aux ultrasons.

F. (× 10 000) détail de E, révélant une endexine lisse intérieurement, et la structuration des têtes des columelles.

Clichés du Laboratoire de Géologie du Muséum National d'Histoire Naturelle de Paris.

PLANCHE 6

A–I: *Trachymene glaucifolia* Benth.

A, B. (× 1000) pollen ovale, vue méridienne de face, ectoaperture longue, endoaperture ovale-rectangulaire, exine bien épaissie dans les zones subpolaires.

C–F. (× 1000) coupes optiques méridiennes de profil successives (C, D: niveaux de l'ectexine) (E, F: niveaux plus profonds montrant l'épaississement marqué de l'endexine avant son interruption au niveau de l'endoaperture et les ailes importantes d'ectexine dans les zones subpolaires).

G. (× 1800) la marge épaissie tout au long de l'ectoaperture est remarquable.

H. (× 9000) surface tectale au niveau d'un mésocolpium montrant l'extrême imbrication des têtes des columelles.

I. (× 4500) détail de G, le mésocolpium étant encadré par les marges des ectoapertures.

Clichés du Laboratoire de Géologie du Muséum National d'Histoire Naturelle de Paris.

PLANCHE 7

A–F : *Trachymene glaucifolia* Benth.

A. (× 1500) cassure longitudinale dûe aux ultrasons.

B. (× 4700) cassure dûe aux ultrasons : endexine détachée de la sole ; columelles avec leurs têtes extraordinaires ; vues de surface tectale ; vue de surfaces arrasées : columelles sectionnées à différents niveaux.

C. (× 10 000) détail de A : endexine (au sens strict) n'est pas compacte, mais est constituée par 2 membranes réunies par des trabécules perpendiculaires ; sole mince sur laquelle reposent les pieds élargis des columelles grandes à têtes à plusieurs niveaux se soudant dans les 3 dimensions.

D. (× 9500) détail de B : columelles reposant sur la sole ; têtes des columelles se soudant à différents niveaux.

E. (× 9500) arrasements provoqués par les ultrasons : columelles sectionnées à différents niveaux. Ectoaperture vue de face, bordée de marges épaissies.

F. (× 19 000) détail de B, où les têtes des columelles ont parfois des formes en osselet très typiques.

Clichés du Laboratoire de Géologie du Muséum National d'Histoire Naturelle de Paris.

PLANCHE 8

A–D : *Cachrys alpina* Bieb.

A. (× 1000) pollen subrectangulaire, en osselet, vue méridienne de trois-quart ; apertures très difficilement visibles.

B. (× 1000) coupe optique méridienne de trois-quart ; épaississement marqué de l'ectexine aux pôles.

D. (× 1000) coupes optiques méridiennes de face successives sur lesquelles la forme subrectangulaire en osselet est très nette ; endoaperture petite, rectangulaire ; ectoaperture pratiquement inexistante ou réduite à un sillon résiduel au niveau de l'endoaperture.

E–H : *Psammogeton crinitum* Boiss.

E. (× 1000) pollen subrectangulaire en osselet (forme définie par le contour de l'endexine), avec un faux aspect d'équatorialo-constricté dû aux épaississements très marqués de l'ectexine dans les zones subpolaires ; endoaperture, petite, rectangulaire ; ectoaperture courte.

F. (× 1000) coupe optique méridienne : importance des columelles dans les zones subpolaires.

G. (× 1000) vue polaire triangulaire.

H. (× 1000) coupe optique équatoriale, montrant les carènes d'exine sur chacun des 3 mésocolpiums.

I–L, O, P : *Diplolophium africanum* Turcz.

I. (× 1000) pollen subrectangulaire, en osselet ; vue méridienne, endoaperture rectangulaire ; ectoaperture courte.

J. (× 1000) coupe optique méridienne montrant la forme nettement en osselet du pollen.

K. (× 2000) la forme en osselet n'est pas visible, elle est cachée par l'ectexine.

L. (× 5000) surface tectale striato-rugulée présentant des corps d'Ubisch (pollen jeune).

O. (× 10 000) détail de L, avec mise au point sur les corps d'Ubisch.

P. (× 10 000) cassure due aux ultrasons : endexine, au sens large, très épaisse ; columelles assez courtes et trappues avec des têtes structurées et soudées en portées qui peuvent avoir des directions privilégiées.

M, N : *Scandix pecten-veneris* L.

M. (× 1000) pollen subrectangulaire en osselet ; vue méridienne, apertures réduites : endoaperture rectangulaire, ectoaperture très courte (grain chloriné).

N. (× 1000) coupe optique méridienne avec épaississement sensible de l'exine dans toute la zone équatoriale (grain chloriné).

Clichés du Laboratoire de Géologie du Muséum National d'Histoire Naturelle de Paris.

PLANCHE 9

A–I : *Cachrys goniocarpa* Boiss.

A–C. (× 1000) pollen subrectangulaire, légèrement en osselet ; coupes optiques méridiennes successives ; endoaperture rectangulaire avec endexine fortement épaissie avant son interruption ; ectoaperture courte ; exine plus épaisse aux pôles.

D. (× 2000) cassure due aux ultrasons au niveau d'une calotte polaire.

E. (× 2200) surface tectale extrêmement heurtée dans les zones aperturales.

F. (× 11 000) détail de D : endexine, au sens large, très épaisse, et relativement lisse intérieurement.

G. (× 22 000) détail de D : endexine au sens strict et sole, très épaisses ; columelles souvent digitées avec des têtes présentant une certaine structuration visible, indépendante des pieds.

H. ($\times 11\,000$) surface tectale dans une zone aperturale: tête des columelles soudées en portées extrêmement enchevêtrées et heurtées.

I. ($\times 11\,000$) surface tectale aux pôles: les têtes des columelles se soudent en portées assez longues qui peuvent s'orienter dans des directions privilégiées: surface striato-rugulée.

Clichés du Laboratoire de Géologie du Muséum National d'Histoire Naturelle de Paris.

PLANCHE 10

A–I: *Echinophora spinosa* L.

A. ($\times 1000$) pollen équatorialo-constricté, vue méridienne de face; pollen à symétrie d'ordre 2; endoaperture rectangulaire, ectoaperture moyenne.

B, C. ($\times 1000$) coupes optiques méridiennes (C: forme équatorialo-constrictée et symétrie d'ordre 2 bien nettes).

D, G. ($\times 1000$) mésocolpium (G: vue méridienne). (D: coupe optique avec les 2 endoapertures qui se font face.)

E. ($\times 2000$) une ectoaperture vue de 3/4.

F. ($\times 2000$) mésocolpium vu de face.

H. ($\times 10\,000$) cassure longitudinale due aux ultrasons: surface tectale micro-réticulée ou striato-réticulée de façon très dense.

I. ($\times 20\,000$) détail de H: endexine au sens large très importante; columelles fines et rapprochées avec des têtes très bien structurées, et cette structuration qui leur est propre forme en surface une micro-réticulation.

Clichés du Laboratoire de Géologie du Muséum National d'Histoire Naturelle de Paris.

PLANCHE 11

A–I: *Pycnocycla ledermanii* Wolff

A. ($\times 1000$) pollen équatorialo-constricté, à symétrie d'ordre 2, vue méridienne de face; endoaperture ovale-rectangulaire; ectoaperture courte et parfois très réduite.

B. ($\times 1000$) coupe optique méridienne de face montrant la forme typique équatorialo-constrictée; les 2 endoapertures sont superposées.

C, D. ($\times 1000$) mésocolpium; (C: vue de surface), (D: coupe optique avec les 2 endoapertures qui se font face).

E. ($\times 1000$) vue polaire ovale, révélatrice de la symétrie bilatérale.

F. ($\times 1000$) coupe optique équatoriale, avec épaississements d'exine qui se font face sur chacun des 2 mésocolpiums.

G. ($\times 20\,000$) surface tectale striato-réticulée de façon très dense: les têtes des columelles sont soudées en portée courtes et rapprochées, quelques fois orientées dans des directions privilégiées.

H. ($\times 2000$) apertures et symétrie d'ordre 2 apparaissent de façon éclatante au microscope électronique à balayage.

I. ($\times 2000$) mésocolpium vu de face.

Clichés du Laboratoire de Géologie du Muséum National d'Histoire Naturelle de Paris.

PLANCHE 12

A–F: *Pycnocycla ledermanii* Wolff

A. (1000) grains vus de face et de profil.

B. ($\times 3300$) cassure transversale due aux ultrasons mettant bien en évidence la symétrie d'ordre 2, avec des épaississements d'exine marqués sur les mésocolpiums qui se font face: endexine au sens large plus épaisse, et columelles plus allongées.

C. ($\times 2000$) grain vu de 3/4: forme équatorialo-constrictée ressortant nettement.

D. ($\times 12\,000$) arrasement provoqué par les ultrasons: columelles entières, puis sectionnées à différents niveaux des pieds qui reposent sur la sole au contact de l'endexine au sens strict.

E. ($\times 10\,000$) surface tectale striato-réticulée dense, avec quelques portées alignées dans des directions privilégiées.

F. ($\times 9000$) cassure transversale due aux ultrasons: endexine au sens large très épaisse, columelles longues, fines et rapprochées, avec des têtes importantes bien structurées, cette structuration étant parfaitement indépendante des pieds sous-jacents: petits éléments en forme de champignons et soudés entre eux.

Clichés du Laboratoire de Géologie du Muséum National d'Histoire Naturelle de Paris.

Planche 13

A–G: *Orlaya grandiflora* (L.) Hoffm.

A. (× 1000) pollen très légèrement équatorialo-constricté (forme peu visible sous l'apaississement de l'ectexine à l'équateur); vue méridienne: endoaperture ovale-rectangulaire; ectoaperture moyenne ou courte.
B, C. (× 1000) coupes optiques méridiennes successives: ectexine épaissie dans la zone équatoriale.
D. (× 2200) grain en vue méridienne avec aperture de face.
E. (× 2200) cassure transversale due aux ultrasons, au niveau de la zone subpolaire: endexine lisse; exine épaissie au niveau des 3 mésocolpiums.
F. (× 11 000) cassure longitudinale due aux ultrasons: têtes globuleuses des columelles, au niveau de l'aperture et surface tectale striato-réticulée de façon très dense ou micro-réticulée.
G. (× 22 000) détail de E: endexine au sens large, très épaisse; columelles grosses et assez allongées avec des têtes très importantes, bien structurées en éléments qui en se soudant, donnent à leur sommet une surface tectale densément striato-réticulée ou micro-réticulée.

Clichés du Laboratoire de Géologie du Muséum National d'Histoire Naturelle à Paris.

Planche 14

A, D: *Lisaea papyracea* Boiss.

A. (× 1000) pollen équatorialo-constricté, vue méridienne de face: avec des ailes d'exine très importantes sur chaque mésocolpium; apertures réduites (la forme équatorialo-constrictée est donnée par le contour de l'endexine).
D. (× 1000) coupe optique au niveau d'une aile de mésocolpium: endexine très épaisse, columelles grandes et digitées, tectum composé de petites columelles.

B, C, E–H: *Turgenia latifolia* (L). Hoffm.

B, C. (× 1000) coupes optiques méridiennes successives montrant la forme équatorialo-constrictée due au contour de l'endexine, de grandes columelles digitées, un tectum composé de petites columelles.
E. (× 1000) coupe optique au niveau d'un mésocolpium.
F. (× 1700) vue d'un mésocolpium.
G. (× 1800) le fort épaississement de l'ectexine, au niveau des 3 mésocolpiums, cache la forme équatorialo-constrictée du pollen. Mésocolpium de face avec les deux zones aperturales qui l'encadrent.
H. (× 5000) surface tectale dans une zone aperturale: micro-réticulation très nette.

Clichés du Laboratoire de Géologie du Muséum National d'Histoire Naturelle de Paris.

Planche 15

A–E: *Turgenia latifolia* (L.) Hoffm.

A. (× 2000) grain en vue méridienne avec aperture de face.
B. (× 2000) cassure transversale due aux ultrasons, dans la zone équatoriale: endexine lisse au sens strict; sole épaisse sur laquelle reposent les columelles qui sont très grandes et digitées au niveau de chacun des 3 mésocolpiums; au sommet de ces columelles, présence d'une membrane sur laquelle reposent les petites columelles propres au tectum.
C. (× 5000) détail de B où l'on peut constater très nettement la présence d'une membrane séparant le tectum (qui a une totale individualisation) des pieds des columelles sous-jacentes.
D. (× 5000) surface tectale dans une zone aperturale montrant une certaine érosion due aux ultrasons.
E. (× 10 000) détail de D: surface tectale micro-réticulée: micro-perforations situées au milieu des micro-mailles formées par les micro-columelles propres au tectum.

Clichés du Laboratoire de Géologie du Muséum National d'Histoire Naturelle de Paris.

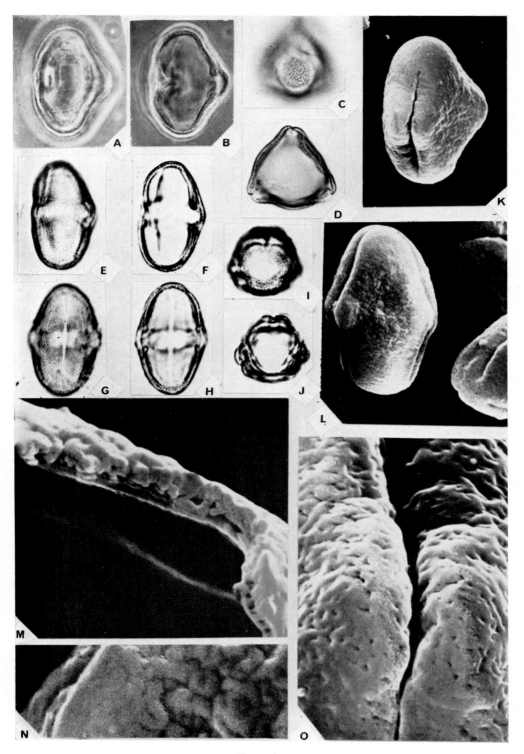

Plate 1

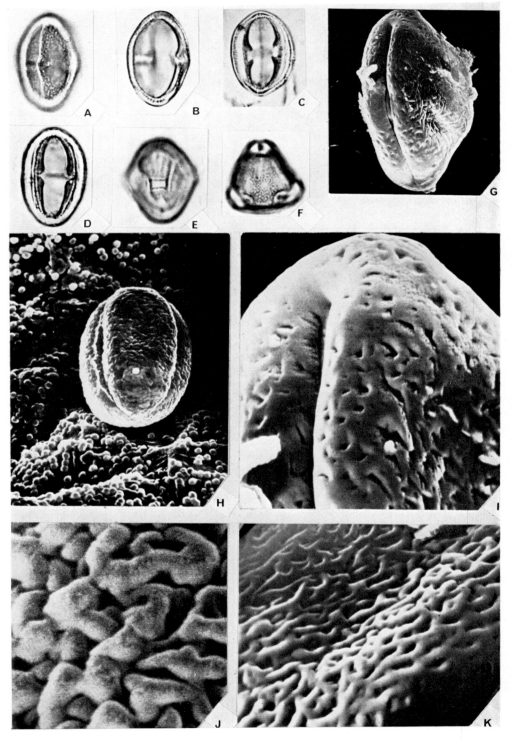

PLATE 2

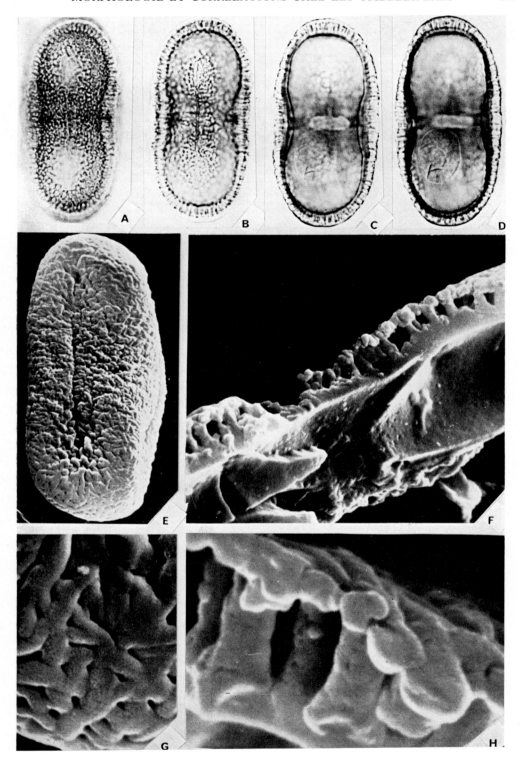

PLATE 3

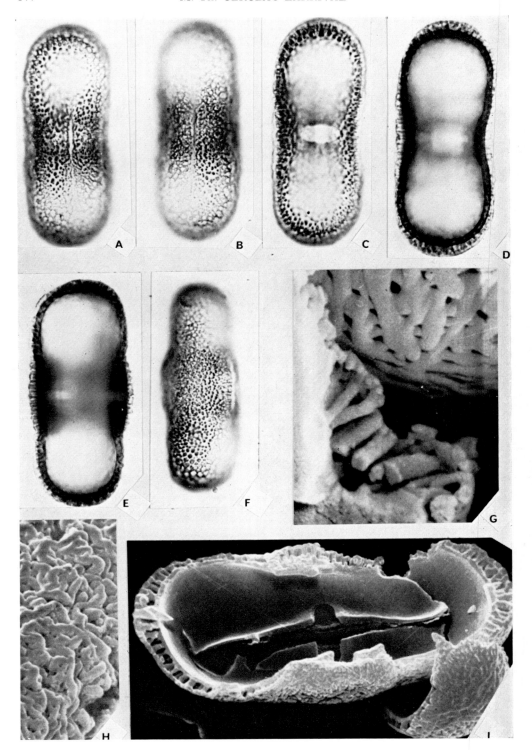

PLATE 4

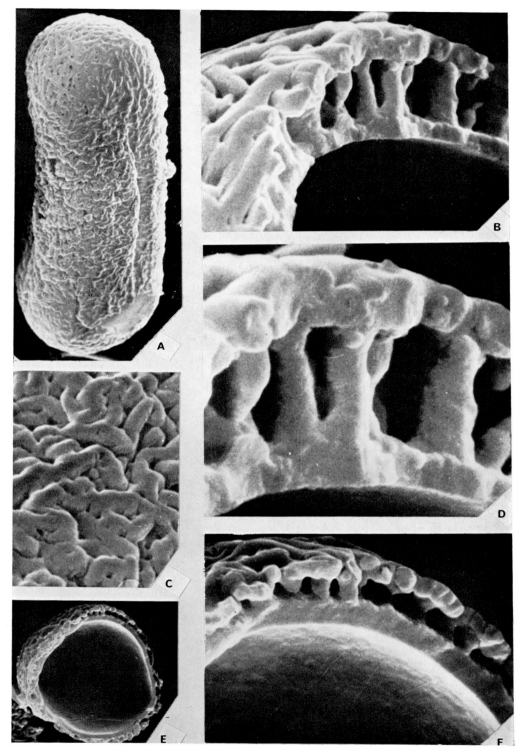

PLATE 5

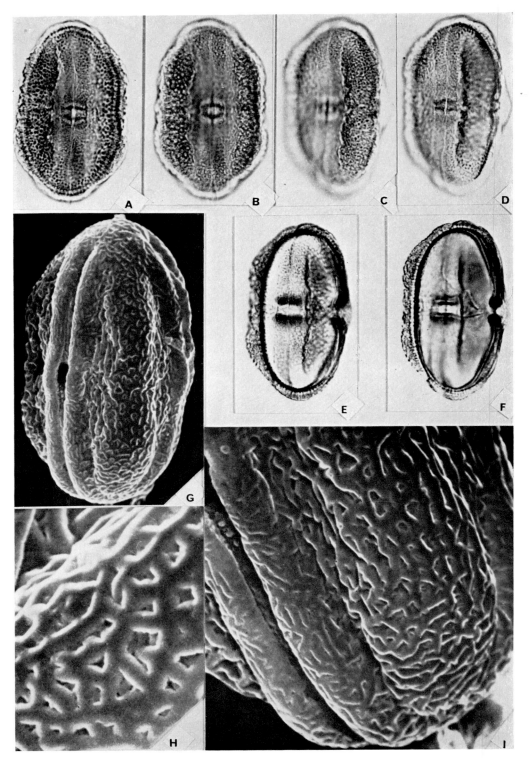

PLATE 6

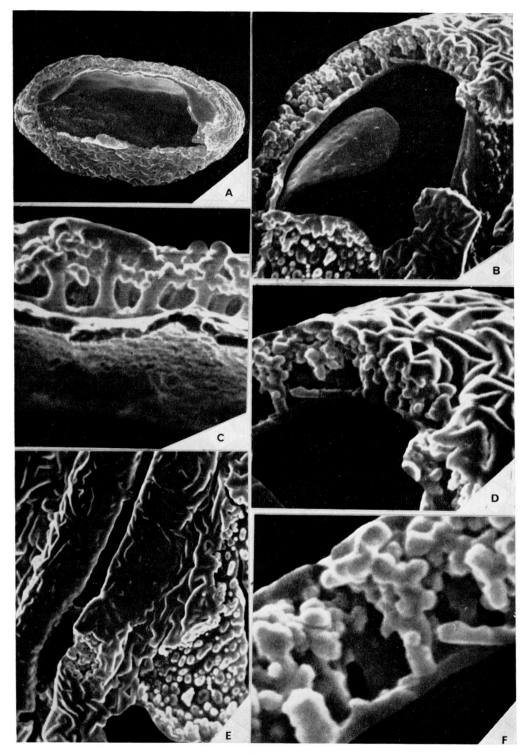

PLATE 7

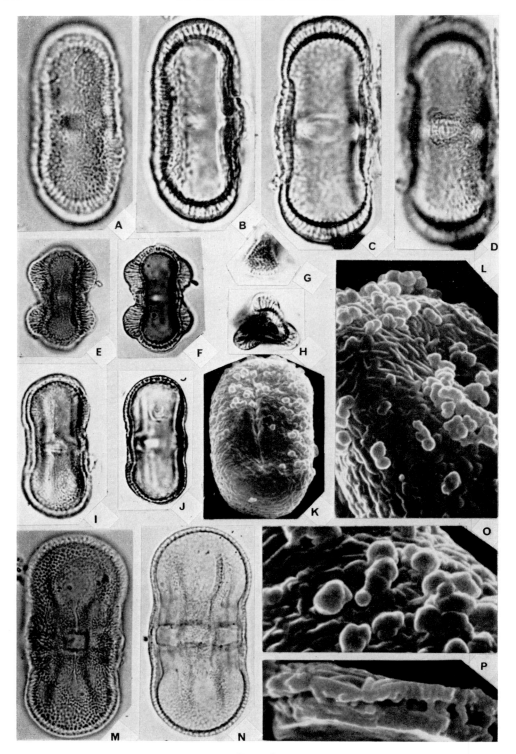

PLATE 8

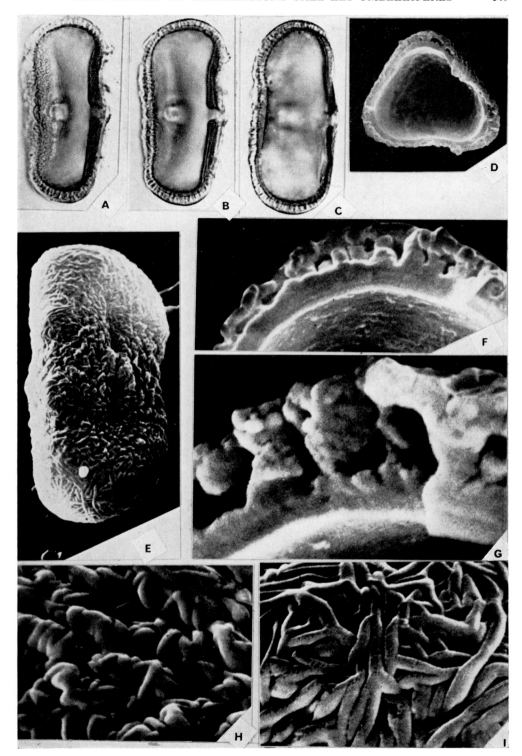

PLATE 9

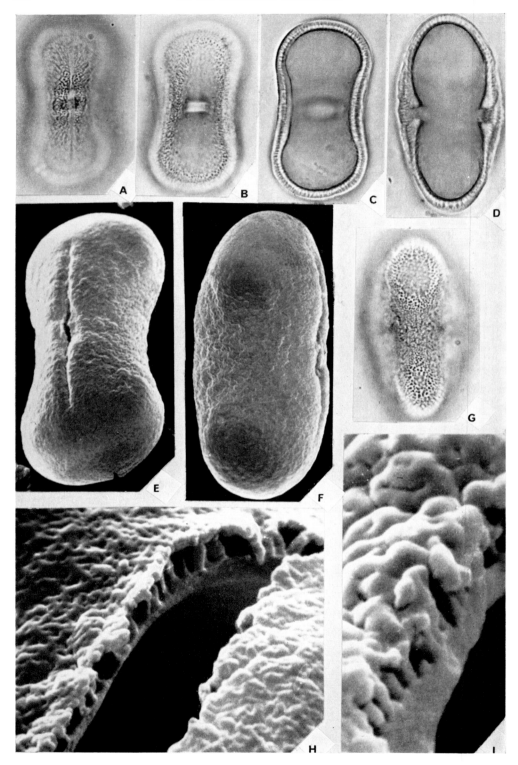

Plate 10

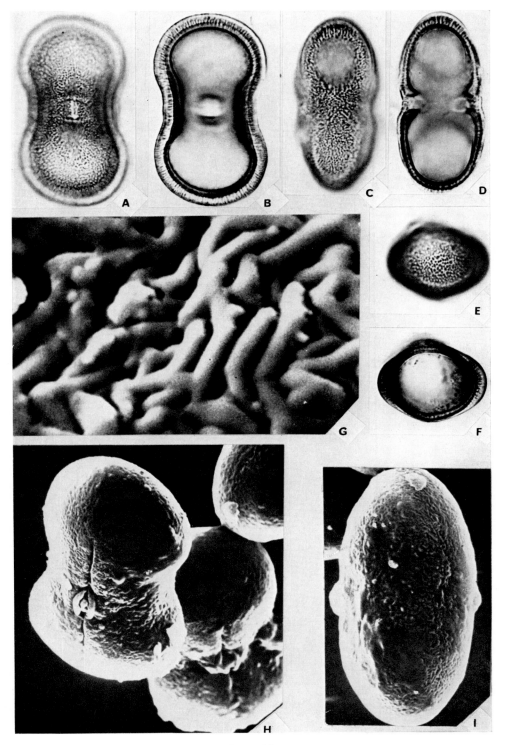

PLATE 11

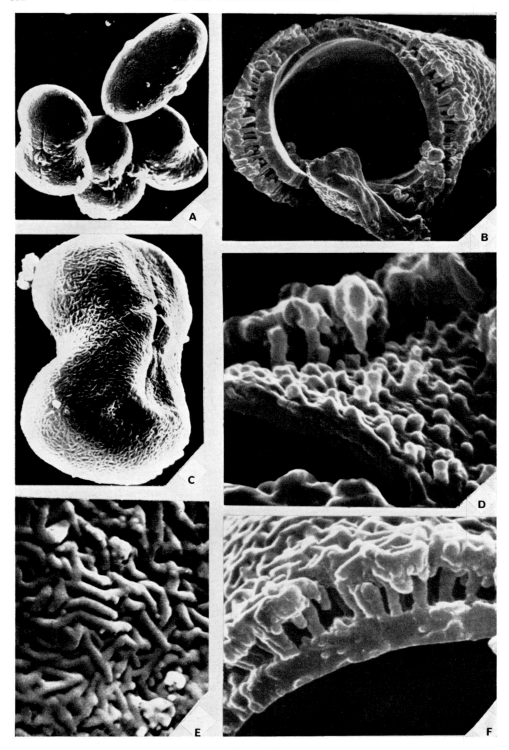

PLATE 12

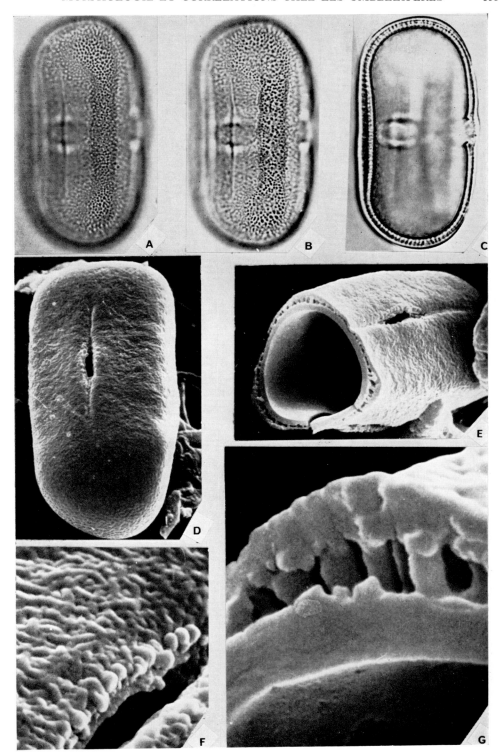

PLATE 13

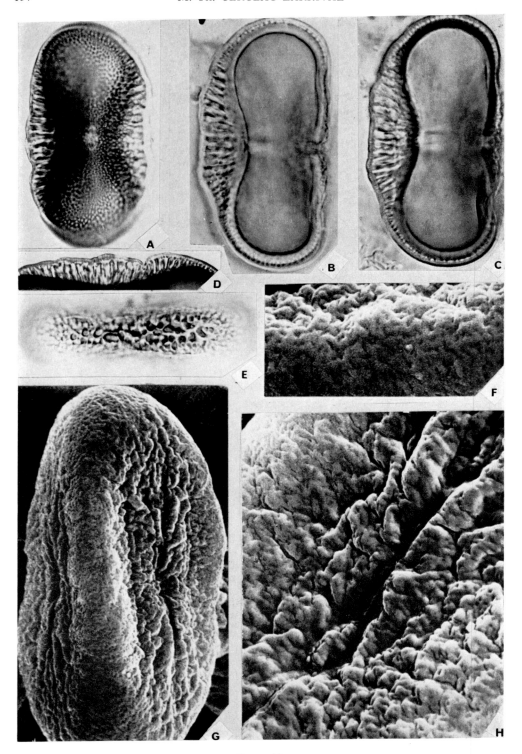

PLATE 14

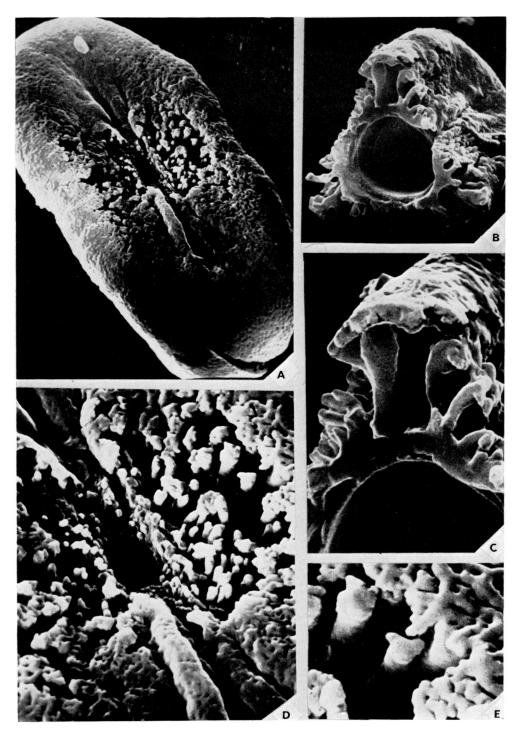

PLATE 15

Inflorescence structure and evolution in Umbelliferae

HANS A. FROEBE

Botanisches Institut der R.W.T.H., Aachen, Germany

Little is known at present concerning the type of inflorescence from which the typical umbel of recent Umbelliferae has originated. It is generally supposed that it has been developed from a polytelic type of inflorescence, specifically a raceme. It is obvious, however, that any other type of inflorescence may be taken theoretically as a starting point giving an umbel by reduction. The Hydrocotyloideae could be regarded as the oldest branch of the Umbelliferae and thus might be expected to have the most primitive inflorescences. It will be demonstrated by means of several examples, taken from the genera *Platysace, Xanthosia, Micropleura* and *Hydrocotyle*, that the primitive inflorescence in question is by no means derived from a raceme but from a monotelic inflorescence system, specifically a thyrse.

CONTENTS

INTRODUCTION

According to Troll (1950, 1961*a*, *b*, 1964–1969) who, on a broad empirical basis attempted to produce a new, natural typology of inflorescences in angiosperms, two types of inflorescence can be distinguished: the *polytelic* and the *monotelic*.*

In the monotelic type of inflorescence, the apex of the main axis as well as those of all floral side branches ends with a terminal flower. In the polytelic type the shoot apex remains indefinite after having produced a greater or lesser number of lateral flowers. There is, therefore, no terminal flower at the summit of the axis.

At first sight this distinction seems very slight—whether or not the inflorescence is formed with a terminal flower. It is, however, very considerable, not only in theory but also in practice. It is this difference alone that enables us to understand the classical forms† of inflorescence in terms of their typological relationships. Again, it is this difference that, by introducing new aspects, has been shown to have considerable systematic value by allowing homologous elements in different inflorescences in many different taxa to be recognized (Weberling, 1965: 216).

---

* In some respects these two types correspond to the 'definite' and 'indefinite' inflorescences recognized by Roeper (1826).

† The classical terms for inflorescences are not directly affected by this change of approach. Thus we can still talk of 'racemes' (as an example of a polytelic inflorescence), 'panicles', 'thyrses' and 'cymes' (as examples of monotelic inflorescences). In spite of the difference noted above all these terms have the same meaning as previously from a terminological point of view.

The basic question of the present investigation is: How did the umbel develop? The umbel is, of course, the type of inflorescence which is as characteristic of the family Umbelliferae as is the capitulum for the Compositae. With good reason these striking inflorescences were used, in both cases, to name these two groups of plants.

The literature dealing with this important question of inflorescence morphology—the evolution of the umbel—is, strangely enough, confined to speculations (Clos, 1855). There is a complete lack of exact morphological studies relating to this problem. Today's generally agreed concept is that the umbellet evolved from a raceme by suppression of the axis, and the umbel therefore from a compound raceme (Fig. 1a, b). This seems to be a very simple explanation, and since it appears so convincing one usually forgets that it is just a working hypothesis (at least as far as the Umbelliferae is concerned). This hypothesis may be right, but not necessarily so. There are other possible ways of deducing the evolution of an umbel: one could start with a panicle for example, or with a thyrse or a dichasial cyme (Fig. 1c, d, e).

FIGURE 1. Schematic figures of umbels showing the derivation of different inflorescence types by suppression of the dotted sections of the axis or branches: (a) umbellet from a raceme (polytelic); (b) umbel from a compound raceme (polytelic); (c) umbel from a panicle (monotelic); (d) umbel from a thyrse (monotelic); (e) umbel from a dichasial cyme (monotelic); (f) general demonstration of the two internodes (hy, hypopodium; me, mesopodium) which must be suppressed in order to get an umbellet.

At this stage of our theoretical considerations it does not seem relevant which of the possibilities is the more suitable or the more realistic one. The main points to be realized are: (1) we could develop the inflorescence of an umbellet or an umbel with almost any type of inflorescence as a starting point, just by suppressing sections of the secondary axis, that is to say of the Hypo- and Mesopodium (Fig. 1f), and (2) the single flowers will have a different value depending on the type of inflorescence we start out with.

In trying now to trace the real derivation of the umbel it seems reasonable to study the inflorescences of that group of umbelliferous plants which can be considered as the most primitive (i.e. ancestral) one, namely the Hydrocotyloideae. Presumably we will find somewhere in this subfamily the most primitive inflorescences; and if the common concept of the evolution of the umbel from a compound raceme is correct we should find some raceme-like type of inflorescence.

RESULTS

The inflorescence of the genus *Platysace* Bunge has proved to be a most primitive type. As will be seen immediately from Plate 1A and Fig. 2(a), the inflorescence of *Platysace dissecta* F. v. Muell. looks like an umbel. It has the characteristic aggregation of the rays of first order and, not so pronounced, those of the rays of second order. Nevertheless, it is not an umbel in the traditional sense: the final units are cymes, the terminal flowers of first order being perfect while the lateral flowers are all male. The organization of the inflorescence of *P. dissecta* is easier to understand if one reverses the shortening of the internodes of the primary, as well as of the lateral axes (Fig. 2b). It is quite obvious then that this inflorescence is a thyrse, more precisely a pleiothyrse. Thus the inflorescence of *P. dissecta* cannot be classified as an umbel in the traditional sense. On a strict morphological basis the organization of this inflorescence (Fig. 2a) is that of a bracteate pleiochasium or a sciadioid (Troll, 1964: 53).

Throughout the genus *Platysace*, the flower-aggregates are umbelloid, in some cases even more so than in *P. dissecta*: they all look like a typical umbel. When examined more closely, however, they all appear to be of the same determinate type described above. The inflorescence of *P. juncea* Benth., for example (Plate 1B, Fig. 2d), at first looks like a threefold umbel. If one examines an umbellet closely (Fig. 2e) it will be seen that not all flowers are perfect; on the contrary, the majority are male as in the case of *P. dissecta*. This sexual dimorphism is easy to explain if one takes one of the inflorescence-branches of *P. dissecta* as a basis for working out the relationships. The scheme of this umbellet, as shown in Fig. 2(e'), corresponds exactly with inflorescence-branch IV of *P. dissecta* if one allows for a considerable reduction. Due to the location of the umbellets in the umbel, the involucellar leaves are shifted to the periphery, the one pointing to the centre of the umbel being suppressed. The compound umbellets at the periphery of the umbel of *P. juncea* (branch I and II in Fig. 2d) have basically the same structure but are slightly more complicated. An empirical diagram is shown in Fig. 2(f). It is not difficult to appreciate the agreement of this structure with those so far described, particularly

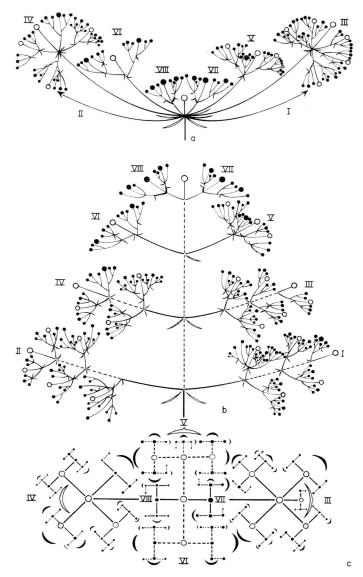

FIGURE 2. (above and opposite) Inflorescence of *Platysace dissecta* (a–c) and *P. juncea* (d–g). The dotted sections of the axis or inflorescence branches indicate suppressed internodes which have been stretched in the schemes (b), (g), (e′) and (f′) to make the facts clearer. I, II ... VIII, inflorescence branches. The dotted circles in (f) indicate umbellets arising on their ray out of the group of the other flowers, as shown in (d) (branch I and II). ○ perfect flowers, ● male flowers. For further explanation see text.

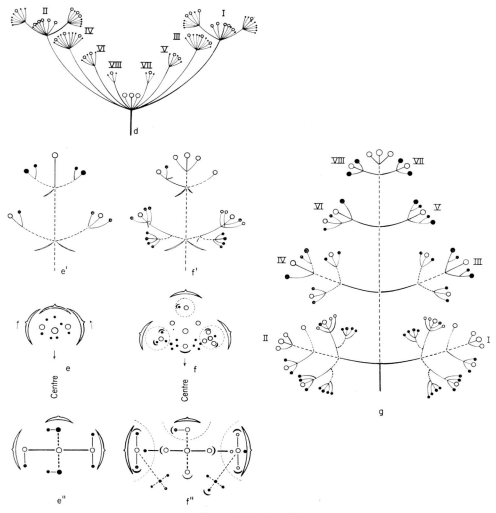

FIGURE 2 (*continued*)

if one compares the schemes Fig. 2(e′) and (f′) and especially the theoretical diagrams (e″) and (f″). The only remarkable point is that the secondary shoot of the lower pair of side branches is not included in the raised umbellet but remains at the base. For this reason, all the flowers originating from the receptacle of the umbellet rank quite differently in this system: they are of the first, second, third and fourth degrees. The basic mechanism, the suppression of the hypopodia, obviously has its explanation in the symmetry of the total umbel, such that all organs orientated towards the centre display some reductive influence. This can be seen most clearly in the second whorl of shoots: the one pointing to the periphery becomes a small umbellet, while the one pointing to the centre has only a small supporting leaf, is reduced to one flower, and remains in the umbellet-unit.

Now we are able to understand completely the umbel of *P. juncea* as pointed out in the scheme Fig. 2(g). It shows the characteristic features of a pleiothyrse, repeating in principle the situation in *P. dissecta*. The only difference is that, by suppression of the hypopodia of the side branches of the second order, groups of flowers are produced which look very much like real umbels. At the same time there is a tendency to reduce the total number of flowers in the branches and to develop the terminal flowers of the side branches of higher orders as perfect flowers.

Our explanation of the organization of the umbellets of *Platysace* receives support from ontogenetic studies. In Fig. 3 umbellets of different size of *P. juncea* are shown in very early stages of development. The size of the flowers reflects their sequence of

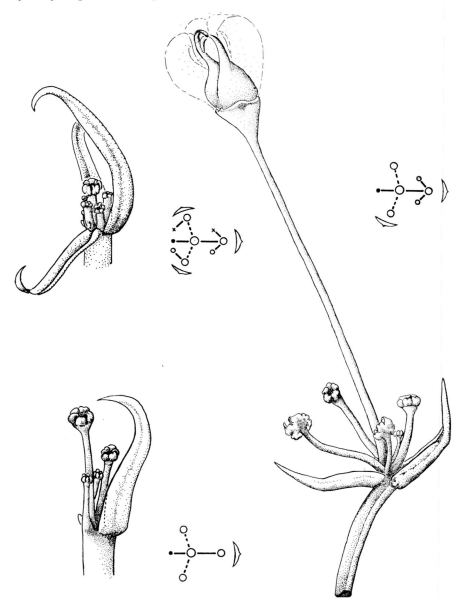

FIGURE 3. Very early stages of development of the umbellets in an umbel of *Platysace juncea*.

emergence. The specific arrangements of the flowers is explained in the empirical diagrams which correspond to the diagrams of Fig. 2.

There are two progressions found in several species of *Platysace*, which should be mentioned. These are apical and proximal dominance. Apical dominance can be found in different examples of the '*effusa*-group', for instance in *P. maxwellii* (F. Muell.) Norm. and one sample of *P. linearifolia* (Cav.) Norm. (material L. A. S. Johnson 30084K). It seems that in relation to the scheme of *P. juncea* (Fig. 4a, a') the whole distal region of the inflorescence including ray III produces exclusively perfect flowers (Fig. 4b, b'). By compression of the internodes these rays come so close together that an umbel evolves, separated by an extended internode from the lower bundle of male umbels. The cluster of male flowers originates from rays I and II only.

Proximal dominance is shown in *P. cirrhosa* Bunge. It is characterized by great reduction in the number of flowers and by the fact that the distal region of the total inflorescence, as well as of the side branches, displays increased maleness (Fig. 4c, c').

As far as I can see, the inflorescences in the old world genera of Hydrocotyloideae are mainly organized in the same way as that of *Platysace* already demonstrated. One always finds a monotelic inflorescence as the basic organization, that is to say, an exact pleiochasium but never a raceme.

We can now survey some suitable examples of *Xanthosia* Rudge. Plate 1C shows a separate inflorescence of *X. rotundifolia* DC. It consists altogether of four umbellets and one centre umbellet without a ray. Each ray rises from the axil of an involucral leaf. Each umbellet has three involucellar leaves which are all petaloid, the lateral ones showing an extremely one-sided development. The exact layout of these flowers can be seen in Fig. 5(a). It is striking to see that male flowers occur only in the parts of umbellets close to the centre of the umbel. In smaller plants or in side umbels the number of male flowers is increased at the expense of the number of perfect flowers. The total number and location of flowers remains the same, but only the female potency is suppressed in the flowers orientated towards the centre of the umbel (Fig. 5b). This is the same phenomenon of peripheral promotion or central reduction, on the basis of symmetry relations of the total umbel, as already pointed out for *Platysace juncea* (see Fig. 2e). But here not only the involucellar leaves orientated towards the centre of the umbel are suppressed, but in addition the lateral ones show an extremely one-sided development (Fig. 5c).

After the foregoing discussion of the inflorescence of *Platysace*, it is evident that in the present case we have the same type of inflorescence, a pleiothyrse, as can be seen in Fig. 5(a'). The inflorescences of *Xanthosia peduncularis* Benth. and *X. atkinsoniana* F. Muell. show exactly the same picture. In comparison, *X. huegelii* Steud. is very much reduced: Fig. 5(d) more or less represents a natural picture of the inflorescence while Fig. 5(d') and (d'') are schematic representations. In *X. huegelii* Steud. the flower triads in Fig. 5(d) are usually reduced to diads and the two upper inflorescence shoots are delayed in their development

In *X. ciliata* Hook. the reduction of the inflorescence branches has progressed much further, resulting in single-flowered branches (Fig. 5e, e', e''). *X. candida* Steud.

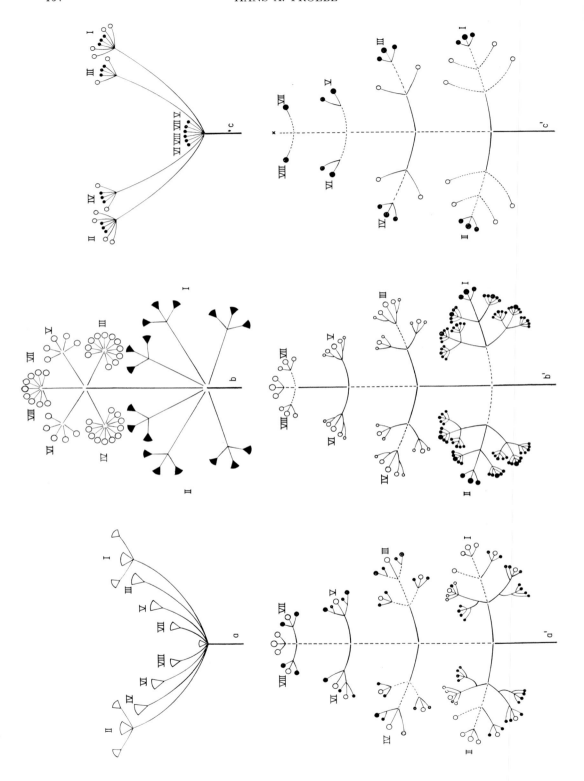

has a similar design, but the highest prophyll is always missing and the supporting leaves of the inflorescence-branches are recaulescently shifted.

In *X. tridentata* DC. and *X. tasmanica* Domin the whole inflorescence is reduced to two flowers; the terminal flower of the whole inflorescence and the terminal flower of the first inflorescence-branch. This inflorescence seems to be laterally attached in position. This apparent lateral attachment results from an overgrowth of the product of the axil of the final leaf below the inflorescence (*). Bearing this in mind, it is clearly seen from Fig. 5(f), (f'), (f") that the inflorescence is terminal.

Also in *X. pusilla* Bunge the distal lateral branch of the synflorescence usually exceeds the terminal inflorescence (s in Fig. 6b) which in most cases is reduced to three flowers. It may happen, however, that the usually elongate distal shoot is very small and almost incorporated into the umbellar-unit (Fig. 6c). An interesting feature of such 'enriched' synflorescences is the rearrangement of the two inflorescence branches, which were originally opposite each other, in relation to the newly joined third one: it results in equal spacing of all three parts of the synflorescence. The terminal flower of the inflorescence has also usually vanished.

The inclusion of so-called 'enriching shoots' in the inflorescence is particularly common in shrubby *Xanthosia* species where the ability to produce flowers is restricted to short shoots, for example, in *X. pilosa* Rudge and *X. vestita* Benth. (Fig. 6d, d'). There the inflorescence proper is restricted to branch I and II as can be seen by comparison with the scheme in Fig. 6a, which is the inflorescence-type of *Xanthosia* as deduced from the drawings shown in Fig. 5. The bracts are white and again petaloid. Both inflorescence-branches are reduced to their terminal flower. The synflorescence is enriched by a side shoot originating in the axil of the uppermost rosette leaf and having the same structure as the main shoot. In *X. montana* Sieb. the terminal flower is lost after the first vegetative period. Afterwards the flowers are formed from rosette shoots (Fig. 6e, e').

Besides the genera where we have no difficulty in demonstrating a thyrsoid inflorescence system, there are others where no direct proof is possible. In all such latter cases the umbel is already too strongly established as the inflorescence. The genus *Trachymene* Rudge should be mentioned here. Its inflorescences appear to be real umbellets in the traditional sense even on very thorough examination. There is not the slightest suggestion that they might be a monotelic type of inflorescence, either by the way of arrangement or separation of the flowers, or by the presence of a terminal flower. Nevertheless it seems quite probable on a basis of natural relationships that this indeterminate umbellet has evolved from a thyrsoid inflorescence system as suggested in Fig. 7(d–f), produced possibly by suppression of the hypopodia as well as by complete reduction of the male flowers and abortion of the apex of the inflorescence. This form of reduction can be followed in *Micropleura renifolia*

FIGURE 4. (opposite) Schematic figures of the inflorescences of *Platysace juncea* (a, a'), *P. linearifolia* (b, b') and *P. cirrhosa* (c, c') showing apical (b) and proximal (c) dominance derived from the same inflorescence type (a). I, II . . . VIII, inflorescence branches. The dotted sections of the axis and inflorescence branches in (a'), (b') and (c') indicate suppressed internodes which have been stretched in the schemes to make the facts more clear. ○ perfect flowers, ● male flowers.

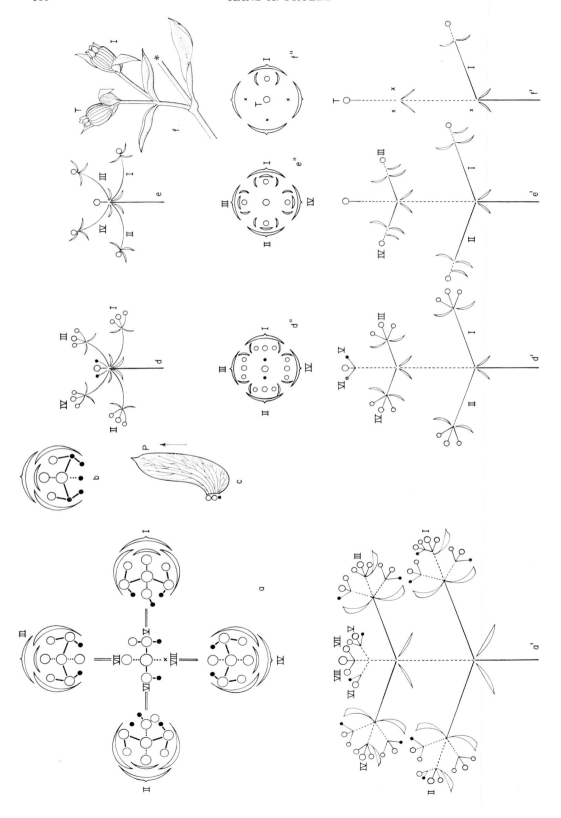

Lagasca, at least as far as the suppression of the hypopodia is concerned. The umbels shown in the Fig. 7(a–c) are somewhat unbalanced; nevertheless, even there one can find almost perfect umbels, in *Micropleura renifolia*. If the small male flowers in the example shown in Plate 1D were missing, and if there were no other examples with unbalanced umbels, it would not be possible to relate this umbel to a thyrsoid inflorescence system.

In the genus *Hydrocotyle* L. the situation is rather different. Despite the fact that here too the umbellets of most species appear remarkably perfect (for instance *H. javanica* Thunb. shown in Plate 2A), there arise doubts as to whether or not these systems are umbelliferous in a traditional sense, especially if one studies *H. verticillata* Thunb., *H. hirsuta* Sw. and *H. bonariensis* (Plate 2B–D).

Any attempt to understand such a complicated system as that of *H. bonariensis* by relating it to a compound raceme will be unsuccessful. Even the nearly correct explanation given by Troll & Heidenhain (1951) is not sufficient since it does not explain how the lateral axis can give rise to new branches. However, if one starts with a thyrsoid inflorescence system, a satisfactory explanation can be given, as shown in Fig. 8(a–c). By compressing the hypopodia in the axes of the third and fourth order, the flower triads in the axes of the second and third order come closer together, leading to a picture of repetitive umbellet formation. Upon suppression of the hypopodia of the axes of the second order, we arrive at exactly the kind of inflorescence as found in *H. bonariensis*, shown in Fig. 8(c) or, slightly altered, in Fig. 8(d). This deduction receives support from the following facts: (1) we started out with a type of inflorescence which is very common in the Hydrocotyloideae; (2) we only used one trend, which is also very common in the Hydrocotyloideae, that is, the compression of hypopodia; (3) in agreement with our theory we find in one single flower-whorl (4-) 6 (-8) flowers, depending on the vigour of the plant; (4) the number of fully developed flowers in a double or quadruple flower-whorl is considerably increased in comparison with the number of flowers in a single flower-whorl.

In young examples it is even possible to demonstrate from which branch the individual flowers of the basic whorl come from. This is quite simple as there are, in general, five or six orthostichies with which all flowers of the different whorls are integrated. Similarly the flowers of the basic whorl are integrated within these orthostichies. One can clearly deduce therefore from Fig. 8(e) that there should be 6×4 (as there are four branches) $= 24$ flowers in the basic whorl. For spatial reasons, however, 12 flowers have been suppressed at the points marked with a cross.

Finally we should not hide the fact that the explanation of the inflorescence of *H. bonariensis* is not as clear-cut as it might appear: the sequence of flower-formation

FIGURE 5. (opposite) Schematic figures of the inflorescences of *Xanthosia rotundifolia*: (a, a′), *X. huegelii* (d, d′, d″), *X. ciliata* (e, e′, e″) and *X. tridentata* (f′, f′, f″). (b), schematic figure of a weak umbellet of *X. rotundifolia* showing the increased number of male flowers at the cost of perfect flowers. (c), lateral involucellar leaf of an umbellet of *X. rotundifolia*. P indicates the periphery of the umbel. T, terminal flower. I, II . . . VIII, inflorescence branches. The dotted sections of the axis and branches indicates suppressed internodes which have been stretched in (a′), (d′), (e′) and (f′). ○ perfect flowers, ● male flowers. For further explanations see text.

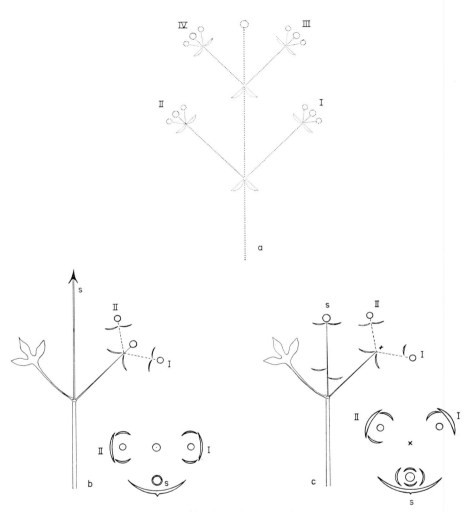

FIGURE 6. (See legend on opposite page.)

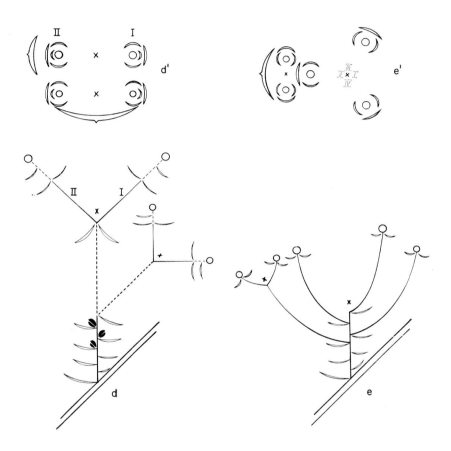

FIGURE 6. Schematic figures of the inflorescence type of *Xanthosia*: (a), the synflorescence of *X. pusilla* (b), *X. pilosa* (d, d′) and *X. montana* (e, e′). S, shoulder product of the distal leaf. x indicates the vanished end of the axis. The dotted sections of the axis or the inflorescence branches in (b), (c), and (d) indicate suppressed internodes which have been stretched in the scheme to make the facts more clear. I . . . IV, inflorescence branches. ○ perfect flowers. For further explanations see text.

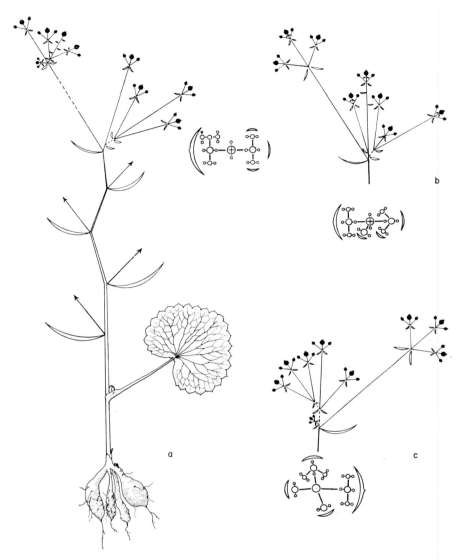

FIGURE 7. (See legend on opposite page.)

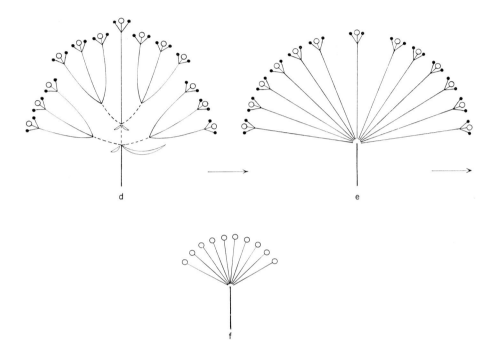

FIGURE 7. Schematic figure of *Micropleura renifolia* (a) and different shapes of its inflorescence (b, c). (d–f): Reduction of a thyrsoid inflorescence system with perfect (○) and male (●) flowers to a sciadioid having only perfect flowers.

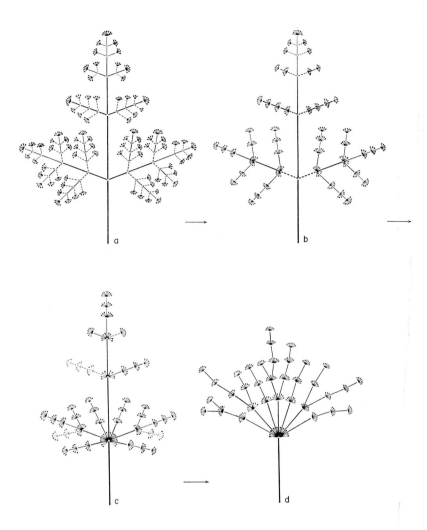

FIGURE 8. (a–d), schematic figures of the reduction of a thyrsoid inflorescence (a) to the inflorescence of *Hydrocotyle bonariensis* (d) by suppression of the hypopodia of different order (dotted sections of the branches in (a) and (d)). The schemes (c) and (d) differ only in the length of several internodes.

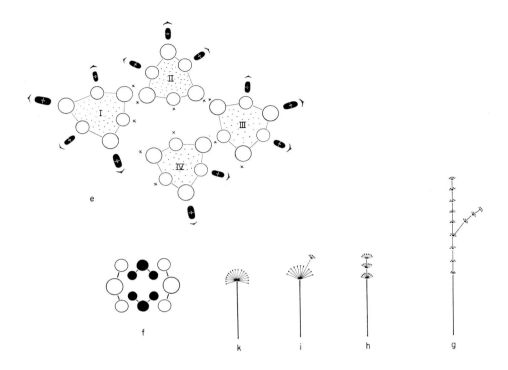

FIGURE 8, (*continued*). (e), diagram of the basic whorl of flowers (black) and the inflorescence branches I–IV. x indicates suppressed flowers of the basic whorl. (f), theoretical diagram of the arrangement supposed in the different whorls (black and white) of flowers on the inflorescence branches. (g–k), schematic figures of *Hydrocotyle verticillata* and *H. hirsuta* (g), *H. vulgaris* (h), *H. umbellata* (i) and *H. javanica* (k) as representative for the majority of species of *Hydrocotyle*.

does not follow our theory, and moreover it requires eight orthostichies (see Fig. 8f), while there are normally only five or six. We have to expect, therefore, that our theory will be modified as time goes by.

Assuming that our interpretation of the inflorescence of *H. bonariensis* is correct, and bearing in mind that there are still unanswered questions, this explanation implies that the simple umbellet in the majority of the species of *Hydrocotyle* is extremely derived. The presence of a series of intermediary types (*H. verticillata*, *H. hirsuta*, *H. vulgaris* L., *H. umbellata* L., see Fig. 8h–k) supports this idea.

In conclusion it can be said that the positive evidence in favour of a thyrsoid inflorescence system in the Hydrocotyloideae leads to the morphologically important conclusion that probably all umbels in the Umbelliferae are determinate or monotelic inflorescences, especially modified thyrsoid systems, and not polytelic inflorescences, and particularly not modified racemes as has so far been generally assumed. A prerequisite for this explanation is, of course, that the whole family is monophyletic and that the Hydrocotyloideae as a taxon are the genuine ancestors of the other Umbelliferae. On the basis of these new findings we are still able to understand the central promotion in the umbellet, already discussed on a previous occasion (Froebe, 1964), which is very common in the Apioideae and especially in the Saniculoideae, as well as all sexual differentiation in the umbels and umbellets.

ACKNOWLEDGEMENTS

Many thanks are due to the Deutsche Forschungsgemeinschaft for financial support of this investigation. I would like to thank Professor V. H. Heywood for revising the English text.

REFERENCES

CLOS, M. D., 1855. L'ombelle, inflorescence définie et indéfinie. *Bull. Soc. bot. Fr.*, **2**: 74–78.

FROEBE, H. A., 1964. Die Blütenstände der Saniculoideen. Eine vergleichend morphologische und entwicklungsgeschichtliche Untersuchung. *Beitr. Biol. Pfl.*, **40**: 325–388.

TROLL, W., 1950. Über den Infloreszenzbegriff und seine Anwendung auf die blühende Region krautiger Pflanzen. *Abh. math.-nat. Kl. Akad. Wiss. Mainz*, no. 15.

TROLL, W., 1961a. Uber die 'Prolificität' von Chlorophytum comosum. *Neue Hefte Morphologie*, **4**: 9–68.

TROLL, W., 1961b. Cochliostema odoratissimum Lem. Organisation und Lebensweise. *Beitr. Biol. Pfl.*, **36**: 325–389.

TROLL, W., 1964/1969. *Die Infloreszenzen. Typologie und Stellung im Aufbau des Vegetationskörpers.* Bd. I (1964), Bd. II/1 (1969). Jena: VEB Gustav Fischer Verlag.

WEBERLING, F., 1965. Typology of inflorescences. *J. Linn. Soc. (Bot.)*, **59**: 215–221.

EXPLANATION OF PLATES

PLATE 1

A. Inflorescence of *Platysace dissecta* F. Muell. (Max Koch 2040, Queenwood, SW-Austr., Okt. 1910. HBG).

B. Inflorescence of *Platysace juncea* Benth. (J. Drummond 16, W-Austr. BM).

C. Inflorescence of *Xanthosia rotundifolia* DC. (Bjuve, H.M.S. *Beagle* 1839–40. BM).

D. Inflorescence of *Micropleura renifolia* Lagasca. (Hinton *et al.* 10683, Pilas, Mexico, 18 Sept. 1937. W).

PLATE 2

A. Inflorescence of *Hydrocotyle javanica* compl. Thunb. (Griffith 2595, E-Himalaya. W).

B. *Hydrocotyle verticillata* Thunb. (no coll. mentioned, Georgia 1833. W).

C. *Hydrocotyle hirsuta* Sw. (P. Sintenis 5863, Pepino, Portorica, 10 Jan. 1887. HBG).

D. Inflorescence of *Hydrocotyle bonariensis* Lam. (no coll. mentioned, prope Arica, Mai 1854. W).

PLATE I

PLATE 2

Comparative anatomical and developmental studies in the Umbelliferae

WILLIAM L. THEOBALD

Biology Department, Occidental College, Los Angeles, California, U.S.A.

A survey of some of the important and classic literature dealing with anatomical and developmental studies of the Umbelliferae is presented. Emphasis is placed on a comparative study of floral and fruit development in the tribe Peucedaneae of the subfamily Apioideae. Studies of floral and fruit morphology and anatomy, venation patterns of flower and fruit, and the developmental changes that occur as the fruit enlarges and matures are described for several representatives of the tribe, including *Angelica, Lomatium, Peucedanum, Heracleum* and *Tordylium*. The comparisons indicate that there are distinctly different patterns of development leading to mature fruits with a similar dorsal flattening and gross morphology. On the basis of these investigations a re-evaluation of generic relationships within the tribe is discussed. The significance of such findings is also discussed with regard to our understanding of relationships in the family.

CONTENTS

INTRODUCTION

Anatomical studies have played a very significant part in the historical development of our present-day concepts of relationships within the Umbelliferae. This is especially true in light of the great importance of fruit structure in the family. As early as 1672, Morison apparently made use of fruit transections in describing his taxa, although none of these were illustrated. Subsequent investigators, including Crantz (1767), Sprengel (1813, 1818), Hoffmann (1816), Koch (1825), and De

Candolle (1829) all utilized similar gross anatomical features in their investigations. With the advent of better lenses and microscopes, it became possible during the second half of the last century (Bartsch, 1882; Courchet, 1882, 1884; Géneau de Lamarlière, 1893; Moynier de Villepoix, 1878) and the early part of this century (Håkansson, 1923; Hoar, 1915; Lemesle, 1926; Liermann, 1926; Ternetz, 1902) to undertake more detailed anatomical studies of all aspects of plant structure in representatives of the family.

The above-mentioned works, and those of the present day, range in scope from studies whose emphasis is on a single cell type, tissue, or organ, to others dealing with a systematic survey of a group of taxa on a comparative basis. The former includes the detailed developmental studies by Esau (1936, 1940) of collenchyma and vascular tissues in petioles of *Apium graveolens* L., and, also, the development of the root of *Daucus carota* L. In addition there are the developmental studies by Majumdar of *Heracleum sphondylium* L. (1942, 1946, 1947, 1948), and the well-known investigations by Steward (1964, 1968, 1970), combining anatomical and physiological aspects of development of isolated phloem parenchyma cells of carrots into fully mature plants. Comparative studies, such as those of Bounaga (1964, 1967), Deutschmann (1969), Espinosa (1932), Guyot (1966), Haccius & Reh (1956), Metcalfe & Chalk (1950), Mittal (1961), Panelatti (1959) Pervukhina (1950), Rodríguez (1957a, b), Tchéou (1930), Tseng (1967) and Veuillet (1959), have also done much to illustrate the usefulness of a careful and detailed survey of particular anatomical aspects.

The present author has attempted to bring together these basic types of information and to use them to demonstrate their value in understanding relationships within the family. In a recent series of studies this type of investigation has been employed in a broad survey of all aspects of vegetative, floral and fruit anatomy in a broad survey of all aspects of vegetative, floral and fruit anatomy in one small tribe, the Hydrocotyleae, of the subfamily Hydrocotyloideae (Theobald, 1967a, b, 1972). In the following account an attempt will be made to show the value of a more limited in scope, detailed survey of floral and fruit anatomy and development in a distinctly different tribe, the Peucedaneae, of the subfamily Apioideae. As a point of reference, Drude's (1897–98) treatment of the family has been accepted, although this treatment can be drawn into question in the light of the studies to be discussed.

FLORAL AND FRUIT DEVELOPMENT IN PEUCEDANEAE

Taxa within the large, world-wide tribe Peucedaneae are generally characterized by a distinct dorsal flattening of the mature fruit with the lateral ribs expanded into wing-like appendages. It is the second largest tribe in the family and includes over 50 genera and some 600–700 species. Drude's treatment (1897–98) recognized three subtribes on the basis of the morphology of the wings: Angelicinae, Ferulinae (Peucedaninae) and Tordyliinae. Angelicinae include *Conioselinum*, *Angelica*, *Levisticum*, *Cymopterus*, *Prionosciadium* and *Rhodosciadium*, for example, and are characterized by separate lateral wings. Ferulinae (Peucedaninae) include *Johrenia*, *Dorema*, *Ferula*, *Ferulago*, *Lomatium*, *Peucedanum* and *Pastinaca*, for example, and are characterized by closely appressed lateral wings. Tordyliinae include *Heracleum*, *Malabaila*, *Zozimia* and *Tordylium*, for example, and are characterized by thickened wing margins.

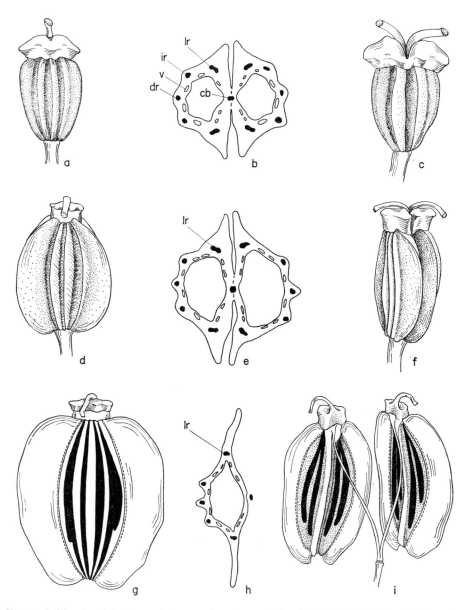

FIGURE 1. Floral and fruit morphology and anatomy of *Angelica triquinata* Michx. (a) Dorsal view of flower shortly after anthesis (×15); (b) median transection (diagrammatic) of developing mericarp shortly after anthesis (×20); (c) lateral view of flower shortly after anthesis (×15); (d) dorsal view of developing fruit (×10); (e) median transection (diagrammatic) of developing fruit (×14); (f) lateral view of developing fruit (×10); (g) dorsal view of mature fruit (×5); (h) median transection (diagrammatic) of mature mericarp (×7); (i) lateral view of mature fruit (×5). [Details: *cb*, carpophore bundles; *dr*, dorsal rib bundle; *ir*, intermediate rib bundle; *lr*, lateral rib bundle; *v*, vitta (secretory canal).]

At anthesis there is little indication of the shape of the mature fruit. The ovaries are often elliptical to terete in transection (Figs 1b, 3b) and the ten ribs (five per mericarp) are more or less of equal size. In each mericarp there are two lateral ribs

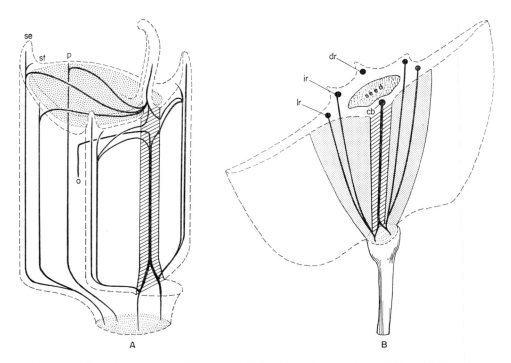

FIGURE 2. Venation pattern of flower and fruit of *Angelica triquinata* Michx. (a) Venation pattern (diagrammatic) of single developing mericarp at anthesis (petals and stamens have been removed) (× 50); (b) venation pattern (diagrammatic) of basal half of mature mericarp (× 12). [Details: *cb*, carpophore bundles; *dr*, dorsal rib bundle; *ir*, intermediate rib bundle; *lr*, lateral rib bundle; *o*, ovule trace; *p*, petal trace; *se*, sepal trace; *st*, stamen trace; diagonal stripes = commissural union.]

adjacent to the commissure, two intermediates, and a single dorsal between the intermediates. The degree of union across the commissure ranges from narrow (Figs 1b, 5b), to broad (Figs 3b, 5a).

Following anthesis, the lateral ribs of adjacent developing mericarps greatly enlarge along their entire length on each side of the body of the fruit in some taxa (Figs 1, 2). In other instances the body of the fruit, which contains the seeds, greatly enlarges, with the lateral ribs being pushed outward (Figs 3, 4). As a result of either of these types of development, the entire fruit takes on a distinct dorsal flattening. By comparison there is only a slight enlargement in a plane perpendicular to the line of contact (commissure) or close proximity of the two mericarps. In some instances, such as taxa within *Angelica, Cymopterus, Pteryxia* and *Glehnia*, the dorsal and intermediate ribs may also develop wings, and as a result the mature fruits superficially appear more rounded. At maturity the two mericarps separate along the commissure and remain attached to the central carpophore which often splits down the middle (Figs 1i, 3f).

Borthwick *et al.* (1931) and Rodríguez (1957*a*) have reviewed earlier literature dealing with the initial stages in the development of the inflorescence and have described these for *Daucus carota* L. and *Myrrhidendron donnell-smithii* C. &

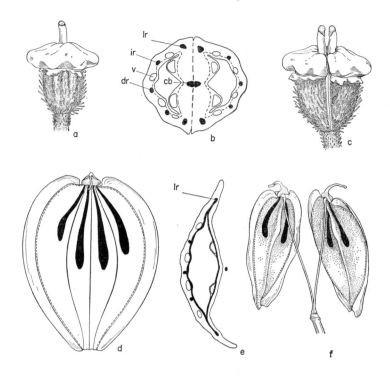

FIGURE 3. Floral and fruit morphology and anatomy of *Heracleum lanatum* Michx. (a) Dorsal view of flower shortly after anthesis (× 18); (b) median transection (diagrammatic) of developing mericarp shortly after anthesis (× 26); (c) lateral view of flower shortly after anthesis (× 18); (d) dorsal view of mature fruit (× 5); (e) median transection (diagrammatic) of mature mericarp (× 7); (f) lateral view of mature fruit (× 5). [Details: *cb*, carpophore bundles; *dr*, dorsal rib bundle; *ir*, intermediate rib bundle; *lr*, lateral rib bundle; *v*, vitta (secretory canal).]

R., respectively. The latter is a member of Peucedaneae. Jackson (1933) has reviewed the literature with regard to patterns of floral venation and nature of the carpophore, and has described the latter for several representatives of the family, including *Pastinaca sativa* L., a member of the tribe. Most studies of other peucedanoid genera, however, have been confined largely to examinations of the gross morphology of flower and fruit and anatomical examination of median transections of mature fruit (Bradley & Fell, 1966; Briquet, 1923, 1924; Drude, 1897–98; Mathias, 1930; Sandina, 1957; Styger, 1919; Tikhomirov & Tretyakova, 1967). Those features which have been most often noted include: shape and size of ribs and seed; location and arrangement of vascular bundles; number and distribution of secretory canals (vittae); presence of lignified cells in the inner layers of the fruit wall; and nature of the pericarp and carpophore. From a survey of such investigations it is apparent that there are considerable differences in the above-mentioned characters, and, in particular, in the relative position of vascular bundles in the flower at anthesis, and in the fruit at maturity. In addition, pericarp structure may vary greatly.

Even though this large body of information is available concerning the gross morphology of flower and fruit, and anatomy of the mature fruit, very little is known concerning floral anatomy and changes that occur between anthesis and fruit maturation. In the following account I would like to describe these changes for two members of the tribe and relate these and other findings to a survey in progress on representative members of the entire tribe. In the past, mature fruit structure has been a critical feature in determining most relationships within this tribe, as well as others of the family. The present investigations point to the erroneous conclusions that have been drawn from such an approach and it is hoped that these continuing investigations, when combined with information obtained from other areas (phytochemistry, cytotaxonomy, palynology, ecology, etc.) will lead to a much clearer interpretation of the relationships of the taxa involved.

Comparison of Angelica and Heracleum

Angelica *L.* (sensu lato)

This large and circumboreal genus includes some 100 species, and has been subdivided in the past into several genera, including *Archangelica* and *Ostericum*. As a point of reference for this and subsequent discussion, the venation pattern and fruit development in *A. triquinata* Michx will be described in some detail, and related to a recent broad survey of the genus by Hsu (1970).

(1) *Venation pattern.* The basic pattern within *Angelica* has been found to be remarkably uniform, aside from a few minor points regarding degrees of union or separation of vascular bundles in the ribs. In *A. triquinata* (Figs 1, 2) it is also very similar to that described earlier by Theobald (1967c) for *Lomatium dasycarpum* (T. & G.) C. & R. However, as one point of difference there are usually two traces evident in those lateral ribs which supply both sepals and petals (Fig. 2a), rather than the single trace observed in *L. dasycarpum*. In both taxa a single bundle is found in those lateral ribs supplying a petal. Secondly, the carpophore bundles are much closer in *A. triquinata* and form a single strand. At the summit of the ovary the two species are also much the same, except for the traces arching into the style within the base of the stylopodium in *A. triquinata* rather than below the disk as in *L. dasycarpum*. At this stage in development the only area of union between adjacent young mericarps is immediately adjacent to the carpophore (Figs 2a, 5b). This is in marked contrast to the condition in *Heracleum, Lomatium, Rhodosciadium*, and *Tordylium* (Fig. 5), as well as other peucedanoid genera.

(2) *Floral and fruit development.* Immediately after pollination the cells above the lateral ribs (in transection) start dividing and enlarging to form the wings characteristic of *A. triquinata* and other members of the genus. There are four such distinct areas on the developing fruit (two per mericarp), and each develops as a separate unit. This is shown in surface view in Figs 1(c), (f) and in transection in Figs 1(b), (e). The epidermis is continuous around these wings, and the narrow region of union between the mericarps remains small (Figs 1e, 2b). The body of the fruit enlarges, but only slightly. At maturity the parenchyma cells along the carpophore collapse and the

mericarps separate, although still attached to the carpophore. All of this is in marked contrast to that described by Theobald (1967c) for *Lomatium dasycarpum*. In the latter the adjacent lateral wings have a single meristematic area and grow as a unit. The resulting commissure is very broad with a collapse of tissues occurring along its entire breadth at maturation (Fig. 5). Both taxa, however, have a parenchymatous pericarp which may become lignified, but which never forms a woody endocarp. Morphologically the two taxa appear similar, and anatomically they superficially appear similar in transection, yet their development is quite distinct.

(3) *Survey of species*. Hsu (1970) has recently examined some 41 species of *Angelica* and found them to be quite uniform in the above-mentioned mode of development. Only moderate variation occurred in the degree of commissural union, which ranged from one-fourth to four-fifths the width of the commissural face. These observations have also been confirmed by the reports of Denisova (1961), Tikhomirov & Galakhova (1965), and Tikhomirov & Tretyakova (1967) with the possible exception of *A. amurensis* Schischk., which has been described in the last mentioned work with a degree of mericarp union more similar to that of *Lomatium* and *Peucedanum*. Only three of the taxa examined by Hsu (1970), *A. edulis* Miyabe, *A. japonica* Gray and *A. longiradiata* Kitagawa, exhibited a possible development similar to *Lomatium*. My own personal observation of the material examined by Hsu leads to some doubt regarding these conclusions, but a final report must await examination of better material. As noted by Hiroe & Constance (1958) the line of demarcation between *Peucedanum* and *Angelica* is particularly difficult, but the above described mode of fruit development lends support to a separation of these genera on the basis of wing formation. As will be noted, subsequently, fruits of *Peucedanum* apparently develop much like *Lomatium*, and never as observed in *Angelica*.

Heracleum *L.*

Some 70 species have been recognized in this large and predominantly Old World genus. In Drude's treatment it falls within the Tordyliinae on the basis of the thickened fruit margin. As a point of reference for this and subsequent discussion, the venation pattern and floral and fruit development of *H. lanatum* Michx will be described in some detail. This will then be related to a broad survey of the genus, and the above discussion of *Angelica*.

(1) *Venation pattern*. The basic pattern at anthesis is quite uniform in *H. lanatum* and other species within the genus. Differences are only minor ones of bundle size, and area of separation in the region of the stylopodium. It is otherwise the same as that of *Angelica* and *Lomatium* (Theobald, 1967c). In many species there is a considerable increase in the size of the upper portion of the ovary (stylopodium), which has led to parts of the vascular system and ovules being found above the level of separation of the traces to the sepals, petals and stamens. As a result, the ovary has taken on a partially superior appearance. This is especially true for those species described by Liehr in 1927 (*H. granatense* Boiss. and *H. mantegazzianum* Som. & Lev.). Eyde & Tseng (1969) have taken note of Liehr's observations and discussed them in light of their findings regarding an example of a hypogynous flower with epigynous ancestors in *Tetraplasandra* of the Araliaceae.

The carpophore bundles also follow the basic pattern found in *Angelica* and *Lomatium* (Theobald, 1967c). There is a broad line of union between the adjacent mericarps similar to that found in *Lomatium*, but distinct from the type described in *Angelica*.

(2) *Floral and fruit development.* Following anthesis the major increase in fruit size in *H. lanatum* is through enlargement of the body of the fruit in a plane parallel to the commissure. There is very little increase in cell number and size in the area above the wing. It is thus quite different from that observed in *Angelica*, *Glehnia*, *Pteryxia* and related genera, as well as *Prionosciadium*, *Rhodosciadium* and *Lomatium*. Throughout development the union of adjacent developing mericarps remains complete (Fig. 4) and it is only at maturation that parenchyma cells along the com-

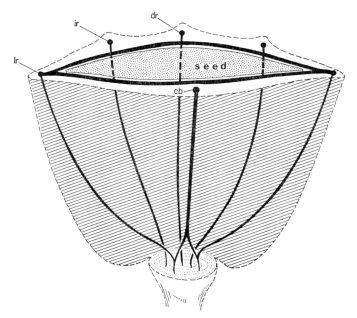

FIGURE 4. Venation pattern (diagrammatic) of basal portion of a mature mericarp of *Heracleum lanatum* Michx (× 8). [Details: *cb*, carpophore bundles; *dr*, dorsal rib bundle; *ir*, intermediate rib bundle; *lr*, lateral rib bundle; diagonal stripes = commissural union.]

missure collapse and bring about separation of the mericarps. A very interesting and distinctive feature in the genus is the formation of a woody endocarp* which often surrounds the seed cavity and extends into the short, thickened, lateral ribs (Figs 3e, 4). It is much the same in transection as that shown in Plate 1B for *Pastinaca*.

This mode of enlargement leads to a mature fruit with an arrangement of vascular bundles (Figs 3e, 4) which is distinct from that of the same flower at anthesis (Fig. 3b) and quite different from that of mature fruits in *Angelica* (Fig. 2b).

---

* There is confusion regarding the true nature of this 'endocarp'. It is sometimes surrounded internally by a single layer of parenchyma, and as a result has been interpreted as part of the mesocarp or inner pericarp. This particular problem has not been studied adequately from a developmental point of view in this investigation, nor in other published reports. Therefore, for purposes of discussion this distinct woody layer will be tentatively referred to as an endocarp. (See also Briquet, 1923.)

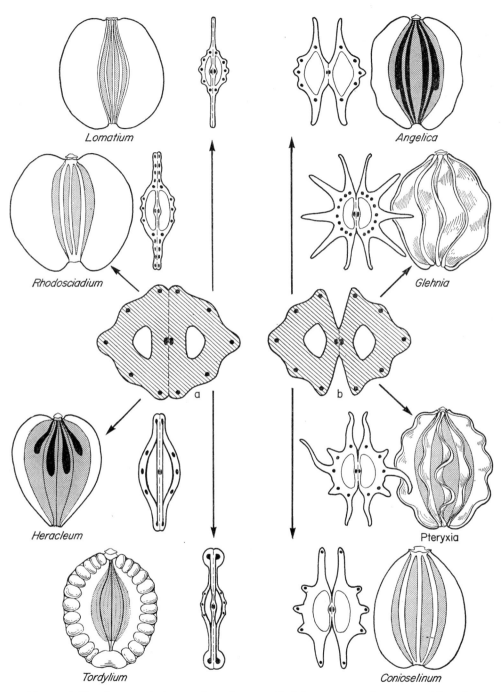

FIGURE 5. Developmental changes from flower to fruit in representative genera of the tribe Peucedaneae. (a) Median transection (diagrammatic) of typical flower of *Lomatium*, *Rhodosciadium*, *Heracleum*, and *Tordylium*. (b) Median transection (diagrammatic) of typical flower of *Angelica*, *Glehnia*, *Pteryxia*, and *Conioselinum*.

(3) *Survey of species.* Some 50 species in the genus have been examined so far
(Lai, 1971) and all are remarkably uniform in fruit anatomy and development. This
has also been confirmed by the reports of Bradley & Fell (1966), Briquet (1924),
Sandina (1957) and Pervukhina (1950). Variation does exist, however, in size and
arrangement of fibres in the 'endocarp', relation of vittae to endocarp position,
location of fibre clusters in the lateral wings, and the relationship of these clusters
to the endocarp. All of this may be of value at the subgeneric and specific level in this
difficult genus.

Survey of Peucedanoid genera

Pteryxia C. & R., Cymopterus Rafin., and Pseudocymopterus C. & R.

Pteryxia is a small genus of some five species found in drier habitats in the western
United States. It has been sometimes treated as a part of *Cymopterus*. The venation
pattern is similar to that of *Angelica*, and the mode of fruit development the same
except for more elaborate wings. These wings form not only on the lateral ribs, but
also on the dorsal and intermediates, as well (Fig. 5). The union of adjacent mericarps is very narrow along the commissure and the wings and pericarp are parenchymatous. These become weakly lignified at maturity. The elaborately developed
wings of *P. terebinthina* (Hook.) C. & R. (Fig. 5, Plate 1A) are formed through cell
divisions and enlargement of the tissue above the vascular bundles, much like
Angelica (Figs 1e, h).

The largest genus of this group, *Cymopterus*, contains some 32 species and is also
found in drier habitats of the western United States. It has sometimes been divided
into several genera (Mathias, 1930), and may represent a reduction series from
Pteryxia-like ancestors. The fruits are much like those of *Pteryxia* with a more
elaborate development of all ribs into wings in some taxa. A survey of the group is
now under way, and the results point to a mode of development similar to that of
Angelica and *Pteryxia*. The lateral ribs develop into wings separately, and the fruits
have a parenchymatous pericarp which becomes lignified with age.

Pseudocymopterus is a small genus of two species, *P. montanus* (Gray) C. & R.
and *P. longiradiatus* Math., Const. & Theobald (1969), also of the southwestern
United States. Both species exhibit the type of development described above.

Glehnia F. Schmidt

This small genus of one or two species is a highly reduced taxon restricted to
sandy beaches along the pacific coast of North America and Asia. It is characterized
by thickened 'corky' wings that allow the seeds to float considerable distances.
In this regard it is similar to *Angelica lucida* L., a species also from coastal beaches
and bluffs, and this probably accounts for their restricted coastal distribution.
Glehnia leiocarpa Mathias exhibits a pattern of development similar to that of both
Angelica and *Pteryxia* with all the ribs developing as separate units (Fig. 5). Vascular
bundles are at the base of the ribs, and the commissural union is from about one-
third to over one-half (Hsu, 1970).

An unusual feature of the genus, and possibly unique in the tribe, is the presence
of more than one bundle at the base of each rib. Instead of the usual solitary bundle

there are several small ones which form a ring of vascular tissue around the seed. As soon as better material of the species becomes available this venation pattern will be investigated in detail. It may represent a secondary adaptation due to the increased fruit size. As noted by Carlquist (1969) an increase in vascularization should be expected as often as reduction. In all other respects this species is much like *Angelica*.

Scandia *Dawson*

Two species were recently segregated from *Gingidium* J. R. & G. Forst. by Dawson (1967b) on the basis of a well-documented series of characters, and were recognized as a new genus *Scandia*. Detailed examination of *S. geniculata* (Forst. f.) Dawson reveals a type of development similar to *Angelica* and probably accounts for its placement in this genus at one time. There is a narrow union at the commissure, separate lateral wing development, and a parenchymatous pericarp which becomes lignified at maturity. Nevertheless, the over-all appearance of the fruit, and especially the epidermis and cuticle, appears distinctive. Because of the quality of material available, it is difficult at this time to pin-point exactly the reasons for such observations. More and better collections are needed of this taxon and the related species *S. rosaefolia* (Hook. f.) Dawson.

Conioselinum *Fisch.*

This small circumboreal genus of some twelve species was considered by Drude to be closely allied to members of the Ammineae subtribe Seselinae, and a link between this group and *Angelica*. The genus has the narrowest degree of mericarp union so far observed, and the wings develop in a manner distinct from any of the other taxa studied. In *C. scopulorum* C. & R. the lateral ribs of adjacent mericarps develop separately into wings, but this is not through cell divisions and enlargement above the bundles. Instead, the divisions and enlargement occur below the ribs and, as a result, the bundles are at the tips of the wings rather than the base (Fig. 5). The same is also true of the dorsal and intermediate ribs, although to a much smaller extent. Superficially the fruit appear similar to *Angelica*, yet they develop quite differently.

Rhodosciadium *S. Wats. and* Prionosciadium *S. Wats.*

These two genera are known from Mexico and adjacent regions of Central America, and contain some twenty-five and sixteen species, respectively. Most are caulescent herbs with a superficial similarity to members of *Angelica*. The fruits are also morphologically similar to those of this genus, as well as to some *Lomatium* and *Peucedanum* species. The similarity with the former probably accounts for Drude's (1898) placement of these two genera in his Angelicinae. On the basis of floral and fruit development, however, this is certainly not correct.

At anthesis the union of adjacent mericarps along the commissure is very broad in both genera and it appears very similar to that described by Theobald (1967c) for *Lomatium dasycarpum*. However, differences become apparent as soon as the fruit begins development. Lateral ribs of the adjacent and united mericarps enlarge as a single unit (Fig. 5) and accessory vascular bundles are formed in the meristematic tissue at the tip of the wings. The number of the accessory bundles apparently depends on the ultimate size of the wings. This has been found to be true in all of the taxa examined so far: *R. diffusum* M. & C., *R. purpureum* M. & C., *P. humile* Rose, *P. cuneatum* C. & R., *P. serratum* C. & R., *P. megacarpum* C. & R. and *P. lineari-folium* C. & R. Accessory bundles also develop in the dorsal and intermediate ribs even though these only increase slightly in size. At maturation the parenchyma cells along the entire length of the commissure collapse and the mericarps separate.

In most of the genera, so far examined (i.e. *Angelica, Conioselinum, Glehnia, Lomatium, Heracleum,* etc.), the seed face is flat or slightly concave in transection. In *Prionosciadium* and *Rhodosciadium*, however, there is an invagination of the peri-carp into the seed, much like that found in members of Drude's tribe Smyrnieae. The significance of this is not yet clear, as similar invaginations have been described by Mathias (1930) for the genus *Cymopterus*, and it may be more common than realized. The shape of such an invagination will vary depending on the region of sectioning. At levels in the upper half of the fruit it may be deep, while transections further down may appear straight or only slightly concave. This presents difficulties in interpretation and comparison, and should be kept in mind when examining material.

Lomatium *Rafin.*

Most taxa within *Lomatium* were initially referred to *Peucedanum* L. but they have since been recognized by Coulter & Rose (1900), Mathias (1930), and Mathias & Constance (1944–45) as distinct. It is the largest umbellifer genus in North America with some 80 species. The floral and fruit development of one of its species *L. dasycarpum* has already been described (Theobald, 1967c) and a study of the rest of the genus is now nearing completion. On the basis of the available information it appears that the development in these taxa is similar to that already described for *L. dasycarpum* with variation occurring only in over-all size of wing, seed and fruit.

The venation pattern is similar to that described for *Angelica*, and the differences are noted in the description of that genus. In all these taxa so far examined, the lateral ribs of adjacent mericarps grow as a single unit and develop through cell divisions and enlargement above the vascular bundle of the rib (Fig. 5). There are no known cases of the formation of accessory vascular bundles found in *Priono-sciadium* or *Rhodosciadium*, nor any instances of the invagination of the pericarp into the seed. At maturation the parenchyma cells along the entire breadth of the com-missure collapse and the mericarps separate. The remaining pericarp is usually made up of lignified parenchyma at maturity.

Peucedanum *L.* (sensu lato)

Unfortunately this genus, the largest in the tribe, is also the one that is least understood. It is very widespread and known from the northern and southern hemispheres, and is particularly abundant in Europe, Asia, the Near East and Africa. It has never undergone a comprehensive revision on a world-wide basis and as Burtt & Davis (1949) have noted, 'It is very difficult to generalize about the genus *Peucedanum.* . . . Even when certain groups such as *Pastinaca* L. and the American *Lomatium* Rafin. are excluded, *Peucedanum* remains a vast assemblage of Old World species which show a wide range of general facies and a considerable variation in details of fruit structure. In this group generic and subgeneric limits are greatly in need of re-definition.'

Briquet (1923) has described in great detail the mature fruit of *P. palustre* (L.) Moench and it is apparent that the development is similar to that of *Lomatium*. Before attempting to analyse the developmental sequences in *Peucedanum*, it has been decided to complete as much as possible of the survey of other genera in order to be better able to determine the significance of any variation that may be observed. This should prove possible in the coming year. As of now, it appears that many of the taxa within *Peucedanum* develop in a manner somewhat similar to that of *Lomatium*. The differences that turn up will probably be ones of internal structure which, in combination with other characters of the taxon, should help to clarify the taxonomy of this genus.

Ferula *L. and* Ferulago *Koch*

Ferula has recently been monographed by Korovin (1947) and this in turn has shed light on its relationship to *Ferulago*. The two genera are quite similar in gross fruit morphology, and the main points of separation have centred around the absence or presence of conspicuous bracts and bractlets. Both are restricted to the Old World with *Ferula* containing some 130 species and *Ferulago* about 50. Although an investigation of the two genera has only just begun, it is evident from available descriptions that these will be both interesting and rewarding. Figures of *Ferula rutbaensis* C. Townsend (1966) indicate that there are either more than the usual five ribs, or that the wings have formed between the lateral and intermediate ribs. Similar illustrations of taxa with more than the normal five ribs are to be found in Drude (1898: 231). It is not yet certain whether these are errors in interpretation or actually exist. They may prove to be clusters of sclerenchyma fibres in a woody 'endocarp', which have been mistaken for vascular bundles.

It is clear that the mode of development in these genera is one of great increase in the body of the fruit. The evidence of a broad union along the commissure, and the development of a woody endocarp may relate *Ferula* and *Ferulago* to *Heracleum*, rather than to other members of the Ferulinae. However, there is so much confusion apparent regarding fruit structure in both these genera, that I hesitate in drawing any conclusions at this time.

Pastinaca *L.*

This small genus of some twelve species was placed by Drude in Ferulinae (Peucedaninae) on the basis of the absence of a thickened fruit margin. It is obvious, however, from studies of floral and fruit anatomy that it is very close to *Heracleum* of Tordyliinae. It is almost identical in all aspects with the latter. In *P. sativa* L. there is a broad union across the commissure and the increase in fruit size is mainly due to increase in the body of the fruit (Fahmy *et al.*, 1958). There is also little or no wing development evident. At maturity there is a very distinctive woody endocarp (Plate 1B) of the type found in *Heracleum*, *Tordylium*, *Malabaila* Tausch, and possibly

Ferula and *Ferulago*. The parenchyma cells along the broad commissure collapse and the two mericarps separate (Plate 1B). Similar woody endocarps have been illustrated for *Stenotaenia* Boiss., *Pastinocopsis* Golosk., *Schummania* Kuntze, *Platytaenia* Nevski & Vved. and *Soranthus* Ldb. (Schischkin, 1951: 285).

Tordylium *L. and* Ainsworthia *Boiss.*

Tordylium is a relatively small genus of sixteen species, especially abundant in the Mediterranean region and the Near East. It has often been subdivided into several genera with *Ainsworthia* and *Hasselquistia* L. as possible segregates. In either circumspection the taxa which make up the group have several distinctive anatomical characters in common. All have a broad union along the commissure at anthesis much like that of *Lomatium, Peucedanum, Ferula* and *Heracleum*. Fruit development is characterized by an enlargement of the seed cavity and a thickening of the lateral ribs. In many cases cell divisions and enlargement occur in the tissues between the edge of the seed cavity and the lateral rib bundles (Fig. 5). It can be described as a specialization of the development described for *Heracleum*. In the latter genus some species begin to approach this type of development (Sandina, 1957). In *T. apulum* L. (Fig. 5) this type of development is carried to an extreme with the lateral rib vascular bundles found at considerable distance from the body of the fruit. In addition, the edge has become thickened and enlarged with a distinct woody endocarp running from around the seed through the wing into the thickened margin. In this regard it is also similar to *Heracleum, Malabaila* and *Zozimia* Hoffm.

DISCUSSION

From the above descriptions it is apparent that there is considerable variation in floral and fruit development. It appears that comparisons of such modes of development, venation patterns and floral and fruit anatomy may be useful in assessing relationships within the group, and between it and other tribes. All of the earlier systems of classification devised for the family, and in particular for the taxa studied, have only varying degrees of similarity to these findings. The early treatments of Koch (1825) and De Candolle (1829, 1830) divided the few known genera of the time among three tribes: Tordylineae, Selineae (Peucedaneae of DC.) and Angeliceae mainly on the basis of the seed and mature fruit. Bentham (1867) in Bentham and Hooker included *Cymopterus* in his sixth subtribe Selineae of his large tribe Seselineae, while *Angelica* and *Levisticum* fell within the seventh subtribe Angeliceae. The remaining genera are within his large tribe Peucedaneae. A later treatment by Calestani (1905) is most similar to Bentham's treatment, aside from changes in rank of the taxa involved.

Drude's treatment (1897–98) is similar to that of Koch and De Candolle with a change from tribe to subtribe for the taxa they recognized. Genera such as *Heracleum* and *Zozimia*, however, were moved to the Tordyliinae from their position in the Selineae of Koch (Peucedaneae of DC.). A more recent, very unusual, and distinctly different treatment was proposed by Koso-Poljansky in 1916. Genera generally treated as part of Drude's subtribe Tordyliinae (*Heracleum, Zozimia, Tordylium*) were united with *Pastinaca*, *Dorema* and *Ferula*, and treated as part of a distinct tribe Pastinaceae, derived from 'Proto-Ligusticeae' ancestors related to members of his subfamily Hydrocotyloideae. One genus, *Symphyoloma* C. A. Mey. of Drude's Ferulinae, was in fact placed in the tribe Azorellae of the Hydrocotyloideae. A recent investigation by Tamamschian (1950) has shown the uniqueness of this genus, which accounts for the widely divergent views of its relationships. Other genera usually recognized in the Peucedaneae were widely scattered among the many tribes he recognized. Although considerable doubt can be shed on some of his supposed relationships, one should not disregard it completely. As has been shown through the anatomical and developmental studies described above, there is strong evidence for believing the Peucedaneae to be an 'unnatural' group.

A more recent reclassification of the family has been proposed by Cerceau-Larrival (1962) based primarily on cotyledon and pollen characteristics in combination with those of fruit, inflorescence and leaves. Numerous tribes have been recognized with Peucedanoid genera falling within the Heracleae, Angeliceae, Peucedaneae, Pastinaceae and Tordylineae. The last mentioned has since been divided into two tribes on the basis of further pollen studies (Cerceau-Larrival, 1963).

When one attempts to relate these systems of classification to the anatomical and developmental investigation described above, one is initially struck by the varied similarities and differences which appear. This is especially true with regard to the degree of union of adjacent developing mericarps at the commissure, and its similarity to genera scattered within Drude's tribes Ammineae (Apieae), Smyrnieae and Coriandreae. The only real differences between Peucedaneae and these tribes centres around the dorsal flattening and wing formation. *Angelica*, *Scandia*, *Gingidium* (Dawson, 1967), *Xanthogalum* Ave-Lallem. (Pimenov, 1967), *Pteryxia*, *Cymopterus*, *Pseudocymopterus*, *Glehnia* and *Conioselinum* are all characterized by such a narrow union and the development of lateral ribs into wings as distinct units. These wings enlarge separately even in those few instances where taxa exhibit a union greater than two-thirds of the commissure (a few *Angelica*, *Glehnia*). *Conioselinum*, although in many ways superficially similar to *Angelica*, exhibits a distinctly different type wing formation, and future examination of taxa within the Ammineae (Apieae) may point to relationships. Much the same is true for *Glehnia* and its formation of extra bundles, although this may be a secondary adaptation to its rather specialized habitat and mode of dispersal.

Dawson (1961, 1967a, b) has clearly shown the value of determining relationships on the basis of a series of vegetative and reproductive features, rather than ones of just fruit morphology. His studies have dealt with two peucedanoid genera, *Scandia* and *Gingidium*, as well as several closely related members of the Ammineae (Apieae), *Lignocarpa* Dawson, *Anisotome* Hook. f., *Aciphylla* J. R. & G. Forst. and Australian *Seseli* L. Earlier confusion in these taxa centred around their initial referral to European genera on the basis of superficial similarity in their mature fruit. Of particular interest is Dawson's placement of two taxa in *Gingidium* which do not develop wings, but which are otherwise similar. These two species were earlier referred to *Ligusticum* (Drude's tribe Ammineae), while the winged species had been referred to both *Ligusticum* and *Angelica* at one time or another. This is an excellent example of the difficulties to be found in trying to place taxa into genera primarily on the basis of mature fruit.

Another example can be found in *Prionosciadium* and *Rhodosciadium* which are definitely out of place in the Angelicinae on the basis of anatomy and development. The broad union across the commissure, the presence of accessory bundles, and the invagination of the pericarp into the seed are distinctive and may point to a possible origin from taxa within the Smyrnieae or Ammineae (Apieae).

Work which is at present concentrating on Drude's Ferulineae (Peucedaninae) already points to distinct differences within the subtribe and between it and the others recognized by Drude. *Lomatium* and *Peucedanum* have both been shown to be quite different from *Angelica*, and the other genera discussed above. It is only a matter of time before it might be possible to better understand *Peucedanum* on the basis of such developmental studies. A survey of the literature indicates that *Ferula* and *Ferulago* are also probably different from *Lomatium* and *Peucedanum*, and more closely allied to *Heracleum* and *Pastinaca*.

In the Tordyliinae there are apparently a greater number of consistencies than in any of the other subtribes described by Drude. This is in part due to its small size and in part due to the combination of characters of flower and fruit that the group have in common. *Heracleum*, *Zozimia* and *Malabaila* are all apparently similar in anatomy and development. *Pastinaca* (tribe Ferulineae) also belongs in this group. *Tordylium* (*sensu lato*) may represent a specialized type derived from one of the former. The latter contains more highly evolved taxa adapted to drier habitats in the Mediterranean and Near East.

With time, close examination of the Ammineae (Apieae) or Smyrnieae may reveal genera or species which exhibit a woody 'endocarp' and broad commissural union like that of *Heracleum* and *Tordylium*. It is not far then to an enlargement of the seed cavity laterally to form the characteristic shape of the Tordyliineae. *Lignocarpa* (Dawson, 1967*b*) is a member of the Ammineae with such woody endocarp, but, unfortunately, it has a narrow union across the commissure. Further studies of peucedanoid taxa may even reveal genera with a narrow union and a woody endocarp. These would then form another distinct group and would not be far removed from *Lignocarpa*. What about derivation of members of the Tordyliinae from Hydrocotyloid-like ancestors as suggested by Koso-Poljansky (1916)? Far-fetched, yes, but not to be over-looked.

No attempt has been made throughout this discussion to propose any new systems of classification, although it is apparent such should be the case. In the Apioideae there is need for more studies like those of Baumann, 1946, 1955; Bell & Constance, 1957, 1960; Crowden *et al.*, 1969; Dawson, 1967*a*, *b*; Harborne, 1967*a*, *b*, 1969; Hedge & Lamond, 1964; Heywood, 1968; Kapoor & Kaul, 1967; Leute, 1969; McNeill *et al.*, 1969; Rodríguez, 1957; Wellendorf, 1966; and Zoz & Prokopenko, 1968, which are helping to clarify problems in the subfamily. The present investigations of floral and fruit anatomy and development point to many independent derivations of peucedanoid taxa from ancestors similar to members of the Ammineae (Apieae), Smyrnieae, or other taxa which are characterized by a narrow to broad union across the commissure. It is quite easy to picture the evolution of dorsal flattening and wing formation as a dispersal mechanism in many independent lines from these less specialized types. It is the author's hope to extend the present studies into a survey of other tribes of the family, such as the Ammineae and Smyrnieae. It is likely that anatomical features in genera of these groups will correspond to the peucedanoid genera studies (i.e. presence of a woody 'endocarp'). During and after the accumulation of this information, an attempt will be made to relate these findings to those of cytology, chemistry, floral biology, and vegetative and reproductive morphology with the aim of bringing these taxa into a clearer perspective. Until this time, however, it would be futile to project a new system of classification. It is apparent that the Peucedaneae is an 'unnatural' group, but it is still unapparent exactly where new lines should be drawn.

ACKNOWLEDGEMENTS

The author would like to thank the National Science Foundation for a grant (BO13316) which has enabled this study to continue, Occidental College for the use of facilities, and Dr Charles R. Metcalfe, former Keeper of the Jodrell Laboratory, Royal Botanic Gardens, Kew, for the use of his facilities when this project was initiated several years ago under a National Science Foundation Postdoctoral Fellowship. Thanks are also due Dr Reed C. Rollins, Gray Herbarium, Harvard University for use of his facilities during an Evolutionary Biology Post-doctoral Fellowship, between the initiation of the project at the Jodrell Laboratory, and its present continuance at Occidental College. I am particularly indebted to Dr Mildred E. Mathias and Dr Lincoln Constance for their valuable criticisms throughout this project; Miss Mary Gregory for her invaluable accumulation of reference material at the Jodrell; Miss Mary Grierson for the preparation of most of the figures, and Mr T. Harwood for assistance in the preparation of the photo-micrographs.

Through the years I have become particularly indebted to the group of under-graduate and graduate students who helped make this study such a pleasure. They include Miss Vina Hsu, Miss Yu-hwa Lai, Mr and Mrs T. Herat, Mr Frank Percival, and especially Miss Sada Okumura and Mr Joseph Krahulik, who made the preparation of the final manuscript possible.

REFERENCES

BARTSCH, E., 1882. *Beiträge zur Anatomie und Entwicklung der Umbelliferen-Früchte*. I. Theil. *Von der Blüthe bis zur Fruchtreife*, 42 pp. Breslau: Diss.

BAUMANN, M. G., 1946. *Myodocarpus* und die Phylogenie der Umbelliferen-Fruchte. *Ber. schweiz bot. Ges.*, **56**: 13–112.

BAUMANN-BODENHEIM, M. G., 1955. Ableitung und Bau bicarpellatmonospermer und pseudomono-carpellater Araliaceen und Umbelliferen-Früchte. *Ber. schweiz. bot. Ges.*, **65**: 481–510.

BELL, C. R. & CONSTANCE, L., 1957. Chromosome numbers in Umbelliferae. *Am. J. Bot.*, **44**: 565–572.

BELL, C. R. & CONSTANCE, L., 1960. Chromosome numbers in Umbelliferae. II. *Am. J. Bot.*, **47**: 24–32.

BENTHAM, G., 1867. Umbelliferae. In Bentham, G. and Hooker, J. D., *Genera Plantarum*, **1**: 859–931, 1008–1009.

BORTHWICK, H. A., PHILLIPS, M. & ROBBINS, W. W., 1931. Floral development in *Daucus carota*. *Am. J. Bot.*, **18**: 784–796.

BOUNAGA, D., 1964. Anatomie du genre *Eryngium* en Afrique du Nord. *Bull. Soc. Hist. nat. Afr. N.* **54**: 7–80.

BOUNAGA, D., 1967. Essai de détermination du mode de ramification anatomique chez *Eryngium tricuspidatum* L. et quelques ombellifères. *Bull. Soc. Hist. nat. Afr. N.*, **58**: 101–132.

BRADLEY, J. M. & FELL, K. R., 1966. The anatomy of the fruit of *Heracleum sphondylium* L. *Planta med.*, **14**: 10–18.

BRIQUET, J., 1923. Carpologie comparée de l'*Archangelica officinalis* Hoffm. et du *Peucedanum palustre* (L.) Moench. *Candollea*, **1**: 501–520.

BRIQUET, J., 1924. L'anatomie du fruit et le comportement des bandelettes dans le genre *Heracleum*. *Candollea*, **2**: 1–62.

BURTT, B. L. & DAVIS, P. H., 1949. *Glaucosciadium*: A new Mediterranean genus of Umbelliferae. *Kew Bull.*, **2**: 225–230.

CALESTANI, V., 1905. Contributo alla sistematica delle ombrellifere d'Europa. *Webbia*, **1**: 89–280.

CARLQUIST, S., 1969. Towards acceptable evolutionary interpretations of floral anatomy. *Phytomorphology*, **19**: 332–362.

CERCEAU-LARRIVAL, M.-T., 1962. Plantules et pollens d'ombellifères. *Mém. Mus. natn. Hist. nat., Paris* sér. B, **14**: 1–166.

CERCEAU-LARRIVAL, M.-T., 1963. Le pollen d'ombellifères Méditerranéennes. II. Tordylinae Drude. *Pollen Spores*, **5**: 297–323.

COULTER, J. M. & ROSE, J. N., 1900. Monograph of the North American Umbelliferae. *Contr. U.S. natn. Herb.*, **7**: 1–256.

COURCHET, L., 1882. *Les ombellifères en général et les espèces usitées en pharmacie en particulier.* 221 pp. Montpellier.

COURCHET, L., 1884. Etude anatomique sur les ombellifères et sur les principales anomalies de structure que présentent leurs organes végétatifs. *Annls Sci. nat., sér. 6*, **17**: 107–129.

CRANTZ, H. I. N., 1767. *Classis Umbelliferarum.* 126 pp. Leipzig: I. P. Kraus.

CROWDEN, R. K., HARBORNE, J. B. & HEYWOOD, V. H., 1969. Chemosystematics of the Umbelliferae— a general survey. *Phytochemistry*, **8**: 1963–1984.

DAWSON, J. W., 1961. A revision of the genus *Anisotome* (Umbelliferae). *Univ. Calif. Publs Bot.*, **33**: 1–98.

DAWSON, J. W., 1967a. New Zealand Umbelliferae *Lignocarpa* Gen. Nov. and *Scandia* Gen. Nov. *N.Z. Jl. Bot.*, **5**: 400–417.

DAWSON, J. W., 1967b. The New Zealand species of *Gingidium* (Umbelliferae). *N.Z. Jl. Bot.*, **5**: 84–116.

DE CANDOLLE, A. P., 1829. *Mémoire sur la Famille des Ombellifères.* Paris: Treuttel & Würz.

DE CANDOLLE, A. P., 1830. Umbelliferae. *Prodromus systematis naturalis regni vegetabilis*, **4**: 55–250, 667–670. Paris.

DENISOVA, G. A., 1961. The development of the fruit of *Archangelica decurrens* Ldb. *Bot. Zh. SSSR*, **46**: 1756–1765. [In Russian]

DEUTSCHMANN, F., 1969. Anatomische Studien über die Exkretgänge in Umbelliferenwurzeln. *Beitr. Biol. Pfl.*, **45**: 409–440.

DRUDE, C. G. O. 1897–1898. Umbelliferae. In Engler & Prantl, *Die natürlichen Pflanzenfamilien*, **3** (8): 63–128, 129–250.

ESAU, K., 1936. Ontogeny and structure of collenchyma and of vascular tissue in celery petioles. *Hilgardia*, **10**: 431–476.

ESAU, K., 1940. Developmental anatomy of the fleshy storage organ of *Daucus carota*. *Hilgardia*, **13**: 175–209.

ESPINOSA, R., 1932. Ökologische Studien über Kordillerenpflanzen (morphologisch und anatomisch dargestellt). *Bot. Jb.*, **65**: 120–211.

EYDE, R. H. & TSENG, C. C., 1969. Flower of *Tetraplasandra gymnocarpa*: hypogyny with epigynous ancestry. *Science, N.Y.* **166**: 506–508.

FAHMY, I. R., SABER, A. H. & KADIR, E. A. E., 1958. A pharmacognostical study of the fruit of *Pastinaca sativa* L. cultivated in Egypt. *J. Pharm. Pharmac.*, **8**: 653–660.

GÉNEAU DE LAMARLIÈRE, L., 1893. *Recherches morphologiques sur la famille des ombellifères.* 200 pp. Lille: Thèse.

GUYOT, M., 1966. Les stomates des ombellifères. *Bull. Soc. bot. Fr.*, **113**: 244–273.

HACCIUS, B. & REH, K., 1956. Morphologische und anatomische Untersuchungen an Umbelliferen-Keimpflanzen. *Beitr. Biol. Pfl.*, **32**: 185–218.

HÅKANSSON, A., 1923. Studien über die Entwicklungsgeschichte der Umbelliferen. *Acta Univ. lund.*, **18**: 1–120.

HARBORNE, J. B., 1967a. Comparative biochemistry of flavonoids. Luteolin 5-glucoside and its occurrence in the Umbelliferae. *Phytochemistry*, **6**: 1569–1573.

HARBORNE, J. B., 1967b. Flavonoids of the Umbelliferae. In Harborne, J. B. (ed.) *Comparative Biochemistry of the Flavonoids*, pp. 180–183. New York: Academic Press.

HARBORNE, J. B., HEYWOOD, V. H. & WILLIAMS, C. A., 1969. Distribution of myristicin in seeds of the Umbelliferae. *Phytochemistry*, **8**: 1729–1732.

HEDGE, I. C. & LAMOND, J. M., 1964. A guide to the Turkish genera of Umbelliferae. *Notes R. bot. Gdn Edinb.*, **25**: 171–177.

HEYWOOD, V. H., 1968. Scanning electron microscopy and microcharacters in the fruits of the Umbelliferae-Caucalideae. *Proc. Linn. Soc. Lond.*, **179**: 287–289.

HIROE, M. & CONSTANCE, L., 1958. Umbelliferae of Japan. *Univ. Calif. Publs Bot.*, **30**: 1–144.

HOAR, C. S., 1915. A comparison of the stem anatomy of the cohort umbelliflorae. *Ann. Bot.*, **29**: 55–63.

HOFFMANN, G. F., 1816. *Genera Plantarum Umbelliferarum.* 2nd ed., 222 pp. Moscow.

HSU, V. W., 1970. *Comparative anatomical studies of floral and fruit development in* Angelica *and related genera (Umbelliferae).* Thesis, Occidental College, Los Angeles, California 55 pp.

JACKSON, G., 1933. A study of the carpophore of the Umbelliferae. *Am. J. Bot.*, **20**: 121–144.

KAPOOR, L. D. & KAUL, B. K., 1967. Studies on the vittae (oil canals) of some important medicinal umbelliferous fruits. I. *Proc. natn. Inst. Sci. India B*, **33**: 1–26.

KOCH, G. D. J., 1825. Generum tribuumque plantarum umbelliferarum nova dispositio. *Nova Acta Acad. Caesar. Leop. Carol.*, **12**: 55–156.

KOROVIN, E. P., 1947. *Generis Ferula (Tourn.) L.—Monographia Illustrata.* 91 pp. Tashkent.

KOSO-POLJANSKY, B. M., 1916. Sciadophytorum systematis lineamenta. II. *Byull. mosk. Obshch. Ispyt. Prir.*, **29**: 93–222.

LAI, Y. H., 1971. *Comparative anatomical studies of floral and fruit development in* Heracleum *and related genera (Umbelliferae).* Thesis, Occidental College, Los Angeles, California.

LEMESLE, R., 1926. Contribution à l'étude structurale des ombellifères xérophiles. *Annls Sci. nat.*, sér. 10, **8**: 1–138.

LEUTE, G.-H., 1969. Untersuchungen über den Verwandtschaftskreis der Gattung. *Ligusticum* L. (Umbelliferae) I. *Annln naturl. Mus. Wien*, **73**: 55–98.

LIEHR, E., 1927. Entwicklungsgeschichtfiche und experimentelle Untersuchungen über die rudimentären Fruchtknoten einiger Umbelliferen. *Mitt. Inst. allg. Bot., Hamb.*, **6**: 361–418.

LIERMANN, K., 1926. *Berträge zur vergleichenden Anatomie der Wurzeln einiger pharmazeutisch verwendeter Umbelliferen.* 98 pp. Basel: Diss.

McNEILL, J., PARKER, P. F. & HEYWOOD, V. H., 1969. A taximetric approach to the classification of the spiny-fruited members (tribe Caucalideae) of the flowering-plant family Umbelliferae. In Cole, A. J. (ed.), *Numerical Taxonomy.* pp. 129–145. London & New York: Academic Press.

MAJUMDAR, G. P., 1942. The organization of the shoot in *Heracleum* in the light of development. *Ann. Bot.*, **6**: 49–81.

MAJUMDAR, G. P. & DATTA, A., 1946. Developmental studies. I. Origin and development of axillary buds with special reference to two dicotyledons. *Proc. Indian Acad. Sci. B*, **23**: 249–259.

MAJUMDAR, G. P., 1947. Growth unit or the phyton in dicotyledons with special reference to *Heracleum. Bull. bot. Soc. Beng.*, **1**: 61–66.

MAJUMDAR, G. P., 1948. Leaf development at the growing apex and phyllotaxis in *Heracleum. Proc. Indian Acad. Sci.*, **28**: 83–98.

MATHIAS, M. E., 1930. Studies in the Umbelliferae. III. A monograph of *Cymopterus* including a critical study of related genera. *Ann. Mo. bot. Gdn*, **17**: 213–476.

MATHIAS, M. & CONSTANCE, L., 1944–1945. Umbelliferae. *N. Am. Flora*, **28b**: 43–295.

MATHIAS, M. E., CONSTANCE, L. & THEOBALD, W., 1969. Two new species of Umbelliferae from the Southwestern United States. *Madroño*, **20**: 214–219.

METCALFE, C. R. & CHALK, L., 1950. *Anatomy of the Dicotyledons.* 2 vols. Oxford: Clarendon Press.

MITTAL, S. P., 1961. Studies in the Umbellales. II. The vegetative anatomy. *J. Indian bot. Soc.*, **40**: 424–443.

MORISON, R., 1672. *Plantarum umbelliferarum distributio nova, per tabulas cognationis et affinitatis ex libro naturae observata et detecta.* Oxford.

MOYNIER DE VILLEPOIX, R., 1878. Recherches sur les canaux secreteurs du fruit des ombellifères. *Annls Sci. nat.*, sér. 6, **5**: 348–365.

PANELATTI, J., 1959. Contribution à l'étude anatomique du genre *Bupleurum* L. au Maroc. *Trav. Inst. scient. chérif.*, **15**, 97 pp.

PERVUKHINA, N. V., 1950. On the phylogenetic significance of some minor structural characters of the fruit of Umbelliferae. *Trudy bot. Inst. Akad. Nauk SSSR*, ser. 7, **1**: 82–120. [In Russian]

PIMENOV, M. G., 1967. A new species of the genus *Angelica* L. from the Transcaucasus. *Byull. mosk. Obshch. Ispyt. Prir.*, **72**: 48–52. [In Russian]

RODRÍGUEZ, R. L., 1957a. Systematic anatomical studies on *Myrrhidendron* and other woody Umbellales. *Univ. Calif. Publs Bot.*, **29**: 145–318.

RODRÍGUEZ, R. L., 1957b. Anotaciones a la anatomía comparada de las umbelíferas. *Revta Biol. trop.*, **5**: 157–171.

SANDINA, I. B., 1957. The significance of the carpological characters for the taxonomy of the genus *Heracleum* L. *Bot. Zh. SSSR*, **42**: 535–555. [In Russian]

SCHISCHKIN, B. K. (ed.), 1951. *Flora SSSR*, **17**: 1–314, 351–359.

SPRENGEL, K. P. J., 1813. *Plantarum Umbelliferarum denuo disponendarum prodromus*. 42 pp. Halle.

SPRENGEL, K., 1818. *Species Umbelliferarum minus cognitae illustratae*. 154 pp. Halle.

STEWARD, F. C., MAPES, M. O., KENT, A. E. & HOLSTEN, R. D., 1964. Growth and development of cultured plant cells. *Science, N.Y.*, **143**: 20–27.

STEWARD, F. C., 1968. *Growth and Organization in Plants*. 564 pp. Reading, Mass.: Addison-Wesley Publishing Co.

STEWARD, F. C., 1970. Totipotency, variation and clonal development of cultured cells. *Endeavour*, **29**: 117–124.

STYGER, J., 1919. *Beiträge zur Anatomie der Umbelliferenfrüchte*. 66 pp. Zürich: Diss.

TAMAMSCHIAN, S. G., 1950. The taxonomy of the genus *Symphyoloma* C.A.M. (Umbelliferae). *Bot. Zh. SSSR*, **35**: 335–342. [In Russian]

TCHÉOU, W. Y. K., 1930. Contribution à l'étude anatomique du fruit des ombellifères tribe des amminees. *Trav. Lab. Matière méd., Paris*, **21**: 88 pp.

TERNETZ, C., 1902. Morphologie und Anatomie der *Azorella selago* Hook. fil. *Bot. Ztg*, **60**: 1–16.

THEOBALD, W., 1967a. Anatomy and systematic position of *Uldinia* (Umbelliferae). *Brittonia*, **19**: 165–173.

THEOBALD, W., 1967b. Comparative morphology and anatomy of *Chlaenosciadium* (Umbelliferae). *J. Linn. Soc.*, **60**: 75–84.

THEOBALD, W., 1967c. Venation pattern and fruit development in *Lomatium dasycarpum* (Umbelliferae). *Ann. Bot.*, **31**: 255–262.

THEOBALD, W., 1972. Comparative anatomical studies in the Hydrocotyleae (Umbelliferae). *Bot. J. Linn. Soc.* (in preparation).

TIKHOMIROV, V. N. & GALAKHOVA, O. N., 1965. A contribution to the morphology of the Angelicinae. I. The investigation of the fruit of *Angelica sylvestris* L. as a lectotype of the genus *Angelica* L. *Byull. mosk. Obshch. Ispyt. Prir.*, **70**: 111–118. [In Russian]

TIKHOMIROV, V. N. & TRETYAKOVA, O. N., 1967. A contribution to the morphology of Angelicinae. II. Comparative anatomy of the fruit of the species belonging to the subgenus *Angelica* of the genus *Angelica* L. *Byull. mosk. Obshch. Ispyt. Prir.*, **72**: 43–54. [In Russian]

TOWNSEND, C. C., 1966. Notes on the Umbelliferae of Iraq: III. *Kew Bull.*, **20**: 77–85.

TSENG, C. C., 1967. Anatomical studies of flower and fruit in the Hydrocotyloideae (Umbelliferae). *Univ. Calif. Publs Bot.*, **42**: 1–58.

VEUILLET, J.-M., 1959. Contribution à l'étude morphologique et anatomique du genre *Elaeoselinum* au Maroc. *Trav. Inst. scient. chérif.*, **18**: 63 pp.

WELLENDORF, M., 1966. Umbelliferous starches. *Dansk Tidsskr. Farm.*, **40**: 164–169.

ZOZ, I. G. & PROKOPENKO, A. P., 1968. Chimiotaxinomie de quelques espèces du genre *Angelica* L. et des genres voisins *Ostericum*, Hoffm., *Archangelica* Hoffm., *Coelopleurum*, Ledeb. *Rastit. Resursy, SSSR*, **4**: 478–485. [In Russian]

EXPLANATION OF PLATE

PLATE 1

Mature fruit structures in peucedanoid genera. A, *Pteryxia terebinthina* C. & R., Median transection of basal portion of lateral wing (× 40). B, *Pastinaca sativa* L., median transection of two mature mericarps splitting along the commissure (× 35). [Details: *e*, 'endocarp'; *lr*, lateral rib bundle; *s*, seed.]

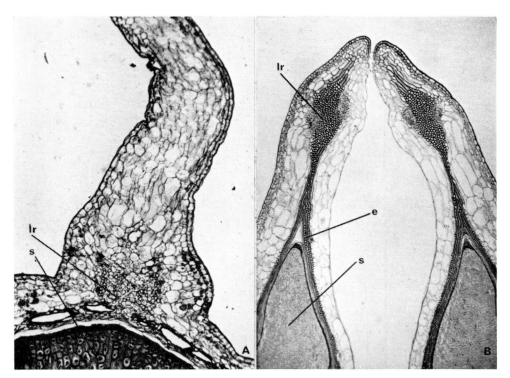

PLATE 1

Phylogenetic and systematic value of stomata of the Umbelliferae

M. GUYOT

Laboratoire de Biologie cellulaire, Faculté des Sciences, Dijon, France

L'étude des épidermes de plus de 150 espèces d'Ombellifères a permis de reconnaître plusieurs types stomatiques entre lesquels ont été établies des relations phylogéniques. L'utilisation de ces types stomatiques permet de distinguer des épidermes à caractères stomatiques primitifs, à caractères stomatiques évolués et à caractères stomatiques intermédiaires.

La répartition de ces caractères épidermiques dans la famille des Ombellifères permet d'accorder au type stomatique une valeur systématique et phylogénique comparable à celle du type pollinique.

La présence simultanée de plusieurs types de stomates sur l'épiderme d'une même feuille est discutée en termes d'influences qui s'exercent au niveau de la cellule méristématique.

The study of the epidermises of more than 150 species of Umbelliferae has made it possible to determine several stomatal types between which phylogenetic relationships have been established.

On the basis of these stomatal types epidermises with primitive, evolved or intermediary stomatal characters can be distinguished.

The distribution of these epidermal characters in the family of Umbelliferae makes it possible to attribute to the stomatal type a systematic and phylogenetic value comparable to that shown by the pollen-type.

The simultaneous presence of several types of stomata on a single leaf is discussed in terms of the influences exerted on the meristemoid cell.

CONTENTS

INTRODUCTION

We have recently resumed the study of the stomata of the Umbelliferae (Guyot, 1965–66) that we began a few years ago; this study had led us to attribute to the stomatal type a systematic and phylogenetic value comparable with that which Cerceau-Larrival (1962) had recognized in the case of pollen.

It is not our purpose here to recount the history of all the attempts to use stomata for taxonomic or phylogenetic purposes which have been made since the works of Vesque (1889); nor will we consider the numerous criticisms to which they have been subjected after Tognini's (1897) observations of several types of stomata on a single plant. The essential references have been given in a previous publication (Guyot, 1966).

It is sufficient to recall the fact that the study of mature stomata, as well as that of their development, has made it possible to establish phylogenetic relationships between the different stomatal types; these relationships are based either upon the existence of stomata with intermediary characters or on the simultaneous presence of several types of stomata on the same plant.

The main relationships are summed up in the following table (Table 1).

Table 1. Phylogenetic relationships between the various types of stomata found in the Umbelliferae

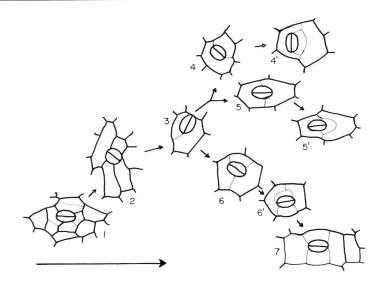

The different types of stomata are drawn diagrammatically:

     1: perigenous anomocytic stoma;
     2: meso-perigenous anomocytic stoma;
     3: meso-perigenous anisocytic stoma;
4, 4′: bicytic paracytic stomata;
5, 5′: bicytic diacytic stomata;
     6: mesogenous anisocytic stoma;
    6′: tetracytic stoma linked up to anisocytic type;
     7: tetracytic stoma.

The arrows indicate the direction of evolution.

DEFINITIONS AND METHODS

In the above system the distinction between these different stomatal types is based both upon the aspect of the mature stomatal apparatus and upon its way of formation. The latter did appear at first necessary to distinguish the types of stomata, but after the study of a great number of epidermises of various ages, we have been able to notice that the simple observation of the mature epidermis (the only possible method or at least the easiest one with plants kept in the herbarium or in alcohol) enables us to distinguish a certain number of epidermal types:

(a) Epidermises whose stomata belong to a rather pure and well-known type. These can be anomocytic without any recognizable companion cell (1) or with a companion cell (2); they may be bicytic paracytic (4), or diacytic (5); they can also be anisocytic (6), or tetracytic (7).

(b) Epidermises where stomata belonging to both types anomocytic and anisocytic and occasionally bicytic can be observed. Here we have epidermises in which the development of the stomata is partly accomplished according to the anisocytic mesoperigenous type, which is why we have chosen it as type (3).

The observations have been made on epidermal peels stripped from fresh leaves or from leaves preserved in alcohol or from herbarium specimens.* Drawings and photographs have been made†, and for most species we have observed the different developmental types.

RESULTS

Distribution of the different types of epidermis in the species studied

Each species has been given a number corresponding to the described type; local variations which may modify the main appearance of the epidermis are noted between brackets.

Actinotus helianthi Labill.	3	
Aegopodium podagraria L.	4	(5)
Aethusa cynapium L.	3	
Ainsworthia trachycarpa Boiss.	5	
Ammi majus L.	3	(5)
A. visnaga (L.) Lam.	3	(5)
Anethum graveolens L.	5	
Angelica silvestris L.	3	
Anthriscus cerefolium (L.) Hoffm.	3	(5)
A. sylvestris (L.) Hoffm.	3	(5)
Apium graveolens L.	3	(5)
A. leptophyllum (Pers.) F. Muell.	3	(5)
Archangelica officinalis Hoffm.	3	
Astrantia major L.	3	(6)
Astydamia canariensis DC.	6	
Azorella trifurcata Hook.	1	
Athamanta cretensis L.	3	(6)
Berula angustifolia Koch	3	(6)
B. erecta (Hudson) Coville	3	(6)

* We are grateful to Mme Cerceau-Larrival (Laboratory of Palynology, Muséum d'Histoire Naturelle, Paris) who gave us many seedlings from her own collection.

† The photographs have been made with a Reichert microscope, type Zetopan, obtained with the aid of the C.N.R.S.

Bifora dicocca Hoffm.		3	
Bowlesia incana Ruiz & Pavón		3	
Bunium incrassatum (Boiss.) Amo		3	(6)
Bupleurum junceum L.		6	
B. ranunculoides L.		6	
B. spinosum Gouan		6	
Cachrys trifida Miller		3	(6)
Capnophyllum dichotomum Lag.		3	(5)
Carum carvi L.		3	
Chaerophyllum aureum L.		3	(5)
C. bulbosum L.		3	(5)
Chamaesciadium flavescens C. A. May.		3	(5)
Cicuta virosa L.	(2)	3	
Cnidium silaifolium (Jacq.) Simonkai		6	
C. dubium (Schkur) Thell.	(3)	4, 5	
Conium maculatum L.		3	(6)
Conopodium bourgaei Coss.	(2)	3	
C. majus (Gouan) Loret	(2)	3	
C. thalictrifolium (Boiss) Calestani	(2)	3	
Coriandrum sativum L.	(3)	6	
Crithmum maritimum L.		6	
Cryptotaenia canadensis DC.		3	(5)
Daucus carota L.		5	
D. maritimus Lam.		5	
Dethawia tenuifolia (Ramond ex DC.) Godron		3	(6)
Dorema aucheri Boiss.		6	(4)
Echinophora spinosa L.		6	(4, 5)
E. tenuifolia L.		6	(4, 5)
Elaeoselinum tenuifolium (Lag.) Lge.		3	(6)
Eleutherospermum grandifolium Koch		3	(5)
Endressia pyrenaica (Gay ex DC.) Gay		6	
Eryngium alpinum L.	(3)	6	
E. amethystinum L.		6	(7)
E. virginianum Lam.		7	
E. barelieri Boiss.		6	
E. billardieri Delar. var. *nigromontanum* Boiss. & Buhse		6	
E. bourgatii Gouan		6	(7)
E. bromeliaefolium Delar.		7	
E. campestre L.		6	(7)
E. caeruleum Bieb.		6	
E. corniculatum Lam.	(3)	6	(7)
E. ebracteatum Lam.		7	
E. elegans Cham.		7	
E. foetidum L.		6	
E. giganteum Bieb.		6	

E. horridum Malme.		7	
E. maroccanum Pitard		6	
E. nasturtiifolium Juss.	3	(6)	
E. oliverianum Delar.		6	
E. palmatum Panč. & Vis.		6	
E. pandanifolium Cham. & Schlecht.		7	
E. paniculatum Cav.		7	
E. planum L.		6	
E. proteaeflorum Delar.		7	
E. rauhianum Mathias & Constance		7	
E. sanguisorba Cham.		7	
E. serbicum Panč.		6	
E. serra Cham.		7	
E. spinalba Vill.		6	
E. tenue Lam.	3	(6)	
E. variifolium Coss.		6	
E. vesiculosum Labill.		6	
E. yuccaefolium Michx		7	
Falcaria vulgaris Bernh.		5	
Ferula glauca L.	(3)	6	
Ferulago galbanifera Koch.		6	
F. campestris (Besser) Grec.		6	
Foeniculum dulce Mill.	(3)	5	
Furnrohria setifolia C. Koch		3	(5)
Grammosciadum pterocarpum Boiss.		3	(5)
Helosciadium nodiflorum Koch		3	
Heracleum sphondylium L.		2	
H. mantegazzianum Som. & Lev.		2	
Hermas capitata L.	(3)	6	
Heteromorpha arborescens Cham. & Schlecht.		2	
Hippomarathrum crispum (Pers.) Koch		3	(6)
H. libanotis Koch		3	(6)
Hydrocotyle javanica Thunb.	(3)	4	
Hydrocotyle vulgaris L.		4	
Kundmannia sicula (L.) DC.		5	
Lagoecia cuminoides L.	4	5	
Laserpitium gallicum L.	3	(4, 6)	
L. latifolium L.	3	(4, 6)	
L. siler L.	(3)	4	
Levisticum officinale Koch	3		
Libanotis montana All.	(3)	6	
L. transcaucasica Schischk.	(3)	6	
Ligusticum huteri Porta & Rigo	3		
L. lucidum Mill.	3		
L. scoticum L.	3		

Magydaris panacifolia (Vahl) Lange		3	
M. pastinaca (Lam.) Paol.		3	(6)
Margotia gummifera (Desf.) Lange		(3)	6
Meum athamanticum Jacq.		3	(6)
M. mutellina Gaertn.		3	(6)
Molopospermum peleponnesiacum (L.) Koch		3	(6)
Myrrhis odorata (L.) Scop.		3	
Myrrhoides nodosa (L.) Cannon		3	(5)
Oenanthe fistulosa L.		6	
O. lachenalii C.C. Gmel.		6	
O. pimpinelloides L.		6	
Opopanax chironium (L.) Koch		(3)	6
O. hispidus (Friv.) Griseb.		(3)	6
Orlaya grandiflora (L.) Hoffm.		5	
Pastinaca sativa L.		3	
Petroselinum crispum (Mill.) A. W. Hill		3	(5)
Peucedanum verticillare (L.) Koch ex DC.		3, 4	
P. austriacum (Jacq.) Koch		3	
P. cervaria (Lap.) Lap.		3	(6)
P. officinale L.		3, 4	
P. oreoselinum (L.) Moench		3	
P. ostruthium (L.) Koch		3	(6)
P. venetum (Spengel) Koch		3, 4	
Physospermum acteaefolium Presl		3	(6)
P. cornubiense (L.) DC.		3	(6)
Pimpinella calicina Maxim.		(3)	5
P. major (L.) Huds.		(3)	5
Pleurospermum austriacum (L.) Hoffm.		3	(4, 6)
Pozoa coriacea Lag.		6	
Ptychotis ammoides Koch (*Ammoides pusilla* (Brot.) Breistr.)		5	
P. saxifraga (L.) Lor. & Barr.		5	
P. timbalii Jord.		5	
Ridolphia segetum Moris		5	
Sanicula europaea L.		6	
Scandix balansae Reut.		5	
Selinum carvifolia (L.) L.		(3, 4)	6
Seseli elatum L.		6	
S. gummiferum Pallas & Sm.		6	
S. libanotis (L.) Koch.		6	
S. montanum L.		6	
Silaum silaus (L.) Schinz & Thell.		6	(5)
Siler trilobum Crantz (*Laser trilobum* (L.) Borkh.)		3	(6)
Sison amomum L.		3	(5)
Sium latifolium L.		(3)	6

S. sisarum L.	(3)	6
Smyrnium olusatrum L.		2 (3)
Stenocoelium divaricatum Turcz.		6
Thapsia villosa L.		2 (3)
Tordylium apulum L.		3 (4, 5)
T. maximum L.		3 (4, 5)
Torilis japonica (Houtt.) DC.		5
T. arvensis (Hudson) Link		5
T. infesta (L.) Hoffm.		5
Trachymene coerulea R. Grah.		6
T. lanceolata Rudge		6
Trinia glauca (L.) Dumort.		6
Trochiscanthes nodiflora (Vill.) Koch		3
Turgenia latifolia (L.) Hoffm.	(3)	5
Xatardia scabra (Lap.) Meissn.		3 (6)
Xanthosia rotundifolia DC.		7
Zizia aurea Koch		6

Distribution of the different epidermal types within the tribes

This was determined by Cerceau-Larrival (1962) from her study of pollen and seedlings.

Series L (long cotyledons)

Bupleureae		6
Hermadideae		6
Endressieae		6
Ammineae		3 (4, 5)
Aegopodium		4 (5)
Ridolphia		5
Scandicineae		3 (5)
Myrrhis		3
Conopodium		2 (3)
Lagoecieae		4, 5
Echinophoreae	(5)	6
Astydamieae	(3, 4)	6
Capnophylleae	3 (5)	3 (6)
Coriandreae		3, 6
Torilineae		5
Caucalideae		5
Thapsieae		2 (3)
Laserpitieae		3 (4, 6)
Dauceae		5
Orlayeae		5

Series R (round cotyledons)

Azorellineae		1	
Hydrocotyleae	(3)	4	
Bowlesiineae		3	
Trachymeneae	(3)	6	
Xanthosieae		7	
Saniculeae	(3)	6	
Eryngieae	(3)	6, 7	
Smyrnieae		2 (3)	
Molopospermeae		2	
Conieae		3 (6)	
Heteromorpheae			
Heteromorpha		2	
Apium,			
Trochiscanthes	3	4, 5	
Cnidium dubium			
Cnidium, Seseli		6	
Oenantheae		6	
Cryptotaenieae	(3)	5	
Pimpinelleae	(3)	5	
Aethuseae		3	
Cachrydeae		3 (6)	
Heracleae		2	
Angeliceae		3	
Peucedaneae		3 (4)	
		3 (6)	
Pastinaceae	3	3 (6)	6
Tordylineae		3	(4, 5)
Turgenieae		5	

CONCLUSIONS

Systematic results

In genera

We notice that in nearly every genus all the species within the genus show more or less the same type of stomata.

The few exceptions are: *Cnidium silaifolium* with stomata entirely anisocytic and *C. dubium* with different types of stomata—anomocytic and anisocytic although mostly diacytic and paracytic; *Eryngium* in which two groups are clearly distinguished: one, European and Asiatic, with type (6) stomata and the other, American, with type (7); certain species have intermediate characters (*E. barelieri, E. corniculatum*).

The genera *Laserpitium* and *Peucedanum* also show differences between species because of their epidermises with stomata having a tendency to be either anisocytic or bicytic.

However, variations which can be observed in bicytic stomata are of little significance; in all the epidermises possessing these, intermediate forms between the paracytic and the diacytic types could be observed. This variation in the direction of the
pore is probably due to the greater or lesser influence of what we have called 'organ
polarity', which no doubt corresponds to the direction of growth of the leaf cells
and which can be disturbed by colchicine (Guyot *et al.*, 1968).

In tribes

As will be seen from the list, only the tribes of the Ammineae, Scandicineae and
of the Heteromorpheae show a greater stomatal heterogeneity than that which can
be observed within a genus.

The tribe Ammineae is rather homogeneous in view of the relationships between
diacytic (5) and paracytic (4) types noted above.

The tribe Scandicineae, composed of genera with diacytic stomata, should not
include the genera *Conopodium* or *Myrrhis* in which such stomata have not been observed.

The tribe Heteromorpheae seems to be worth revising, isolating the genus
Heteromorpha and regrouping the other genera in the Apieae for instance.*

The use of the stomatal characters, based either on the developmental mode or
on the distribution of stomatal types in mature epidermises, allows us to keep—and,
in doing so, to confirm—the classification established on the basis of pollen grain
characters (Cerceau-Larrival, 1962).

Phylogenetic results

If we consider the table summarizing the phylogenetic relationships between the
different types of stomata, we can clearly distinguish:

(a) tribes with primitive† stomatal characters: epidermal types 1, 2, 3:

in series L:	Thapsieae	2 (3)
series R:	Azorellineae	1
	Bowlesiineae	3
	Smyrnieae	2 (3)
	Molopospermeae	2 (3)
	Aethuseae	3
	Heracleae	2
	Angeliceae	3
	Heteromorpha	2

(b) tribes with evolved† stomatal characters: shown in species with stomata mostly
of the same type, either bicytic (4, 5) or anisocytic and tetracytic (6–7):

in series L:	Bupleureae	6
	Endressieae	6

* These modifications in the constitution of the tribes of the Scandicineae and Heteromorpheae
agree with the observations of Mme Cerceau-Larrival (oral communication).

† The terms of primitive and evolved must not be understood in a strict sense; they only indicate a
level of complexity in development reached by stomata and do not mean any direct filiation between
species, or genera or tribes.

	Lagoecieae	(4) 5
	Echinophoreae	6
	Torilineae	5
	Caucalideae	5
	Dauceae	5
	Orlayeae	5
in series R:	Trachymeneae	6
	Xanthosieae	7
	Eryngieae	6, 7
	Oenantheae	6
	Turgenieae	5

Table 2. Hypothetic phylogenetic relationships between the different tribes of Umbelliferae. Series L (long cotyledons); Series R (round cotyledons)

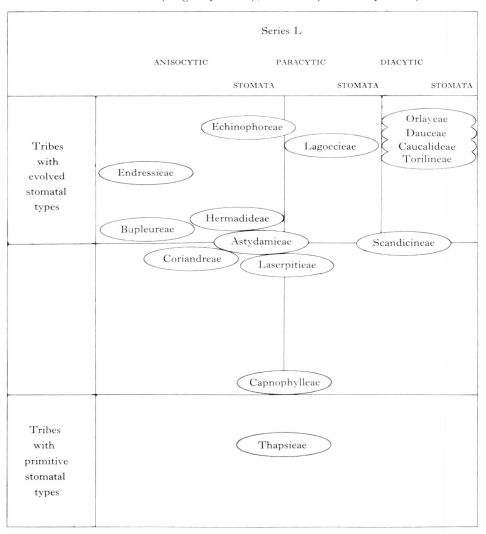

(c) tribes most often comprising species with different types of stomata or stomata of intermediary types.

If we consider, in each of the series L and R, the tendency to produce either bicytic stomata or anisocytic and other types, we may try to represent schematically the hypothetical phylogenetic relationships between the different tribes (Table 2).

It will be seen that in the L series bicytic stomata are the most frequent, whereas in the R series anisocytic ones are the commonest. In the latter we mostly find tribes with primitive characters.

Table 2 (*continued*).

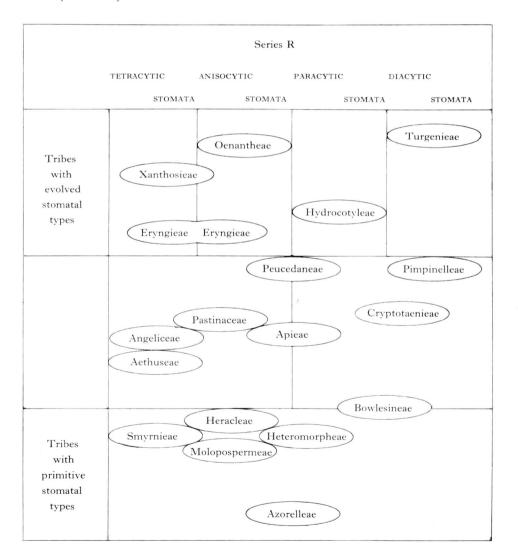

DISCUSSION

The use of the stomata in classification dates back, as we said, to the end of the last century. We have employed them in the family of Umbelliferae and have shown that the stomatal type, as a taxonomic feature, is as valuable as the pollen-type (Guyot, 1966).

If we try and find the reasons why stomata have been discredited as taxonomic characters after Vesque (1889) had demonstrated their value in a certain number of families we come to the conclusion that it is mainly because of the fact that on a same plant we can find several types of stomata. The work of Indian botanists has shown this abundantly quite recently (Inamdar, 1969; Inamdar & Chohan, 1969).

This variability has, apparently, discouraged taxonomists who prefer stable characters. It is true that it is impossible to give each Dicotyledon family a precise stomatal definition, particularly the family Umbelliferae.

Curiously enough, if we consider only the guard cells we can contrast the constancy of their composition with the variability of the stomata in their distribution among the other epidermal cells. Here is a remarkable example of cell differentiation in which, starting from a meristematic epidermal cell which is indistinguishable from the others, a stomatal mother cell is formed after one, two, three or more cell divisions.

It is this number of divisions that forms the basis of any classification into stomatal types; if we add to it the different positions of the guard cells in relation to the walls of the meristematic cell and of the neighbouring epidermal cells, we arrive at the definition of the different types of stomata that we proposed in 1966 and which is summarized in Table 1.

The links which obviously exist ontogenetically between the different types led us to connect them with arrows, leading from the type in which the meristematic cell has few divisions to the type where it has the largest number of divisions.

This direction of these links was chosen for several reasons: (a) because it leads to a diversification of the stomatal types, (b) because the first anomocytic (1, 2) types correspond to the Ranunculaceae whereas the last ones correspond respectively to the Rubiaceae (4), the Acanthaceae (5), the Cruciferae (6), (c) finally because on a young epidermis the first stomata to be recognized are generally anomocytic.

From all this it seems justifiable to speak of primitive stomatal types and of evolved stomatal types, which does not necessarily mean that there are direct links between the present-day tribes of Umbelliferae in which we find them.

The data we have adduced show that in certain species the stomata have remained primitive in character, while in others they have reached an evolved state, and in some cases they have mixed characters. It is very remarkable that the study of stomatal types should reveal evolutionary tendencies expressed in different stomatal types on the same epidermis at the same time. This is probably a reflection of the precarious balance between, on the one hand, the influences operating at the level of the meristemoid cell and which tend to cause the formation there of a stomatal mother cell with circular walling (Humbert & Guyot, 1969), and, on the other hand, the influences operating, in part, at least, at the organ level and which are involved in the orientation of the cell divisions (Guyot *et al.*, 1968; Humbert & Guyot, 1969; Guyot, 1969).

It is probable that other stomatal characters such as the size of the stomata or their shape would help to make the connections more precise. It is also likely that the study of all the epidermal cells (stomata, trichomes, ordinary epidermal cells) would add much information.

The results we have obtained in the fields of systematics and phylogeny already show the value of the study of the plant epidermis. Those results have been confirmed by a similar research in other families [Polygonaceae by Husson (1966); Mesembryanthemaceae by Dupont (1968); Saxifragaceae by Moreau & Gorenflot (1970); Gorenflot & Moreau (1970)].

REFERENCES

Cerceau-Larrival, M.-Th., 1962. Plantules et pollens d'Ombellifères. *Mém. Mus. natl Hist. nat. Paris*, nouv. série, B, Bot., **14**: 1166.

Dupont, S., 1968. Epidermes et plantules de Mesembryanthémacées. *Bull. Soc. Hist. nat. Toulouse*, **104**: 7–64.

Gorenflot, R. & Moreau, F., 1970. Types stomatiques et phylogénie des Saxifraginées (Saxifragacées). *C. r. Acad. Sci. Paris*, **270**: 2802–2805.

Guyot, M., 1965. Les types stomatiques et la classification des Ombellifères. *C. r. Acad. Sci. Paris*, **260**: 3739–3742.

Guyot, M., 1966. Les stomates des Ombellifères. *Bull. Soc. bot. Fr.*, **113**: 244–273.

Guyot, M., 1969. Action de la colchicine sur la différenciation des cellules stomatiques. *Bull. Soc. bot. Fr.* (sous presse).

Guyot, M., Pikusz, A. & Humbert, C., 1968. Action de la colchicine sur les stomates de *Dianthus caryophyllus*. *C. r. Acad. Sci. Paris*, **266**: 1251–1252.

Humbert, C. & Guyot, M., 1969. Action de la colchicine sur le développement des stomates paracytiques. *Bull. Soc. bot. Fr.*, **116**: 301–310.

Husson, P., 1966. Stomates et cellules annexes: types stomatiques chez les Polygonacées. *Bull. Soc. Hist. nat. Toulouse*, **102**: 1–11.

Inamdar, J. A., 1969. Epidermal structure and ontogeny of stomata in some Verbenaceae. *Ann. Bot.*, **33**: 55–66.

Inamdar, J. A. & Chohan, A. J., 1969. Epidermal structure and stomatal development in some Malvaceae and Bombacaceae. *Ann. Bot.*, **33**: 865–878.

Moreau, F. & Gorenflot, R., 1970. Les types stomatiques dans la sous-tribu des Saxifraginées (Saxifragacées). *C. r. Acad. Sci. Paris*, **270**: 686–689.

Tognini, F., 1897. Contribuzione allo studio della organogenia comparata degli stomi. *Atti Ist. bot. Univ. Pavia*, 2ᵉ série, **4**: 1–56.

Vesque, J., 1889. De l'emploi des caractères anatomiques dans la classification des végétaux. *Bull. Soc. bot. Fr.*, Congrès Bot. août, **36**: 41–89.

EXPLANATION OF PLATES

Plate 1

A. *Heteromorpha arborescens*. Anomocytic stomata.
B. *Aethusa cynapium*. Anomocytic stomata.
C. *Bowlesia incana*. Anomocytic stomata.
D. *Physocaulis nodosus*. Anomocytic and diacytic stomata.
E. *Ammi majus*. Anisocytic and diacytic stomata.
F. *Tordylium maximum*. Anomocytic and diacytic stomata.

Plate 2

G. *Aegopodium podagraria*. Paracytic stomata.
H. *Turgenia latifolia*. Diacytic stomata.
I. *Ainsworthia trachycarpa*. Diacytic stomata.
J. *Eryngium alpinum*. Anisocytic stomata.
K. *Eryngium rauhianum*. Tetracytic stomata.
L. *Xanthosia pusilla*. Tetracytic stomata.

Photographs of epidermal peels, from leaves of plants which have been preserved in alcohol (Plate 1, A–F, and Plate 2, G–K) or as herbarium specimens (Plate 2L). The scale indicated applies to all the figures.

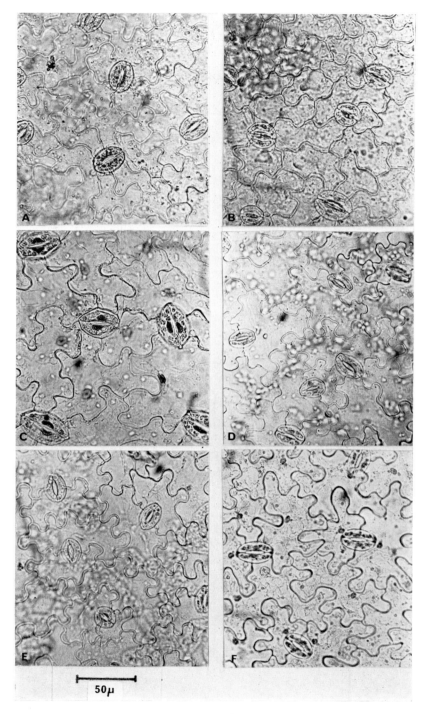

50μ

PLATE 1

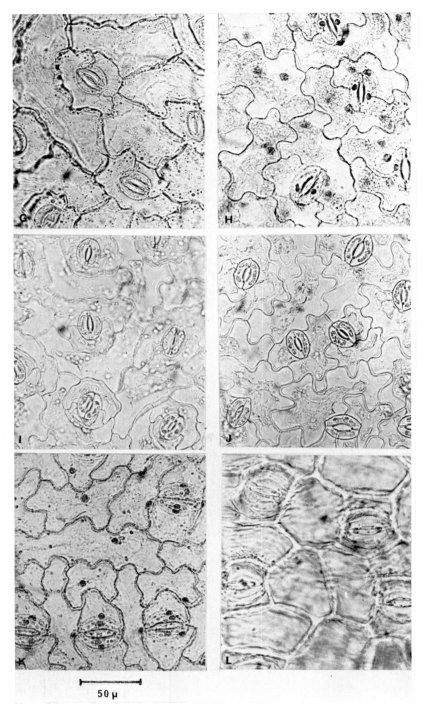

50 μ

PLATE 2

Fruit structure in the Umbelliferae-Caucalideae

V. H. HEYWOOD, F.L.S.

Department of Botany, University of Reading, Reading, England

AND

K. M. M. DAKSHINI

Department of Botany, University of Delhi, India

The classification of the Umbelliferae at the generic level and above is traditionally based largely on the general form and arrangement of spines and ridges on the fruit (mericarp). However, in taxonomic descriptions these details are rather imprecise and this causes difficulties in identification and delimitation of taxa. Scanning electron microscope (SEM) studies of mericarps of 40 species belonging to 12 genera of Umbelliferae-Caucalideae have improved the existing information on fruit characters and have shown that the apparently trivial characters are in fact complex and divisible into a series of separate microcharacters. These points are illustrated and the value of these microcharacters in delimiting taxa will be discussed.

CONTENTS

INTRODUCTION

Most classifications of the Umbelliferae rely, at the generic level and above, to a large extent on features of the fruits (mericarps) and to a lesser extent on details of inflorescence, floral and vegetative structure. In recent years additional kinds of characters have been used—pollen and seedlings (Cerceau-Larrival, 1962, 1965, 1971), chemical constituents (for summaries see Crowden *et al.*, 1969; Harborne, 1971; Hegnauer, 1971), stomatal structure (Guyot, 1966, 1971)—but they have complemented rather than replaced data derived from the fruits. The general shape of the mericarps, the presence or absence of wings, the form and arrangement of spines and ridges, as well as anatomical and embryological features are widely used to characterize genera or to separate species although many taxonomists have felt uneasy at the use of such apparently 'trivial' characters. Very little is known about their functional or adaptive value. Indeed, little attempt has been made to examine fruit characters in detail, largely due to difficulties of observation and the limitations of the light microscope, although last century several Umbellifer authors achieved a remarkable amount in observing and drawing fruit ornamentation despite the primitive optical aids available to them. In most Floras, however, the level of accuracy of the descriptions of the mericarps is not very high and many features are either ignored, oversimplified or misinterpreted.

With the introduction of the scanning electron microscope it is now possible to study the surface features of fruits in great detail with comparative ease. Preliminary studies have shown the potential value of this technique and indicated the wealth of microtopological detail that can be revealed (Heywood, 1968a, 1969, 1971a) in fruits of the Caucalideae group of genera. This work has been extended and the aim of this paper is to present the results of a comparative study of the fruits of a wide range of representatives of this group. It forms part of a much wider programme of multivariate and chemotaxonomic studies (McNeill et al., 1969; Crowden et al., 1969; Heywood, 1971a).

The tribe Caucalideae sensu Boissier was chosen because of its fairly compact distribution (mainly Europe, N. Africa and S.W. Asia), convenient size (18 genera and 80–100 species), considerable diversity of structure at a conspicuous level and disputes about generic limits and positioning of several species in the genera.

MATERIALS AND METHODS

Mericarps of 40 species belonging to 12 genera of the Caucalideae have been examined by scanning electron microscopy. The material has been taken from plants of wild or known origin, either from herbarium specimens or from material cultivated in glasshouses. Most of the material is of the same origin as that used for chemotaxonomic, cytotaxonomic and other studies in the wider programme.

The mericarps were dried naturally and then coated with a thin layer of gold, gold/palladium alloy, or platinum, in a JEOL vacuum coating unit with a revolving stage. Uncoated fruits or fruits sprayed with an antistatic agent were also examined in some instances although these did not give as satisfactory results at higher magnifications as the coated specimens. All the specimens were examined in a JSM-2 scanning electron microscope in the Electron Microscope Laboratory, Department of Botany, University of Reading, at accelerating voltages of 10 or 15 kV.

RESULTS

The basic structure of all the mericarps studied is similar: they are oblong-elliptical in outline with five primary ridges (one dorsal, two lateral and two commissural) and four vallecular ('secondary') ridges, all of which run longitudinally from the base to the stylar end of the fruit. These ridges vary considerably in their degree of development and prominence, the vallecular ones often being more strongly developed than the primary, and they usually bear spines or hairs.

Only those features which lend themselves to detailed analysis by scanning electron microscopy were recorded, as noted below, but it must be mentioned that other morphological features such as the type and degree of compression of the fruits, size and colour show taxonomically valuable variation.

Primary ridges

The primary ridges are prominent at an early stage of development of the mericarps before the elongation of the spines on the vallecular ridges but in the mature mericarp they are seldom conspicuous. They usually bear hairy outgrowths which can be divided into four groups in terms of their distribution, pattern and position: (a) hairs pointing to the stylar end of the mericarp and more or less appressed to the surface of the ridge, e.g. *Torilis*; (b) hairs spreading sideways in relation to the ridge, e.g. *Daucus, Cuminum*; (c) hairs simple, more or less erect (i.e. at right angles to the surface of the mericarp), e.g. *Caucalis, Orlaya, Pseudorlaya, Turgenia, Psammogeton, Chaetosciadium*; (d) hairs variously branched and erect, e.g. *Artedia, Astrodaucus*.

The surface pattern of these hairs varies: (a) papillate-tuberculate in *Torilis* and *Chaetosciadium*; (b) smooth or striate in *Astrodaucus, Turgenia, Psammogeton, Orlaya, Pseudorlaya, Cuminum* and *Caucalis*; (d) papillate-glandular in *Daucus* spp. and *Artedia*.

The attachment of the hairs to the primary ridge is often characteristic: the base may be simple as in *Astrodaucus, Turgenia, Psammogeton, Pseudorlaya, Artedia, Cuminum* etc. or variously lobed as in *Torilis* and *Daucus*. Other variations shown by these hairs are described under the individual genera below.

Vallecular ridges

The vallecular ('secondary') ridges are usually distinct and prominent but are suppressed or less well developed in *Chaetosciadium, Turgenia* and some *Torilis* spp., and winged in *Artedia*. In most species the ridges bear spiny outgrowths ('spines') which may be long or short in relation to the width of the mericarp. The bases of the spines are either separate, e.g. *Torilis* spp., *Daucus* spp., *Turgenia, Psammogeton* or are fused to some degree, often forming a prominent overgrown longitudinal ridge, e.g. *Astrodaucus, Orlaya, Daucus* spp. In several genera the surface of the spines and of the mericarp is smooth and striate or ridged, e.g. *Daucus* spp., *Caucalis, Orlaya, Artedia*, but tuberculate/papillate in *Daucus* spp., *Torilis, Turgenia, Lisaea, Psammogeton*. The tubercles or papillae vary in prominence and shape— they may be simple and conical (*Torilis*), elongate (*Daucus* spp.), peg-like (*Astrodaucus*), and sometimes with distinct rounded heads (*Astrodaucus, Psammogeton*). In some species of *Torilis* and in *Turgenia* and *Chaetosciadium* the tubercles are complex multi-lobed structures as described below. The apex of the spines may be (a) simple, tapering, acute, e.g. *Daucus* spp., *Caucalis, Orlaya, Pseudorlaya*; (b) glochidiate, e.g. *Torilis, Daucus* spp.; (c) tuberculate e.g. *Torilis* spp., *Turgenia, Chaetosciadium*, or (d) multi-branched e.g. *Psammogeton*.

Descriptions of the genera

Daucus L.

The genus *Daucus* is the largest in the tribe Caucalideae, with some 24 species, excluding the various segregates of the *D. carota* complex (cf. Thellung, 1925, 1926a; Heywood, 1968b). It has been variously subdivided into sections, subgenera or even separate genera, based partly on mericarp anatomy and morphology (e.g. Baillon, 1880, Drude, 1898, Calestani, 1905). The treatment followed here is that of Thellung (1926b) although this will require further revision; it is, however, the one that reflects most closely the microcharacters of the mericarps as shown by SEM. Sect. *Daucus* can be exemplified by the type-species, *D. carota* L. The primary ridges are prominent and strongly striate, bearing hairs in two rows, spreading sideways more or less at right angles to the ridge, and varying from subappressed to semi-erect in relation to the surface of the mericarp (Plate 1A). The hairs are more or less flattened and shallowly grooved and the surface is strongly tuberculate; the base is multicellular and glandular, the cells forming an irregular, lobed pattern (Plate 1B).

The vallecular ridges are distinct and prominent, bearing spines in a single row. These spines are striate, etuberculate and sometimes with a glochidiate apex (Plate 1C). The surface of the mericarps is smooth. Other species of Sect. *Daucus* examined show a basically similar pattern. They differ in the degree of development of the base of the hairs on the primary ridges—more prominent and many-celled in *D. guttatus* Sibth. & Sm., or scarcely differentiated (*D. syrticus*) (Plate 1D). The spines on the vallecular ridges vary in length and may be tuberculate (*D. guttatus*) (Plate 1E) and their bases distinct or united, sometimes forming an overgrown ridge. The glochidiate apex varies in form, number of rays and in having a smooth or tuberculate surface. The body of the mericarp between the spines may also be tuberculate in some species.

Sect. *Anisactis* DC. (= *Durieua* Boiss. & Reuter)

Although recognized mainly on the basis of inflorescence and stylar characters, the species of this section are distinct from those of sect. *Daucus* in the microcharacters of the mericarps. We have examined three of the five species referred to this section, namely *D. durieua* Lange, *D. abyssinicus* Hochst. and *D. glochidiatus* (Labill.) Fischer & Meyer.

In *D. durieua* the most conspicuous feature of the mericarps under the SEM is the marked development of the primary ridges and of the hairs borne on them. The latter are abundant, in several rows, filling the whole space between the vallecular ridge spines (Plate 2A). They spread sideways and are subappressed in relation to the mericarp surface. Their base is prominent, multicellular, and the main unicellular upper part of the hair is flattened and strongly tuberculate. The spines on the vallecular ridges are furrowed and bear numerous peg-like projections with the apex irregularly capitate and possibly glandular. The apex of the spines themselves is glochidiate and smooth (Plate 2B, C).

In *D. glochidiatus* the hairs on the primary ridges are also well developed and in several rows, but not so numerous as in *D. durieua*, shorter and variable in posture from subappressed to semi-erect (Plate 2D). The base of the hairs is much less prominent than in *D. durieua*, and the main unicellular portion is rounded at the base. The spines on the vallecular ridges and on the rest of the body of the mericarp are conspicuously tuberculate, the tubercles being triangular and somewhat lobed. The apex of the spines is glochidiate and tuberculate (Plate 2E).

In *D. abyssinicus* the hairs of the primary ridges are in two to three rows, variable in posture and angle and with the basal portion not well developed (Plate 2F). The hairs are more similar in general appearance to those of *D. glochidiatus* than to those of *D. durieua*. The spines on the vallecular ridges are strongly tuberculate and the apex is glochidiate and weakly tuberculate.

Sect. *Leptodaucus* Thellung

This section was created by Thellung (1926*b*) for two species previously included by other authors in sect. *Anisactis*—*D. pusillus* Michx from W. North America and *D. montevidensis*. Link ex Sprengel (*D. australis* Poeppig) from S. South America. There is some debate as to the identity and distribution of the latter species but this will be discussed in a separate paper.

In *D. pusillus* the hairs on the primary ridges show a remarkable development, unlike anything observed elsewhere in the genus. The basic shape of the hairs is similar to that of other species of *Daucus*—with a multicellular basal portion and a large unicellular main upper portion which is flattened and somewhat grooved below and cylindrical and pointed above. The arrangement, orientation, posture and size of the hairs is, however, very irregular (Plate 3A, B). They more than fill the space between the vallecular spines and overlap with the bases of the latter. The vallecular spines themselves are ridged and sparsely tuberculate, with a glochidiate apex. Further investigation of this critical species is under way.

The most conspicuous feature of *D. montevidensis* is the remarkable development of the base of the hairs on the primary ridges. The ridges themselves are prominent and the hairs borne in two to three rows. Most of the hairs are semi-erect; their base is very irregular, lobed, multicellular and often strongly asymmetrical (Plate 3C, D). The vallecular ridges are grooved and tuberculate, the tubercles being more frequent in the lower portion. The apex is glochidiate and more or less smooth.

Sect. *Chrysodaucus* Thellung

This monotypic section was described by Thellung (1915) for *D. aureus*, a W. Mediterranean–Canary Island species. It differs from all other species in the genus in having the whole fruit surface densely covered with conical papillae which are often grouped into concentric clusters (Plate 4A, B). The primary ridges are inconspicuous and bear semi-erect hairs with a conspicuous, multicellular, papillate base. The vallecular spines are ridged-tuberculate or papillate, the papillae being much less conspicuous than on the surface of the mericarp.

Sect. *Ctenolophus* Batt.

This section, which is recognized by Drude, contains a small number of N.W. African species which are sometimes treated as a separate genus (*Ctenodaucus*

Pomel) or placed in the genus *Laserpitium* as by Koso-Poljansky (1915) who treats them as sect. *Ctenodaucus*. We have examined two species in this group, *D. reboudii* Cosson and *D. laserpitioides* DC.: they differ in mericarp structure from *Daucus* in the absence of hairs on the primary ridges and seem indeed closer to *Laserpitium* but further study is needed.

Astrodaucus *Drude*

The three species of this genus (*A. orientalis* (L.) Drude, *A. littoralis* (Bieb.) Drude and *A. persicus* (Boiss.) Drude) from S.E. Europe, S.W. Asia and the U.S.S.R. have been variously placed—in *Daucus* by Boissier, in *Caucalis* by Čelakowsky and in *Torilis* by Calestani. The three species differ markedly from each other in mericarp structure and further work is required before a proper assessment of generic status can be made. A fourth species, *A. leptocarpus* (Hochst.) Drude is shown below to belong to the genus *Torilis*.

In *A. orientalis* the hairs on the primary ridges are complex multi-branched structures at the base, sometimes ending in a simple, tuberculate, cylindrical-grooved portion. The hairs form a dense intertwined mass on the primary ridges (Plate 4C, D). The vallecular ridges bear abundant, long, peg-like projections with a rounded, capitate, rugose apex (Plate 4E, F). Considerable variation is shown by this species in details of mericarp morphology and further study is needed.

In *A. persicus* the hairs on the primary ridges are stalked, branching above into numerous flattened arms (Plate 5A). The spines on the secondary ridges are densely covered with long or short peg-like projections (Plate 5B), similar to those of *A. orientalis* and also with a capitate-tuberculate-rugose apex.

Orlaya *Hoffm.*

This genus of three species has a relatively simple mericarp morphology as seen under the SEM. The primary ridges are slender, with the hairs semi-erect, in one or two rows. The vallecular ridges are equally prominent and bear striate spines which are simple and uncinate at the apex.

Pseudorlaya *Murb.*

There are only two species recognized in this genus, *P. pumila* (L.) Grande and *P. minuscula* (Pau) Laínz. They differ considerably in the gross morphology of the mericarps and this is reflected in the microcharacters shown under the SEM.

In *P. pumila* the primary ridges are conspicuous and bear several rows of flattened, strap-like hairs, some of which are united at the base (Plate 5C). The base is prominent and multi-cellular as in some species of *Daucus*. The vallecular ridges bear spines which vary in size according to whether they are dorsal or lateral. The spines are all ridged, etuberculate, and glochidiate at the apex.

In *P. minuscula* the primary ridges are less conspicuous with shorter, less numerous hair which are not united at the base. The vallecular ridges are all similar as are the spines borne on them: the spines are short, united at the base and appear to be in two to three rows, strongly tuberculate and glochidiate at the apex (Plate 5D). The degree of variability of these two species needs further assessment but it does appear from both the macro- and micro-characters of the fruit surface that they may belong in different genera. Their anatomy, palynology and phytochemistry are being investigated to help arrive at a decision.

Caucalis *L.*

This genus has had a remarkable history. In addition to the type-species, *C. platycarpos* L., it has had included in it species which are today considered as referable to *Torilis* (see below), *Turgenia, Agrocharis, Astrodaucus* and *Yabea*! There are several tropical African species which have yet to be studied by us (*C. incognita* Wolff, *C. pedunculata* Engler and *C. longisepala* Engler) and which are probably referable to *Agrocharis* or *Caucaliopsis*. It seems likely that the genus is in fact monotypic.

The fruit structure of *C. platycarpos* is very distinctive and not closely approached by any other species of any other genus of the tribe, except perhaps *Orlaya*. Its micro-characters by SEM are illustrated in earlier papers (Heywood, 1968*a*, 1971*b*). The primary ridges are slender and bear a few semi-erect, flattened hairs which are prominently swollen at the base, in a single row. The spines on the prominent vallecular ridges are large, cylindrical, striate and uncinate-aculeate.

Turgenia *Hoffm.*

The fruits of the monotypic genus have an extremely complex surface ornamentation. They have already been fully illustrated in previous papers (Heywood, 1968*b*, 1969, 1971*b*). The most characteristic features are the castellated spine-masses between the tuberculate spines. These spine-masses vary considerably in size and development (Plate 6A). Despite the fact that a more complete contrast with *Caucalis* can scarcely be envisaged, *Turgenia latifolia* has frequently been included in the former genus.

Lisaea *Boiss.*

This genus contains four E. Mediterranean-S.W. Asian species, only one of which, *L. syriaca* Boiss., has been studied by us so far. It is remarkably similar in the detailed micro-characters of the mericarps to *Turgenia* so that we are inclined to agree with Koso-Poljansky (1915) in uniting the two genera as subgenera under *Turgenia*. *L. syriaca* shares with *T. latifolia* the remarkable development of spine-masses, and the vallecular spines are also similar (Plate 6B, C, D).

Torilis *Adanson*

This is the second largest genus in the tribe, containing some 14 species, half of which have been studied by us with the SEM. As would be expected in a genus of this size, there is considerable variation in fruit structure, but in all the species we have examined, the basic features are similar. The primary ridges are slender and bear one to four rows of more or less appressed hairs directed towards the stylar end of the mericarp. These hairs are tuberculate and vary in length in the different species but are characteristic of the genus and have not been found elsewhere in the tribe.

Those species which were previously included in the genus *Caucalis* and which are now regarded as belonging to *Torilis* subg. *Pseudocaucalis* Drude have this same type of hair on the primary ridges.

The vallecular ridges bear conspicuous tuberculate spines or rarely tubercles only, the spines being suppressed. Variation in the development of spines and tubercles in the genus is very considerable and is linked with questions of fertilization; it will be considered in detail in a separate paper.

The case of *Daucus leptocarpus* Hochst. can be considered here. Drude (1898) transferred it to the genus *Astrodaucus*. We have, however, studied material of this species from Anatolia and examination by the SEM indicates clearly that it belongs to the genus *Torilis* (Plate 7A) with which it agrees in the details of the hairs on the primary ridges, spines on the vallecular ridges and in all other respects. Townsend's transfer of this species to *Torilis* [*Kew Bull.*, **17**: 434 (1964)] is therefore fully justified.

Chaetosciadium *Boiss.*

The fruits of this monotypic genus are remarkable in the tribe for their covering of fine bristles which hide the body of the mericarp. Because of this the single species *C. trichospermum* (L.) Boiss. is immediately recognizable. Its affinities have been somewhat obscured by these characteristic hairs. Calestani regarded it as forming a separate subtribe Chaetosciadieae of the tribe Ligusticeae showing little affinity with *Torilis*, while Koso-Poljansky (1915) placed it in the Daucinae beside *Torilis* and *Cuminum* noting that it was closely related to *Psammogeton*. Under the SEM the bristles of *Chaetosciadium* have been shown to possess a remarkable structure, being made up of tube-like elements and unlike any other type of hair found in the Caucalineae (Heywood, 1971*b*). On the other hand the hairs on the primary ridges are very similar in shape, posture and orientation to those found in *Torilis*. In other respects, too, such as developmental anatomy, chromosome number and chemical constituents, this genus shows a close affinity with *Torilis*. Further studies are in progress.

Psammogeton *Edgew.*

Only one of the four species of this S.W. Asian genus had been studied by SEM so far, namely *P. setifolium* (Boiss.) Boiss. It bears simple, erect hairs on the primary ridges and elongate outgrowths on the strongly ridged vallecular spines. These latter show some similarity to those of *Chaetosciadium* and the relationships of the two genera are being further investigated.

Cuminum *L.*

Of the two species in this genus only *C. cyminum* L. has been studied by SEM, but further work is needed. The primary ridges are slender and bear laterally spreading hairs as in *Daucus*. The vallecular ridges are more prominent and bear short, striate spines which are simple, acute and tapering at the apex.

Artedia L.

The most outstanding feature of this monotypic genus is the development of the lateral vallecular ridges in the form of a deeply lobed, scaly, expanded wing (Plate 7B). The primary ridges and the other vallecular ridges are slender and filiform. The hairs on the primary ridge are branched and erect.

DISCUSSION

Although this study of the mericarps of Caucalideae is far from complete it is already clear that the micro-characters shown by SEM are of very great assistance in clarifying the relationships of the component genera. The diversity of structure found is surprisingly great and much further work will have to be undertaken to consider the genetic control, variability and adaptive significance of the features of surface ornamentation. It is possible, however, at this stage to say that in most cases the genera can be clearly and unambiguously characterized by the characters of the primary and vallecular ridges and their hairy outgrowths. As a result the genera can now be readily identified.

Naturally we cannot advocate the use of the SEM as a routine identification instrument, but fortunately most of the micro-characters can be recognized, now that we know their detailed nature, by the use of a simple dissecting microscope. Yet the dissecting microscope alone has not permitted us previously to elucidate these features.

From the point of view of generic classification and relationships the evidence from SEM studies must be considered along with other features of the mericarps such as their gross morphology, anatomy and chemistry, together with information from other parts of the plant such as pollen, stomata, chemical constituents. A synthesis of these various classes of data is being prepared and will be presented as a later paper. In very many instances, it does already appear that the micro-characters of the mericarps show a high correlation with these other kinds of character which confirms the reliability of using them as a simple means of identification.

This kind of SEM study is therefore of great practical value as well as contributing to our understanding of the variation in structure of the plants concerned. Taxonomists can perhaps take comfort in the knowledge that the mericarp characters used as the basis for tribal and generic classification in the Umbelliferae are not so much 'trivial' as simply small-scale but none the less valid for that.

ACKNOWLEDGEMENTS

We wish to record our gratitude to Mr S. K. Irtiza-Ali for his skilled technical assistance with the scanning electron microscopy and photography. Dr D. M. Moore very kindly read through the manuscript and made valuable suggestions for its improvement. One of us (KMMD) is grateful to the Centre of Advanced Study in Botany, University of Delhi and UNESCO for the grant of a fellowship to carry out this project, and to the British Council for making all the arrangements.

REFERENCES

BAILLON, H. E., 1880. *Histoire Naturelle des Plantes.* **7**. Paris.

CALESTANI, V., 1905. Contributo alla sistematica delle Ombrellifere d'Europe. *Webbia*, **1**: 89–280.

CERCEAU-LARRIVAL, M.-TH., 1962. *Plantules et pollens d'Ombellifères. Mém. Mus. natn Hist. Paris*, sér. B. (Bot.), **14**: 1166.

CERCEAU-LARRIVAL, M.-TH., 1965. Le pollen d'Ombellifères méditerranéennes. III—Scandicineae Drude, IV—Dauceae Drude. *Pollen Spores*, **7**: 35–62.

CERCEAU-LARRIVAL, M.-TH., 1971. In *The Biology and Chemistry of the Umbelliferae*, London & New York: Academic Press.

CROWDEN, R. K., HARBORNE, J. B. & HEYWOOD, V. H., 1969. Chemosystematics of the Umbelliferae— A general survey. *Phytochemistry*, **8**: 1963–1964.

DRUDE, C. G. O., 1898. Umbelliferae: Apioideae. In Engler, A. & Prantl, K. (eds), *Die natürlichen Pflanzenfamilien*, **3** (8): 145–250.

GUYOT, M., 1966. Les stomates des Ombellifères. *Bull. Soc. bot. Fr.*, **113**: 244–273.

GUYOT, M., 1971. In *The Biology and Chemistry of the Umbelliferae*, London & New York: Academic Press.

HARBORNE, J. B., 1971. In *The Biology and Chemistry of the Umbelliferae*, London & New York: Academic Press.

HEGNAUER, R., 1971. In *The Biology and Chemistry of the Umbelliferae*, London & New York: Academic Press.

HEYWOOD, V. H., 1968a. Scanning electron microscopy and microcharacters in the fruits of the Umbelliferae-Caucalideae. *Proc. Linn. Soc. London*, **179**: 287–289.

HEYWOOD, V. H., 1968b, *Daucus* L. In Tutin, T. G., Heywood, V. H. *et al.* (eds.), *Flora Europaea*, **2**: 373-375. Cambridge: Cambridge University Press.

HEYWOOD, V. H., 1969. Scanning electron microscopy in the study of plant materials. *Micron*, **1**: 1–14.

HEYWOOD, V. H., 1971a. Chemosystematic studies in Daucus and allied species. *Boissiera*, **19**: 289–295.

HEYWOOD, V. H., 1971b. The characteristics of the scanning electron microscope and their importance in biological studies. In Heywood, V. H. (ed.), *Scanning Electron Microscopy*, 1–16. London & New York: Academic Press.

KOSO-POLJANSKY, B., 1915. Sciadophytorum systematis lineamenta. *Bull. Soc. nat. Hist. Moscow*, n.s., **29**, 93–222; 279–290.

McNEILL, J., PARKER, P. F., & HEYWOOD, V. H., 1969. A taxometric approach to the classification of the spiny-fruited members (tribe Caucalideae) of the flowering-plant family Umbelliferae. In Cole, A. J. *Numerical Taxonomy*, pp. 129–147. London & New York: Academic Press.

THELLUNG, A., 1925. Umbelliferae. In Hegi, G., *Illustrierte Flora von Mitteleuropa, V/2*.

THELLUNG, A., 1926a. Die Linneschen Daucus-Arten in Lichte der original-Herbarexemplare. *Repert. Spec. Nov. Regni Veg.*, **22**: 300–315.

THELLUNG, A., 1926b. Daucus-Studien. *Repert. Spec. Nov. Regni Veg.*, **23**: 147–159.

EXPLANATION OF PLATES

PLATE 1

A. *Daucus carota:* part of primary ridge of mericarp showing hairs spreading sideways ($\times 150$).
B. *Daucus carota:* base of hair on primary ridge ($\times 380$).
C. *Daucus carota:* glochidiate apex of spine on vallecular ridge ($\times 680$).
D. *Daucus syrticus:* hairs on primary ridge showing their scarcely differentiated bases ($\times 150$).
E. *Daucus guttatus:* part of mericarp surface showing a primary ridge with hairs which are multi-cellular at the base, and the bases of tuberculate spines on a vallecular ridge ($\times 80$).

PLATE 2

A. *Daucus durieua:* primary ridge with hairs in several rows filling the space between the vallecular spines ($\times 40$).
B. *Daucus durieua:* prominent multi-cellular base of hair on primary ridge ($\times 315$).
C. *Daucus durieua:* portion of a spine on a vallecular ridge showing peg-like projections with an irregularly capitate apex ($\times 1140$).
D. *Daucus glochidiatus:* primary ridge showing hairs in several rows and variable in posture ($\times 100$).
E. *Daucus glochidiatus:* part of vallecular ridge spine with a glochidiate and tuberculate apex ($\times 90$).
F. *Daucus abyssinicus:* primary ridge showing hairs in two to three rows and variable in posture ($\times 25$).

PLATE 3

A. *Daucus pusillus:* primary ridge showing irregular development of hairs filling the space between the vallecular spines ($\times 30$).
B. *Daucus pusillus:* base of hairs on primary ridge showing the multi-cellular base ($\times 380$).
C. *Daucus montevidensis:* primary ridge showing hairs in two or three rows and basal portion of vallecular spines ($\times 75$).
D. *Daucus montevidensis:* base of hair on primary ridge showing a very irregular, lobed, multi-cellular and asymmetrical base ($\times 600$).

PLATE 4

A. *Daucus aureus:* part of primary ridge showing hairs and the dense covering of papillae on the mericarp surface ($\times 190$).
B. *Daucus aureus:* concentric cluster of papillae on mericarp surface ($\times 630$).
C. *Astrodaucus orientalis:* primary ridge showing multi-branched hairs and basal portions of spines on vallecular ridges ($\times 40$).
D. *Astrodaucus orientalis:* detail of hairs on primary ridge ($\times 95$).
E. *Astrodaucus orientalis:* portion of spine on vallecular ridge showing long, peg-like projections ($\times 190$).
F. *Astrodaucus orientalis:* capitate rugose apex of peg-like projections on spine on vallecular ridge ($\times 700$).

PLATE 5

A. *Astrodaucus persicus:* primary ridge bearing stalked hairs which are branched above, and bases of spines on vallecular ridges ($\times 30$).
B. *Astrodaucus persicus:* detail of spines on vallecular ridges showing peg-like projections ($\times 300$).
C. *Pseudorlaya pumila:* part of primary ridge showing flattened, strap-like hairs, some of which are joined at the base ($\times 55$).
D. *Pseudorlaya minuscula:* general view of mericarp surface showing primary ridge bearing hairs, and vallecular ridges with strongly tuberculate spines united at the base ($\times 20$).

PLATE 6

A. *Turgenia latifolia:* general view of mericarp surface showing strongly tuberculate spines and castellated spine-masses at their base and between them ($\times 19$).
B. *Lisaea syriaca:* general view of mericarp surface showing strongly tuberculate spines and castellated spine-masses ($\times 19$).
C. *Lisaea syriaca:* detail of spine-masses on mericarp surface ($\times 190$).
D. *Lisaea syriaca:* detail of a single spine-mass ($\times 375$).

PLATE 7

A. *Torilis leptocarpa:* general view of mericarp surface showing ridges bearing appressed papillate hairs, and vallecular ridges with tuberculate spines ($\times 65$).
B. *Artedia squamata:* portion of margin of fruit showing part of lobed, wing-like lateral vallecular ridges and the scaly surface of fruits ($\times 35$).

PLATE 1

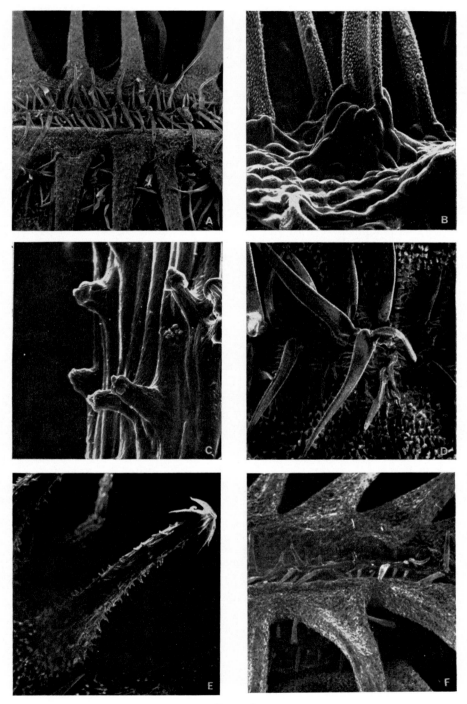

PLATE 2

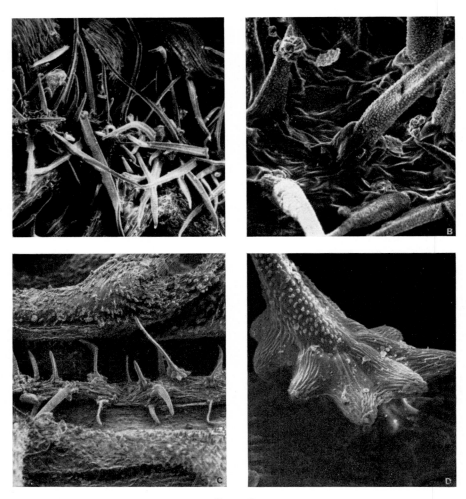

PLATE 3

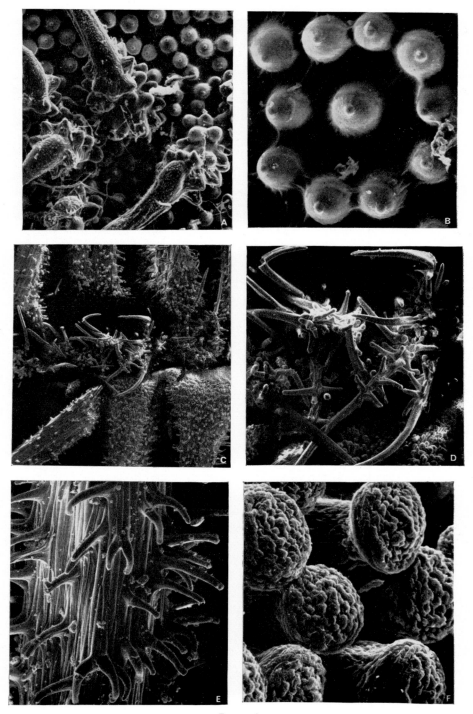

PLATE 4

PLATE 5

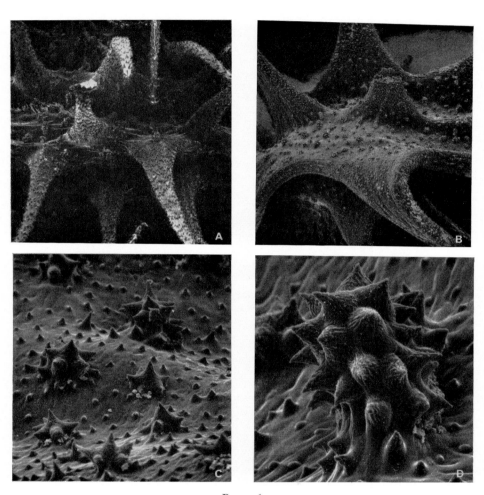

PLATE 6

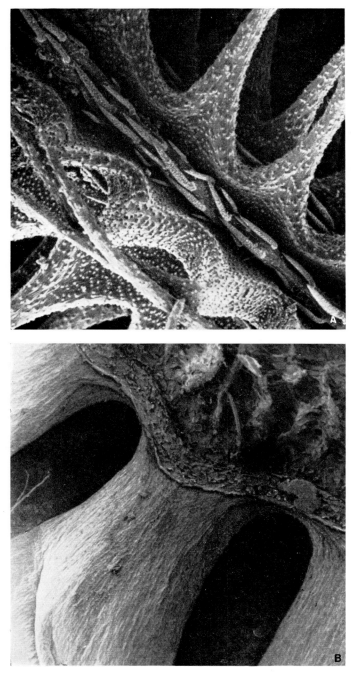

PLATE 7

Chromosome studies in the Umbelliferae

D. M. MOORE, F.L.S.

Department of Botany, University of Reading, Reading, England

During the past two decades the number of species of Umbelliferae for which there is any information on the chromosomes has almost trebled so that about 30% of the species, belonging to 175 genera, have now been subjected to at least a preliminary study. Naturally occurring meiotic irregularities appear to be rare, even in hybrids, and supernumerary chromosomes appear to have been recorded with certainty in only one genus (*Dethawia*). With one or two exceptions there is no cytological evidence on the interrelationships of the karyotypes present in the Umbelliferae so that it is necessary to stress the limitations of the chromosome data currently available and, in particular, the lack of experimental studies yielding cytogenetical information. At this stage, therefore, most discussions must revolve around the observed chromosome numbers—umbelliferous cytotaxonomy is still at the 'alpha' level.

Haploid chromosome numbers (n) in the family range from 4 to 84, from which the primary basic numbers (x) 4–12 can be derived with $x = 8$ being commonest in the Hydrocotyloideae and Saniculoideae and $x = 11$ in the Apioideae. The relevance of these basic numbers to the subfamilial and tribal groupings within the Umbelliferae and to the relationships with other related families is discussed and the general lack of chromosomal evidence for a linear arrangement of the major groupings is stressed. The chromosomes are of very variable taxonomic utility at the generic and specific levels.

Aneuploidy and polyploidy both seem to have played an important role in the evolution of the Umbelliferae. As in other large families for which there are comparable data, about a quarter of the genera show intraspecific variation in chromosome number, although the proportion being greater in the Saniculoideae, but there is little information on the extent to which this variation is correlated with other factors. Generic endemism, which is common in the Umbelliferae, does not generally appear to be associated with distinctive chromosome characteristics, but there is some evidence for a concentration of apparent 'palaeopolyploids' in Mexico and neighbouring regions of Central America.

CONTENTS

INTRODUCTION

In 1949 Gardé & Malheiros-Gardé summarized all the published information on chromosome numbers in the Umbelliferae, including that of such earlier workers as Melderis (1930), Ogawa (1929), Schulz-Gaebel (1930), Tamamschjan (1933) and Wanscher (1931, 1932, 1933, 1934), whose contributions had laid the foundations for chromosome studies in the family. Bell & Constance (1957) noted that by 1955 information was available on the chromosomes of about 214 taxa, comprising less than 10% of the recognized species, and that this was largely derived from Eurasia, particularly Europe. From that time there has been a continual increase in the annual output of chromosome data for all groups of plants (cf. Moore, 1968) and it is particularly appropriate to measure the improved information for the Umbelliferae since then because Bell & Constance (1957), in presenting the first of their major contributions on the chromosomes of the Umbelliferae, emphasized the need to extend greatly such studies to areas of the world, particularly North America and the Southern Hemisphere, for which such data were then almost completely lacking.

In trying to review the current state of chromosome studies in the Umbelliferae an attempt has been made to take account of all the published work, though there will be inevitable deficiencies, together with much unpublished information which has kindly been made available (see acknowledgements). There are now chromosome data for about 840 species, comprising some 30% of the family, an increase of about 250% in just over two decades. These data are summarized in Appendix A, from which can be seen that there is some information on 175 genera scattered through the three subfamilies and all the tribes currently recognized.

There appear to be very few programmes of experimental hybridization within the family and, so far as I am aware, there is no cytogenetical information derived from such work. Such information is an essential step in interpretative cytological studies and consequently most of what follows is based on observational data. Furthermore, although a few authors (e.g. Runemark, 1968; Cauwet, 1967, 1968; Činčura & Hindáková, 1963; Reese, 1969) have studied the structure of the karyotype in groups of related species, the bulk of the available data refer to chromosome number only and consequently at almost every level in the Umbelliferae we are still at the stage of 'α cytotaxonomy'.

CHROMOSOME STUDIES AND TAXONOMY

Subfamilies

Earlier work showed that members of the Hydrocotyloideae and Saniculoideae were most likely to have $x = 8$ while members of the Apioideae most frequently had $x = 11$. From Fig. 1 it can be seen that this general difference between the subfamilies is confirmed by the more abundant data now available. When presumed primary basic chromosome numbers are considered (Table 1) 61·3% of the Apioideae have $x = 11$, compared with 0·6% in the Saniculoideae and 15·4% in the Hydrocotyloideae, while only 8·5% of the Apioideae have $x = 8$, compared with 73·5% and 46% in, respectively, the Saniculoideae and Hydrocotyloideae, the latter also having a significant proportion (19%) with $x = 10$. It

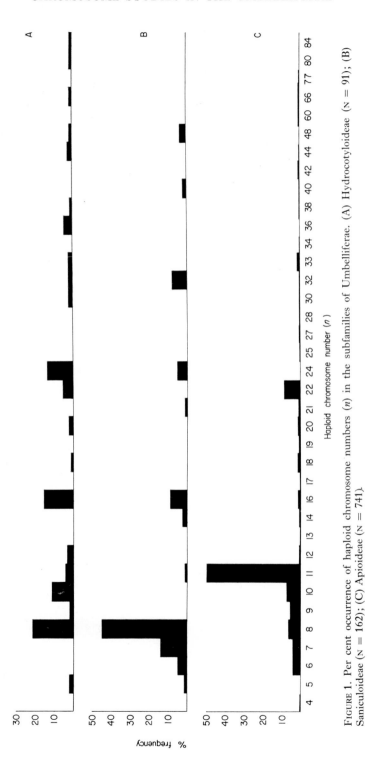

FIGURE 1. Per cent occurrence of haploid chromosome numbers (n) in the subfamilies of Umbelliferae. (A) Hydrocotyloideae ($N = 91$); (B) Saniculoideae ($N = 162$); (C) Apioideae ($N = 741$).

Table 1. Per cent occurrence of presumed primary basic chromosome numbers derived from haploid numbers available for each of the subfamilies of Umbelliferae

	Presumed primary basic chromosome number										Total counts
	4	5	6	7	8	9	10	11	12	13	
Hydrocotyloideae		2·2			46·2	3·3	18·7	15·4	14·3		92
Saniculoideae		1·8	4·9	17·3	73·5			1·8	0·6		162
Apioideae	0·1		4·2	6·8	8·5	8·0	10·1	61·3	0·9	0·2	741

should be noted, however, that the subfamilies have relatively broad and overlapping spectra of haploid numbers, most presumed primary basic numbers occurring in all three subfamilies (Table 1). Clearly, the available chromosome data do not permit any arrangement of the subfamilies in a linear sequence and it seems preferable to consider that they have exploited modally different parts of the chromosome numbers spectrum. The exact routes followed during this exploitation are impossible to determine in view of the lack of experimental cytogenetical evidence but the widespread occurrence of $x = 8$ and $x = 11$ in very different taxa suggests that these are the original basic numbers in the family. Whilst it is conceivable that the original basic number was $x = 4$, as suggested by Wanscher (1933), the absence or paucity of the numbers which would then be diploid, hexaploid, etc. (e.g. 8, 24, etc.) makes this very unlikely. Furthermore, this hypothetical basic number is not present in any related families (Table 3).

Tribal differences

Although most people nowadays follow Drude (1897–98) in recognizing the three subfamilies referred to above, there is a much greater diversity of opinion concerning the number and delimitation of tribes, of which there have been variously considered to be 10, 11, 12, 27 or 31 (Crowden et al., 1969: 1980). In view of this uncertainty

Table 2. Haploid chromosome numbers (n) recorded in the Umbelliferae.

	4	5	6	7	8	9	10	11	12	13	14	16	17	18	19	20
Hydrocotyloideae																
Hydrocotyleae					1	1	4	3				4		1		2
Mulineae		2		22		2	10					12				
Saniculoideae																
Saniculeae		3	8	22	74		1				4	15				
Lagoecieae				1	1											
Apioideae																
Echinophoreae																
Scandiceae (Scandicinae)			1	6	7	6	?1	15	1	?1		2	1		1	
Scandiceae (Caucainae)			6		5	3	3	4	3			1		1		
Dauceae				1	5	3	5	8								
Coriandreae						2	3									
Smyrnieae			11	1	1	?1	2	13			3	1		3		3
Apieae			12	23	32	30	35	168	2	1	3	5	2	7	7	9
Peucedaneae	1		1	1	1	2	10	148	1		2					
Laserpitieae					1			16								

it is not easy to consider the relevance of the chromosome data to the tribal distinctions but an attempt has been made to do so in Table 2, which summarizes the numbers known for each of the twelve tribes recognized by Drude.

The clearest agreement between chromosome studies and tribal delimitation is shown by the two tribes of the Hydrocotyloideae, which generally exploit different basic numbers and in a rather different manner (Fig. 2). In the Hydrocotyleae the

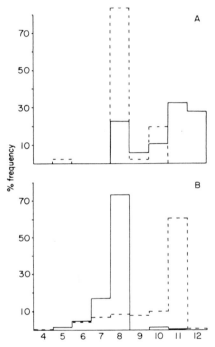

FIGURE 2. Per cent occurrence of presumed primary basic chromosome numbers (x) in: (A) subfamily Hydrocotyloideae-tribe Mulineae (––––) and tribe Hydrocotyleae (–––––), and: (B) subfamilies Saniculoideae (–––––) and Apioideae (––––).

Figures indicate the number of species in which each number is recorded

21	22	24	ca.25	27	28	30	32	33	34	36	38	40	42	44	48	60	66	77	80	84
	5	9				2	1	2		4	1			2	1		1		1	1
		4					1													
		9					12					3		5						
1																				
						1														
	1																			
	2																			
	1							1												
3	18		1	1	1		1		1		1	1	2	1						
2	23				2	1	1	2				1		1		1				
3	21							4						1				1	1	
	1							1												

commonest basic numbers are $x = 11$ (33%) and $x = 12$ (28%). Although $x = 8$ occurs in 23% of cases it should be noted that these are all at the polyploid level and, indeed, polyploidy is much more prevalent in the Hydrocotyleae than in the Mulineae, 80% of the available counts being above the assumed range of diploid numbers. In the Mulineae, on the other hand, 38% of the counts are polyploid. In this tribe 76% of the numbers are based on $x = 8$, including all counts known from *Azorella* Lam., *Bolax* Comm. *Bowlesia* Ruíz & Pav., *Homalocarpus* Hook. & Arn., *Mulinum* Pers., *Schizeilema* Domin and *Spananthe* Jacq. from South America, and the Canarian endemic *Drusa* DC. Most of the remaining species (21%) are based on $x = 10$. *Asteriscium* Cham. & Schlecht. and the closely related *Gymnophyton* Clos and *Pozoa* Lag. have only been found with $n = 10$ while the third related genus, *Eremocharis* Phil., has $n = 10$, 8 and 5 and although it is tempting, as suggested by Mathias & Constance (1962), to consider the last two numbers to be derived there is clearly a great need for detailed karyotype studies to investigate further the relationships between the species with $n = 8$ in this and the other seven genera of Mulineae. It is interesting to note that the two European representatives of this largely South American tribe, presumably indicative of a fairly old separation, have two basic numbers, $x = 8$ in *Drusa* and $x = 10$ in the Balearic Islands *Naufraga* Constance & Cannon.

In the Saniculoideae the chromosome data neither support nor contradict the recognition of Drude's two tribes. Most of the data are derived from members of the tribe Saniculeae, in which $x = 7$ and 8 predominate, while the only three records known from the tribe Lagoecieae conform to these two base numbers (Table 2).

Although more chromosomal data are known for the Apioideae than for the other two subfamilies it is also the largest subfamily and within it tribal boundaries are particularly open to question. At this stage in our knowledge of the subdivision of the Apioideae it is therefore perhaps not surprising that the chromosomal data show no particularly close relationship to the tribal system used as a framework here. The Echinophoreae and Coriandreae, which are chromosomally the poorest known tribes, are based on $x = 10$ or 11, the Laserpiteae all have $x = 11$ apart from one species of *Siler* Crantz with $n = 8$, while the Peucedaneae mostly have $x = 10$ or 11. On the other hand the Scandicinae, Dauceae, Smyrnieae and Apieae, although most commonly with $x = 11$, as would be expected in this subfamily, have exploited most numbers between $x = 6$ and $x = 11$. These modal differences, if valid, can be seen from Table 2, but their significance is not clear. It is tempting to consider that the most successful tribes may constitute the group having the greatest chromosomal diversity but much more cytological information is needed before any conclusions can be attempted. It is interesting to note that the crude chromosomal groupings referred to cannot be correlated with the tentative groupings of the tribes of the Apioideae based on the presence or absence of flavones and flavonols (Crowden *et al.*, 1969). However, the close similarity between the distributions of numbers in the Scandiceae and Dauceae supports their close relationship on chemical evidence (Crowden *et al.*, 1969) as opposed to the location of the latter after the Laserpitieae as under the Drude arrangement.

Genera and species

Most taxonomic difficulties in the Umbelliferae are experienced at the generic level and there is every need for as wide an approach as possible to the problem of generic delimitation. Chromosomal information is clearly of potential value in this as in other families, although the widespread occurrence of $x = 8$ and $x = 11$ means that the chromosomes may be of less use than other forms of data. Thus, problems of generic delimitation are not aided by the available chromosomal data in *Bowlesia* and *Drusa* (Mathias & Constance, 1965) with $x = 8$, *Gingidium* F. Muell., *Ligusticum* L., *Angelica* L. and *Aciphylla* J. R. & G. Forst. (Dawson, 1967), which all have $x = 11$, or the disputed separation of *Limnosciadium* Mathias & Constance and *Cynosciadium* DC., both with $x = 11$. On the other hand, the separation of *Turgenia* Hoffm. ($n = 9, 16$) and *Caucalis* L. ($n = 10, 11, 22$) is supported by chromosome information. The role of chromosome studies at the generic level is well exemplified by *Naufraga*, recently discovered endemic of the Balearic Islands. Although of uncertain affinities, this genus has tentatively been suggested to be closest to *Schizeilema* (Constance & Cannon, 1967), which has $x = 8$. However, *Naufraga* has $n = 10$, indicating possible affinities with *Asteriscium* and its relatives in which this number predominates. Furthermore, the presence of two telocentric chromosomes in the haploid complement of *Naufraga* (Marchant, unpub.) may suggest that it is derived from ancestors with $x = 9$, a number only known within the tribe for the endemic Andean genera *Laretia* Gill. & Hook. and *Huanaca* Cav. Clearly, in such cases as this widely based and detailed cytological studies are necessary to assist in determining more precisely the generic affinities.

The role of chromosome data in the delimitation of species certainly parallels the situation outlined above for the generic level. Such genera as *Apium* L., *Ligusticum*, *Heracleum* L., *Lomatium* Raf., and *Laserpitium* L. show considerable uniformity in chromosome number and any possible application to problems of species delimitation would require more detailed studies of the structure and behaviour of the karyotype. On the other hand *Bupleurum* L., which is discussed in the next paper (p. 257), is an example of the way in which the chromosomes have proved helpful in assessing the status of related species (Cauwet, 1967, 1968).

Related families

There seems little doubt that the Araliaceae is the family most closely related to the Umbelliferae; indeed they have been united into one family by several workers (most recently by Thorne, 1968). Compared with the diversity of presumed basic numbers in the Umbelliferae the Araliaceae have $x = 9, 10, 11, 12$ and 13 (Table 3), of which 12 is much the most frequent. Although $x = 12$ occurs in the Umbelliferae it is found at a rather low frequency and it is tempting to consider the Araliaceae with the subfamilies of Umbelliferae so that, of the presumed diploid base numbers, the Saniculoideae have exploited 8, the Hydrocotyloideae 8 and 10, the Apioideae 11 and the Araliaceae 12, thus chromosomally putting them at comparable hierarchical levels. If some sort of sequence is sought then it is perhaps relevant that most Umbelliferae with $x = 12$ are in the Hydrocotyloideae, tribe Hydrocotyleae, and almost all the remainder in the Saniculoideae.

Table 3. Presumed basic chromosome numbers in Umbellales, Cornales, Sapindales (*sensu* Cronquist, 1968)

Umbellales										
Umbelliferae	4	5	6	7	8	9	10	11	12	13
Araliaceae						9*	10*	11	12?	13
Cornales										
Cornaceae					8	9	10	11		
Alangiaceae					8			11		
Garryaceae								11		
Rhizophoraceae					8*	9*				
Nyssaceae							10*	11*		
Sapindales										
Staphyleaceae									12	13
Melianthaceae						9*				
Connaraceae				7*						13
Sapindaceae				7*	8*			11	12	
Hippocastanaceae							10*			
Aceraceae										13
Burseraceae								11	12	13
Anacardiaceae				7	8*		10*		12	
Rutaceae				7	8	9		11	12*	13
Meliaceae				7*			10	11	12	
Zygophyllaceae			6		8	9	10	11	12	13

Data for families other than the Umbelliferae taken from Bolkhovskikh *et al.* (1969). Numbers marked with an asterisk are not known within the diploid range in the family but are deduced from haploid numbers of 14 or more.

The Araliaceae and Umbelliferae have traditionally been included in the same order with the Cornaceae and their allies. However, Cronquist (1968) has separated the Umbellales, comprising the first two families, from the Cornales and considers them to be most closely related to the Sapindales. The presumed basic chromosome numbers for the families in the Umbellales, Cornales and Sapindales, as delimited by Cronquist, are shown in Table 3. It can be seen that $x = 8$ and 11 occur in both the Cornales and Sapindales, though at a rather higher frequency in the former, and on this basis families in both orders could be suggested as of close chromosomal affinity to the Umbelliferae, e.g. Cornaceae, Alangiaceae, Sapindaceae, Rutaceae and Zygophyllaceae. It is worth pointing out that $x = 12$, which is largely characteristic of the Araliaceae and which is also present in some genera of Umbelliferae (see pp. 236–68), does not occur at all in the Cornales, while in the Sapindales it is found in seven of the eleven families for which chromosome data are available. Of the families listed in Table 3 it is interesting that it is the Umbelliferae, with a high frequency of herbaceous types, that have most exploited chromosomal variation, although followed rather closely by the generally shrubby Zygophyllaceae which appears to be a derived family within the Sapindales.

CHROMOSOME STUDIES AND EVOLUTION

In contrast to the purely phenetic value of the chromosome data available for the Umbelliferae it is worth here considering what role they have in the evolution and differentiation of the family. As mentioned earlier (p. 234) the lack of experimental cytogenetical information in the Umbelliferae severely limits the interpretative chromosomal studies so necessary for the subject of this section and what follows is a summary of relevant information gleaned from the observational data that are available.

Chromosomal variation

Meiotic irregularities

As noted earlier (p. 234) chromosome information is now available for some 840 species, and in about three-quarters of these it has been derived from examination of meiosis. In the overwhelming majority of these cases there is no indication that anything other than normal bivalent pairing occurred but occasional examples of meiotic irregularities can be cited. Thus, in *Sanicula crassicaulis* Poepp. ex DC. Bell (1954) found multivalents in some hexaploids and octoploids, although none were observed in the tetraploids, but there are few other such examples. Even where natural hybrids have been studied, as in *Apium* (Beuzenberg & Hair, 1963), *Eryngium* L. (L. Constance *et al.*, unpublished) and *Sanicula* (Bell, 1954), meiosis appears normal, the only exception to this being a hybrid between diploid and tetraploid populations of *Eryngium campestre* L. (Reese, 1969) in which 35–40% of the pollen mother cells showed univalents and multivalents and abnormalities such as lagging chromosomes. In a natural hybrid between *Eryngium campestre* ($n = 7$) and *E. planum* L. ($n = 8$) seven bivalents and one univalent were found at meiosis by Reese (1969) and it is possible that a similar set of circumstances accounts for the report of eleven bivalents and one univalent in *Seseli montanum* L. (Gardé & Malheiros-Gardé, 1954), although it may equally indicate the presence of supernumerary chromosomes.

Supernumerary chromosomes

The only definite record is that of Favarger & Huynh (1964), who found four B-chromsomes in *Dethawia tenuifolia* (Ramond ex DC.) Godron, but the report of $2n = 33$ for *Centella asiatica* (L.) Urban by Mitsukuri & Kurahori (1959) may suggest a supernumerary chromosome. As noted in the previous paragraph, *Seseli montanum* may also be cited here.

Aneuploidy and polyploidy

It is often noted in the literature that aneuploidy is frequent and polyploidy is rare in the Umbelliferae; indeed, it was recently stated (Cauwet, 1970) that polyploidy is known in only six genera. A glance at Fig. 1 or Appendix A, however, shows that while aneuploidy is common in the family, so is polyploidy. The extent of intrageneric aneuploid and polyploid variation in those genera for which more than one count is available is summarized in Table 4 and, for comparison, data for two other large groups—the Leguminosae and, in the Compositae, the tribe Astereae, which has recently been the subject of intensive chromosome studies (Solbrig *et al.*, 1969). From these data it can be seen that the Umbelliferae are not too different from the other two groups. The higher proportion of Umbellifer genera showing variation is due to the Apioideae and, particularly, the Saniculoideae and it is interesting to note the differences between the three subfamilies with regard to the various components of this variation. Thus, there are no genera in the Saniculoideae in which only polyploid variation occurs, while such variation is found to a comparable extent in the Apioideae and the Leguminosae where it is about half as frequent as in the Hydrocotyloideae and Astereae. On the other hand, aneuploid variation alone is virtually identical in the Leguminosae and Astereae, rather more frequent and very similar in the Saniculoideae and Apioideae, and much less common in the Hydrocotyloideae. Again, within the Umbelliferae, genera showing both polyploid and aneuploid variation are least common in the Hydrocotyloideae, but are markedly still less frequent in the Astereae. Whilst sampling error may account for the universal occurrence of chromosomal variation in the four saniculoid genera considered, it will be interesting to see whether future studies confirm or otherwise the trends indicated here which suggest that the patterns of chromosomal variation may differ somewhat in the subfamilies of the Umbelliferae. It is particularly interesting that, within the family, the Hydrocotyloideae seem chromosomally most conservative and closest to the Astereae and Leguminosae, and furthermore that their variation is perhaps due more to multiplication of genomes than to aneuploidy involving changes in base number.

Although allopolyploidy is more likely to be commoner than autopolyploidy in the Umbelliferae, as appears to be the case in most plants, there is evidence for the occurrence of both in the family. Thus, polyploids in *Sanicula crassicaulis* are morphologically and ecologically intermediate between the diploid species *S. laciniata* Hook. & Arn. and *S. hoffmannii* (Munz) Shan & Constance, and Bell (1954) considers the tetraploid populations to be allotetraploids while the hexa- and octo-polyploids are probably autoallopolyploids, although some of the latter also perhaps derive from hybridization between hexaploid *S. crassicaulis* and the diploid *S. bipinnatifida* Dougl. ex Hook. In *Eryngium*, on the other hand, the 28-chromosome forms of *E. campestre* seem likely to be autotetraploids since they have a karyotype which duplicates in every detail that of the diploid complement (Reese, 1969).

Intraspecific chromosome variation

It is interesting to note from Table 5 that the Umbelliferae are closely similar to both the Astereae and Leguminosae in that about a quarter of the genera appear to show some intraspecific variation in chromosome number. When the subfamilies are considered separately it can be seen that two of them are very similar indeed to the non-umbelliferous groups while the Saniculoideae show a much higher variation which, as indicated above, may be a spurious effect of the small sample. The chromosome variation due to polyploidy is likely to be reasonably accurately recorded in the data summarized in Table 4 and although aneuploidy is undoubtedly over-estimated because of inaccurate and conflicting counts this is probably a factor of similar magnitude in the three families considered.

There is little information on the extent to which the observed intraspecific chromosome variation is correlated with other factors. In the *Sanicula crassicaulis* complex Bell (1954) could not find any correlation between the variation associated with individual plants or populations and the chromosome level of those plants or

Table 4. Occurrence of variation in chromosome number in genera of Umbelliferae, Compositae-Astereae (data from Solbrig et al., 1969) and Leguminosae (data from Bolkhovskikh et al., 1969) for which more than 1 count is known

	Polyploidy	Aneuploidy	Polyploidy + aneuploidy	Total show- ing variation	Total genera
Astereae	14(33·33%)	8(19·05%)	8(19·05%)	30(71·43%)	42
Hydrocotyloideae	4(36·36%)	1(9·09%)	3(27·27%)	8(72·72%)	11
Saniculoideae	0	1(25·00%)	3(75·0%)	4(100%)	4
Apioideae	13(16·25%)	21(26·25%)	32(40·0%)	66(82·5%)	80
[Umbelliferae total]	17(17·9%)	23(24·3%)	38(41%)	78(83·2%)	95
Leguminosae	25(17·60%)	27(19·0%)	48(33·8%)	100(70·04%)	142

Table 5. Number of genera apparently showing intraspecific variation in chromosome number in Umbelliferae, Compositae-Astereae and Leguminosae (for sources of data see Table 4)

Astereae	15/63	23·8%	
Hydrocotyloideae	4/18	22·2%	
Saniculoideae	3/6	50·0%	} 28%
Apioideae	41/147	27·9%	
Leguminosae	66/254	26·0%	

populations, while he considered that the few correlations he did find between chromosomes and distribution were not significant and likely to disappear with increased data. An interesting situation is reported from *Perideridia* Reichenb. (Chuang & Constance, 1969) in which the populations with the presumed diploid numbers ($n = 8, 9, 10$) were the most difficult to separate and were therefore provisionally treated as a single polymorphic species, while the taxa at polyploid levels were reasonably distinct. This is the reverse of the situation usually reported in such cases where the blurring of morphological boundaries occurs at polyploid levels and has given rise to the concept of 'pillar complexes'.

Chromosome variation in large genera

As might be expected, the greatest variation in chromosome number is shown by the large genera. However, the reverse is not necessarily true and a wide variety of situations exists in these presumably successful genera for which we have a reasonable amount of information. Thus, for example, *Hydrocotyle* L. shows a wide range of polyploids up to 15-ploid, together with aneuploidy at all levels. *Eryngium*, *Pimpinella* L. and *Seseli* L. are largely diploid, with some polyploidy and aneuploidy at the diploid level, while *Angelica* L., *Bupleurum*, *Ligusticum*, *Lomatium*, *Peucedanum* L. and *Sanicula* show a similar pattern with the exception that there is relatively little aneuploidy at any level. *Donnellsmithia* Coulter ex Rose has one diploid species, all the others exploiting aneuploidy at the tetraploid and hexaploid levels, while in complete contrast *Daucus* L., which is mostly diploid with $n = 10$ and 11, has two polyploids and is otherwise aneuploid at the diploid level. Finally, three widespread and well-developed genera are all diploid, *Apium* with $n = 11$ except for two species with $n - 6$, *Laserpitium* L. with $n = 11$ and *Oreomyrrhis* Endl. with $n = 6$ except for one record of $n = 7$.

Interrelationships of presumed primary basic numbers

As pointed out earlier (p. 236), within the range of presumed diploid numbers the Umbelliferae contains all gametic numbers between $n = 4$ and $n = 13$ and these may be considered the presumed primary basic numbers of the family. In addition, of course, there are the aneuploid numbers at polyploid levels which clearly constitute a group of secondary basic numbers, but it should also be stressed that some of the numbers in the range $x = 4$ to $x = 13$ may also be secondary numbers. It is clearly very important for understanding chromosomal evolution in the Umbelliferae to be able to determine which of the presumed primary basic numbers are original and which are derived, but the lack of relevant information has already been mentioned (p. 236). The predominance of $x = 8$ and $x = 11$ in the family, and their widespread occurrence in related families, other than the Araliaceae which have already been considered as a special case (p. 239), suggests that these might be the original numbers within the Umbelliferae. If this is so, then it might be suspected that the other primary basic numbers have mostly been derived from them by reduction, since it seems generally easier to lose than to gain centromeres. There is very little direct evidence on these points. In *Bupleurum* Cauwet (1968) has shown that the 7-chromosome species seem to be more derived than those with $x = 8$, and in *Tordylium* L. (Runemark, 1968) the change is presumed to be from $x = 10$ to $x = 9$. Centromeric gain is validly assumed in *Centella* L. by Hair (1966), who proposed that the New Zealand endemic *C. uniflora* (Col.) Nannf. ($n = 38$) is a secondary octoploid ($x_2 = 19$) by comparison with the widespread diploid species *C. asiatica* ($n = 9$).

Even if future detailed cytological evidence should confirm 8 and 11 as original primary basic numbers in the Umbelliferae, the reported occurrence of both these numbers in such genera as *Bupleurum*, *Daucus*, *Ptilimnium* Rafn., *Seseli* and *Spermolepis* Brongn. ex Griseb. suggests that one of the numbers, presumably $x = 8$, can also be derived secondarily in these genera. Again, it could be supposed that the group of genera in the Hydrocotyloideae-Mulineae with $x = 10$ are derived from 11-chromosome ancestors, but Runemark (1968) has suggested that in *Tordylium* the original primary basic number is $x = 5$, which has given rise to the only species known in the family with $n = 4$ by centromeric loss following a reciprocal translocation, and that most species known cytologically in the genus, which have $n = 10$, are tetraploid.

Chromosomes and generic endemism

The level of generic endemism is high in the Umbelliferae but there do not generally appear to be any distinctive chromosomal characteristics of such genera. Thus, for example, endemic genera in the Apioideae are more likely than not to have $x = 11$, those in the other two subfamilies to have $x = 8$; exceptions are no more frequent among the endemic than the widespread genera. However, the chromosome data summarized in Appendix A do reveal one point of potential interest in this respect. There are seventeen genera in which all representatives so far examined are polyploid. According to the concepts of Favarger (1961, 1967, 1969) these may be considered as palaeopolyploids, since diploid relatives are not known, and their occurrence in a particular region may indicate evolutionary antiquity. It is therefore interesting to note that, of these seventeen genera, there is one each in Japan (*Nothosmyrnium* Miq.), Australia (*Actinotus* Labill.) and Argentina (*Oligocladus* Chodat ex Wilczek), two in North America (*Oreoxis* Rafn., *Oxypolis* Rafn.) and three in the Mediterranean region (*Echinophora* L., *Molopospermum* Koch, *Prangos* Lindl.). All the others, comprising over half the total, occur in Mexico and neighbouring regions of Central America—*Arracacia* Bancroft, *Coaxana* Coulter & Rose, *Coulterophytum* Robinson, *Enantiophylla* Coulter & Rose, *Neogoezia* Hemsley, *Neonelsonia* Coulter & Rose, *Ottoa* Humb., Bonpl. & Kunth, *Prionosciadium* Wats. and *Rhodosciadium* Wats. It will be interesting to see how far this picture is supported by future work but it is perhaps noteworthy that Mathias (1965) considered the Mexican highlands and Central America to be one of the two centres of distribution of Apioideae in the western Northern Hemisphere. It is possible that the concentration of apparent palaeopolyploids in this region is somehow connected with the suggestion that the genera there are the modern derivatives of the Madro-Tertiary Geoflora (Mathias, 1965). The other centre of distribution, in Pacific North America (including the Rocky Mountains), which holds very few such polyploid genera, has a flora of much more diverse affinities, but interestingly one of the two apparent palaeopolyploid genera in this region, *Oreoxis*, is given as an example of a montane relict by Mathias (1965). The two above regions together comprise one of the major centres of differentiation of the Umbelliferae. In contrast, the other centre, with about three times as many species, is concentrated around the Mediterranean, where a great deal of generic endemism has occurred at the diploid level and suspected palaeopolyploids appear to be relatively infrequent.

ACKNOWLEDGEMENTS

It is a pleasure to thank Dr Lincoln Constance for placing at my disposal his complete file of published chromosome numbers in the Umbelliferae, together with much as yet unpublished information. I am also very grateful to Dr J. B. Hair, Christchurch, New Zealand, and Dr C. J. Marchant, Royal Botanic Gardens, Kew, for kindly providing unpublished information for use in this account.

REFERENCES

BAQUAR, S. R., 1967–1968. Chromosome numbers in some vascular plants of East Pakistan. *Rev. Biol.*, 6: 440–448.

BEGHTEL, F. E., 1925. The embryogeny of *Pastinaca sativa*. *Am. J. Bot.*, 12: 327–337.

BELL, C. R., 1954. The *Sanicula crassicaulis* complex (Umbelliferae). *Univ. Calif. Publs Bot.*, 27: 133–230.

BELL, C. R. & CONSTANCE, L., 1957. Chromosome numbers in Umbelliferae. *Am. J. Bot.*, 44: 565–572.

BEUZENBERG, E. J. & HAIR, J. B., 1963. Contributions to a chromosome atlas of the New Zealand flora — 5. Miscellaneous families. *N.Z. Jl Bot.*, 1: 53–67.

BOLKHOVSKIKH, Z., GRIF, V., MATVEJEVA, T. & ZAKHARYEVA, O., 1969. *Chromosome numbers of flowering plants.* Leningrad: Acad. Sci. U.S.S.R.

BORHIDI, A., 1968. Karyological studies on south-east European plant species. I. *Acta Bot. Acad. Sci. Hung.*, **14**: 253–260.

CAUWET, A., 1967. Contribution à l'étude caryosystématique du genre *Bupleurum* L. I. *Bull. Soc. bot. Fr.*, **114**: 371–386.

CAUWET, A., 1968. Contribution à l'étude caryologique des Ombellifères de la partie orientale des Pyrénées. *Nat. Monspel. Sér. Bot.*, **19**: 5–27.

CAUWET, A., 1970. *Contribution à l'étude caryosystématique du genre* Bupleurum (Tourn.) L. Thèse, Fac. Sci. Univ. Montpellier.

CHESNOY, L., 1962. *Étude caryologique du* Bupleurum lancifolium *et données sur deux espèces voisines.* Paris: D.E.S.

CHUANG, T-I. & CONSTANCE, L., 1969. A systematic study of *Perideridia* (Umbelliferae-Apioideae). *Univ. Calif. Publs Bot.*, **55**: 1–74.

CONSTANCE, L. & CANNON, J. F. M., 1967. *Naufraga*—a new genus of Umbelliferae from Mallorca. *Feddes Repert.*, **74**: 1–4.

COOK, C. D. K., 1968. In I.O.P.B. chromosome number reports XVIII. *Taxon*, **17**: 419–422.

CRONQUIST, A., 1968. *The Evolution and Classification of Flowering Plants.* London & Edinburgh: Nelson.

CROWDEN, R. K., HARBORNE, J. B. & HEYWOOD, V. H., 1969. Chemosystematics of the Umbelliferae— a general survey. *Phytochemistry*, **8**: 1963–1984.

DAMBOLDT, J., 1968. In I.O.P.B. chromosome number reports XV. *Taxon*, **17**: 91–104.

DAWSON, J. W., 1961. A revision of the genus *Anisotome* (Umbelliferae). *Univ. Calif. Publs Bot.*, **33**: 1–98.

DAWSON, J. W., 1967. The New Zealand species of *Gingidium* (Umbelliferae). *N.Z. Jl Bot.*, **5**: 84–116.

DELAY, J., 1968. Halophytes II. *Inf. Ann. Caryosyst. Cytogénét.*, **2**: 17–22.

DRUDE, C. G. O., 1897–1898. In Engler, A. & Prantl, K. (eds) *Die natürlichen Pflanzenfamilien*, 3 (8): 63–150.

ENGSTRAND, L., 1970. Studies in the Aegean flora XVIII. Notes and chromosome numbers in Aegean Umbelliferae. *Bot. Not.*, **123**: 384–393.

FAVARGER, C., 1961. Sur l'emploi des nombres de chromosomes en géographie botanique historique. *Ber. geobot. Inst. Rübel*, **32**: 119–146.

FAVARGER, C., 1967. Cytologie et distribution des plantes. *Biol. Rev.*, **42**: 163–206.

FAVARGER, C., 1969. In I.O.P.B. chromosome number reports XXII. *Taxon*, **18**: 434–435.

FAVARGER, C. & HUYNH, K. L., 1964. In I.O.P.B. chromosome number reports II. *Taxon*, **13**: 201–209.

FAVARGER, C. & KÜPFER, P., 1968. Contribution à la cytotaxinomie de la flore alpine des Pyrénées. *Collect. Bot.*, **7**: 325–352.

GADELLA, T. W. J. & KLIPHUIS, E., 1968. Chromosome numbers of flowering plants in the Netherlands IV. *Proc. Roy. Netherlands Acad. Sci. ser. C.*, **71**: 168–183.

GARDÉ, A. & MALHEIROS-GARDÉ, N., 1949. Contribuição para o estudio cariologico da familia Umbelliferae. I. *Agron. Lusit.*, **11**: 91–140.

GARDÉ, A. & MALHEIROS-GARDÉ, N., 1954. Contribuiçao para o estudio cariologico da familia Umbelliferae. III. *Brotéria*, **23**: 5–35.

HAIR, J. B., 1966. Biosystematics of the New Zealand flora 1945–1964. *N.Z. Jl Bot.*, **4**: 559–595.

HSU, C.-C. 1968. Preliminary chromosome studies on the vascular plants of Taiwan. I. *Taiwania*, no. 13: 117–130.

HUNKELER, C. & FAVARGER, C., 1967. Contribution à la cytotaxinomie du genre *Pimpinella* L. *Bull. Soc. Neuchat. Sci. Nat.*, **90**: 219–239.

JOHNSON, A. W. & PACKER, J. G., 1968. Chromosome numbers in the flora of Ogotoruk Creek, N.W. Alaska. *Bot. Not.*, **121**: 403–456.

JOSHI, S., 1968. A comparative study in Umbellifers of artifically induced polyploids and structural hybridity with special reference to change in the expression of gene (genes) controlling the pollen shapes. *Cytologia*, **33**: 345–356.

JOSHI, S. & RAGHUVANSHI, S. S., 1965. *Coriandrum sativum*: mutation, polyploidy, non-dividing pollen mother cells and pollen variability. *Can. J. Genet. Cytol.*, **7**: 223–236.

KAPOOR, B. M. & LÖVE, Á., 1969. In I.O.P.B. chromosome number reports XX. *Taxon*, **18**: 214.

KUROSAWA, S., 1966. Cytological studies on some Eastern Himalayan plants. In Hara, H. (ed.), *The Flora of Eastern Himalaya*, pp. 658–670. Univ. Tokyo Press.

LEE, Y. N., 1967. Chromosome numbers of flowering plants in Korea I. *J. Korean Cult. Res. Inst.*, **11**: 455–478.

LEE, Y. N., 1969. Chromosome numbers of flowering plants in Korea II. *J. Korean Inst. Better Living*, **2**: 141–145.

LÖVE, Á. & KAPOOR, B. M., 1967. In I.O.P.B. chromosome number reports XIV. *Taxon*, **16**: 552–571.

LÖVE, Á. & LÖVE, D., 1965. In I.O.P.B. chromosome number reports IV. *Taxon*, **14**: 86–92.

MATHIAS, M., 1965. Distribution patterns of certain Umbelliferae. *Ann. Mo. Bot. Gdn*, **52**: 387–398.

MATHIAS, M. & CONSTANCE, L., 1955. The genus *Oreomyrrhis* (Umbelliferae). *Univ. Calif. Publs Bot.*, **27**: 347–416.

MATHIAS, M. & CONSTANCE, L., 1962. A revision of *Asteriscium* and some related hydrocotyloid Umbelliferae. *Univ. Calif. Publs Bot.*, **33**: 99–184.

MELDERIS, A., 1930. Chromosome numbers in Umbelliferae. *Acta Horti Bot. latv.*, **5**: 1–8.

MITRA, K. & DATTA, N., 1967. In I.O.P.B. chromosome number reports XIII. *Taxon*, **16**: 445–461.

MITSUKURI, Y. & KURAHORI, Y., 1959. Cytogenetical studies in Umbelliferae II. The chromosome numbers and karyotypes of some Japanese species. *La Kromosomo*, **40**: 1354–1361.

MOORE, D. M., 1967. Chromosome numbers of Falkland Islands angiosperms. *Br. Antarct. Surv. Bull.*, no. 14: 69–82.

MOORE, D. M., 1968. The karyotype in taxonomy. In Heywood, V. H. (ed.), *Modern Methods in Plant Taxonomy*, pp. 61–75. London: Academic Press.

MULLIGAN, G. A., 1967. In I.O.P.B. chromosome number reports XIV. *Taxon*, **16**: 552–571.

MURÍN, A. & CHAUDRI, I. I., 1970. In I.O.P.B. chromosome number reports XXVI. *Taxon*, **19**: 266–268.

OGAWA, K., 1929. Chromosome arrangement. V. Pollen mother cells in *Torilis anthriscus* Bernh. and *Peucedanum japonicum* Thunb. *Mem. Coll. Sci. Kyoto Imp. Univ. B*, **4**: 309–322.

PETERSEN, H. E., 1914. Indledende Studier over Polymorphien hos *Anthriscus silvestris* (L.) Hoffm. *Diss. Univ. Copenhagen*: 1–40.

PODLECH, D. & DIETERLE, A., 1969. Chromosomenstudien an afghanischen Pflanzen. *Candollea*, **24**: 185–243.

RAGHUVANSHI, S. S. & JOSHI, S., 1966. *Foeniculum vulgare*: Polyploidy, translocation heterozygosity and pollen variability. Part I. Cytology. *Cytologia*, **31**: 43–58.

REESE, G., 1961. In Löve, Á. & Löve, D., Chromosome numbers of central and northwest European plant species. *Op. bot. Soc. bot. Lund*, **5**: 1–371.

REESE, G., 1969. Cytotaxonomische Untersuchungen an di- und tetraploiden Sippen von *Eryngium campestre* L. und einem Artbastard mit $2n = 15$. *Öst. bot. Z.*, **117**: 223–247.

ROGERS, J. L., 1965. Documented plant chromosome numbers 65:1. *Sida*, **2**: 163–165.

RUNEMARK, H., 1968. Studies in the Aegean flora, XIII. *Tordylium* L. (Umbelliferae). *Bot. Not.*, **121**: 233–258.

SCHULZ-GAEBEL, H. H., 1930. Entwicklungsgeschichte-zytologische Studien an der Umbelliferen-Unterfamilie der Apioideen. *Beitr. Biol. Pfl.*, **18**: 345–398.

SMITH, E. B. In I.O.P.B. chromosome number reports XVII. *Taxon*, **17**: 285–288.

SNOGERUP, S., 1962. Studies in the Aegean flora IV. *Bupleurum flavum* Forsk. and related species. *Bot. Not.*, **115**: 357–375.

SOKOLOVSKAYA, A. P., 1968. A karyological investigation of the flora of the Korjakian Land. *Bot. Zh.*, **53**: 99–105. [In Russian]

SOLBRIG, O. T., ANDERSON, L. C., KHYOS, D. W. & RAVEN, P. H., 1969. Chromosome numbers in Compositae VII: Astereae III. *Am. J. Bot.* **56**: 348–353.

SUSNIK, F. & DRUSKOVIC, B., 1968. Prisevek k morfologiji in citologiji taksona *Pastinaca fleischmannii* Hladnik ex Koch. *Biol. Vestn.*, **16**: 29–38.

TAMAMSCHJAN, S., 1933. Materialen zur Caryosystematik der kultivierten und wilden Umbelliferen. *Bull. Appl. Bot. Genet. Pl. Breed.* II, **2**: 137–161.

TAYLOR, R. L., 1968. In I.O.P.B. chromosome number reports XIX. *Taxon*, **17**: 577.

TAYLOR, R. L. & MULLIGAN, G. A., 1968. *Flora of the Queen Charlotte Islands. Part 2. Cytological aspects of the Vascular Plants.* Ottawa: Queen's Printer.

THEOBALD, W. L., 1966. The *Lomatium dasycarpum-mohavense-foeniculaceum* complex. *Brittonia*, **18**: 1–18.

THORNE, R. F., 1968. Synopsis of a putatively phylogenetic classification of flowering plants. *Aliso*, **6**: 57–66.

WANSCHER, J. H., 1931. Studies on the chromosome numbers of the Umbelliferae. *Hereditas*, **15**: 179–184.

WANSCHER, J. H., 1932. Studies on the chromosome numbers of the Umbelliferae. II. *Bot. Tidsskr.*, **42**: 49–58.

WANSCHER, J. H., 1933. Studies on the chromosome numbers of the Umbelliferae. III. *Bot. Tidsskr.*, **42**: 384–399.

WANSCHER, J. H., 1934. Secondary (chromosome) associations in Umbelliferae and Bicornes. *New Phytol.*, **33**: 58–65.

APPENDIX A

	4	5	6	7	8	9	10	11	12	13	14	16	17	18	19	20	n 21
HYDROCOTYLOIDEAE																	
HYDROCOTYLEAE																	
Actinotus																1	
*Centenella						1						1					
*Hydrocotyle								2		3		3		1			
Micropleura							1										
Trachymene								2								1	
MULINEAE																	
Asteriscium							2										
Azorella					8							2					
Bolax												1					
Bowlesia					4												
Drusa					1												
*Eremocharis			2		2		2										
Gymnophyton							3										
Homalocarpus					1												
Huanaca						1											
Laretia						1											
*Mulinum					4							2					
Naufraga							1										
Pozoa							2										
Schizeilema					1							7					
Spananthe					1												
SANICULOIDEAE																	
SANICULEAE																	
*Astrantia				5	1						3						
*Eryngium		3	8	17	47						1	14					
Hacquetia					1												
*Sanicula					25			1				1					
LAGOECIEAE																	
Lagoecia				1	1												
Petagnia																	
APIOIDEAE																	
ECHINOPHOREAE																	
Echinophora																	
SCANDICEAE-SCANDICINEAE																	
Ammoselinum									1					1			
*Anthriscus				3	2	5											
*Chaerophyllum			1	1				8									
Molopospermum																	
Myrrhis								1									
*Myrrhoides				1				1				1					
Osmorhiza								4									
*Scandix				1	5	1	1?			1?		1	1				
Tinguarra								1									
SCANDICEAE-CAUCALINEAE																	
Astrodaucus							1										
*Caucalis							1	2									
Chaetosciadium			1														
*Orlaya					2	2	1										
*Torilis			5		2			1	3					1			
*Turgenia					1							1					
DAUCEAE																	
Ammodaucus					1												
Artedia					1												
*Daucus				1	2	3	5	8									
Pseudorlaya					1												

22	24	ca. 25	27	28	30	32	33	34	36	38	40	42	44	48	60	66	77	80	84	Source†
																				1
1																				1, 2, 10, 22, 35
	9				2	1	2		1	1			1	1				1	1	1, 10, 20, 21, 22, 28, 36, 46
									3											
																				1
4													1		1					1, 10
																				1
																				1, 10, 36, 37
																				37
																				1, 10
																				1
																				1, 10
																				1, 10
																				1
																				37
																				1
	1																			10
																				33
																				1
	3				1						1									21, 36
																				1
																				1, 6, 17
	8						11				3			5						1, 5, 9, 10, 14, 41
																				1
	1						1													1, 10, 28, 52
1																				1, 10, 15
																				1
						1														1, 6
																				10
																				1, 6, 15, 40
																				1, 6, 10
1																				1, 6
																				1, 6
																				1, 10, 49
																				1, 10, 52
																				1, 6, 10, 15, 41
																				10
																				1, 10
1																				1, 10, 49
																				10, 49
																				1, 15
1																				1, 5, 10, 15, 41, 49
																				1, 10, 49
																				10
																				15
1								2												1, 10, 15, 25, 27, 37, 41, 49, 51
																				1, 15

APPENDIX A—*contd.*

	4	5	6	7	8	9	10	11	12	13	14	16	17	18	19	20	n 21
CORIANDREAE																	
*Bifora							2	2									
Coriandrum								1									
SMYRNIEAE																	
Apiastrum								1									
*Arracacia (Velaea)											1						
Cachrys								2									
*Conium					1			1									
*Donnellsmithia								1								2	3
Erigenia						?1											
*Neogoezia																	
Neonelsonia																	
Oreomyrrhis			11	1													
*Ottoa																1	
Oxypolis											2	1		2			
Pleurospermum								1									
Prangos														1			
Scaligeria							2										
Smyrnium								3									
Tauschia								5									
APIEAE																	
Aciphylla								15									
*Aegopodium								1									
*Aethusa							1	1									
Alboria							1										
*Ammi							1	3									
Ammoides		1															
Anethum								1									
Anisotome								9									
Aphanopleura							1	1									
Apium				2				14									
Astydamia								1									
Athamanta								3									
*Berula		1				2											
Brachyapium							1										
Bunium								2									
*Bupleurum			2	14	26			3			3	3					1
*Carum						1	4	5	1								
Cenolophium								1									
Chamaele								1									
*Cicuta								6									
*Cnidium							2	4	1								
Coaxana																	
Conioselinum				1				2									
Conopodium								1									
Cortia								1									
*Crithmum							1	1									
*Cryptotaenia						1	3	3									
Cuminum				1													
Cymopterus								4									
Cynosciadium			1														
Daucosma (Discopleura)					1												
Dethawia								1									
Endressia								1									
Eurytaenia				2													
Falcaria								1									
Foeniculum								5									
Frommia								1									
Gingidium (Coxella)								4									
Glehnia								1									
Harbouria							1										
Heteromorpha								1									
Kundmannia								1									
*Ligusticum								14									
Lilaeopsis								2									

22	24	ca. 25	27	28	30	32	33	34	36	38	40	42	44	48	60	66	77	80	84	Source†
																				1
																				1, 25, 26, 49
																				1
13						1														1, 10
																				1
																				1, 10
2								1		1	1	2	1							1, 10
																				10
1			1	1																10
1																				1
																				1, 10, 34, 36
1																				10
																				1
		1																		1
																				41
																				15
																				1, 6, 15
																				1, 10
																				1, 21
4																				1
																				1, 6
																				10
																				1, 5, 15, 39
																				1
																				1, 10, 25
																				13, 21
																				1, 41
																				1, 10, 15, 36
																				1
																				1
																				1
																				5
																				1, 5
																				1, 5, 7, 10, 17, 18, 24, 29, 30, 42, 47
																				1, 6, 10, 15, 38
																				1
																				1
4																				1, 10, 32
																				1, 10, 48
3																				10
2																				1, 24, 52
																				1
																				1
																				1, 6
																				1
																				1, 25
																				1, 10
																				10
																				1
																				1
																				6
																				1
																				1
																				1, 10, 43
																				10
																				1, 13
																				1, 52
																				1
																				10
																				1
1			1				2													1, 6, 10, 16, 52
2																				1, 10, 36, 52

APPENDIX A—contd.

	4	5	6	7	8	9	10	11	12	13	14	16	17	18	19	20	n 21
Limnosciadium			1														
Meum								1									
Microsciadium			1														
Muretia								1									
Nirarathamnos								1									
*Nothosmyrnium														1			
Oenanthe							4	11								?1	
*Oreoxis																	
*Perideridia (Eulophus)					1	1	1			1			2	4	7	6	
*Petroselinum						1		1									
*Pimpinella					12		7	3						2		1	
Pituranthos							1	1									
Pteryxia								1									
*Ptilimnium			2	2	1			1				1					
Ptychotis								1									
Ridolfia								1									
Selinum								3									
*Seseli					1	7	3	12				1					1
Silaum								1									
Sison				1													
*Sium			2				2	2								1	
Spermolepis					2			1									
Sphenosciadium								1									
Taenidia								1									
Thaspium								3									
Todaroa								2									
*Trachyspermum						1		1									
Trepocarpos						1											
Trinia						3	1										
Trochiscanthes								1									
Xatardia								1									
Zizia								3									
PEUCEDANEAE																	
Ainsworthia				1													
*Angelica								41			2						
Capnophyllum							1	1									
Coelopleurum								2									
Coulterophytum																	
Dorema								1									
Ducrosia								1									
Elaeoselinum								2									
Enantiophylla																	
Erythroselinum								1									
Ferula							1	9									
Ferulago								1									
Heracleum								12									
*Laser						1		1									
Levisticum								1									
*Lomatium								38									
Lophosciadium								1									
Malabaila								3									
Oligocladus																	
Opopanax								1									
Pastinaca					1?			4									
Peucedanum			1					21	1								
Polytaenia								1									
Prionosciadium																	2
Pseudocymopterus								1									
Pseudotaenidia								1									
*Rhodosciadium																	1
Scandia								2									
Synelcosciadium							1										
Thysselinum								1									
Tordylium	1					1	6	1									
Zozimia							1										

22	24	ca. 25	27	28	30	32	33	34	36	38	40	42	44	48	60	66	77	80	84	Source†
																				1
																				1, 5, 6
																				15
																				1
																				10
1																				1
3																				1, 5, 10, 11, 52
					1								1							1, 3
1												1		1						1, 8, 10
1																				1
																				1, 6, 10, 15, 23, 25
1																				1, 10, 39
																				1
																				1, 10
																				1, 6
																				1
																				1, 6
																				1, 5, 6, 10, 12, 16, 35
																				1, 10
																				10
																				1
						1														1, 10
																				1
																				1
																				1, 10
																				1, 10
																				1, 10, 25
																				1
																				1, 6
																				1
																				6
																				1
																				10
2								2												1, 6, 10, 24, 52
																				1, 10
																				1
1																				1, 10
																				1
																				10
																				1, 5
																				10
																				10
1																				1, 6, 10, 15
																				1
1																				1, 6, 10, 41, 52
																				1
																				1
7																		1	1		1, 10, 53
																				1
																				1, 15, 37
1																				1
																				1
																				1, 3, 6, 44, 50
								2												1, 4, 6, 19
																				1
5																				1, 10
																				1
																				1
3												1								1, 10
																				1
																				10
																				1
																				1, 45
																				10

D. M. MOORE

APPENDIX A—*contd.*

	4	5	6	7	8	9	10	11	12	13	14	16	17	18	19	20	n 21
LASERPITIEAE																	
Laserpitium								12									
Melanoselinum								1									
Siler					1			1									
Thapsia								2									

Appendix A. Haploid chromosome numbers known for the genera of Umbelliferae, showing the number of species in a genus for which each number has been reported.

* Asterisk indicates those genera within which intraspecific chromosome number differences have been recorded.

† Sources are indicated by numbers which refer to the publications whose authors are shown below and which are given in the list of references at the end of the paper. Individual mention is only made of those papers not listed in the recent compilation of Bolkhovskikh *et al.* (1969) from which details of all other sources can be obtained. (1) Bolkhovskikh *et al.*, 1969; (2) Baquar, 1967–1968; (3) Beghtel, 1925; (4) Borhidi, 1968; (5) Cauwet, 1967; (6) Cauwet, 1968; (7) Chesnoy, 1962; (8) Chuang & Constance, 1969; (9) Coleman & Smith, 1969; (10) Constance & Chuang, unpublished; (11) Cook, 1968; (12) Damboldt, 1968; (13) Dawson, 1961; (14) Delay, 1968; (15) Engstrand, 1970; (16) Favarger, 1969;

22	24	ca. 25	27	28	30	32	33	34	36	38	40	42	44	48	60	66	77	80	84	Source†
																				1, 6
																				1
																				1, 10
1								1												1, 5, 6

(17) Favarger & Huynh, 1964; (18) Favarger & Küpfer, 1968; (19) Gadella & Kliphuis, 1968; (20) Hair, 1966; (21) Hair, unpublished; (22) Hsu, 1968; (23) Hunkeler & Favarger, 1967; (24) Johnson & Packer, 1968; (25) Joshi, 1968; (26) Joshi & Raghuvanshi, 1965; (27) Kapoor & Löve, 1969; (28) Kurosawa, 1966; (29) Lee, 1967; (30) Lee, 1969; (31) Löve & Kapoor, 1967; (32) Löve & Löve, 1965; (33) Marchant, unpublished; (34) Mathias & Constance, 1955; (35) Mitra & Datta, 1967; (36) Moore, 1967; (37) Moore, unpublished; (38) Mulligan, 1967; (39) Murín & Chaudri, 1970; (40) Petersen, 1914; (41) Podlech & Dieterle, 1969; (42) Reese, 1961; (43) Raghuvanshi & Joshi, 1966; (44) Rogers, 1965; (45) Runemark, 1968; (46) Smith, 1968; (47) Snogerup, 1962; (48) Sokolovskaya, 1968; (49) Stewart, unpublished; (50) Susnik & Druskovic, 1968; (51) Taylor, 1968; (52) Taylor & Mulligan, 1968; (53) Theobald, 1966.

Caryosystématique du genre *Bupleurum* L.

A.-M. CAUWET

Laboratoire de Botanique, Collège Scientifique Universitaire, Perpignan, France

Les nombres chromosomiques que nous avons pu établir jusqu'ici dans le genre *Bupleurum* [Tourn.] L. ajoutés à ceux déjà connus nous ont permis de confirmer certaines sections ou sous-sections définies d'après des données morphologiques mais nous ont également amenée à en modifier quelques autres.

La sous-section *Nervosa* (Godron) Briq. a été divisée en deux séries ; l'une à nombre de base 7, l'autre à nombre de base 8. La sous-section *Marginata* Godron a été supprimée et remplacée par la sous-section *Rigida* Drude emend. Cauwet ; elle comprend uniquement *B. rigidum* L. Les paléopolyploides (*B. fruticescens* L., *B. spinosum* Gouan, *B. dianthifolium* Guss. et *B. salicifolium* Soland.) ont été réunis dans la sous-section *Fruticescentia* Cauwet.

L'évolution du genre semble s'être faite parallèlement à partir d'espèces à nombre de base 8, dans deux foyers de différenciation : le Bassin Méditerranéen et les chaînes asiatiques.

Chromosome numbers, previously recorded and those found by the author, in the genus *Bupleurum* [Tourn.] L., lead her to maintain some sections and subsections and to modify some others. Subsection *Nervosa* (Godron) Briq. is divided into two series, one with 7 as base number, the other with 8 as base number. Subsection *Marginata* Godron is replaced by subsection *Rigida* Drude emend. Cauwet; it contains only *B. rigidum* L. The palaeopolyploids (*B. fruticescens* L., *B. spinosum* Gouan, *B. dianthifolium* Guss. & *B. salicifolium* Soland.) are united in the subsection *Fruticescentia* Cauwet.

The genus seems to have undergone an evolution from species with eight as base number in two areas of differentiation : the Mediterranean basin and the mountains of Asia.

TABLE DES MATIÈRES

INTRODUCTION

Depuis Ogotoruk Creek près du Cercle Polaire en Alaska, où a été signalé *B. americanum* Coult. & Rose (Johnson & Packer, 1968) jusqu'à l'Ile de Ceylan qui abrite *B. mucronatum* Wight & Arnott, le genre *Bupleurum* L. peuple, entre 0 et

4200 m, de nombreux territoires de l'hémisphère nord. Dans l'hémisphère sud, seuls la province du Cap et le Transvaal abritent *B. mundtii* Cham. & Schlecht.

Le genre est essentiellement euro-asiatique représenté par de très nombreuses espèces sur le pourtour du Bassin Méditerranéen. Deux espèces seulement ont été signalées en Amérique du Nord: *B. triradiatum* Adams (Wolff, 1910, 117) en Alaska et *B. americanum* Coult. & Rose (Wolff, 1910, 122) de l'Alaska au Wyoming. Cette dernière espèce, diploide ($2n = 14$) dans la partie nord de son aire de répartition est tétraploide ($2n = 28, 32$) au sud de celle-ci (Johnson & Packer, 1968: 447). Nous sommes entièrement de l'avis de ces auteurs lorsqu'ils écrivent: 'It would seem reasonable to suppose that *Bupleurum* is Old World in origin and that its advent into N. America is fairly recent. . . . However, the entry of the genus certainly predates the last glaciation, for the distribution, . . . suggest survival both north and south of the last ice sheet.' Il ne fait aucun doute, le genre *Bupleurum* a émigré de l'Asie vers l'Amérique du nord par le Détroit de Béring.

Systématiquement, ce genre a été placé par Drude (1898: 115) dans la sous-famille des *Apioidées* (Ombelles composées), tribu des *Amminées* et sous-tribu des *Carininées* (fruit comprimé latéralement, méricarpe dépourvu de côtes secondaires et à côtes primaires égales, filiformes ou ailées, graine à face commissurale plane). L'absence de dents calicinales et la présence d'un stylopode plat le distinguent des genres: *Hohenackeria* Fischer & Meyer, *Nirarathamnos* Balf., *Heteromorpha* Cham. & Schlecht., *Rhyticarpus* Sond. & *Hermas* Reichenb. qui sont morphologiquement voisins.

La plantule est du 'type cotyledonaire long' (Cerceau-Larrival, 1962). Le pollen étudié par ce même auteur est considéré comme un pollen subrhomboïdal à exine mince. Ce pollen de type primitif serait le point de départ de plusieurs séries dans la lignée de 'type cotylédonaire long'.

Possédant de nombreuses espèces endémiques groupées essentiellement sur le pourtour de Bassin Méditerranéen et au niveau des chaînes asiatiques (Cauwet, 1970*b*), ce genre se caractérise par la présence de plusieurs taxons polyploïdes, fait assez rare chez les Ombellifères.

Dans l'état actuel de nos connaissances caryologiques, il n'est pas encore possible de savoir si les espèces endémiques sont isolées systématiquement; seule, la connaissance de leur nombre chromosomique devrait nous permettre de reconsidérer leurs affinités. Avant nous, les travaux de cytologie effectués dans le genre *Bupleurum* avaient amené leurs auteurs à signaler quatre nombres de base différents:

$x = 6$ chez *B. kaoi* Liu, Chao, Chuang (Liu, Chao, Chuang, 1961) et *B. sacchalinense* Schmidt (Suzuka, 1953);

$x = 11$ chez *B. rotundifolium* L. (Melderis, 1930) et *B. americanum* Coult. & Rose (Bell & Constance, 1966);

$x = 7$ et $x = 8$ chez toutes les autres espèces. Ces deux derniers nombres de base étant d'ailleurs les seuls que nous ayons nous même rencontrés (Cauwet, 1970*a*).

Afin d'aboutir à une révision du genre, aussi complète que possible, nous nous sommes intéressée non seulement au nombre chromosomique mais également au caryotype et à la structure quiescente du noyau; à ces trois critères sont venus s'ajouter la répartition géographique de la plante, sa biologie et son écologie. A l'exception de *B. tianschanicum* Freyn et de *B. salicifolium* Soland., 21 espèces que nous avons examinées sont toutes des espéces européennes.* Nous les avons étudiées dans l'ordre où elles sont citées par Tutin (1968: 345–350). La connaissance de nombres chromosomiques nouveaux ainsi que la présence dans certaines sections ou sous-sections d'espèces qui n'en sont pas le type nous ont amenée à apporter quelques modifications à la classification proposée par cet auteur. Nous examinerons donc successivement les sections ou sous-sections qui restent inchangées, puis celles que nous avons remaniées.

SUBDIVISIONS INCHANGÉES DANS LA CLASSIFICATION DU GENRE

Section Bupleurum *Tutin*

La section *Bupleurum* Tutin groupe deux espèces *B. rotundifolium* L. et *B. lancifolium* Hornem.; leur nombre chromosomique est: $2n = 16$. La structure quiescente du noyau est uniforme: sur un fond granuleux se détachent 15 à 25 chromocentres de taille inégale.

Section Diaphyllum (*Hoffm.*) *Dumort.*

La section *Diaphyllum* (Hoffm.) Dumort. ne comprend qu'une seule espèce: *B. longifolium* L. Les deux sous-espèces considérées par Tutin, subsp. *longifolium* et subsp. *aureum* (Hoffm.) Soó ont toutes deux $2n = 16$ pour nombre chromosomique.

Section Reticulata *Godron*

La section *Reticulata* Godron groupe uniquement deux espèces:

B. angulosum L. endémique des Pyrénées, et
B. stellatum L. endémique des Alpes cristallines et de la Corse.

Les deux espèces sont diploïdes et ont pour nombre de base 7, ce qui les sépare du *B. longifolium* L. auquel de très nombreux auteurs les avaient rattachées.

Chez *B. angulosum* L. chacune des trois variétés: *latifolium* Lap., *pyrenaeum* Gouan et *alpinum* Lap. a pu être caractérisée par un caryotype différent (Fig. 1). La comparaison des plaques métaphasiques de *B. angulosum* L. et *B. stellatum* L. nous a permis de constater que les deux espèces possédaient dans leur caryotype des chromosomes *a, b, c* et *d* morphologiquement identiques. On peut donc considérer qu'elles sont issues d'une souche commune dans le caryotype de laquelle, les quatre premiers chromosomes seraient identiques à *a, b, c, d*. Nous nous rallions à Favarger et Kupfer (1968) pour considérer ces espèces comme des '*schizoendémiques* faisant partie d'une flore orophile commune aux Alpes et aux Pyrénées'.

Section Coriacea *Godron*

La section *Coriacea* Godron semble également parfaitement homogène. Sur les trois espèces qu'elle comporte, deux ont un nombre chromosomique connu. *B. gibraltaricum* Lam. et *B. fruticosum* L. sont diploïdes à $2n = 14$.

---

* Tutin (1968: 345–350) en cite 39. Vingt-trois nombres chromosomiques sont actuellement connus.

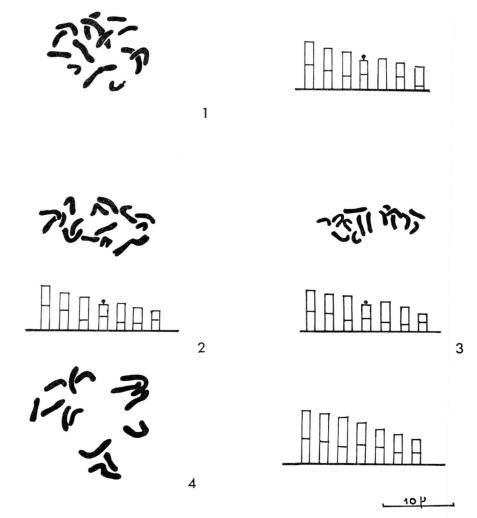

FIGURE 1. Plaques métaphasiques et caryogrammes. 1. *B. stellatum* L. (2*n* = 14); 2. *B. angulosum* L. var. *latifolium* Lap. (2*n* = 14); 3. *B. angulosum* L. var. *alpinum* Lap. (2*n* = 14); 4. *B. angulosum* L. var. *pyrenaeum* Gouan (2*n* = 14).

Section Isophyllum (*Hoffm.*) *Dumort.*

La section *Isophyllum* (Hoffm.) Dumort. groupe actuellement, en Europe, 31 espèces. Ce nombre élevé et les différences morphologiques ou anatomiques que l'on rencontre chez ces espèces ont amené Tutin à la subdiviser en six sous-sections. Si certaines d'entre elles présentent une grande homogénéité, nous avons été amenée à modifier, dans cette section, les sous-sections *Nervosa* (Godron) Briq. et les sous-sections *Rigida* (Drude) Wolff et *Marginata* (Godron) Wolff.

Sous-sections Juncea *Briq.*, Trachycarpa (*Lange*) *Briq.*, Aristata (*Godron*) *Briq.*

Les comptages que nous avons établi, nous permettent, jusqu'ici, de considérer $x = 8$ comme nombre de base des sous-sections *Juncea* Briq. et *Trachycarpa*

(Lange) Briq. Les nombres chromosomiques connus dans la sous-section *Aristata* (Godron) Briq. sont, pour l'instant, $x = 7$ et $x = 8$. Personnellement nous avons seulement rencontré ce dernier, mais Snogerup (1962) ayant établi $2n = 14$ chez *B. aira* Snog. et *B. gracile* d'Urv. nous attendrons de nouveaux comptages pour remanier cette sous-section.

SUBDIVISIONS MODIFIÉES DANS LA CLASSIFICATION DU GENRE

Sous-section Nervosa (*Godron*) *Briq.*

La sous-section *Nervosa* (Godron) Briq. compte, telle que la définit Tutin, six espèces en Europe. Si deux d'entre elles, *B. bourgaei* Boiss. & Reut. et *B. elatum* Guss. sont considérées comme des endémiques, et si *B. petraeum* L. a une aire de répartition parfaitement bien définie et peu étendue, les trois autres espèces, en l'occurrence *B. multinerve* DC., *B. ranunculoides* L. et surtout *B. falcatum* L. ont une aire de répartition très vaste qui déborde largement l'Europe.

Quatre des six espèces qui composent cette sous-section, ont un nombre chromosomique connu et les nombres de base qu'ils ont permis de définir sont $x = 7$ et $x = 8$. Nous proposons donc de la subdiviser en deux séries: la série *Ranunculoidea* (Wolff) emend. Cauwet qui groupe, pour l'instant, *B. petraeum* L., *B. ranunculoides* L. et *B. multinerve* DC. (son nombre de base est $x = 7$), et la série *Falcata* Wolff emend. Cauwet qui comprend seulement, actuellement, *B. falcatum* L. et quelques unes de ses variétés* chez lesquelles il nous a été possible d'établir le nombre chromosomique (son nombre de base est $x = 8$).

Les deux représentants principaux de chacune de ces séries, en l'occurrence *B. ranunculoides* L. et *B. falcatum* L. sont remarquables par les races chromosomiques qu'ils ont différenciées. Chez *B. ranunculoides* L. quatre races chromosomiques sont actuellement connues (Cauwet, 1970c); chez *B. falcatum* L. la race tétraploide a été signalée par Baksay (1956) chez *B. dilatatum* Schur. Nous rattachons ces deux espèces aux *néopolyploides*† définis par Favarger (1965).

Sous-section Fruticescentia *Cauwet*

Par suite de l'absence de *B. rigidum* L. dans la sous-section *Rigida* (Drude) Wolff dans laquelle Tutin place *B. spinosum* Gouan, *B. fruticescens* L., *B. dianthifolium* Guss., *B. barceloi* Coss. et *B. acutifolium* Boiss., il n'est pas possible de conserver cette dénomination pour cette sous-section. Nous proposons: sous-section *Fruticescentia* Cauwet et nous prenons pour type de celle-ci *B. fruticescens* L.

Trois nombres chromosomiques sont actuellement connus chez les espèces européennes de cette sous-section, il s'agit de ceux de *B. spinosum* Gouan, *B. fruticescens* L. (Cauwet, 1970a) et *B. dianthifolium* Guss. (Fabbri, 1969). Les trois espèces sont tétraploides: $2n = 32$ ($x = 8$). Nous les considérons comme des espèces très anciennes et les assimilons aux *paléopolyploides*** définis par Favarger (1965).

---

* Il s'agit de: var. *sibthorpianum* (Smith.) Wolff en provenance du Mt Kyllini (Grèce); var. *parnassicum* (Halacsy) Wolff en provenance du Mt Parnasse (Grèce); var. *olympicum* (Boiss.) en provenance de l'Olympe de Thessalie.

† Le terme de néopolyploide a été créé par Monnier (1960).

** Le groupe de paléopolyploides comprend également *B. salicifolium* Soland, endémique des îles Canaries et de Madère, chez lequel nous avons compté, de même, $2n = 32$.

Sous-section Rigida *Drude emend. Cauwet*

À la suite de Wolff (1910, 152) Tutin place *B. rigidum* L. dans la sous-section *Marginata* Godron ainsi appelée par suite de la présence d'une 'nervure marginale' (Godron, 1848: 725) chez les espèces qui en font partie: *B. rigidum* L. et *B. falcatum* L. Il ne semble pas possible de conserver ce nom à cette sous-section. En effet, il existe d'une part, *B. marginatum* Noë [*B. rotundifolium* L. (Wolff, 1910: 41)] et *B. marginatum* Wall. [*B. falcatum* L. var. *marginatum* (Wall.) C.B. Clarke (Wolff,

Table 1. Nombres chromosomiques actuellement connus chez les espèces europèenes du genre *Bupleurum* [Tourn.] L.

	n	*2n*
Section *Bupleurum* Tutin ($x = 8$)		
B. rotundifolium L.	8	16
B. lancifolium Hornem.		16
Section *Diaphyllum* (Hoffm.) Dumort. ($x = 8$)		
B. longifolium L.		
subsp. *longifolium*	8	16
subsp. *aureum* (Hoffm.) Soó	8	
Section *Reticulata* Godron ($x = 7$)		
B. angulosum L.	7	14
B. stellatum L.	7	14
Section *Coriacea* Godron ($x = 7$)		
B. gibraltaricum Lam.		14
B. fruticosum L.		14
Section *Isophyllum* (Hoffm.) Dumort.		
sous-sect. *Aristata* (Godron) Briq. ($x = 7, 8$)		
B. gracile d'Urv.		14
B. aira Snog.		14
B. glumaceum Sibth & Sm.	8	16
B. karglii Vis.		16
B. baldense Turra		16
Sous-sect. *Juncea* Briq. ($x = 8$)		
B. prealtum L.		16
B. gerardi All.		16
B. affine Sadl.		16
Sous-sect. *Trachycarpa* (Lange) Briq. ($x = 8$)		
B. tenuissimum L.		16
B. semicompositum L.	8	
Sous-sect. *Nervosa* (Godron) Briq.		
(a) Série *Ranunculoidea* Wolff emend. Cauw. ($x = 7$)		
B. petraeum L.		14
B. ranunculoides L.	7, 14	14, 21, 28, 42
B. multinerve DC.		14
(b) Série *Falcata* Wolff emend. Cauwet ($x = 8$)		
B. falcatum L.		16
var. *falcatum*		
var. *sibthorpianum* Smith.		
var. *parnassicum* Halácsy		
var. *olympicum* Boiss.		
Sous-sect. *Rigida* Drude emend. Cauw. ($x = 8$)		
B. rigidum L.		16
Sous-sect. *Fruticescentia* Cauwet ($x = 8$)		
B. fruticescens L.		32
B. spinosum Gouan		32
B. salicifolium Soland.		32
B. dianthifolium Guss.		16–32

1910: 193)] hors de la sous-section *Marginata* Godron, et d'autre part, cette sous-section comprend uniquement *B. rigidum* L. pris par Drude (1898, 181) comme espèce type de la sous-section *Rigida*.

Nous proposons donc de placer *B. rigidum* L., qui jusqu'ici s'est toujours avéré diploide à $2n = 16$, dans la sous-section *Rigida* Drude emend. Cauwet qui, désormais comprend seulement cette espèce.

En tenant compte des résultats caryologiques acquis et des modifications que nous avons apportées, la classification des espèces du genre *Bupleurum* L. est actuellement celle que nous indiquons dans le tableau ci-joint.

PREMIÈRES HYPOTHÈSES SUR LA PHYLOGÉNIE DU GENRE

À la suite de ce travail sur le genre *Bupleurum* nous constatons que celui-ci présente le fait peu répandu chez les Ombellifères de posséder plusieurs espèces polyploïdes.

Ces polyploides rattachés aux *paléopolyploides* et aux *néopolyploides* semblent avoir pris naissance pour les premiers depuis très longtemps ; pour les seconds plus récemment mais à partir de sippes très anciennes.

Les relations géographiques qui existent entre ces taxons polyploides et les foyers d'endémisme (Cauwet, 1970*b*) nous amènent à penser que le genre possède deux foyers de différenciation possibles ; l'un au niveau de l'ancien massif betico-rifain effondré, l'autre au niveau des chaînes asiatiques. Cette macroévolution selon deux phyllum séparés possède-t-elle une souche commune ?

Les espèces appartenant au foyer 'méditerranéen' (fig. 2) auraient pour origine le

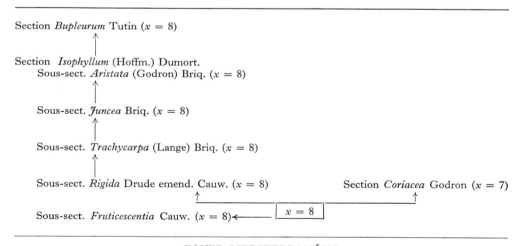

Section *Bupleurum* Tutin ($x = 8$)

Section *Isophyllum* (Hoffm.) Dumort.
  Sous-sect. *Aristata* (Godron) Briq. ($x = 8$)

  Sous-sect. *Juncea* Briq. ($x = 8$)

  Sous-sect. *Trachycarpa* (Lange) Briq. ($x = 8$)

  Sous-sect. *Rigida* Drude emend. Cauw. ($x = 8$)   Section *Coriacea* Godron ($x = 7$)

  Sous-sect. *Fruticescentia* Cauw. ($x = 8$) ⟵ $x = 8$

FOYER MÉDITERRANÉEN

FIGURE 2. Hypothèses sur la phylogénie du genre *Bupleurum* [Tourn.] L.: foyer méditerranéen.

diploide, sans doute disparu, duquel sont issus les paléopolyploides que nous avons pu observer (*B. spinosum* Gouan, *B. fruticescens* L. et *B. dianthifolium* Guss.) De cette souche se seraient diversifiées deux branches : l'une à nombre de base 8 conduirait au *B. rotundifolium* L. que, nous considérons de par sa structure morphologique, comme une espèce évoluée; l'autre à nombre de base 7, obtenu après des remaniements cytologiques, comprendrait uniquement les espèces de la section *Coriacea* Godron.

Les espèces appartenant au foyer asiatique (Fig. 3) auraient de la même manière

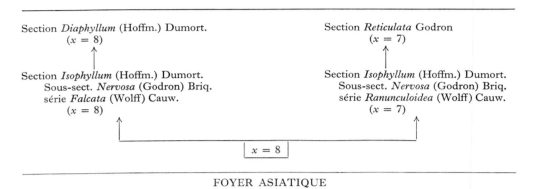

Section *Diaphyllum* (Hoffm.) Dumort.
(*x* = 8)

Section *Isophyllum* (Hoffm.) Dumort.
Sous-sect. *Nervosa* (Godron) Briq.
série *Falcata* (Wolff) Cauw.
(*x* = 8)

Section *Reticulata* Godron
(*x* = 7)

Section *Isophyllum* (Hoffm.) Dumort.
Sous-sect. *Nervosa* (Godron) Briq.
série *Ranunculoidea* (Wolff) Cauw.
(*x* = 7)

$x = 8$

FOYER ASIATIQUE

FIGURE 3. Hypothèses sur la phylogénie du genre *Bupleurum* [Tourn.] L.: foyer asiatique.

une espèce souche ayant 8 pour nombre de base. Il ne nous est pas possible pour l'instant de nommer plus précisément cette espèce, mais c'est de cette souche que se seraient également différenciées deux branches l'une à $x = 8$ qui conduirait au *B. falcatum* L. puis au *B. longifolium* L.; l'autre à $x = 7$ d'où seraient issues les espèces asiatiques morphologiquement proches du *B. ranunculoides* L. à partir duquel se seraient différenciées: *B. petraeum* L., *B. angulosum* L. et *B. stellatum* L. Cette dernière espèce à involucelle gamophylle représentant le stade ultime de l'évolution.

Il semble donc qu'il y ait eu dans les deux branches principales une micro-évolution identique: espèce souche à $x = 8$ puis diversification de deux branches, l'une à $x = 8$, l'autre à $x = 7$. La question reste posée de savoir qu'elle est dans les deux cas l'espèce souche. Y a-t-il eu pour les deux phyllums un tronc commun? C'est à ces questions que nous nous efforcerons de répondre en poursuivant plus loin nos investigations cytologiques dans le genre *Bupleurum*.

BIBLIOGRAPHIE

BAKSAY, L., 1956. Cytotaxonomical studies on the Flora of Hungary. *Ann. hist. nat. Mus. Natl. Hung.*, Nov. Ser., **7**: 321–334.

BELL, C. R. & CONSTANCE, L., 1966. Chromosome numbers in Umbelliferae. III. *Am. J. Bot.*, **53**: 512–520.

BOKOVSKIKH, Z., GRIF, V., MATVEJEVA, T. & ZAKHARYEVA, O., 1969. *Chromosome Numbers of Flowering Plants*. 926 pp. Leningrad.

CAUWET, A.-M., 1967. Contribution à l'étude caryosystématique du genre *Bupleurum* L. I. *Bull. Soc. bot. Fr.*, **114**: 371–386.

CAUWET, A.-M., 1968a. Contribution à l'étude caryosystématique du genre *Bupleurum* L. II. *Bull. Soc. bot. Fr.*, **116**: 19–28.

CAUWET, A.-M., 1968b. A propos du *Bupleurum laricense* Gaut. et Timb.-Lagr. et du *Bupleurum ramosum* Gaut. et Timb.-Lagr. de la montagne d'Alaric (Corbières audoises-France). *Bull. Soc. bot. Fr.*, **116**: 97–102.

CAUWET, A.-M., 1970*a*. *Contribution à l'étude caryosystématque du genre Bupleurum (Tourn.) L.*— Thèse de spécialité, 166 pp., 10 pl., 16 cartes. Montpellier.

CAUWET, A.-M., 1970*b*. Polyploidie et répartition géographique dans le genre *Bupleurum* (Tourn.) L. *C.r. Soc. biogéog.* (à paraître).

CAUWET, A.-M., 1970*c*. Races chromosomiques, écologie et biologie du *Bupleurum ranunculoides* L. dans la partie orientale des Pyrénées. *Bull. Soc. bot. Fr.* (à paraître).

CERCEAU-LARRIVAL, M.-TH., 1962. Plantules et pollens d'Ombellifères. Thèse de Doctorat, 166 p. 10 tab. 26 pl. Paris.

CHESNOY, L., 1962. Étude caryologique du *B. lancifolium* L. et données sur deux espèces voisines. Paris: D. E. S.

DRUDE, C. G. O., 1898. Umbelliferae. In Engler, A. & Prantl, K. (eds), *Die natürlichen Planzenfamilien*, 3 (8): 175–182.

FABBRI, F., 1969. Il numero cromosomico di '*Bupleurum dianthifolium* Guss.' endemismo de Marettimo (Isole Egadi). *Informatore Botanico Italiano*, 1 (3): 164–167.

FAVARGER, C., 1964. Cytotaxinomie et endémisme. *C.R. Soc. biogéog.*, 357: 23–44.

FAVARGER, C., 1965. Notes de caryologie alpine IV. *Bull. Soc. Neuch. Sci. Nat.*, 88: 5–60.

FAVARGER, C. & CONTANDRIOPOULOS, J., 1961. Essai sur l'endémisme. *Bull. Soc. bot. Suisse*, 71: 384–408.

FAVARGER, C. & KÜPFER, PH., 1968. Contribution à la cytotaxinomie de la flore alpine des Pyrénées. *Coll. Bot.*, 7: 325–355.

JOHNSON, A. W. & PACKER, J. G., 1968. Chromosome numbers in the Flora of Ogotoruk Creek, N.W. Alaska. *Bot. Not.*, 121: 403–456.

KÜPFER, PH., 1968. Nouvelles prospections caryologiques dans la Flore orophile des Pyrénées et de la Sierra Nevada. *Bull. Soc. neuch. Sci. nat.*, 91: 87–104.

KÜPFER, PH., 1969. Recherches cytotaxinomiques sur la flore des montagnes de la Péninsule ibérique. *Bull. Soc. neuch. Sci. nat.*, 92: 31–48.

KÜPFER, PH. & FAVARGER, C., 1967. Premières prospections caryologiques dans la flore orophile des Pyrénées et de la Sierra Nevada. *C. r. Acad. Sci. Paris*, 264: 2463–2465.

LARRIVAL, M.-T., 1952. Révision de l'espèce pyrénéenne: *Bupleurum angulosum* L. *Bull. Soc. Hist. nat.* Toulouse, 87: 225–254. Voir également Cerceau-Larrival M.-Th.

LIU, T. S., CHAO, C. Y. & CHUANG, T. I., 1961. Umbelliferae of Taïwan. *Q. Jl Taiw. Mus.*, 14: 15–47.

LÖVE, Á. & LÖVE, D., 1961. Chromosome numbers of central and north west European plant species. *Bot. Not.*, supplément; *Opera Botanica* no. 5, 581 pp. Lund.

MONNIER, P., 1960. Biosystématique de quelques *Spergularia* méditerranéens. *C. r. Acad. Sci.*, Paris, 251: 117–119.

SNOGERUP, S., 1962. Studies in the Aegean Flora IV. *Bupleurum flavum* Forsk. and related species. *Botaniska Notiser*, 115: 357–375.

SPRENGEL, A., 1814. Der Gesselschaft Naturforschender Freunde zu Berlin Magazin, pp. 255–261.

SUZUKA, O., 1953. Chromosome numbers in pharmaceutical plants II. *Seiken Zihô*, 6: 79.

TUTIN, T. G., 1968. *Bupleurum*. In Tutin, T. G. *et al.*, *Flora Europaea*, 2: 345–350.

WOLFF, H., 1910. Umbelliferae. In Engler, A. *Pflanzenreich*, IV (228): 1–214.

Chemical patterns and relationships of Umbelliferae

R. HEGNAUER

Laboratorium voor Experimentele Plantensystematiek van de Rijksuniversiteit te Leiden, 5e Binnenvestgracht 8, Leiden, Netherlands

The chemistry of Umbelliferae is reviewed and compared with chemical features of other taxa (Table 2). The overall chemical evidence so far available favours the following hypotheses:

(1) Umbelliferae and Araliaceae are related taxa, which may be regarded as constituting the order Umbellales.

(2) Umbellales do not represent a climax group, but rather the stock from which Asterales evolved.

(3) Umbellales may have evolved from the Rutalean stock.

CONTENTS

INTRODUCTION

Umbellifers were recognized long ago as a natural assemblage of plants. James Petiver (1699) used 'Herbae Umbelliferae' together with two other very natural plant groups, Labiatae and Cruciferae, to discuss and illustrate the hypothesis that morphologically similar plants produce constituents with similar therapeutical effects. During the eighteenth and nineteenth century the conviction became firmly established among scientists that a natural classification of plants was of practical interest to man for the discovery of new plant resources. Many textbooks of Materia Medica of the nineteenth century included in the descriptions of plant families notes on characteristic constituents (e.g. Guibourt-Planchon, 1876). Hoffmann (1846) even went a step further. In his treatise of the families of flowering plants represented in Germany, he reserved much space for the description of the chemical make-up of each of them. He was convinced that phytochemistry offered a new possibility of checking proposals of classification based exclusively on morphology. During the more than a hundred years since Hoffmann's book was published, plant taxonomy has learned to use many new types of characters for classificatory purposes. Chemical characters, however, were neglected for a long time because thorough information in most groups was too scanty. A radical change took place two decades ago and at present we are already in a much better position for a phytochemical approach to plant systematics.

The purpose of this symposium is to discuss morphological and non-morphological characters of Umbelliferae and their impact on the classification of these plants. It is my task to give a summary of our phytochemical knowledge and to try to interpret the chemical pattern in the frame of plant systematics at family level. This implies a general survey of chemical characters and of some of the recent proposals of classification.

CHEMISTRY OF UMBELLIFERS

Essential oils and biogenetically related non-volatile constituents

All Umbellifers are aromatic plants. They produce essential oils and biogenetically related resins which are excreted in schizogenous canals in roots, stems, leaves, inflorescences and, if present, in the so-called vittae of the fruits. As in other plant families the essential oils contain mainly monoterpenes, sesquiterpenes and phenylpropanoid compounds. Many well-known essential oil constituents were isolated for the first time from an umbelliferous plant and were named accordingly after this source. Three examples are given in Fig. 1; none of these compounds is typical of the Umbelliferae.

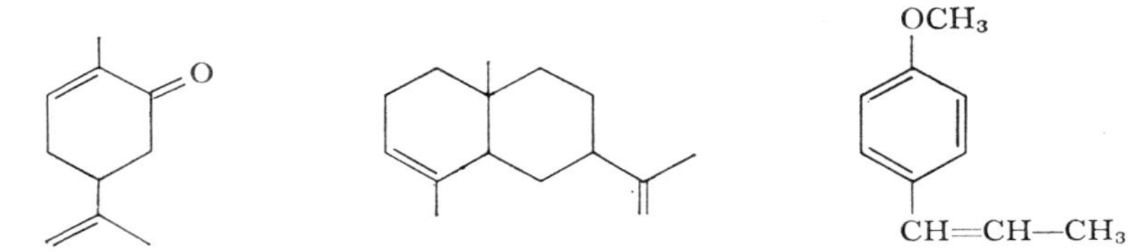

		OCH₃
Carvone	α-Selinene	Anethole
(*Carum carvi* L.)	(from selinon, an old name of celery, *Apium graveolens* L.)	(*Pimpinella anisum* L.)

FIGURE 1. Three essential oil constituents named after umbelliferous plants.

There are, however, some constituents of essential oils and intimately related non-volatile sesquiterpenes which seem to be much more characteristic of Umbelliferae or of some of their genera at least. Among them are the daucan-type sesquiterpenes, esters of monoterpene aldehydes, the acetogenic (Mitsuhashi-Nomura, 1966) ligustilide-type compounds and the guaianolide- and germacranolide-type lactones (Herout, 1970). An example of each of these five classes of metabolites is given in Fig. 2.

Ligustilide-type compounds were demonstrated to be present in members of some genera of Apieae (*Apium, Cnidium, Ligusticum, Meum*) and Peucedaneae (*Angelica, Conioselinum, Levisticum*) and guaianolides and germacranolides are

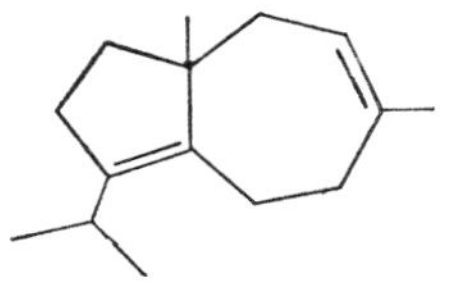

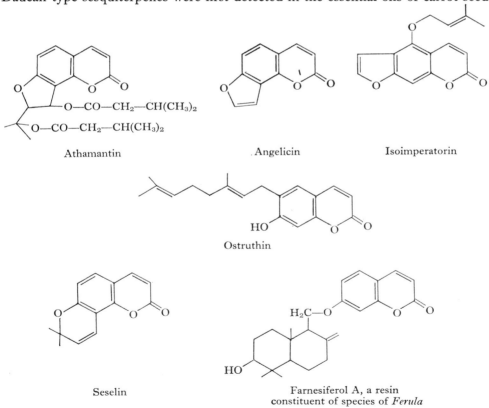

Daucene

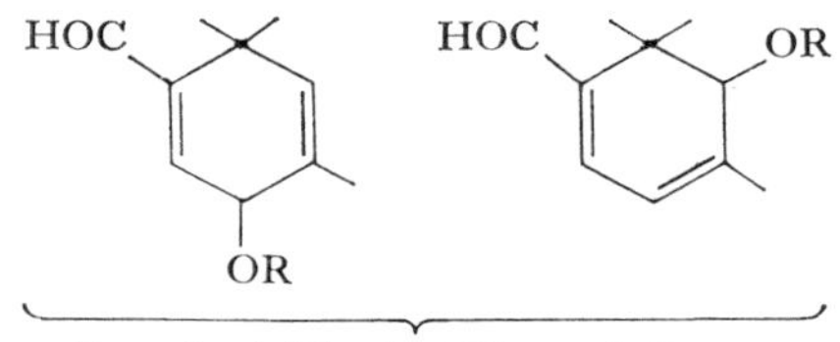

R = Acyl (*Ferula, Silaum, Selinum* and other taxa)

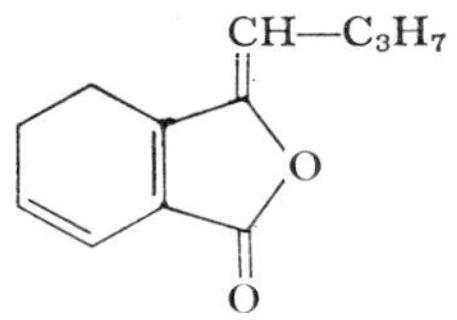

Ligustilide

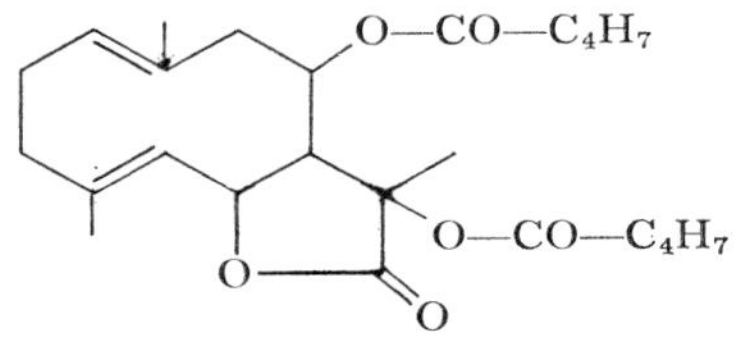

Laserolide

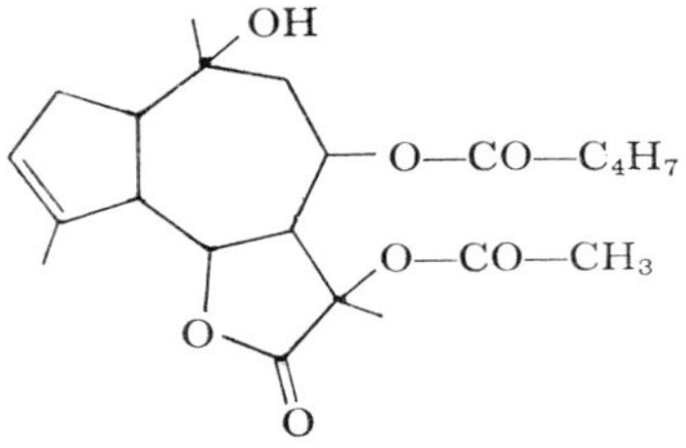

Montanolide

FIGURE 2. Typically umbelliferous metabolites occurring in essential oils or which are intimately connected with essential oil synthesis.

known to occur in *Ferula* (*Peucedaneae*) and *Laser* and *Siler* (both *Laserpitieae*). Daucan-type sesquiterpenes were first detected in the essential oils of carrot seeds

Athamantin

Angelicin

Isoimperatorin

Ostruthin

Seselin

Farnesiferol A, a resin constituent of species of *Ferula*

FIGURE 3. Some umbelliferone-derived types of coumarins characteristic for umbelliferous plants.

(fruits of *Daucus carota* L.) but later detected also in *Laserpitium latifolium* L., whose bitter principle, latifolin, is a complex derivative of daucan (Holub *et al.*, 1965, 1967).

Coumarins

Furo- and dimethylpyranocoumarins are discussed in Nielsen's paper, p. 325. They are very characteristic metabolites of many umbelliferous plants but have not yet been isolated from members of Hydrocotyloideae and Saniculoideae. According to observations of Crowden *et al.* (1969) furanocoumarins, however, do occur in both taxa. Biogenetically, all coumarins of Umbelliferae seem to be derived from umbelliferone. The constituents of the resins of species of *Dorema*, *Ferula* and *Opopanax* likewise are biogenetically linked with umbelliferone. Figure 3 illustrates some structural types of umbelliferone-derived umbelliferous constituents.

Acetylenic compounds

Acetylenic compounds form an outstanding feature of Umbelliferae. They are treated in detail in Bohlmann's paper, p. 279. It should suffice, therefore, to point to their rather general distribution (Crowden *et al.*, 1969) and to the fact that a chain length of C-17 (e.g. falcarinone and falcorinol [= panaxynol = carotatoxin]) is most common in the family. C-13 and C-15 compounds, however, co-occur or replace the C-17 compounds in some species (Fig. 4). Some of the umbelliferous polyacetylenic metabolites are highly toxic. Dangerous plants of this family (*Cicuta*, *Oenanthe* p.p. and to a less extent *Aethusa*, *Chaerophyllum* p.p., wild carrots) generally store such compounds in relatively large amounts. *Conium* with its α-substituted piperidine alkaloids and members producing photodynamically active furanocoumarins form an exception to the rule that toxic effects of Umbelliferae are caused by acetylenic compounds.

$$
\begin{array}{l}
\overset{R}{\underset{\|}{}} \\
H_2C{=}CH{-}\overset{\|}{C}{-}[C{\equiv}C]_2{-}CH_2{-}CH{=}CH{-}[CH_2]_7H \\
HOCH_2{-}CH{=}CH{-}[C{\equiv}C]_2{-}[CH{=}CH]_2{-}[CH_2]_2{-}CH(OH){-}[CH_2]_3H \\[6pt]
HOCH_2{-}[CH_2]_2{-}[C{\equiv}C]_2{-}[CH{=}CH]_3{-}CH(OH){-}[CH_2]_3H \\
H_3C{-}CH{=}CH{-}[C{\equiv}C]_2{-}[CH{=}CH]_2{-}CH_2{-}CH_3 \\
H_3C{-}CH{=}CH{-}[C{\equiv}C]_2{-}[CH{=}CH]_2{-}CH(OH){-}[CH_2]_3H
\end{array}
$$

$\begin{cases} R = O \\ R = H, HOH \end{cases}$ Falcarinone (I) \
Falcarinol (II) \
Oenanthotoxin (III) \
Cicutoxin (IV) ⎫ C-17

Aethusin (V) C-13

Carbinol from *Oenanthe crocata* L. (VI) ⎫ C-15

FIGURE 4. Some umbelliferous polyacetylenes (III and IV are extremely toxic; I, II, V and VI are much less toxic).

Triterpenes and saponins

Triterpenes occur widely in Umbelliferae. It seems, however, significant to note that free triterpenes in high concentrations are rather rare. Umbelliferous waxes are mainly composed of alkanes and ketonic alkanes but not of triterpenic acids. The latter occur esterfied with sugars (e.g. asiaticoside) or glycosylated (saponins). In most instances, however, umbelliferous sapogenins seem not to be triterpenic

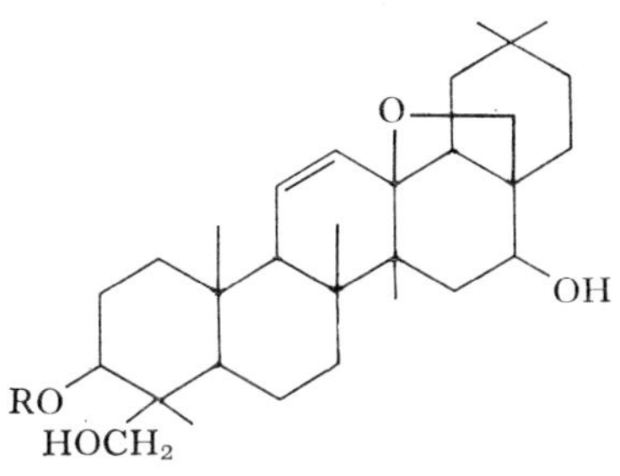

Constituents of *Bupleurem*:

R = H: Saikogenin F

R = sugar: Saikosid Ia

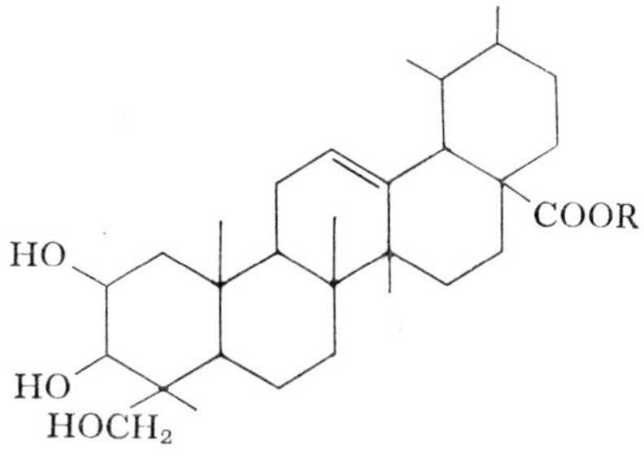

Constituents of *Centella*:

R = H: Asiatic acid

R = sugar: Asiaticoside

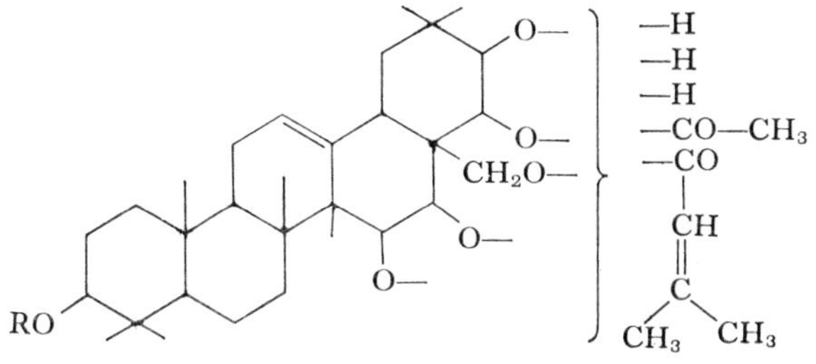

Constituents of *Eryngium* and *Sanicula*:

R=H: Saniculagenin A

R = sugar: *Sanicula*-saponins A and B

FIGURE 5. Some triterpenes and glycosylated triterpenes of umbelliferous plants.

acids but triterpenic polyols (Fig. 5). At the same time the available information suggests that saponins occur with a higher frequency in Hydrocotyloideae and Saniculoideae than in Apioideae (Table 1).

Table 1. Frequency of occurrence of hemolytically active or otherwise saponin-like substances in Umbelliferae

Subfamilies	Saponins present[1]	Saponins absent	Percentage of positive species	Total number of species tested
Hydrocotyloideae	19	47[2]	28·8	66
Saniculoideae[3]	7	13	35	20
Apioideae	5	65	7·1	70

[1] According to observations of Cambie et al. (1961), Ricardi et al. (1958), Simes et al. (1959) and Wall et al. (1951–1961).

[2] Asiaticoside-type esters do not hemolyze and escape attention in most screening procedures for saponins.

[3] Saponins seem to occur even more frequently. All the uses mentioned by Wolff (1913) for Saniculoideae point to the presence of saponins and Hiller & Linzer (1966, 1967) found saponins in most species of *Astrantia*, *Eryngium* and *Sanicula* investigated by them.

Seed oils

Umbelliferae produce seeds containing large amounts of fatty oils and of proteins organized in the characteristic aleurone grains. At the same time polysaccharides of still unknown composition are deposited in the cell walls of the endosperm. The chemical make-up of the glycerides is taxonomically very interesting. All members of the family investigated so far contain petroselinic acid (Fig. 6) as one of the major fatty acids of their seed fats.

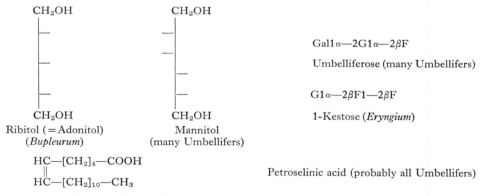

$$Gal1\alpha—2G1\alpha—2\beta F$$

Umbelliferose (many Umbellifers)

$$G1\alpha—2\beta F1—2\beta F$$

1-Kestose (*Eryngium*)

CH₂OH

Ribitol (=Adonitol) (*Bupleurum*)

CH₂OH

Mannitol (many Umbellifers)

$$HC—[CH_2]_4—COOH$$
$$\|$$
$$HC—[CH_2]_{10}—CH_3$$

Petroselinic acid (probably all Umbellifers)

FIGURE 6. Some characteristic storage metabolites of Umbellifers
(Gal = galactose; G = glucose; F = fructose).

Oligosaccharides and polyols

Biennial and perennial species store mainly starch and oligosaccharides in roots and rhizomes. In many species these carbohydrates are accompanied by considerable amounts of hexitols or pentitols. The raffinose isomer umbelliferose is rather characteristic of the family; it is replaced completely by sucrose in *Sanicula*, by kestose in *Eryngium* and by centellose in *Centella*. Mannitol is the chief hexitol of Umbelliferae; it is replaced by ribitol in *Bupleurum* (Fig. 6).

Cinnamic acids and flavonoids

With regard to phenolic constituents, which are treated separately by Harborne, Umbelliferae are characterized by a total lack of true tannins (including gallic and ellagic acids and catechins and leucoanthocyanins). Flavonols, except myricetin, are present in rather high amounts in many species, just as are esters of caffeic acid. Flavonols are often replaced, especially in more advanced taxa (Harborne, 1967), by flavones (apigenin and luteolin) and their monomethyl ethers (especially diosmetin and chrysoeriol). Flavanones seem to be rare; hesperidin was isolated from *Cnidium silaifolium* Simonk. and selinon (Fig. 7) from *Selinum vaginatum* Clarke.

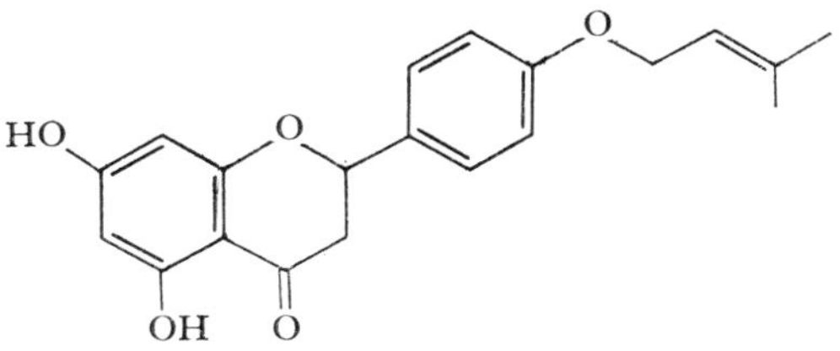

FIGURE 7. Selinon, a flavanone of Umbelliferae.

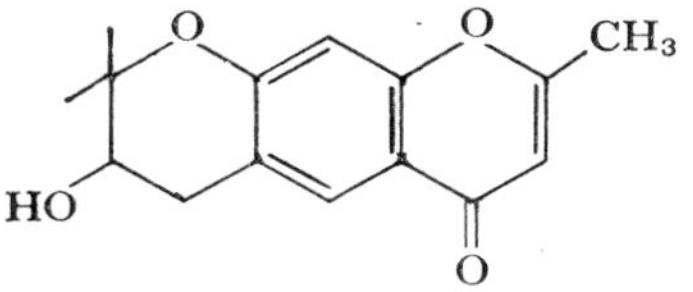

Hamaudol,
a 2-methylchromone

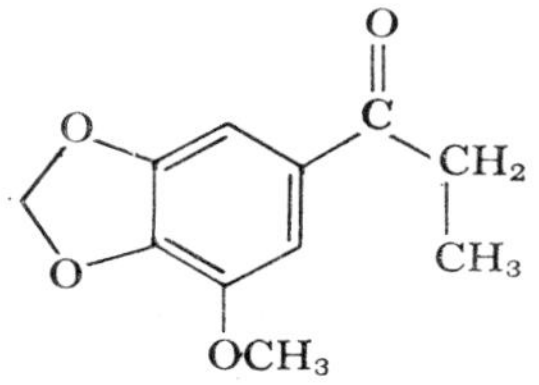

Crocatone (=latifolone),
a derivative of iso-myristicin

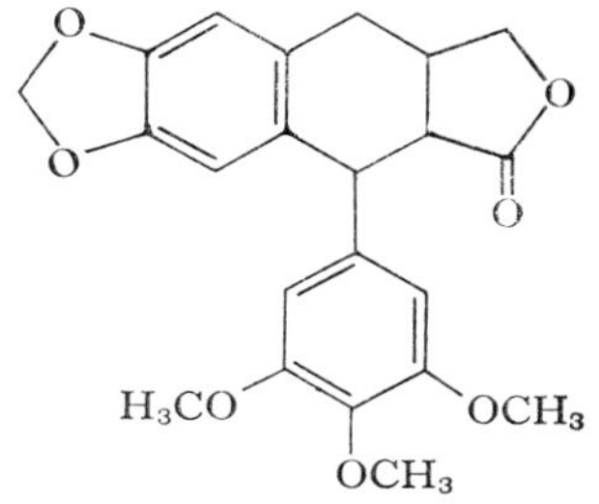

Desoxypodo phyllotoxin
(=anthricine = cicutin),
a naphthalide-type lignan

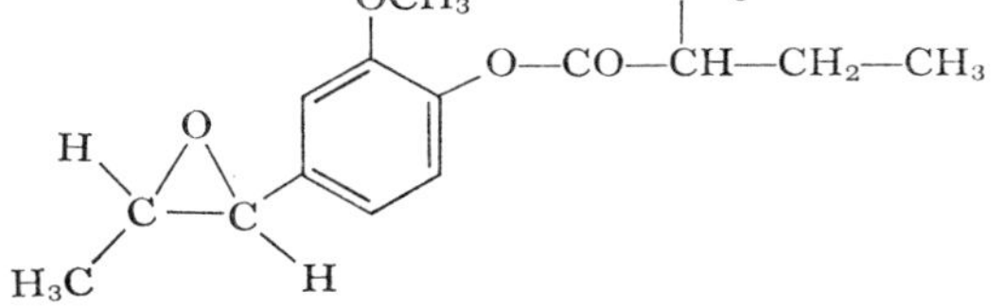

Ester of isoeugenolepoxide with 2-methylbutyric acid

FIGURE 8. Some characteristic compounds found so far only in a few umbelliferous genera.

Miscellaneous compounds

Finally, several chemical trends are known in members of the family. Future research has still to demonstrate if they represent characters at a higher level or are exclusively of generic or specific interest. This category of phytoconstituents includes malonic acid, which is stored in exceptionally large amounts by the umbelliferous plants investigated by Bentley (1952) and the classes of compounds illustrated in Fig. 8: crocatone and similar derivatives of isomyristicin (*Oenanthe, Laserpitium*), naphthalide-type lignans (*Anthriscus, Cicuta*), 2-methylchromones (*Ammi, Angelica, Peucedanum*) and esters of isoeugenolepoxide (*Pimpinella*).

RELATIONSHIPS OF UMBELLIFERS

Most authors, except Hutchinson (1969), agree that Umbelliferae and Araliaceae are closely related. These two families alone form the order Umbellales in the classification proposed by Cronquist (1968). The affinities of Umbellales, however, are

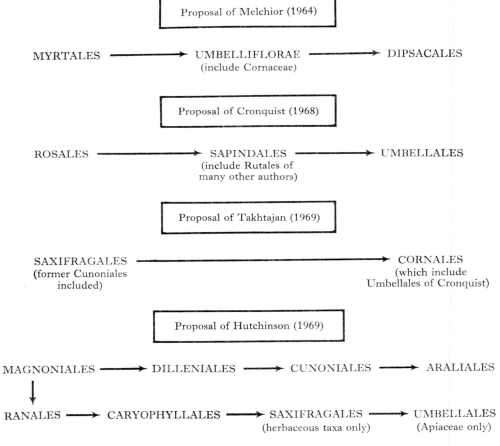

FIGURE 9. The position of Umbellales (*sensu* Cronquist) in four recent proposals for the classification of Dicotyledons.

rather obscure. Rosiflorae, Myrtales, Celastrales, Rhamnales and Sapindales (including Rutales) have been variously considered as ancestral by taxonomists. At the same time Umbellales are often believed to represent a climax group. Difficulties connected with the classification of Umbellales may be illustrated by four recent proposals for the classification of Dicotyledons (Fig. 9).

I realize well that it is premature to put too much weight on chemical evidence in matters of plant classification. Nevertheless, some striking resemblances, summarized in Table 2, merit to be mentioned.

Table 2. Characteristic chemical patterns of Umbelliferae and their occurrence in other taxa

Type of chemical compounds and frequency of occurrence in Umbelliferae	Presence in other taxa
(1) Essential oils and resins in schizogenous cavities or canals: ubiquitous.	Araliaceae, Compositae, Pittosporaceae, Burseraceae, Simaroubaceae, Rutaceae (lysigenous) and other taxa.
(2) Furanocoumarins: frequent.	Rutaceae, Pittosporaceae, Leguminosae, Moraceae.
(3) Pyranocoumarins: frequent.	Rutaceae.
(4) Other isopentenyl-substituted coumarins: frequent.	Rutaceae, Ptaeroxylon, Cedrelopsis, Compositae (Aster).
(5) Polyacetylenic compounds: frequent; especially falcarinone-type C-17 compounds.	Araliaceae (especially falcarinone-type), Compositae (including falcarinone-type), Pittosporaceae, Campanulaceae.
(6) Oleanene- and ursene-type triterpenic sapogenins: several genera.	Araliaceae, Pittosporaceae, Compositae, Berberidaceae, Ranunculaceae and many other taxa.
(7) Seed fats with petroselinic acid: general.	Araliaceae, Simaroubaceae (Picrasma).
(8) True tannins: lacking.	Araliaceae, Pittosporaceae, Compositae and many other taxa.
(9) 2-Methylchromones.[1]	Ptaeroxylon, Ranunculaceae, Myrtaceae; 2,2-dimethylchromenes in Compositae and Rutaceae.
(10) Guaianolides.[1]	Compositae.
(11) Germacranolides.[1]	Compositae, Magnoliaceae (Michelia, Liriodendron).
(12) Esters of isoeugenolepoxide.[1]	Compositae (Coreopsis).

[1] Distribution given in the text.

Evidently, Umbellales *sensu* Cronquist form a metabolically natural group. They share the biochemical characters 1, 5, 6, 7, and 8 of Table 2. Additionally they have similar spectra of flavonoid compounds and esters of caffeic acid. A major difference is indicated by the absence of coumarins from Araliaceae. This difference may be real. As Araliaceae have been studied far less intensively by phytochemists the possibility exists, however, that the difference is only an apparent one.

If we accept Umbellales as a natural group, chemical comparison of this order with other families and orders of Dicotyledons yields two main suggestions (cf. Hegnauer, 1964, 1969).

(1) Umbellales are not a climax group, but may represent the stock from which Asterales evolved.

(2) Umbellales may derive from the rutalean stock. This suggestion is in line with Cronquist's proposal.

Evidently chemical characters represent only one of the many sets of evidence needed to arrive ultimately at an optimal classification of flowering plants. It is my conviction, however, that the contribution of phytochemistry to classification is a valuable one in this part of the system of angiospermous taxa.

REFERENCES

BENTLEY, L. E., 1952. Occurrence of malonic acid in plants, *Nature, Lond.*, **170**: 847–848.

CAMBIE, R. C., CAIN, B. F. & LA ROCHE, S., 1961. A New Zeal. Phytochemical Survey. 2. Dicotyledons, *N.Z. Jl Sci.*, **4**: 604–663.

CRONQUIST, A., 1968. *The evolution and classification of flowering plants.* Boston: Houghton Mifflin Company.

CROWDEN, R. K., HARBORNE, J. B. & HEYWOOD, V. H., 1969. Chemosystematics of the Umbelliferae—a general survey. *Phytochemistry*, **8**: 1963–1984.

GUIBOURT, N. J. B. G. & PLANCHON, G., 1876. *Histoire naturelle des drogues simples*, 7ᵐᵉ éd., et fils, Baillière, Paris. (Araliaceae and Umbelliferae in tome 3, pp. 197–250.)

HARBORNE, J. B., 1967. *Comparative biochemistry of the flavonoids*, pp. 180–183, London & New York: Academic Press.

HEGNAUER, R., 1964. *Chemotaxonomie der Pflanzen*, Bd. **3**, Araliaceae, pp. 183–184; Compositae, pp. 542–544, Basel: Birkhäuser Verlag. (Umbelliferae will be treated in Bd. 6, which is in preparation.)

HEGNAUER, R., 1969. Chemical evidence for the classification of some plant taxa. In *Perspectives in Phytochemistry*, pp. 121–138. Swain, T. & Harborne, J. B. (eds). London & New York: Academic Press.

HEROUT, V., 1970. Personal letter 11.3. See also HOLUB, M., DE GROOTE, R., HEROUT, V. & ŠORM, F., Oxygen containing components of light petroleum extract of *Laser trilobum* (L.) Borkh. root. Structure of laserine, *Coll. Czech. Chem. Commun.*, **33**: 2911–2917 (1968); HOLUB, M., ZAMEK, Z., POPA, D. P., HEROUT, V. & ŠORM, F., The structure of laserolide, a sesquiterpenic lactone from the roots of *Laser trilobum* (L.) Borkh., *Coll. Czech. Chem. Commun.*, **35**: 284–294 (1970); HOLUB, M., POPA, D. P., ZAMEK, Z., HEROUT, V. & ŠORM, F., Neutral components of the light petroleum extract of the root of *Laserpitium siler* L. The structure of the sesquiterpenic lactone monanolide, *Coll. Czech. Chem. Commun.*, **35**: 3296–3308 (1970).

HILLER, K. & LINZER, B., 1966. Zur Kenntnis der Inhaltsstoffe der Saniculoideae. 2. Mitt.: Das Vorkommen von Saponinen und deren hämolytische Aktivität, *Pharmazie*, **21**: 245–250.

HILLER, K. & LINZER, B., 1967. Zur Kenntnis der Inhaltsstoffe einiger Saniculoideae. 5. Mitt.: Hämolytische Aktivität von *Eryngium*-Species sowie jahreszeitliche Schwankungen im hämolytischen Index von *Sanicula europaea* L. und *Eryngium planum* L., *Pharmazie*, **22**: 321–324.

HOFFMANN, H., 1846. *Schilderung der deutschen Pflanzenfamilien vom botanisch-descriptiven und physiologisch-chemischen Standpunkte*, Giessen: G. F. Heyer's Verlag.

HOLUB, M., HEROUT, V., ŠORM, F. & LÍNEK, A., 1965. Constitution of laserpitine—a sesquiterpenic compound from *Laserpitium latifolium* L. roots, *Tetrahedron Letters*: pp. 1441–1446.

HOLUB, M., ZAMEK, Z., HEROUT, V. & ŠORM, F., 1967. The constitution of laserpitine—a sesquiterpenic compound from *Laserpitium latifolium* root, *Coll. Czech. Chem. Commun.*, **32**: 591–609. Die Konstitution von Isolaserpitin, Desoxodehydrolaserpitin und Laserpitinol, *Mh. Chem.*, **98**: 1138–1153.

HUTCHINSON, J., 1969. *Evolution and phylogeny of flowering plants.* London & New York: Academic Press.

MELCHIOR, H., 1964. Umbelliflorae. In Engler, A. *Syllabus der Pflanzenfamilien*, 12. Aufl., Bd. 2, Berlin: Gebrüder Bornträger.

MITSUHASHI, M. & NOMURA, M., 1966. Studies on the constituents of Umbelliferae Plants. XII Biogenesis of 3-butylphthalide (1), *Chem. Pharm. Bull. (Tokyo)*, **14**: 777–778.

PETIVER, J., 1699. Some attempts made to prove that herbs of the same make or class for the generality, have the like virtue and tendency to work the same effects, *Phil. Trans. (London)*, **21**: 289–294.

RICARDI, M., MARTICORENA, C., SILVA, M. and TORRES, F., 1958. Detección de saponinas en Angiospermae Chilenas, *Bol. Soc. Biol. Concepción (Chile)*, **33**: 29–94.

SIMES, J. J. H., TRACEY, J. G., WEBB, L. J. and DUNSTAN, W. J., 1959. Australian Phytochemical Survey. III Saponins in Eastern Australian Flowering Plants, *Bull. No. 281, C.S.I.R.O., Australia*, Melbourne.

TAKHTAJAN, A., 1969. *Flowering plants. Origin and dispersal*, Edinburgh: Oliver and Boyd.

WALL, M. E., WILLAMAN, J. J., CORRELL, D. S., SCHUBERT, B. G. & GENTRY, H. S. (with partial collaboration of others), 1954–1961. Steroidal sapogenins XIII (1954), XV (1954), XXVI (1955) (*Supplementary tables of data* AIC-363, AIC-367, ARS-73-4, U.S. Dept. Agric., Agric. Res. Service);
XLIII (1957), *J. Am. Pharm. Ass.*, **46**: 653–668; LV (1959), *J. Am. Pharm. Ass.*, **48**: 695–722;
LX (1961), *J. Pharm. Sci.*, **50**: 1001–1034.

WOLFF, H., 1913. Umbelliferae-Saniculoideae. In Engler, A. *Das Pflanzenreich*, Heft **61**, Reprint 1968.

Acetylenic compounds in the Umbelliferae*

F. BOHLMANN

Organisch-Chemisches Institut der Technischen Universität Berlin, 1 Berlin 12, Germany

Up to the present eighty acetylenic compounds have been isolated from different species of the Umbelliferae. C_{17}-compounds such as falcarinone (9) and related compounds are the most common while C_{13}- and C_{15}-chains are restricted to a few species. Acetylenes have been found in 75% of the species so far investigated. Many of the structures show that there is a close relationship between the Umbelliferae, Araliaceae and Compositae.

CONTENTS

INTRODUCTION

The large family Umbelliferae is rich in secondary constituents, especially in coumarins, flavones, terpenes, aromatic and acetylenic compounds.

In 1952 Lythgoe and his co-workers elucidated the structures of the toxic principles of *Oenanthe crocata* L. (1–3) and *Cicuta virosa* L. (4–5). Some years later some further acetylenes were isolated from *Aethusa cynapium* L. (Bohlmann *et al.*, 1960) (6–8), *Falcaria vulgaris* L. (Bohlmann *et al.*, 1961) (9) and some other Umbelliferae:

$$HOCH_2CH{=}CH{-}(C{\equiv}C)_2{-}(CH{=}CH)_2CH_2CH_2CHC_3H_7$$
$$\underset{OH}{|}$$
(1)

$$HOCH_2CH{=}CH{-}(C{\equiv}C)_2{-}(CH{=}CH)_2C_6H_{13}$$
(2)

$$H_3CCH{=}CH{-}(C{\equiv}C)_2{-}(CH{=}CH)_2CH_2CH_2COC_3H_7$$
(3)

$$HOCH_2CH_2CH_2{-}(C{\equiv}C)_2{-}(CH{=}CH)_3CHC_3H_7$$
$$\underset{OH}{|}$$
(4)

$$HOCH_2CH_2CH_2{-}(C{\equiv}C)_2{-}(CH{=}CH)_3C_4H_9$$
(5)

* Dedicated to Professor K. Mothes h.c. mult, on the occasion of his seventieth birthday.

$$H_3C—CH=CH—(C\equiv C)_2—(CH=CH)_2CH_2CH_3$$
(6)

$$HOCH_2—CH=CH—(C\equiv C)_2—(CH=CH)_2CH_2CH_3$$
(7)

$$H_3C—CH=CH—(C\equiv C)_2—CH=CHCHC_3H_7$$
$$|$$
$$OH$$
(8)

$$H_2C=CHCO(C\equiv C)_2—CH_2CH\underset{c}{=}CH—C_7H_{15}$$

(9)

METHODS OF STRUCTURE ELUCIDATION

The structures of 1–9 have been elucidated by classical chemical methods but now more effective methods are available for structure determination of such highly unstable compounds which are often isolated in only very small amounts. Besides, uv-spectra, which are sometimes characteristic, nmr together with mass spectroscopy are powerful methods for structure elucidation, especially in this field. The main problem now is usually the isolation of the acetylenic compounds which occur very often as complex mixtures in low concentrations in the extracts of plant material. In several cases, therefore, special chemical methods are necessary for the separation of such mixtures.

A typical example is a group of alcohols isolated from the roots of *Oenanthe crocata* L. Partial oxidation with manganese dioxide gives among other products in small amounts a ketone which could be isolated in the pure state (Bohlmann & Rode, 1968). The not very characteristic uv spectrum of this ketone is in agreement with an ene-diyne-diene-one-chromophore. From the nmr spectrum the end groups can easily be detected and the mass spectrum gives the structural formula together with some typical fragments. The only remaining structure for this ketone is 10 and the natural product therefore is the carbinol 11:

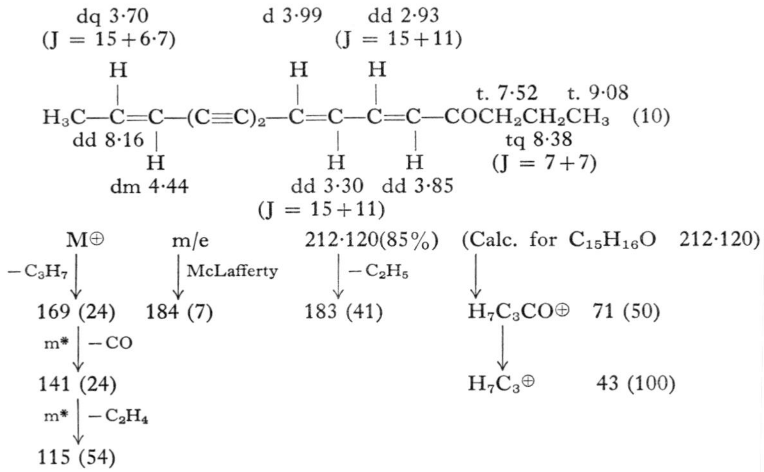

FIGURE 1. Nmr spectral assignments and mass spectral fragmentation of ketone (10).

$$H_3CCH=CH[C\equiv C]_2(CH=CH)_2CH(OH)C_3H_7$$
(11)

ACETYLENIC COMPOUNDS FROM UMBELLIFERAE

Using these methods several earlier investigations have been repeated. In this way the extracts of the roots and aerial parts of *Aethusa cynapium* L. give at least 25 acetylenes (Bohlmann *et al.*, 1968).

Table 1. Acetylenes from *Aethusa cynapium* L.

$H_3C = \equiv_2 =_2 CH_2CH_3$
(6)

$H_3C = \equiv_2 CH_2 = CH_2CH_2CH_3$
(12)

$H_3C =_2 \equiv =_2 CH_2CH_3$
(13)

$H_3C = \equiv_2 = CHC_3H_7$
|
OR
(R = H) (8) (R = Ac) (14)

$H_3C = \equiv_2 = COC_8H_7$
(15)

$HOCH_2 = \equiv_2 =_2 CH_2CH_3$
(7)

$AcOCH_2 —$
(16)

$HOCH_2CH_2CH_2 \equiv_2 =_2 CH_2CH_3$
(14)

$H_3C = \equiv_2 =_2 CH_2CH_2CH_2OH(C_{14})$
(18)

$HOCH_2 = \equiv_2 = CH_2CH_3$
O
(19)

$H_3CCH_2 =_2 \equiv = CH_3$
OH OH
(20)

$H_3C = \equiv_2 CH_2CH_2CHC_3H_7$
|
OH
(21)

$H_3C = \equiv_2 = CH_2CH_3$
O
(22)

$H_3C = \equiv_2 = CH_2CH_3$
O
(23)

$H_3C = \equiv_2 CH_2 CH_2CH_2CH_3$
O
(24)

$H_3C = \equiv_2 = CHO(C_{10})$
(25)

$H_3C =_2 \equiv = CHO$
(26)

$H_3CCH_2 =_2 \equiv = CHO(C_{11})$
(27)

$H_3C = \equiv_2 = CH_2COCH_2CH_3$
(28)

$H_3C = \equiv_2 CH_2CH_2COC_3H_7$
(29)

$H_3C =_2 \equiv_2 COC_3H_7$
(30)

$H_3CCH_2 =_2 \equiv = COCH_2CH_3$
(31)

$H_3C =_2 \equiv = CH_2OH(C_{10})$
(32)

$H_3CCH_2 =_2 \equiv = CH_2OH(C_{11})$
(33)

Most of these compounds have C_{13}-chains while only a few have also 10 or 11 carbons. One is a C_{14}-compound which is biogenetically important as shown later.

A reinvestigation of *Falcaria vulgaris* L. (Bohlmann *et al.*, 1966) gave also several further acetylenes which are summarized in Table 2:

Table 2. Acetylenes from *Falcaria vulgaris* L.

$= CO \equiv_2 CH_2 = C_7H_{15}$

$= CH \equiv_2 CH_2 = C_7H_{15}$
|
OH
(34)

$= CO \equiv =_3 C_6H_{13}$
(35)

$HOCH_2CH_2CO \equiv_2 = C_8H_{19}$
(36)

$= CH \equiv_2 CH = C_7H_{15}$
| |
OH   OH
(37)

$HOCH_2CH_2CO \equiv_2 CH_2 = C_7H_{15}$
(38)

$HOCH_2CH_2CH_2 \equiv_2 CH_2 = C_7H_{15}$
(39)

The more detailed investigation of *Oenanthe crocata* L. (Bohlmann & Rode, 1968) and *Cicuta virosa* L. (Bohlmann & Hänel, 1969) shows that the extracts contain many new compounds (see Tables 3 and 4):

Table 3. Acetylenes from *Oenanthe crocata* L.

$HOCH_2= \equiv_2 =_2 CH_2CH_2CHC_3H_7$
                  $|$
                  OH
(1)

$HOCH_2= \equiv_2 =_2 C_6H_{13}$
(2)

$H_3C= \equiv_2 =_2 CH_2CH_2COC_3H_7$
(3)

$H_3C= \equiv_2 =_2 C_6H_{13}$
(40)

$H_3C= \equiv_2 =_2 C_4H_9(C_{15})$
(41)

$H_3C= \equiv_2 CH_2\overline{\underset{c}{=}}C_7H_{15}$
(42)

$H_3C= \equiv_2 =(CH_2)_4COC_3H_7$
(43)

$H_3CCH_2CH_2 \equiv_2 =_2 CH_2CH_2COC_3H_7$
(44)

$AcOCH_2= \equiv_2 =_2 C_6H_{13}$
(45)

$AcOCH_2CH_2CH_2 \equiv_2 =_2 C_6H_{13}$
(46)

$=CH \equiv_2 CH_2\overline{\underset{c}{=}}C_7H_{15}$
 $|$
OH
(34)

$=CH \equiv_2 =_2 C_6H_{13}$
 $|$
OH
(47)

$HOCH_2CH_2CH_2 \equiv_2 =(CH_2)_4COC_3H_7$
(48)

$HOCH_2CH_2CH_2 \equiv_2 =_2 CH_2CH_2CHC_3H_7$
                       $|$
                       OH
(49)

$H_3C= \equiv_2 =CHC_5H_{11}(C_{15})$
              $|$
              OH
(50)

$HOCH_2= \equiv_2 CH_2\overline{\underset{c}{=}}C_7H_{15}$
(51)

$HOCH_2CH_2CH_2 \equiv_2 =_2 C_6H_{13}$
(52)

$H_3C= \equiv_2 =_2 CHC_3H_7(C_{15})$
                $|$
                OH
(53)

$H_3C= \equiv_2 =_2 CH_2CH_2CHC_3H_7$
                     $|$
                     OH
(54)

$HOCH_2CH_2CH_2 \equiv_2 CH_2\overline{\underset{c}{=}}C_7H_{15}$
(55)

$=CH \equiv_2 CH\overline{\underset{c}{=}}C_7H_{15}$
 $|$ $|$
OH OH
(57)

$OCH= \equiv_2 =CHC_7H_{15}$
           $|$
           OH
(56)

$AcOCH_2CH_2CH_2 \equiv_2 =CHC_7H_{15}$
                    $|$
                    OH
(57)

$AcOCH_2= \equiv_2 =_2 CH_2CH_2CHC_3H_7$
                    $|$
                    OH
(58)

$AcOCH_2CH_2CH_2 \equiv_2 =_2 CH_2CH_2CHC_3H_7$
                            $|$
                            OH
(59)

$HOCH_2= \equiv_2 =_2 CH_2CH_2COC_3H_7$
(60)

$HOCH_2CH_2CH_2 \equiv_2 =_2 CH_2CH_2COC_3H_7$
(61)

Table 4. Acetylenes from *Cicuta virosa* L.

$HOCH_2CH_2CH_2 \equiv_2 =CHC_7H_{15}$
$\qquad\qquad\qquad |$
$\qquad\qquad\qquad OH$
(62)

$HOCH_2CH_2CH_2 \equiv_2 =_2 C_6H_{13}$
(63)

$HOCH_2CH_2CH_2 \equiv_2 =_2 COC_5H_{11}$
(64)

$HOCH_2CH_2CH_2 \equiv_2 =_2 CHC_5H_{11}$
$\qquad\qquad\qquad\qquad |$
$\qquad\qquad\qquad\qquad OH$
(65)

$HOCH_2CH_2CH_2 \equiv_2 =_3 C_4H_9$
(5)

$H_3C= \equiv_2 =_3 COC_3H_7$
(66)

$HOCH_2CH_2CH_2 \equiv_2 =_3 COC_3H_7$
(67)

$HOCH_2CH_2CH_2 \equiv_2 =_3 CHC_3H_7$
$\qquad\qquad\qquad\qquad |$
$\qquad\qquad\qquad\qquad OH$
(4)

$HOCH_2CH_2CH_2 \equiv_2 =_2 CH_2CH_2COC_3H_7$
(68)

$HOCH_2CH_2CH_2 \equiv_2 =(CH_2)_4COC_3H_7$
(69)

Again most of the compounds have a C_{17}-chain, like the compounds isolated from *Opopanax chironium* Koch (Bohlmann & Rode, 1968), (see Table 5):

Table 5. Acetylenes from *Opopanax chironium* Koch

$=CO \equiv_2 CH_2 \overline{\underset{c}{=}} C_7H_{15}$
(9)

$=CO \equiv_2 CO \overline{\underset{c}{=}} C_7H_{15}$
(70)

$=CO \equiv_2 CH \overline{\underset{c}{=}} C_7H_{15}$
$\qquad\quad |$
$\qquad\quad OH$
(71)

$H_3C= \equiv_2 =_2 CH_2CH_2COC_3H_7$
(3)

$AcOCH_2= \equiv_2 =_2 C_6H_{13}$
(45)

$HOCH_2—$
(2)

$OCH—$
(72)

$=CH \equiv_2 CH_2 \overline{\underset{c}{=}} C_7H_{15}$
$\quad |\qquad\qquad (34)$
$\quad OH$

$=CH \equiv_2 =_2 C_6H_{13}$
$\quad |$
$\quad OH \qquad (47)$

$HOCH_2= \equiv_2 CH_2 \overline{\underset{c}{=}} C_7H_{15}$
(51)

$HOCH_2= \equiv_2 =CHC_7H_{15}$
$\qquad\qquad\quad |$
$\qquad\qquad\quad OH$
(73)

$HOCH_2CH_2CH_2 \equiv_2 =CHC_7H_{15}$
$\qquad\qquad\qquad\qquad |$
$\qquad\qquad\qquad\qquad OH$
(74)

$=CH \equiv_2 CH=C_7H_{15}$
$\quad |\qquad\quad |$
$\quad OH\quad\; OH$
(37)

Up to now the only species besides *Aethusa cynapium* L. containing C_{13}-acetylenes is *Laserpitium archangelica* Wulf (Bohlmann *et al.*, unpubl.) (see Table 6):

Table 6. Acetylenes from *Laserpitium archangelica* Wulf

$H_3C=\equiv_2=_2 CH_2CH_3$
(6)

$H_3C=\equiv_2=\underset{O}{\diagdown\diagup} CH_2CH_3$
(22)

$AcOCH_2=\equiv_2=_2 CH_2CH_3$
(16)

$H_3C=\equiv_2 CH_2\underset{C}{=}C_3H_7$
(12)

$H_3C=\equiv_2=CHC_3H_7$
$\quad\quad\quad\quad\mid$
$\quad\quad\quad\quad OAc$
(14)

$H_3C=\equiv_2=CHC_3H_7$
$\quad\quad\quad\quad\mid$
$\quad\quad\quad\quad OH$
(8)

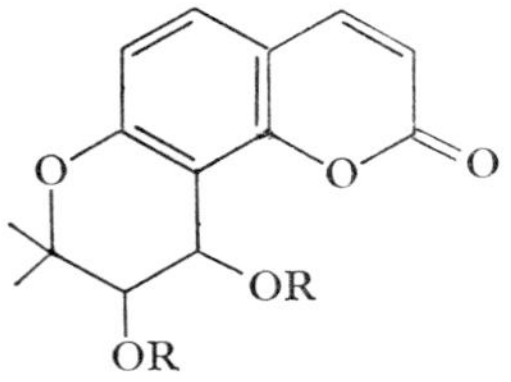

Again C_{17}-acetylenes together with a C_{15}-compound have been isolated from an *Azorella* species (Bohlmann *et al.*, unpubl.). The structures are most closely related to those of *Oenanthe* species (see Table 7):

Table 7. Acetylenes from *Azorella trifurcata* Pers.

$HOCH_2=\equiv_2 CH\underset{C}{=}C_7H_{15}$
$\quad\quad\quad\quad\mid$
$\quad\quad\quad\quad OH$
(75)

$AcCH_2=\equiv_2 CH\underset{C}{=}C_7H_{15}$
$\quad\quad\quad\quad\mid$
$\quad\quad\quad\quad OH$
(76)

$AcCH_2=\equiv_2 CH\underset{C}{=}C_5H_{11}$
$\quad\quad\quad\quad\mid$
$\quad\quad\quad\quad OH$
(77)

All the other investigated species contain already known compounds. Most widespread are falcarinone (9) and related acetylenes.

BIOGENETIC PATHWAYS

As in the family Compositae oleic acid is the common precursor for all these acetylenes, but the typical vinyl end group of the Compositae acetylenes is missing in all Umbelliferae compounds. Therefore this family seems to produce a special enzyme which reduces the vinyl groups. In Tables 8–11 the biogenetic relationships are summarized:

Table 8. Biogenetic relationships (C_{17})

$$H_3C(CH_2)_7 \overset{C}{=\!=\!=} (CH_2)_7CO_2R \qquad\qquad =CO \equiv_2 \overset{OH}{\underset{C}{CH}\!=\!\!=} C_7H_{15}$$

$\downarrow -[H] \qquad\qquad\qquad\qquad\qquad \uparrow [O]$

$$[H_7C_3 \equiv_2 \overset{C}{CH_2}\!=\!\!= (CH_2)_7CO_2R] \qquad =CH \equiv_2 \underset{OH}{\overset{C}{CH}\!=\!\!=} C_7H_{15}$$
$$\underset{OH}{} $$

$\downarrow [O],[H] \qquad\qquad\qquad\qquad\qquad \uparrow [O]$

$$[H_7C_3 \equiv_2 \overset{C}{CH_2}\!=\!\!= C_7H_{15}] \xrightarrow[{[O]}]{-[H]} =CH \equiv_2 \underset{OH}{CH_2}\!=\!\!\overset{C}{=} C_7H_{15}$$

$\downarrow -[H] \qquad\qquad\qquad\qquad\qquad OH \quad \downarrow [O]$

$$H_3C\!=\!\! \equiv_2 \overset{C}{CH_2}\!=\!\!= C_7H_{15} \qquad\qquad =CO \equiv_2 CH_2\!=\!\!\overset{C}{=} C_7H_{15}$$

$\downarrow [O]$

$$HOCH_2\!=\!\! \equiv_2 CH_2\!=\!\!\overset{C}{=} C_7H_{15} \xrightarrow{[H]} HOCH_2CH_2CH_2 \equiv_2 CH_2\!=\!\!\overset{C}{=} C_7H_{15}$$

$\downarrow [O] \qquad\qquad\qquad\qquad\qquad \downarrow [O],-H_2O$

$$HOCH_2\!=\!\! \equiv_2 \underset{OH}{CH\!=\!\!\overset{C}{=}} C_7H_{15} \qquad ROCH_2CH_2CH_2 \equiv_2 \equiv_2 C_6H_{13}$$

$\downarrow \qquad\qquad\qquad\qquad\qquad\qquad \xrightarrow{-H_2O} ROCH_2\!=\!\! \equiv_2 \equiv_2 C_6H_{13}$

$$HOCH_2\!=\!\! \equiv_2 \underset{OH}{=\!\!CHC_7H_{15}} \qquad\qquad —$$

$\downarrow [H] \quad OH \qquad\qquad\qquad\qquad \xrightarrow{[O]}$

$$ROCH_2CH_2CH_2 \equiv_2 \underset{OH}{=\!\!CHC_7H_{15}} \qquad OCH\!=\!\! \equiv_2 \underset{OH}{=\!\!CHC_7H_{15}}$$

Table 9. Biogenetic relationships (C_{17})

$$H_3C\!=\!\! \equiv_2 \equiv_2 CH_2CH_2COC_3H_7 \xrightarrow{[H]} H_7C \equiv_2 \equiv_2 CH_2CH_2COC_3H_7$$
$$\qquad\qquad\qquad\qquad\qquad\qquad + H_3C\!=\!\! \equiv_2 =\!(CH_2)_4COC_3H_7$$

$\uparrow [H]$

$$H_3C\!=\!\! \equiv_2 \equiv_3 COC_3H_7 \xleftarrow[{-H_2O,[O]}]{[O]} H_3C\!=\!\! \equiv_2 \equiv_2 C_6H_{13} \longrightarrow HOCH_2\!=\!\! \equiv_2 \equiv_2 C_6H_{13}$$

$\downarrow [O],[H] \qquad\qquad\qquad\qquad\qquad\qquad\qquad\qquad \downarrow [H]$

$$ROCH_2\!=\!\! \equiv_2 \equiv_2 CH_2CH_2COC_3H_7 \qquad\qquad HOCH_2CH_2CH_2 \equiv_2 \equiv_2 C_6H_{13}$$

$\downarrow [H] \qquad\qquad\qquad\qquad\qquad\qquad\qquad\qquad \downarrow [O]$

$$ROCH_2\!=\!\! \equiv_2 \equiv_2 \underset{OH}{CH_2CH_2CHC_3H_7} \qquad HOCH_2CH_2CH_2 \equiv_2 \equiv_2 \underset{OH}{CHC_5H_{11}}$$

$\downarrow [H] \qquad\qquad\qquad\qquad\qquad\qquad\qquad\qquad \downarrow -H_2O$

$$ROCH_2CH_2CH_2 \equiv_2 \equiv_2 \underset{OH}{CH_2CH_2CHC_3H_7} \qquad HOCH_2CH_2CH_2 \equiv_2 \equiv_3 C_4H_9$$

$\downarrow [O] \qquad\qquad\qquad\qquad\qquad\qquad\qquad\qquad \downarrow [O]$

$$ROCH_2CH_2CH_2 \equiv_2 \equiv_2 CH_2CH_2COC_3H_7 \qquad HOCH_2CH_2CH_2 \equiv_2 \equiv_3 COC_3H_7$$

$\downarrow [H] \qquad\qquad\qquad\qquad\qquad\qquad\qquad\qquad \downarrow [H]$

$$ROCH_2CH_2CH_2 \equiv_2 =\!(CH_2)_4COC_3H_7 \qquad HOCH_2CH_2CH_2 \equiv_2 \equiv_2 CH_2CH_2COC_3H_7$$

Table 10. Biogenetic relationships (C_{17} and C_{15})

$$=CH \equiv_2 =_2 C_6H_{13} \qquad =CO \equiv =_3 C_6H_{13}$$

$$\underset{\overset{|}{OH}}{=CH} \equiv_2 CH_2 \underset{C}{=} C_7H_{15} \longrightarrow =CO \equiv_2 CH_2 \underset{C}{=} C_7H_{15} \longrightarrow \underset{(79)}{H_3CCH_2CO} \equiv_2 \underset{(9)}{CH_2 = C_7H_{15}}$$

$$\underset{\overset{|}{OAc}}{=CH} \equiv_2 CO = C_7H_{15} \quad H_3CCH_2CH_2 \equiv_2 CH_2 \underset{C}{=} C_7H_{15} \qquad HOCH_2CH_2CO \equiv_2 CH_2 \underset{C}{=} C_7H_{15}$$

$$\underset{(78)}{} \quad \underset{(12)}{}$$

$$[H_3CCH_2CH_2 \equiv_2 CH_2 \underset{C}{=} (CH_2)_7CO_2R] \longrightarrow =CO \equiv_2 CH_2 \underset{C}{=} (CH_2)_6CHO$$
$$\underset{(80)}{} \qquad \underset{(13)}{}$$

$$(H_3CCH_2CH_2 \equiv_2 CH_2 \underset{C}{=} C_5H_{11}]$$

$$\underset{\overset{|}{OH}}{=CH} \equiv_2 CH_2 \underset{C}{=} C_5H_{11} \qquad\qquad H_3C = \equiv_2 CH_2 \underset{C}{=} C_5H_{11}$$
$$\qquad\qquad\qquad\qquad\qquad\qquad\qquad ROCH_2 = \equiv_2 \underset{\overset{|}{OH}}{CH \underset{C}{=} C_5H_{11}}$$

$$\underset{\overset{|}{OH}}{=CH} \equiv_2 =_2 C_4H_9 \qquad\qquad H_3C = \equiv_2 \underset{\overset{|}{OH}}{=CHC_5H_{11}}$$

$$=CO \equiv_2 =_2 C_4H_9 \qquad\qquad H_3C = \equiv_2 =_2 C_4H_9 \longrightarrow OCH = \equiv_2 =_2 C_4H_9$$
$$\qquad\qquad\qquad\qquad\qquad\qquad\qquad\qquad \underset{(81)}{}$$

$$H_3C = \equiv_2 =CH_2CH_2COC_3H_7 \overset{[O]}{\underset{[H]}{\longleftarrow}} H_3C = \equiv_2 =_2 \underset{\overset{|}{OH}}{CHC_3H_7}$$

In the case of the *Aethusa*-polyynes (see Table 11) most of these steps are established by feeding experiments (Bohlmann *et al.*, 1968). As in the case of Compositae-C_{13}-compounds, C_{14}-chains are the precursors and again the vinyl end group is biochemically reduced.

Hydrogenations of double bonds are also important in the case of *Oenanthe* and *Cicuta* acetylenes as shown again by tracer studies. Up to now the only known way of introducing an oxygen function is by allylic oxidation. In all cases where the polyynes have a non-allylic hydroxyl or keto group, an allylic precursor could be pointed out. If we put together all the necessary reactions, we can see that besides

Table 11. Biogenetic relationships (C_{13})

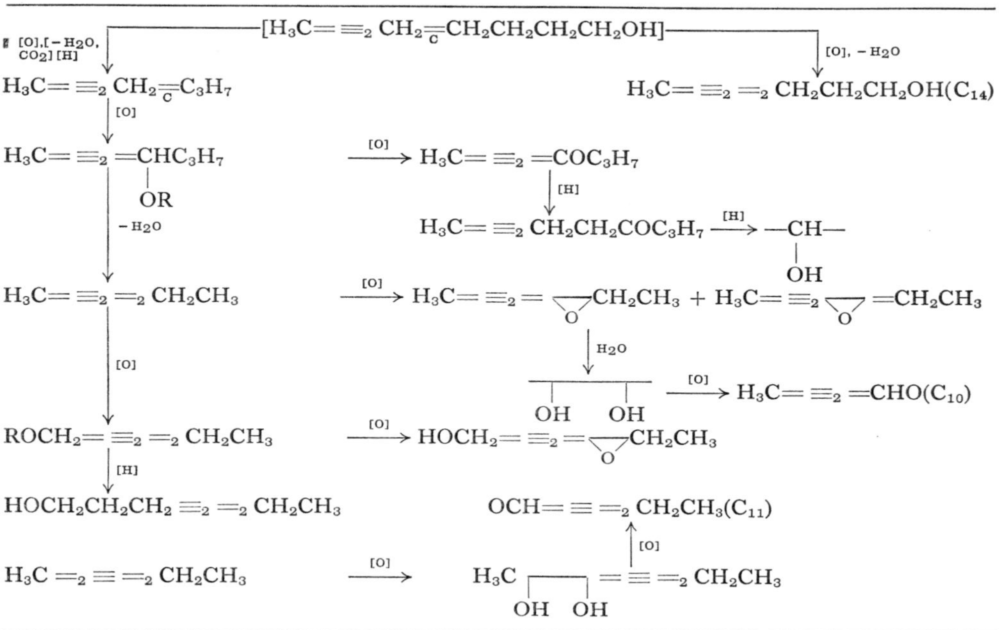

$$[H_3C\!=\!\equiv_2 CH_2\overline{\overline{=}}CH_2CH_2CH_2CH_2OH]$$

$$\begin{array}{l} \text{[O],[}-H_2O, \\ CO_2]\text{ [H]} \end{array}\Big\downarrow \qquad\qquad\qquad\qquad\qquad\qquad\qquad\qquad \Big\downarrow\,\text{[O], }-H_2O$$

$$H_3C\!=\!\equiv_2 CH_2\overline{\overline{=}}C_3H_7 \qquad\qquad\qquad\qquad H_3C\!=\!\equiv_2\,=_2 CH_2CH_2CH_2OH(C_{14})$$

$$\Big\downarrow\text{[O]}$$

$$H_3C\!=\!\equiv_2\,=\!CHC_3H_7 \qquad\xrightarrow{\text{[O]}}\; H_3C\!=\!\equiv_2\,=\!COC_3H_7$$

$$\begin{array}{c}|\\OR\end{array} \qquad\qquad\qquad\qquad\qquad\qquad\Big\downarrow\text{[H]}$$

$$\Big\downarrow\,-H_2O \qquad H_3C\!=\!\equiv_2 CH_2CH_2COC_3H_7 \xrightarrow{\text{[H]}}\; -CH-$$

$$\qquad\qquad\qquad\qquad\qquad\qquad\qquad\qquad\qquad\qquad\begin{array}{c}|\\OH\end{array}$$

$$H_3C\!=\!\equiv_2\,=_2 CH_2CH_3 \qquad\xrightarrow{\text{[O]}}\; H_3C\!=\!\equiv_2=\!\underset{O}{\triangledown}CH_2CH_3 + H_3C\!=\!\equiv_2\underset{O}{\triangledown}=\!CH_2CH_3$$

$$\Big\downarrow\text{[O]} \qquad\qquad\qquad\qquad\qquad\qquad\qquad\qquad\Big\downarrow H_2O$$

$$\qquad\qquad\qquad\qquad\qquad\qquad\qquad\underset{OH\quad OH}{|\qquad|}\xrightarrow{\text{[O]}} H_3C\!=\!\equiv_2\,=\!CHO(C_{10})$$

$$ROCH_2\!=\!\equiv_2\,=_2 CH_2CH_3 \qquad\xrightarrow{\text{[O]}}\; HOCH_2\!=\!\equiv_2=\!\underset{O}{\triangledown}CH_2CH_3$$

$$\Big\downarrow\text{[H]}$$

$$HOCH_2CH_2CH_2\equiv_2\,=_2 CH_2CH_3 \qquad\qquad OCH\!=\!\equiv\,=_2 CH_2CH_3(C_{11})$$

$$\qquad\qquad\qquad\qquad\qquad\qquad\qquad\qquad\qquad\qquad\uparrow\text{[O]}$$

$$H_3C\,=_2\equiv\,=_2 CH_2CH_3 \qquad\xrightarrow{\text{[O]}}\qquad H_3C\underset{OH\quad OH}{\overline{|\qquad|}}=\!\equiv\,=_2 CH_2CH_3$$

dehydrogenation to the triple bond nearly all the reactions are normal biochemical pathways:

Table 12. Necessary biochemical reactions

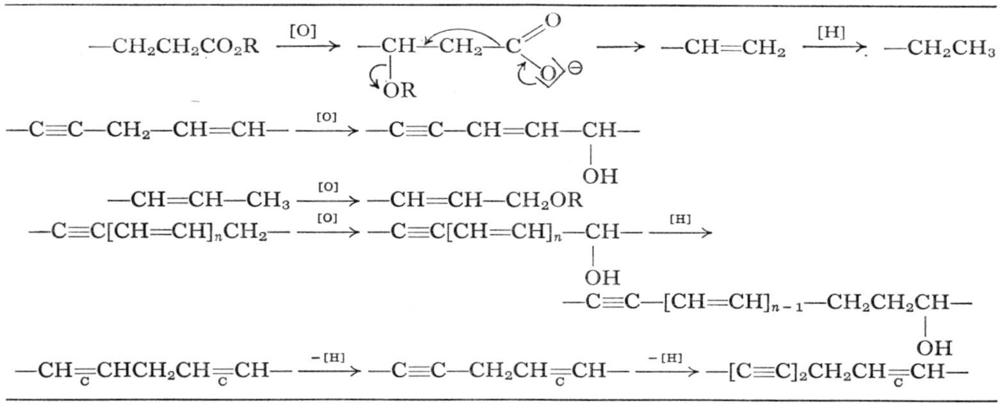

$$-CH_2CH_2CO_2R \xrightarrow{\text{[O]}} -CH\overset{\nearrow CH_2\searrow}{\underset{\begin{array}{c}|\\OR\end{array}}{}}C\overset{\nwarrow O}{\underset{\searrow O^\ominus}{}} \longrightarrow -CH=CH_2 \xrightarrow{\text{[H]}} -CH_2CH_3$$

$$-C\equiv C-CH_2-CH=CH- \xrightarrow{\text{[O]}} -C\equiv C-CH=CH-CH-$$

$$\qquad\qquad\qquad\qquad\qquad\qquad\qquad\qquad\qquad\begin{array}{c}|\\OH\end{array}$$

$$-CH=CH-CH_3 \xrightarrow{\text{[O]}} -CH=CH-CH_2OR$$

$$-C\equiv C[CH=CH]_n CH_2- \xrightarrow{\text{[O]}} -C\equiv C[CH=CH]_n-CH- \xrightarrow{\text{[H]}}$$

$$\qquad\qquad\qquad\qquad\qquad\qquad\qquad\qquad\qquad\qquad\qquad\begin{array}{c}|\\OH\end{array}$$

$$\qquad\qquad\qquad\qquad\qquad\qquad -C\equiv C-[CH=CH]_{n-1}-CH_2CH_2CH-$$

$$\qquad\qquad\qquad\qquad\qquad\qquad\qquad\qquad\qquad\qquad\qquad\qquad\qquad\begin{array}{c}|\\OH\end{array}$$

$$-CH\overline{\overline{=}}CHCH_2CH\overline{\overline{=}}CH- \xrightarrow{-\text{[H]}} -C\equiv C-CH_2CH\overline{\overline{=}}CH- \xrightarrow{-\text{[H]}} -[C\equiv C]_2CH_2CH\overline{\overline{=}}CH-$$

DISTRIBUTION OF ACETYLENES IN THE UMBELLIFERAE

If we look at the distribution of the acetylenes in the Umbelliferae we can see (Tables 13 and 14) that these compounds are present in all three subfamilies. So far species of only 25% of the Umbelliferae genera have been investigated so that the systematic importance of acetylenes is still not clear. It will be necessary to survey more species and to consider other constituents before a proper assessment can be made.

Table 13. Umbelliferae species known to contain acetylenes
(F = Falcarinone or derivatives)

Subfamily HYDROCOTYLOIDEAE
  Tribe 1. Hydrocotyleae
Didiscus coeruleus DC.   F (9)
D. pilosus Domin   F (9, 34)
Trachymene australis Benth.   F (71)

  Tribe 2. Mulineae
Bowlesia tenera Spr.   F (9)
B. incana Ruíz & Pavón   F (9)
B. tenella Meyer   F (9)
Azorella trifurcata Pers. C_{17}, C_{15} (see Tables 8–11)

Subfamily SANICULOIDEAE
  Tribe 1. Saniculeae
Eryngium planum L.   F (9, 34, 71)

  Tribe 2. Lagoecieae
Lagoecia cuminoides L.   —C≡C—

Subfamily APIOIDEAE
  Tribe 1. Scandiceae
Anthriscus cerefolium (L.) Hoffm.   —C≡C—
Astrodaucus orientalis (L.) Drude   —C≡C—*
Caucalis platycarpos L.   F (9, 71)
Chaerophyllum aromaticum L.   —C≡C—
C. temulentum L.   F (9)
Chaetosciadium trichospermum (L.) Boiss.   —C≡C—*
Myrrhis odorata (L.) Scop.   —C≡C—
Myrrhoides nodosa (L.) Cannon   —C≡C—
Orlaya daucorlaya Murb.   —C≡C—*
O. grandiflora (L.) Hoffm.   F (9, 34)
Osmorhiza aristata Makino   —C≡C—†
Physocaulis nodosus (L.) Koch   F (9, 71)
Scandix balansae Reut.   F (9)
S. pecten-veneris L.   —C≡C—
Torilis arvensis (Hudson) Link   F (9)
T. japonica (Houtt.) DC.   F (9, 34)
T. nodosa (L.) Gaertn.   —C≡C—†
Turgenia latifolia (L.) Hoffm.   —C≡C—*

  Tribe 4. Smyrnieae
Conium maculatum L.   F (9, 71, 79)

  Tribe 5. Apieae
Aegopodium podagraria L.   F (70, 71)
Aethusa cynapium L. C_{13} (see Table 1)
Ammi visnaga (L.) Lam.   F (71)
Anethum graveolens L. C_{17} (45)
Apium graveolens L.   F (9, 37, 71)
Berula erecta (Hudson) Coville   F (9, 71)
Bunium bulbocastanum L.   F (9, 34, 45, 71)
Bupleurum rotundifolium L. C_{17} (2, 52)
B. gerardi All. C_{17} (2, 52)†
B. longiradiatum Turcz.   —C≡C—
Carum carvi L.   F (37, 71)
C. verticillatum (L.) Koch   F (37, 71)
Cenolophium denudatum (Hornem.) Tutin   F (71)
Cicuta douglasii Coult. & Rose C_{17} (see Table 4)
C. virosa L. C_{17} (see Tables 8–10)
Crithmum maritimum L.   F (71)
Cryptotaenia canadensis (L.) DC.   F (71)
Cuminum cyminum L.   F (37, 70, 71)
Falcaria vulgaris Bernh.   F (see Table 2)
Foeniculum vulgare Miller   —C≡C—
Helosciadium inundatum (L.) Koch   —C≡C—

Kundmannia sicula (L.) DC.	F (9, 71)
Libanotis buchtormensis DC.	F (9)
Ligusticum mucronatum Hort.	—C≡C—*
L. lucidum Miller	—C≡C—
Meum athamanticum Jacq.	F (71)
Oenanthe aquatica (L.) Poir.	F (9) + C_{17} (similar to *Oenanthe crocata* + 81, 82)
O. crocata L.	F (9) + C_{17} (see Tables 8–10)
O. fistulosa L.	F (9) + C_{17}
O. globulosa L.	C_{17}
O. lachenalii Gmelin	C_{17}
O. peucedanifolia Poll.	F (9)
O. pimpinelloides L.	F (9, 34, 37, 71) + C_{17} (2, 45, 46, 52)
O. silaifolia Bieb.	F (9) + C_{17} (see Table 3)
Petroselinum crispum (Miller) A. W. Hill	F (71)
P. segetum (L.) Koch	F (9, 34)
Pimpinella major (L.) Huds.	F (9)
P. koreana	—C≡C—†
P. saxifraga L.	—C≡C—*
Ptychotis saxifraga (L.) Loret & Barrandon	F (9, 71)
Ridolfia segetum Moris	F (9)
Selinum carvifolia (L.) L.	F (9)
Seseli osseum Crantz	F (9)
S. dichotomum Pall. ex Bieb.	F (9)
S. glabratum Willd. ex Schultes	F (9, 71)
S. gummiferum Pall. ex Sm.	F (34)
S. leucospermum Waldst. & Kit.	F (34, 71)
S. montanum L.	F (9, 71)
S. varium Trevir.	F (9, 71)
Sison amomum L.	F (9)
Silaum besseri DC.	F (9)
S. latifolium L.	F (71)
S. nodifolium L.	F (9, 34)
S. sisaroideum DC.	—C≡C—
S. sisarum L.	F (71, 72)
S. suave Walter	—C≡C—*
Thaspium aureum Nutt.	F (9) + C_{17}
T. trifoliatum (L.) Gray	—C≡C—*
Trachyspermum ammi Spr.	C_{17}
Trinia glauca (L.) Dumort.	F (9, 71)
T. kitaibelii Bieb.	F (9)
Zizia aurea Koch	F (9, 34, 71)

Tribe 6. Peucedaneae

Ainsworthia trachycarpa	F (80)
'*Angelica deculsiva*'	—C≡C—†
A. miqueliana	—C≡C—†
A. polymorpha	—C≡C—†
A. sylvestris L.	—C≡C—*
Capnophyllum dichotomum Lag.	F (37)
C. peregrinum (L.) Lange	F (37)
Conioselinum chinense	—C≡C—†
Ferula assa-foetida L.	F (71)
Opopanax chironium (L.) Koch	F (9, 37, 72) + C_{17} (see Tables 8–10)
O. hispidius (Friv.) Griseb.	C_{17}
Pastinaca sativa L.	F (9) + C_{17} + 80
Phellopterus littoralis Buth.	—C≡C—†
Tordylium maximum L.	F (9)

Tribe 7. Laserpitieae

Laserpitium archangelica Wulf.	C_{13} (see Table 11)
L. hispidum Bieb.	—C≡C—*
Thapsia villosa L.	—C≡C—*

[*continued overleaf*]

[Table 13—*continued*.]

Tribe 8. Dauceae	
Daucus aureus Desf.	—C≡C—*
D. carota L.	F (34, 37, 71)
D. crinitus Desf.	—C≡C—*
D. guttatus Sibth.	—C≡C—*
D. pusillus Michx.	—C≡C—*
Pseudorlaya pumila (L.) Grande	F (9)

* Crowden *et al.* (1969).
† Yoshioka *et al.* (1966).

Table 14. Distribution of acetylenes in the Umbelliferae

	Tribes	No. of genera with acetylenes	Typical compounds	Others
I.	Hydrocotyleae	2	F	$HOCH_2 = \equiv_2 CH = C_7H_{15}$
				$\mid$
				OH
	Mulineae	2	F	
II.	Saniculeae	1	F	
	Lagoecieae	1	?	
III.	Echinophoreae	?	—	
	Scandiceae	13	F	
	Coriandreae	?	—	
	Smyrnieae	1	F	
	Apieae	33	F	many C_{17}-, C_{13}- and some C_{15}-acetylenes
	Peucedaneae	9	F	
	Laserpitieae	2	$C_{13}(H_3C = \equiv_2 =_2 CH_2 CH_3)$	
	Dauceae	2	F	

(F means $=CO \equiv_2 CH_2 \underset{C}{=} C_7H_{15}$ or derivatives.)

RELATIONSHIPS WITH OTHER FAMILIES

Up to the present the only relationships to other families that are more or less clear are those shown in Table 15. Considering the structure of the acetylenes and

Table 15. Relationships with other families

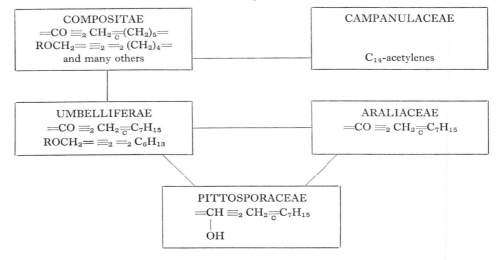

also of several other constituents, the Umbelliferae are closely related to the Araliaceae and the Compositae. Further relationships with the Campanulaceae and Pittosporaceae are also evident but more samples will have to be studied to clarify the situation further.

REFERENCES

ANET, E. F. L., LYTHGOE, B., SILK, M. H. & TRIPETT, S., 1953. Oenanthotoxin and cicutoxin, isolation and structure. *J. Chem. Soc.*, 309–322.

BENTLEY, R. K., BHATTACHARJEE, D., JONES, E. & THALLER, V., 1969. Natural acetylenes, Part XXVIII. C_{17}-polyacetylenic alcohols from the umbellifer *Daucus carota* L. (carrot). Alkylation of benzene by acetylenyl (vinyl) carbinols in the presence of toluene-*p*-sulphonic acid. *J. Chem. Soc.* C, 685–688.

BOHLMANN, F., ARNDT, C., BORNOWSKI, H. & HERBST, P., 1960. Polyacetylenverb. XXV. Die Polyine aus *Äthusa cynapium* L. *Chem. Ber.*, **93**: 981–987.

BOHLMANN, F., ARNDT, C., BORNOWSKI, H. & KLEINE, K. M., 1961. Polyacetylenverb. XXXI. Über die Polyine aus der Familie der Umbelliferen. *Chem. Ber.*, **94**: 958–967.

BOHLMANN, F., FANGHÄNEL, L., WOTSCHOKOWSKY, M. & LASER, J., 1968. Polyacetylenverb. **154**. Über die Isolierung weiterer Acetylenverbindungen aus *Äthusa cynapium* L. und über die Biogenese der Hauptinhaltsstoffe. *Chem. Ber.*, **101**: 3510–2518.

BOHLMANN, F., NIEDBALLA, U. & RODE, K. M., 1966. Polyacetylenverb. CXVIII. Über neue Polyine mit C_{17}-Kette. *Chem. Ber.*, **99**: 3552–3558.

BOHLMANN, F. & RODE, K. M., 1968. Polyacetylenverb. 147. Die Polyine aus *Oenanthe crocata* L. *Chem. Ber.*, **101**: 1163–1175.

BOHLMANN, F. & HÄNEL, P., 1969. Polyacetylenverb. 168. Über die Polyine aus *Cicuta virosa* L. *Chem. Ber.*, **102**: 3293–3297.

BOHLMANN, F. & RODE, K. M., 1968. Polyacetylenverb. CXLIII. Die Polyine aus Opopanax chironium Kch. *Chem. Ber.*, **101**: 525–531.

CROWDEN, R. K., HARBORNE, J. B. & HEYWOOD, V. H., 1969. Chemosystematics of Umbelliferae—a General Survey. *Phytochemistry*, **8**: 1963–1984.

JONES, E., SAFE, S. & THALLER, V., 1966. Natural acetylenes, Part XXIII. A C_{18}-polyacetylenic keto-aldehyde related to falcarinone from an umbellifer (*Pastinaca sativa* L.). *J. Chem. Soc.*, C 1220–1221.

YOSHIOKA, I., KIMURA, T., IMAGAWA, H. & TAKARA, K., 1966. Polyacetylenic compounds (I) Occurrence in higher plants. *Yakugoku Zazhi*, **86**: 1216–1220.

Flavonoid and phenylpropanoid patterns in the Umbelliferae

J. B. HARBORNE

Phytochemical Unit, Department of Botany, University of Reading, Reading, England

Surveys of leaf flavonoids have shown that there is a steady progression within the family from taxa with only flavonols (kaempferol and/or quercetin) to those with only flavone (luteolin). Flavonol groups include all the tribes of the Hydrocotyloideae and Saniculoideae and the tribes Echinophoreae, Coriandreae, Smyrnieae and Peucedaneae of the Apioideae. Intermediate groups with both flavone and flavonol are the Apieae, Laserpitieae and Dauceae. The only flavone group is the Scandiceae. Flavonoids associated in the angiosperms generally with woody habit (e.g. leucocyanidin) are almost completely absent, apart from isolated occurrences in the Apieae. By contrast, more complex (or more 'highly evolved') flavonoids such as chrysoeriol (luteolin 3′-methyl ether) are known in the Dauceae and Scandiceae. Sugars found attached to flavonoids also vary in the family from glucose and rutinose in the flavonol groups to apiosylglucose and as yet incompletely characterized di- and triglucoses, arabinosylglucoses and arabinosylglucosylrhamnoses attached to luteolin in the Scandiceae.

Another character of interest at the tribal and generic levels is the hallucinogenic phenylpropanoid myristicin, which occurs in the seed of Apieae (especially *Oenanthe*), Peucedaneae (e.g. *Pastinaca*) and Dauceae (*Daucus* and *Pseudorlaya*). Again, surveys have indicated that while the caffeic acid ester chlorogenic acid is ubiquitous, it is replaced by the related isochlorogenic acid in the leaves of the single genus, *Astrodaucus*.

The taxonomic and evolutionary significance of these results will be discussed in relation to tribal classification within the family and to the classification of the Caucalineae-Dauceae alliance.

CONTENTS

INTRODUCTION

Flavonoid pigments are favoured compounds as taxonomic markers in the angiosperms because they are ubiquitous whereas most other classes of secondary constituents have a more limited distribution. Thus in the family under discussion, the Umbelliferae, flavonoids occur universally whereas alkaloids, for example, are restricted to a single taxon, *Conium maculatum* (see Fairbairn's paper, p. 361). Another potent reason for the popularity of flavonoids as taxonomic markers is the fact that (with the exception of the anthocyanins) they are remarkably stable substances and can readily be detected in plant tissue taken from herbarium sheets which are as much as 100 to 150 years old. This factor has been very important in our own survey of the Umbelliferae (Crowden *et al.*, 1969) and has allowed a much broader survey than would otherwise have been possible. By contrast, polyacetylenes can only be surveyed using completely fresh plant material (cf. Bohlmann's paper, p. 279).

Perhaps the most cogent reason of all for studying the distribution patterns of flavonoids in higher plants is that they appear to show much promise as phyletic markers (Harborne, 1966, 1971). Thus, studies of broad distribution patterns among the angiosperms have indicated that several evolutionary (and biosynthetic) progressions in flavonoid types are present. In the flower, the evolutionary trend is from cyanidin as the simplest or most primitive anthocyanidin towards pelargonidin and apigeninidin (to give orange red colour) or towards delphinidin and malvidin (to give blue colour) depending on the pollinating vectors involved. In the leaf, the most striking evolutionary change is associated with the changeover from woody to herbaceous habit. The 'woody' flavonoid pattern consists of the flavonols kaempferol (1), quercetin (2) and especially myricetin (3), together with leucoanthocyanidins based on cyanidin (4) and delphinidin (5). On the other hand, in herbaceous plants, kaempferol (1) and quercetin (2) are often present but they are progressively replaced by the flavones luteolin (6) and apigenin (7); and leucoanthocyanidins are completely lacking. Many other structural features in the flavonoid molecule (e.g. A-ring hydroxylation, *C*-glycosylation, etc.) also change with evolutionary advancement. It should be noted that two of the major changes in leaf pattern involve loss mutations, i.e. the loss of the ability to add a 3-hydroxyl group to give flavones instead of flavonols and the loss of the ability to add a third hydroxyl to the B-ring (disappearance of myricetin and leucodelphinidin). These general patterns have been established by comparing flavonoid distributions with the broad views of angiosperm evolution as outlined in Davis & Heywood (1963), Cronquist (1969) and Takhtajan (1969). They become of value when considering evolutionary trends within individual families and this is certainly true of the Umbelliferae as much as any other group.

Until our recent survey of the Umbelliferae, little was known of the flavonoid patterns in this large family. However, a number of compounds had been isolated from individual members, particularly those of culinary and medicinal usage, and it is interesting to note that one of the very first flavone glycosides to be characterized chemically was the unusual apiosylglucoside of apigenin, apiin, which was isolated from celery seed as long ago as 1843. While the Umbelliferae is not quite as rich in interesting and structurally diverse flavonoids as certain other families such as the Leguminosae or Compositae, nevertheless, as will be shown here, it contains a sufficiently wide assemblage of compounds for taxonomic scrutiny.

In the present paper, it is the intention to review the flavonoids found in the family, to discuss their distribution patterns and then to consider in more detail

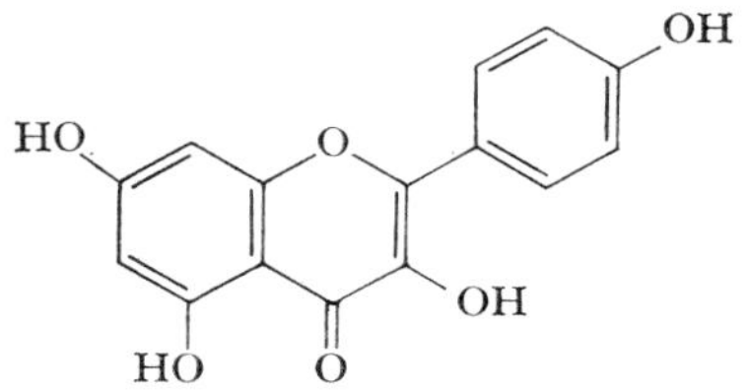

(1) Kaempferol

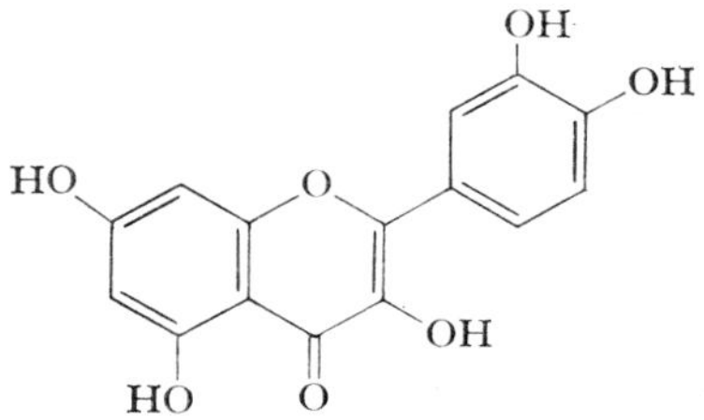

(2) Quercetin

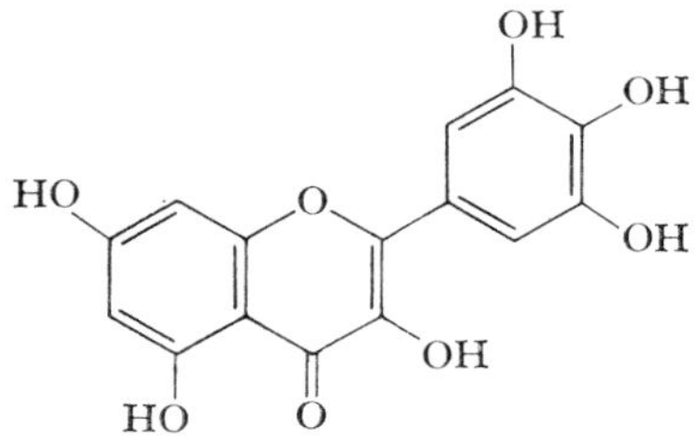

(3) Myricetin

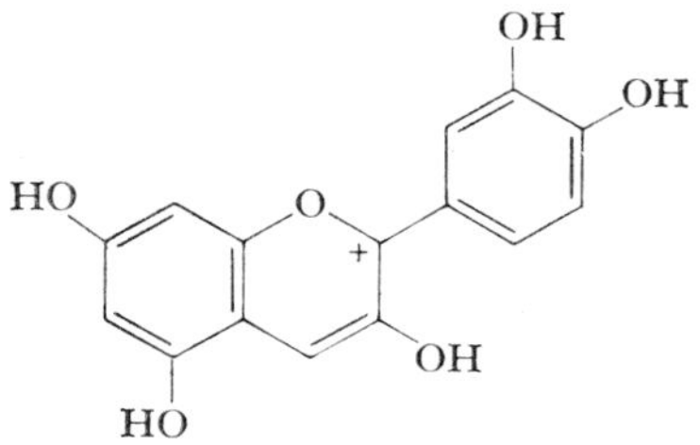

(4) Cyanidin

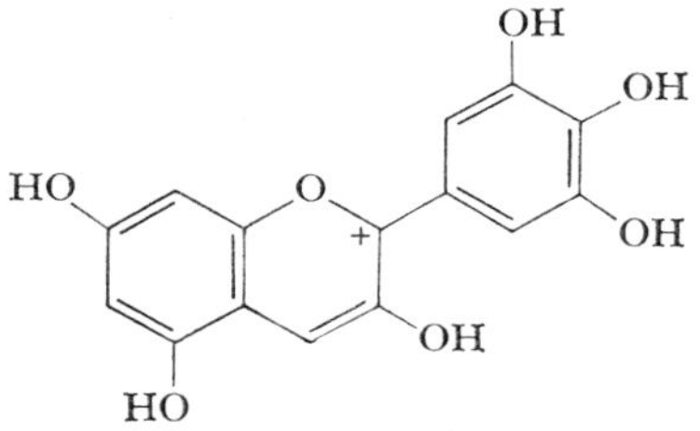

(5) Delphinidin

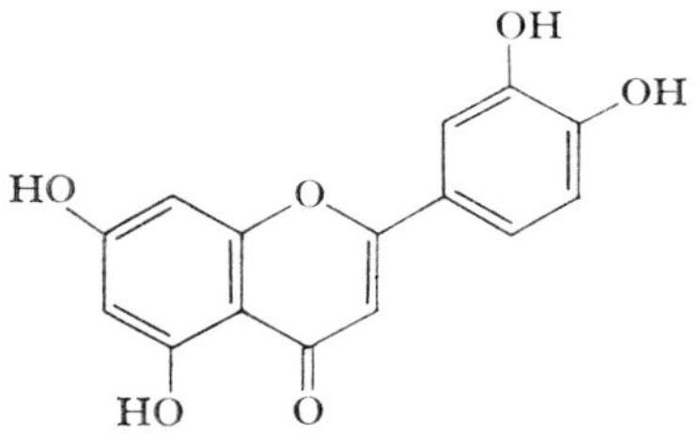

(6) Luteolin

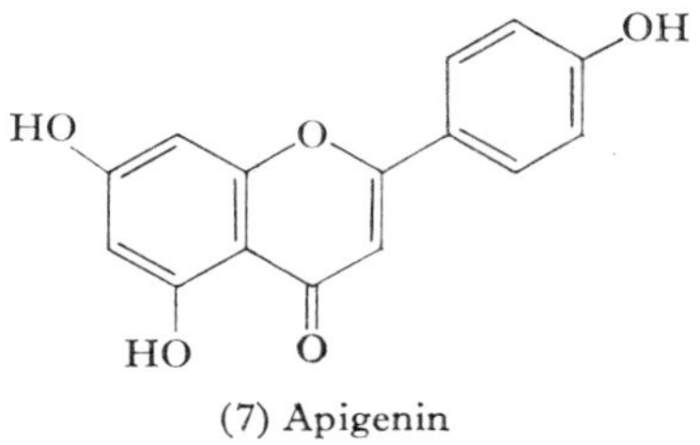

(7) Apigenin

these patterns in a single tribe, the Caucalideae, which has been the subject of an intensive joint biological and chemical investigation (see also pp. 215–232). The phenylpropanoids, which are closely related biosynthetically to the flavonoids, have been screened for during these investigations and the distribution of some of these derivatives are also considered here.

FLAVONOIDS OF THE UMBELLIFERAE

Aglycones

Information on the flavonoids in the Umbelliferae presented here is based on

(i) isolated reports from the earlier literature (for reference, see Geissman 1962; Harborne, 1967), (ii) a search of Chemical Abstracts up to November 1970, (iii) our own broad survey of leaf and fruit constituents (Crowden *et al.*, 1969; Harborne *et al.*, 1969) and (iv) our detailed study of flavonoids in leaf, flower and fruit of the Caucalideae (Harborne, 1967*b* and unpublished). As a result, a total of eleven aglycones have been isolated from the family (Table 1).

It is clear from leaf surveys that there are three major regular constituents: kaempferol, quercetin and luteolin. In this respect, it is the characteristic pattern to be expected in a predominantly herbaceous, highly specialized family. One may note also that myricetin (3), a regular constituent in many primitive woody families (see Bate-Smith, 1962) is completely absent and also that leucoanthocyanidins are likewise absent or very rare. Leucocyanidin was provisionally detected in but one species (*Apiastrum angustifolium*) from 300 surveyed, while an earlier report of the same compound in *Hacquetia epipactis* could not be confirmed (Crowden *et al.*, 1969).

Another 'primitive' flavonoid class, glycoflavone, is also very rare in the family, being possibly present in *Laretia* (tribe Mulineae) and *Cryptotaenia* (tribe Apieae). A related C-glycoside, the xanthone mangiferin (8) has also been found in the family, but this again is very rare, appearing as it does in the leaf of just two *Heptaptera* species, *H. triquetra* and *H. angustifolia*. With regard to other occurrences of more 'primitive' flavonoid types in the family, examination of some of the more strikingly woody members of the family such as *Myrrhidendron* (see Rodríguez' paper, p. 63) would be of especial interest, since the flavonoid pattern might indicate whether the woodiness here is primary or secondary in nature.

O-Methylation of flavonoid hydroxyl groups is generally regarded as an advancement over its absence so that it is interesting that no less than five *O*-methylated flavonoids are present. Four are related either to the common flavones, i.e. chrysoeriol (9), diosmetin (10) and acacetin (11) or to the common flavonols, i.e. isorhamnetin (12). The fifth is more unusual: it is the flavanone hesperitin (13), reported in the leaf of *Cnidium silaifolium* by Plouvier (1969) as occurring in the form of the 7-rutinoside, hesperidin. The only other flavanone found in the family is selinone (14), an *O*-isoprene substituted derivative of naringenin, occurring in the root of *Selinum vaginatum* (Seshadri & Sood, 1967). Both these flavanones are of systematic interest since they indicate the presence of chemical link between the Umbelliferae and a neighbouring family, the Rutaceae. Thus, hesperidin is best known as a regular constituent of *Citrus* fruits, while a flavanone with terpenoid substitution very similar to selinone has been isolated by Geissman (1958) from *Melicope sarcococca* (see Harborne, 1967*a*: pp. 174–180).

The only anthocyanidin reported in the family appears to be the phylogenetically simplest member of the series, cyanidin (4). This is hardly surprising since no strong selective pressures for bright anthocyanin flower colour seems to have occurred in the family at large. At least, the majority of umbellifers of temperate climates have dull flower colours, often white, occasionally yellow and sometimes pale pink. Anthocyanin pigment, when it is present, seems to be concentrated more in the stem (*Heracleum mantegazzianum*, *Conium maculatum*), in the leaf (*Chaetosciadium*,

Torilis) or in the root (high concentrations of cyanidin glycoside are present in the so-called 'black' carrot cultivar of India).

A number of so far unidentified (and possibly novel) flavonoids have been detected in the family during leaf surveys (e.g. in *Eryngium*, *Eriosynaphe* and *Magydaris*) and their structural elucidation may well throw further light on family relationships. One such compound, present in the fruit of *Daucus*, has the colour properties of an aurone. This would be an interesting discovery since aurones occur typically in the Compositae and their presence thus appears to represent phyletic advancement.

Glycosides

Each of the eleven aglycones found in the Umbelliferae (Table 1) is capable of occurring in the living cell as a range of different glycosides. Since glycosylation is

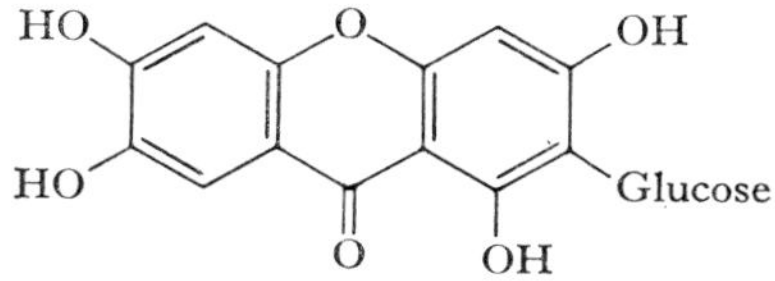

(8) Mangiferin

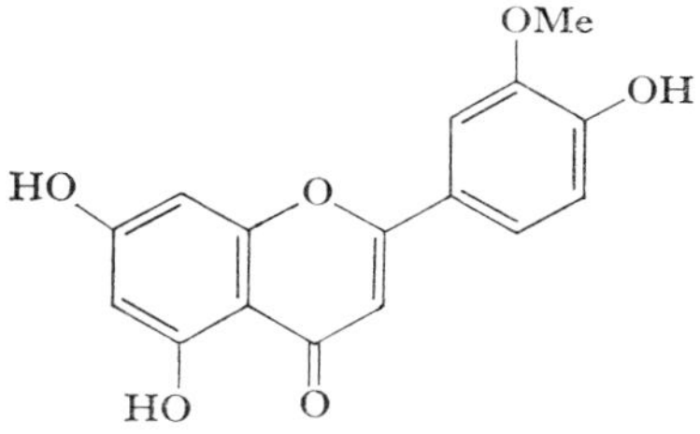

(9) Chrysoeriol

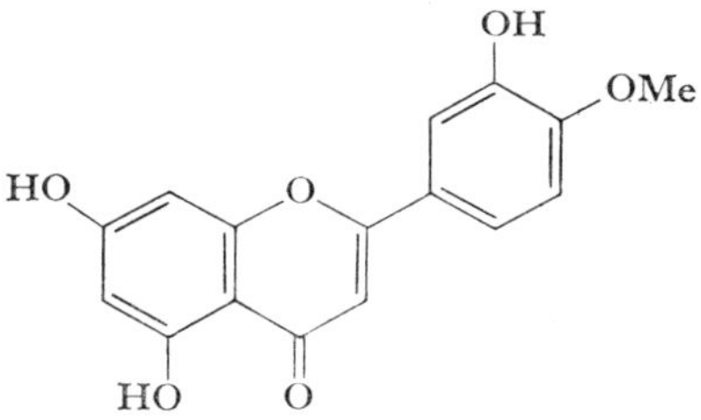

(10) Diosmetin

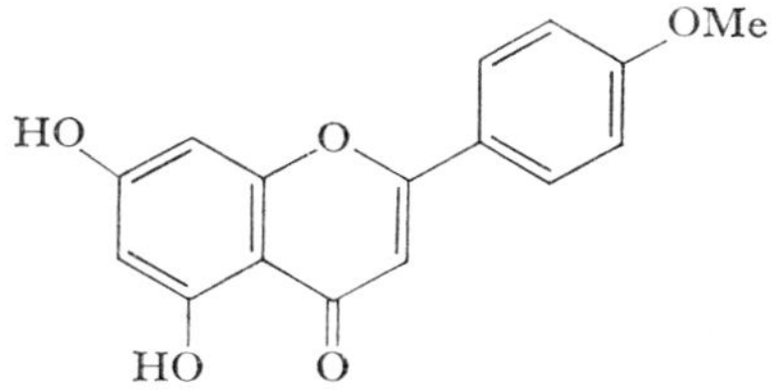

(11) Acacetin

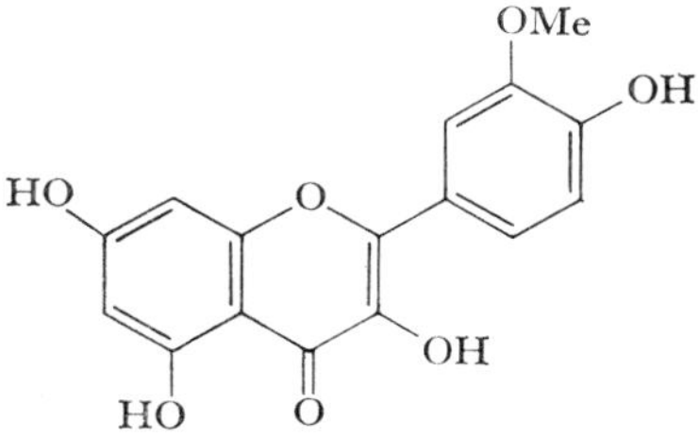

(12) Isorhamnetin

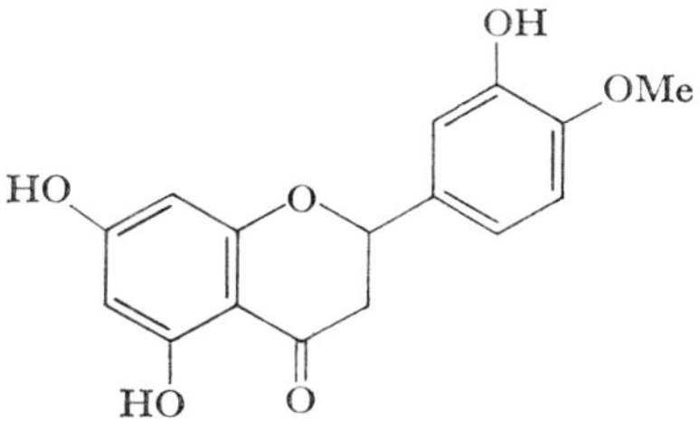

(13) Hesperitin

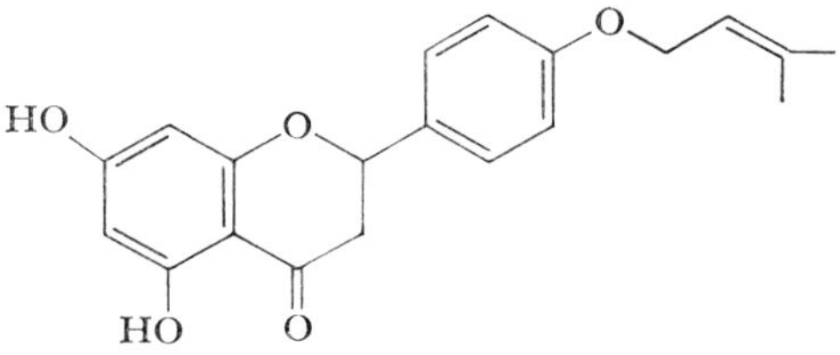

(14) Selinone

often very consistent taxonomically and also quite complex in some cases, its study provides much of interest to the systematist. The glycosidic variation as at present known among the flavones and flavonols of umbellifers is outlined in Tables 2–3. Many of the types listed (e.g. flavonol 3-glucosides and 3-rutinosides, flavone 7-glucosides) are relatively common both in the family and in the angiosperms generally. It is the more unusual types, i.e. those with an unusual sugar, combination

Table 1. Flavonoid aglycones in the Umbelliferae

Class	Compound and formula	Distribution
Flavonols	Quercetin (2)	Widespread; in leaves of 62% of a 300 spp. sample, also frequent in flower and fruit.
	Kaempferol (1)	Widespread; in leaves of 40% of a 300 spp. sample, also frequent in flower and fruit.
	Isorhamnetin (12)	Uncommon; in *Bupleurum, Oenanthe*, and *Pastinaca*.
Flavones	Luteolin (7)	Widespread; in leaves of 26% of a 300 spp. sample, also found in flower and fruit.
	Apigenin (6)	Uncommon; in *Apium, Daucus, Laserpitium, Peucedanum*.
	Chrysoeriol (9) (Luteolin 3′-methyl ether)	Uncommon; in *Apium, Daucus, Petroselinum, Pseudorlaya, Torilis, Turgenia*.
	Diosmetin (10) (Luteolin 4′-methyl ether)	Uncommon; in *Angelica, Cnidium, Conopodium*, and *Trinia*.*
	Acacetin (11)	Rare: in *Ammi visnaga*.
Anthocyanidin	Cyanidin (4)	Uncommon; in *Chaetosciadium, Daucus, Heracleum, Torilis*.
Flavanones	Hesperitin (9)	Rare; as 7-rutinoside hesperidin in *Cnidium silaifolium*.
	Selinone (10)	Rare; free in roots of *Selinum vaginatum*.

* Also reported incorrectly as occurring in *Conium maculatum* leaf (cf. Crowden *et al*., 1969) and in parsley seed (cf. Nordström *et al*., 1953).

Table 2. Flavonol glycosides of the Umbelliferae

Flavonol glycoside	Occurrence	Leading reference
Kaempferol		
3-Glucoside	Common, e.g. *Daucus carota* flower	Rahman *et al*., 1963
3-Rutinoside	In *Bifora testiculata* leaf	Crowden *et al*., 1969
3-Glucuronide ⎱ 3-Arabinoside ⎰	In *Foeniculum vulgare* leaf	Harborne & Saleh, 1971
3-Diglucoside	In *Daucus carota* flower	Rahman *et al*., 1963
Quercetin		
3-Glucoside	Common, e.g. *Hydrocotyle* spp. leaf	Crowden *et al*., 1969
3-Rutinoside	Very common, e.g. *Bupleurum falcatum*	Rabaté, 1930
3-Glucuronide ⎱ 3-Arabinoside ⎰	In *Foeniculum vulgare* leaf	Ohta & Miyazaki, 1959; Harborne & Saleh, 1971
3-Galactoside	In *Orlaya kochii* fruit	J. B. Harborne, unpublished
3-Rhamnoside	In *Pimpinella procumbens* leaf	Crowden *et al*., 1969
Isorhamnetin		
3-Rutinoside	In *Bupleurum multinerve* leaf	Minaeva & Volkhonskaya, 1964
3-Glucoside-4′-rhamnoside	In *Pastinaca sativa* fruit	Maksyutina & Litvinenko, 1966
3-Potassium hydrogen sulphate	In *Oenanthe stolonifera* flower	Matsushita & Iseda, 1965

Table 3. Flavone glycosides of the Umbelliferae

Flavone glycoside*	Occurrence	Leading reference
Apigenin		
7-Glucoside	In *Peucedanum villosum* leaf	Crowden *et al.*, 1969
7-Apiosylglucoside	In *Apium graveolens* fruit	Vongerichten, 1876
7-Rhamnosylglucoside	In *Torilis* spp. fruit ⎫	
7-Diglucoside	⎬ In *Pseudorlaya pumila* fruit	J. B. Harborne & C. A. Williams, unpublished
7-Arabinosylrhamnosylglucoside ⎰		
7-Glucosylglucuronide	In *Orlaya daucorlaya* fruit ⎭	
Luteolin		
7-Glucoside	Common, e.g. in *Daucus carota* leaf	Crowden *et al.*, 1969
7-Apiosylglucoside	In *Petroselinum crispum* fruit	Nordström *et al.*, 1953
7-Rhamnosylglucoside	In *Torilis* spp. fruit ⎫	
7-Diglucoside	In *Torilis nodosa* fruit ⎪	
7-Triglucoside	In *T. leptophylla* fruit ⎬	Harborne 1967*b*; J. B. Harborne & C. A. Williams, unpublished
4'-Glucoside ⎱	In *Turgenia latifolia* fruit ⎪	
4'-Diglucoside ⎰	⎭	
Chrysoeriol		
7-Glucoside ⎱	In *Pseudorlaya pumila* fruit	J. B. Harborne & C. A. Williams, unpublished
7-Diglucoside ⎰		
7-Apiosylglucoside	In *Apium graveolens* leaf	Farooq *et al.*, 1953
Diosmetin		
7-Rutinoside	In *Trinia glauca* leaf	Plouvier, 1969

* The apiosylglucose in the flavone glycosides is known to be β-D-apiofuranosyl ($1 \rightarrow 2$) β-D-glucose but the structures of the remaining di- and trisaccharides attached in the 7-position still await full characterization. At least two series of isomeric 7-diglucosides are present in Caucalideae fruit tissues.

of sugars or type of linkage, that are of most interest. Some of these types are discussed below.

One of the most distinctive sugars of the Umbelliferae is the five carbon branched pentose apiose, first isolated from Nature in combined form as apiin, the 7-apiosylglucoside of apigenin (15), from celery seeds by Bracconnet in 1843 and later

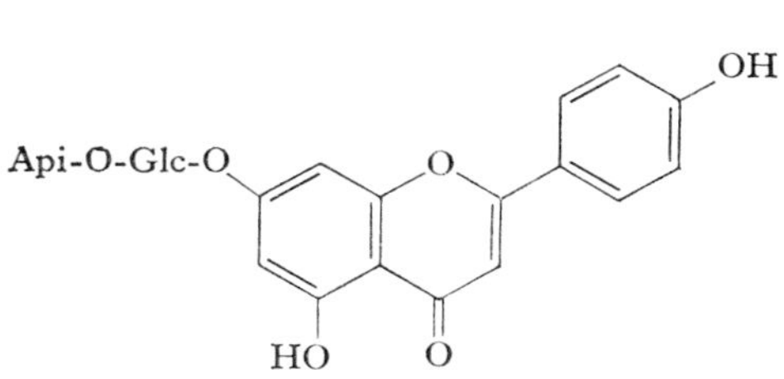

(15) Apiin

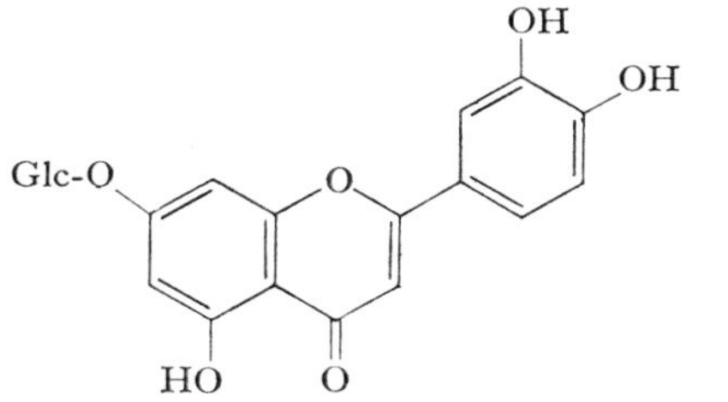

(16) Luteolin 7-glucoside

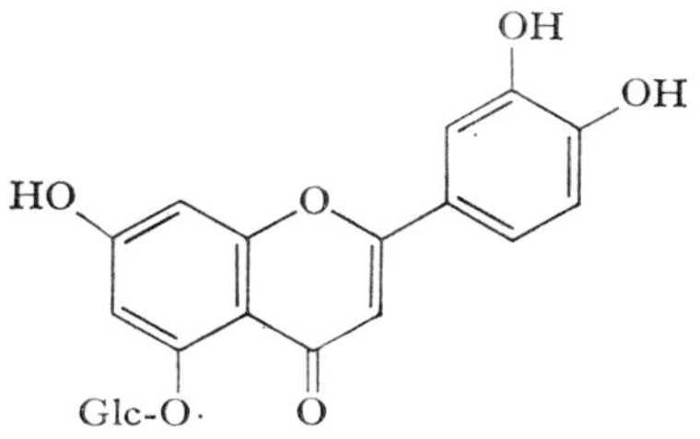

(17) Luteolin 5-glucoside

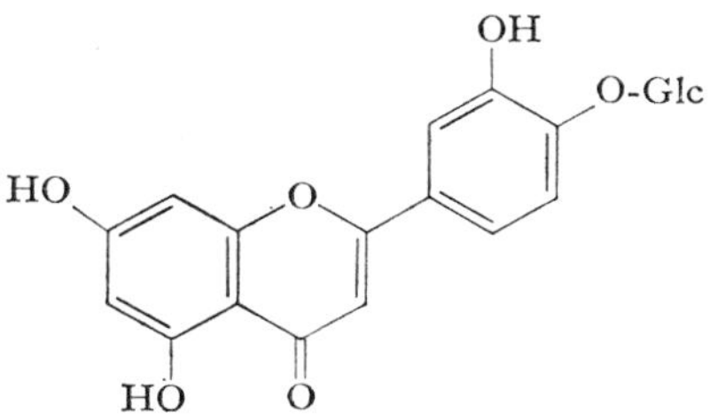

(18) Luteolin 4'-glucoside

characterized by Vongerichten in 1876. Apiose has subsequently been found else-where in the plant kingdom, particularly combined as polysaccharide, but the Umbelliferae still remain a notable source. Within the family, the 7-apiosylglucosides of apigenin and luteolin, both present in celery and parsley, are not widespread. However, apiose has been detected both in the soluble sugar fraction and combined as polysaccharide in a number of other umbellifers (see Crowden *et al.* 1969).

While attachment of sugars to the 7-position of flavones is very common—luteolin 7-glucoside (16) is the most widespread flavone glycoside in the Umbelliferae—attachment of sugars to other less reactive hydroxyl groups is much rarer. Two such types are known in the family: the 5- and 4'-glucosides of luteolin. Luteolin 5-glucoside, or galuteolin (17), occurs in three related umbellifer sources, in *Chaetosciadium*, *Daucus* and in *Torilis*. This substance is also known in the Leguminosae (*Galega officinalis*, *Genista* spp.), in the Compositae (*Cotula turbinata*) and the Caprifoliaceae (*Leycesteria formosana*) and seems to represent an advanced character in the angiosperms at large (Glennie & Harborne, 1971). Luteolin 4'-glucoside (18), accompanied by the 4'-diglucoside, occurs again in two related umbellifer sources, in *Turgenia latifolia* and in some accessions of *Daucus carota*. The 4'-glucoside also has a disparate distribution elsewhere in the angiosperms, being reported from *Spartium junceum* (Leguminosae), *Pyrus* (Rosaceae), *Gnaphalium affine* (Compositae) and *Acer cissifolium* (Aceraceae) (for references see Harborne, 1967).

Flavonols occur generally in umbellifers in unexceptional glycosidic form, e.g. as the 3-glucoside or 3-rutinoside (Table 2). An unusual type unique to the family is the 3-glucoside 4'-rhamnoside of isorhamnetin (19) (pasternoside) found in parsnip seeds by Maksyutina & Litvinenko (1966). The occurrence of 3-glucuronides and 3-arabinosides of kaempferol and quercetin in leaf of fennel, *Foeniculum vulgare*, is also noteworthy (Harborne & Saleh, 1971). This is a very unusual pair of glycosides to be found together. In fact, the arabinoside character varies within the species. A survey of 19 accessions from different parts of Europe showed it was restricted to two-thirds; however, its presence was not clearly correlated with either geography or subspecies classification. Finally, mention must be made of the combined form in which isorhamnetin occurs in *Oenanthe*; this is not a glycoside but as a potassium hydrogen sulphate salt (20) (Matsushita & Iseda, 1965). Such flavonoid salts are a rarity in Nature; it has been suggested that their occurrence is associated with aquatic habit (McClure, 1970). This suggestion is supported by the recent discovery of these compounds in two moisture-loving composite plants, *Lasthenia conjugens* and *L. fremontii* (Saleh *et al.*, 1971).

(19) Pasternoside   (20) Persicarin

The simple anthocyanidin pattern in the Umbelliferae has already been commented on above; glycosidic variation in this series is likewise not very great. Unpublished work from this laboratory suggests that the main pigments in carrot root and flower, *Torilis arvensis* and *Chaetosciadium* leaf are the 3-rutinoside and/or 3-sophoroside (diglucoside) of cyanidin. Another relatively common pigment, cyanidin 3-sambubioside, was similarly found in the stem of the giant hogweed *Heracleum mantegazzianum*.

PHENYLPROPANOIDS

Hydroxycinnamic acids

There is as rich a variety of phenylpropanoids in the family as there are of flavonoids. These compounds are often isolated in the essential oil fraction of fruits or roots and some compounds, e.g. *p*-coumaric acid, occur combined with terpenes. Only two classes of phenylpropanoids are considered here: the hydroxycinnamic acid derivatives and the phenylpropenes. Other phenylpropanoids of taxonomic interest are the coumarins, discussed in Nielsen's paper, p. 325, and 2-methylchromones, mentioned in Hegnauer's paper, p. 267.

A leaf survey in our laboratory of 38 umbellifer taxa (mainly Caucalideae with representatives of other tribes) showed that the hydroxycinnamic acid pattern was typical for an advanced angiosperm family (cf. Bate-Smith, 1962). Thus, caffeic acid was universal, while ferulic, sinapic and *p*-coumaric acids were regularly present. In the same survey, two other compounds, gentisic acid and scopoletin, were found as frequent constituents but the distribution patterns in both cases were too sporadic to be meaningful.

A wide survey of leaf constituents in the family showed that the major cinnamic ester universal in the group was the simple caffeic acid ester, chlorogenic acid (Crowden *et al.*, 1969). However, caffeic acid does occur in more unusual forms of taxonomic interest. Thus, it is present as an ester with 3,4-dihydroxyphenyl-lactic acid, i.e. rosmarinic acid (21), in several members of the Saniculoideae (see Hiller's paper, p. 369). It also occurs as the dicaffeoyl quinic ester, isochlorogenic acid in many members of the Caucalideae. Isochlorogenic acid is normally accompanied by larger amounts of chlorogenic, but exceptionally, occurs alone in the leaf of all three known species of *Astrodaucus* (see p. 307). Finally there is a recent report of caffeic acid being covalently linked to the seed protein of anise and caraway (Brieskorn & Mosandl, 1970).

No simple esters of *p*-coumaric acid (e.g. *p*-coumaroylquinic acid) have been isolated from the family but this compound has been found in unusual combination with a monoterpene and with a sesquiterpene. The first compound is *p*-coumaroyl-fenchone (22), isolated from the roots of *Seseli sibiricum* by Kapoor *et al.*, 1968, the second is farnesiferol B (23) from *Ferula assa-foetida* (Caglioti *et al.*, 1958). This second compound is of biosynthetic interest because of the close structural relationship of its sesquiterpene moiety to the plant growth regulator, abscisic acid (24).

Phenylpropenes

A considerable number of phenylpropenes occur in the Umbelliferae and at least

(21) Rosmarinic acid   (22) p-Coumaroylfenchone

(23) Farnesiferol B   (24) Abscisic acid

(25) Myristicin

one, myristicin (25) occurs relatively widely (in 14 genera from 3 tribes) (Harborne *et al.*, 1969). Myristicin has a bitter taste and is present, not surprisingly, in a number of those umbellifers used for seasoning foods. It is also of pharmaceutical interest, since it is either hallucinogenic itself or gives rise to hallucinogenic compounds *in vivo* (Shulgin, 1967). The known umbellifer phenylpropenes fall into five classes, according to the hydroxylation (or methoxylation), pattern of the benzene ring, i.e. 4-OH, 3,4-diOH, 3,4,5-triOH, 2,4,5-triOH and 2,3,4,5-tetraOH.

The simplest phenylpropene is anethole (26) reported in *Pimpinella anisum* by Dumas as long ago as 1833. More recently, the related isoeugenol epoxide (27) was found in *Pimpinella saxifraga* as an ester with 2-methylbutyric acid (Bohlmann & Zdero, 1969). The only phenylpropene with 3,4-dihydroxy substitution is methyl-eugenol or 3,4-dimethoxyallylbenzene reported in carrot root by Buttery *et al.* (1968). The 3,4,5-trihydroxy pattern is exemplified by myristicin (25), which has been found in root, seed or leaf oil of many economically important umbellifers, such as celery, dill, fennel, parsley, parsnip and carrot. It also occurs widely in *Oenanthe*, so it is not surprising that a related ketone crocatone (28) is present in *Oenanthe* and also in *Laserpitium* (Plat *et al.*, 1963). Another myristicin analogue, dihydromyristi-cin is known; this occurs in the root of the carrot (Buttery *et al.*, 1968). By contrast

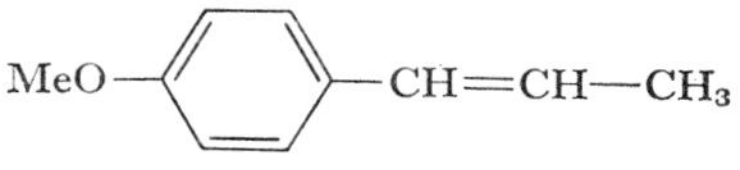

MeO—⟨benzene⟩—CH=CH—CH₃

(26) Anethole

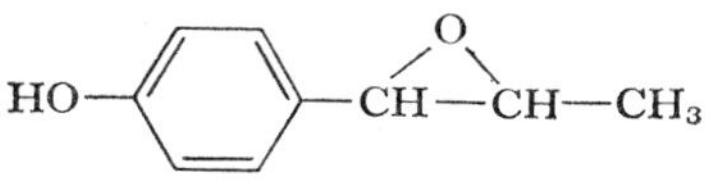

HO—⟨benzene⟩—CH—CH—CH₃ (epoxide O)

(27) Isoeugenol epoxide

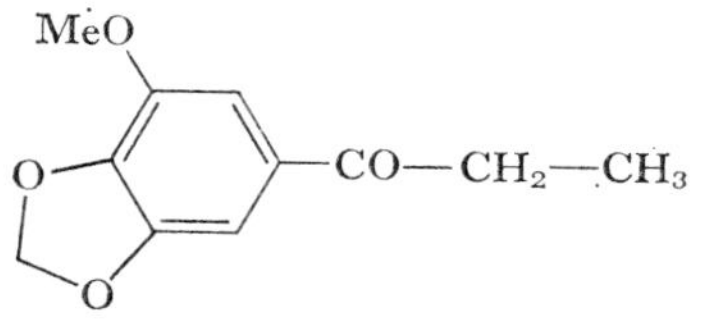

MeO / O—CH₂—O (methylenedioxy) ⟨benzene⟩—CO—CH₂—CH₃

(28) Crocatone

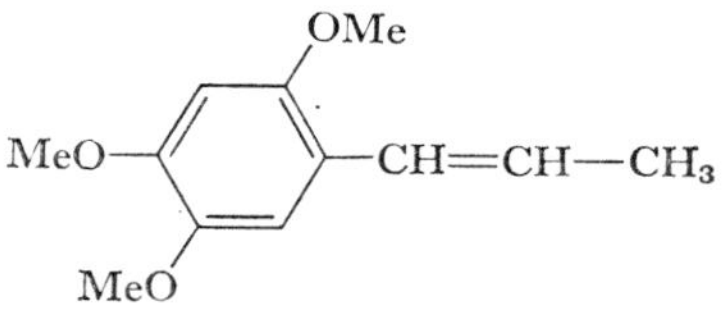

OMe / MeO—⟨benzene⟩—CH=CH—CH₃ / MeO

(29) Asarone

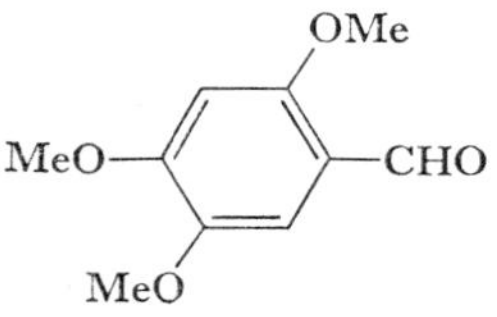

OMe / MeO—⟨benzene⟩—CHO / MeO

(30) Asaronaldehyde

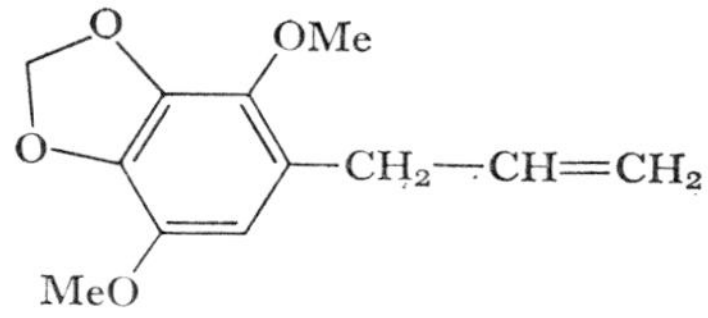

O—CH₂—O / OMe ⟨benzene⟩—CH₂—CH=CH₂ / MeO

(31) Parsleyapiole

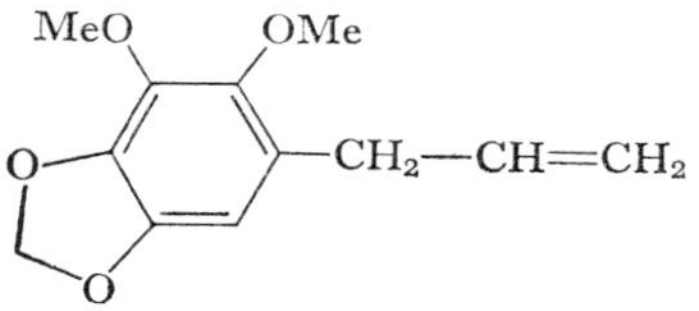

MeO OMe / O—CH₂—O ⟨benzene⟩—CH₂—CH=CH₂

(32) Dillapiole

MeO OMe / MeO—⟨benzene⟩—CH₂—CH=CH₂ / MeO

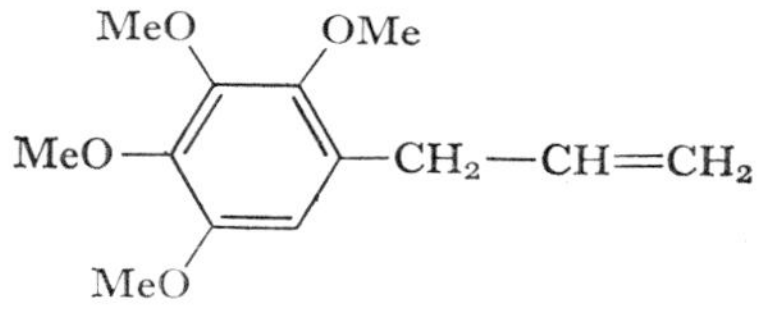

(33) 2,3,4,5-Tetramethoxyallylbenzene

with the 3,4,5-substitution pattern in myristicin, the isomeric 2,4,5-pattern is rare. Compounds of this type are confined to the carrot and include asarone (29) and the related benzaldehyde, asaronaldehyde (30) (Starkovsky, 1962) which was first isolated from *Asarum europeum* (Aristolochiaceae).

Finally, mention must be made of parsley-apiole and dillapiole, the isomeric dimethoxymethylenedioxybenzenes (31) and (32). The first occurs characteristically in *Petroselinum sativum* (Vongerichten, 1876) and the second in dill, *Anethum graveolens* (Ciamician & Silber, 1896). One or both also occur in *Crithmum maritimum*, *Anethum sowa* and *Ligusticum scoticum*. A third compound of this type, 2,3,4,5-tetramethoxyallylbenzene (33) accompanies apiole and myristicin in parsley seed (Wagner & Hölzl, 1968).

FLAVONOID PATTERNS AT THE FAMILY AND TRIBAL LEVELS

From the systematic viewpoint, the most significant discovery arising from the flavonoid leaf survey in the family (the results of which are summarized in Table 4) is that nearly all species have *either* flavonols *or* flavones but not both, some *Daucus* and *Laserpitium* species being rare exceptions. Furthermore, flavones are found almost entirely in taxa generally considered to be advanced or more specialized (e.g. *Daucus*, *Scandix*, *Torilis*) while flavonols predominate in the less advanced genera (e.g. *Hydrocotyle*). Thus, the replacement of flavonol by flavone appears to have evolutionary significance within the family, as it probably has among the angiosperms generally.

Table 4. Distribution of flavonoids in the Umbelliferae

Subfamily and tribe*	No. of species with Flavonol	Flavone	Generic ascertainment	Methylated flavonoids	Phenyl-propenes
Hydrocotyloideae					
1. Hydrocotyleae	16	0	13/34	—	—
2. Mulineae	7	0			
Saniculoideae					
1. Saniculeae	26	0	7/9	—	—
2. Lagoecieae	2	0			
Apioideae					
1. Echinophoreae	2	0	2/5	—	—
2. Scandiceae					
(a) Scandicinae	1	16	17/21	—	—
(b) Caucalinae	2	19		+	+
3. Coriandreae	3	0	2/5	—	—
4. Smyrnieae	21	5	22/29	—	—
5. Apieae	79	20	52/85	+	+
6. Peucedaneae	46	1	23/41	+	+
7. Laserpitieae	7	11	4/8	—	+
8. Dauceae	5	7	3/4	+	+

* Classification according to Drude (1898).

On the basis of the flavonoid data, tribes can be divided (Table 4) into two broad groups: the majority of nine in which flavones are rare or absent; and four in which flavones are common or predominant (Apieae, Dauceae, Laserpitieae and Scandiceae). This division correlates reasonably well with accepted evolutionary lines within the family, particularly those at the subfamily level. Thus, the Hydrocotyloideae which lacks flavones is less typically umbelliferous than the Apioideae and closer to the Araliaceae in possessing a woody endocarp, no separate carpophore and frequent absence of vittae. It is interesting to note here that flavones are also completely absent from the Araliaceae, all species examined in this neighbouring family having kaempferol and/or quercetin (J. B. Harborne, unpublished results). Again, the Saniculoideae which also lacks flavones altogether, is regarded as having probably evolved separately from the rest of the family for a long time. This subfamily has a distinctive chemistry in other regards (see Hiller's paper, p. 369). Finally, there is the third subfamily the Apioideae, which separates from the other two by presence of flavones, of methylated flavonoids and of phenylpropenes.

These three chemical characters are by no means uniformly distributed throughout the Apioideae. However, one can discern a progression in flavonoid pattern from the Echinophoreae, Coriandreae, Peucedaneae and Smyrnieae (flavones rare) through the Apieae (flavones in 20% of species) to the Scandiceae, Laserpitieae and Dauceae (flavones in over 50% of species). This evolutionary trend is correlated with morphology in so far as the Echinophoreae is regarded as the more primitive and the Laserpitieae and Dauceae the more advanced tribes within the subfamily.

While the distribution of methylated flavonoids and of phenylpropenes is not as well documented as that of the basic flavonoids, it is worth noting that these two biosynthetically distinct characters co-occur in the four groups: Apieae, Peucedaneae, Scandiceae (Caucalinae) and Dauceae. Phenylpropenes have also been detected in the Laserpitieae (J. W. Adcock, unpublished results) which suggests that more detailed examination of the flavonoids in this tribe might well reveal some methylated derivatives as being present.

FLAVONOID AND OTHER CHEMICAL PATTERNS IN THE CAUCALIDEAE

Flavonoids and phenylpropanoids

Our interest in the flavonoids of the Umbelliferae at large arose from a more detailed programme of research on the phytochemistry of the Caucalideae tribe. This research programme, initiated in 1965 by V. H. Heywood and supported by the U.K. Science Research Council, has been concerned with accumulating data of all types (chemical, anatomical, morphological, cytological) on a small group of 'taxonomically difficult' plants in order to determine whether newer methods of analysis, and particularly numerical analysis, would provide a more objective and ultimately more useful systematic classification.

The group of plants under study are essentially all those umbellifer taxa with spines on both the primary and secondary ridges of the fruit. They are classified all together as the Caucalideae by Bentham & Hooker (1867) and Boissier (1872) but separated into two groups, the tribe Dauceae and the subtribe Caucalinae, tribe Scandiceae, by Drude in the Englerian system (1898). In all, there are some 80–100 species divided into some 14 genera, the plants being of European, North African or S.W. Asian origin. The most important and largest genus is *Daucus*, which includes the cultivated carrot *D. carota*, and which is also the most variable morphologically. The only other large genus (10–15 species) is *Torilis*, the European hedge- or bur-parsley. The remaining genera are represented by 1–3 species: *Orlaya*, *Caucalis*, *Turgenia*, *Chaetosciadium*, *Artedia*, *Pseudorlaya* and *Astrodaucus*.

The richest variation in the various chemicals present in these plants was detected in the flavonoids and a detailed analysis of these constituents has been carried out, especially those in the fruit and to a lesser extent those in leaf and flower. The main results are presented in Table 5, while a summary of these results considered as generic characters is presented in Table 6. Before discussing variation within species, it is perhaps useful to consider the systematic significance of these new data at the generic level, as indicated in Table 6.

The ten chemical characters included in this table are reasonably consistent at the generic level, with the exception of some variation in *Daucus*. This is not surprising, however, since *Daucus* is the largest genus under study: it is also very variable morphologically and there are reasons (see Heywood & Dakshini, p. 215) for promoting some of the individual sections in the genus into separate genera. Apart from this, nearly all the genera can be distinguished from each other on the basis of the flavonoid pattern.

As can be seen, the nine genera in Table 6 are divided into four groups on the basis

Table 5. Flavonoids in the fruits of the Caucalideae

Species	FLAVONES Aglycones Lu	Ap	Chr	Glycosides 5G	4'G	7RG	7GG	7GGlur	FLAVONOLS Aglycones Qu	Km	Glycosides
Artedia squamata L.	—	—	—	—	—	—	—	—	+	+	—
Astrodaucus orientalis (L.) Drude	—	—	—	—	—	—	—	—	+	—	—
Caucalis platycarpos L.	+	—	—	—	—	+	+	—	—	—	—
Chaetosciadium trichospermum (L.) Boiss.	+	+	—	—	—	—	—	—	—	—	—
Daucus aureus Desf.	+	+	+	+	—	—	—	—	—	—	—
D. australis Kotov	+	+	—	—	—	—	—	—	+	—	—
D. carota ssp. *sativus*	+	+	—	—	+	+	+	—	+	—	—
D. carota ssp. *carota*	+	—	—	—	+	+	—	—	+	—	—
D. crinitus Desf.	+	—	—	—	—	+	—	—	+	+	3RG
D. glochidiatus (Labill.) Fischer & C. A. Meyer	—	—	—	—	—	—	—	—	+	—	—
D. littoralis Sibth. & Sm.	+	—	—	—	—	—	—	—	+	—	3GG
D. muricatus (L.) L.	+	—	—	—	+	—	—	—	—	—	—
D. pusillus Michx	+	+	—	—	—	+	—	—	+	+	—
D. setifolius Desf.	+	+	—	—	—	+	—	+	+	—	—
D. syrticus Murb.	+	+	—	—	—	—	—	—	+	—	—
D. sp.	+	+	+	—	—	+	—	—	—	—	—
Orlaya kochii Heywood	+	—	—	—	—	—	+	—	+	—	3Gal
O. grandiflora (L.) Hoffm.	—	—	—	—	—	—	—	—	+	—	—
O. daucorlaya Murb.	+	—	—	—	—	—	—	+	+	+	3Glur
Pseudorlaya minuscula (Pau) Laínz	+	—	—	—	—	—	—	—	+	—	3RG
P. pumila (L.) Grande	—	+	+	—	—	—	+	—	+	—	3GG
Torilis arvensis (Huds.) Link	+	—	—	—	—	+	—	—	—	—	—
T. japonica (Houtt.) DC.	+	—	+	—	—	+	—	—	—	—	—
T. leptophylla (L.) Reichenb. f.	+	—	—	—	—	+	+	—	—	—	—
T. nodosa (L.) Gaertner	+	—	—	+	—	+	+	—	—	—	—
T. tenella (Delile) Reichenb. f.	+	+	—	—	—	+	+	—	—	—	—
Turgenia latifolia (L.) Hoffm.	+	—	+	—	+	—	—	—	—	—	—

KEY: Lu, luteolin; Ap, apigenin; Chr, chrysoeriol; 5G, 5-glucoside; 4'G, 4'-glucoside; 7RG, 7-rhamnosylglucoside; 7GG, 7-diglucoside; 7GGlur, 7-glucosylglucuronide; Qu, quercetin; Km, kampeferol; 3RG, 3-rutinoside; 3GG, 3-diglucoside; 3Gal, 3-galactoside; 3Glur, 3-glucuronide. Since in all species, flavones occurred as 7-glucosides and flavonols as 3-glucosides, these glycosidic forms are omitted from the table. Additional compounds were present as follows: unknown aglycone, *D. carota* subsp. *carota* and *D. crinitus*; luteolin 7-triglucoside, *T. leptophylla*; luteolin 7-arabinoside and 7-arabinosylglucoside, *Turgenia*; luteolin 7-arabinosylrhamnosylglucoside, *P. pumila*; quercetin 3-triglucoside, *D. littoralis*. Luteolin 4'-glucoside was usually accompanied where it occurred by the 4'-diglucoside.

of their fruit aglycones: two with flavonols alone, three with flavonols plus flavones and four with flavones alone. These groupings suggest that there is an evolutionary progression within the Caucalideae with *Artedia* being the most primitive and *Torilis* or *Turgenia* the most advanced. It will also be noticed there is some correlation between chromosome number and chemistry, but this is by no means complete.

Of the many interesting interrelationships suggested by the above data, it is worth mentioning three:

(i) the monotypic genus *Turgenia latifolia*, once included in *Caucalis*, is clearly distinct both chemically and in its unique chromosome number. A pre-

Table 6. Chemical groupings of the genera of the Caucalideae

Genus and chromosome nos.	Flavonols		Flavones			Flavone glycosides			Phenyl propanoids	
	Qu	Km	Lu	Ap	Chr	5G	4'G	GGlur	Mr	Iso
Artedia (8)	+	+	—	—	—	—	—	—	—	—
Astrodaucus (10)	+	—	—	—	—	—	—	—	—	+
Daucus (9, 10, 11)	+	+	+	+	+	+	+	+	+	—
Orlaya (9)	+	+	+	+	—	—	—	+	—	—
Pseudorlaya (8)	+	+	+	+	—	—	—	—	+	—
Caucalis (10)	—	—	+	—	—	—	—	—	—	—
Torilis (6, 12)	—	—	+	+	+	+	—	—	—	—
Chaetosciadium (6)	—	—	+	+	—	+	—	—	—	—
Turgenia (16)	—	—	+	—	+	—	+	—	—	—

KEY: Qu = quercetin; Km, kaempferol; Lu, luteolin; Ap, apigenin; Chr, chrysoeriol; 5G, luteolin 5-glucoside; 4'G, luteolin 4'-glucoside; GGlur, luteolin 7-glucosylglucuronide; Mr, myristicin; Iso, isochlorogenic acid. All characters are in the fruit, except isochlorogenic acid, which is a leaf character. Some of the fruit characters (e.g. 5-glucoside, 7-glucosylglucuronide) do extend to the leaf as well.

liminary numerical analysis, based on both biological and flavonoid leaf characters, also clearly separated *Turgenia* from *Caucalis* (McNeill *et al.*, 1969).

(ii) *Chaetosciadium* and *Torilis* have very similar chemical patterns (note especially the presence in both of luteolin 5-glucoside) although the fruit anatomy is superficially different, sufficiently so for Calestani (1905) to consider separating *Chaetosciadium* into a separate tribe. The chromosome data are also consistent with a close link between these taxa so there seems no justification now for such a tribal separation.

(iii) *Pseudorlaya* and *Daucus*, included together in the tribe Dauceae by Drude, show many similarities in chemical pattern. In particular, myristicin occurs in both known *Pseudorlaya* species (in leaves, seeds), in *Daucus glochidiatus*, *D. australis* (in leaves, seeds) and in *D. carota* (in root) but nowhere else in the group.

Turning now to the flavonoid patterns within genera, it has been found that species can satisfactorily be distinguished in almost all cases on the basis of two-dimensional chromatograms of the fruit flavonoids (see e.g. Fig. 1). For this purpose, two or three individual fruits provide sufficient material for analysis and the flavonoids are separated by chromatography on paper in *n*-butanol-acetic acid-water and in 15% acetic acid. In order to detect very minor constituents, the papers are finally treated with alcoholic aluminium chloride, which converts the flavonoids into fluorescent spots, thus increasing the sensitivity and the number of detectable constituents. While most of the major flavonoids have been identified (Table 5), many of the minor compounds are as yet unknown.

Variation within genera is most pronounced in *Daucus* (see Table 5 and Fig. 1). By contrast, the five *Torilis* species studied are relatively uniform, containing as they do mainly luteolin derivatives. Within *Torilis*, the species do, however, differ from each other by at least one character. In fact, there is an interesting progression in relation to the increasing number of glucose residues attached to the 7-position of

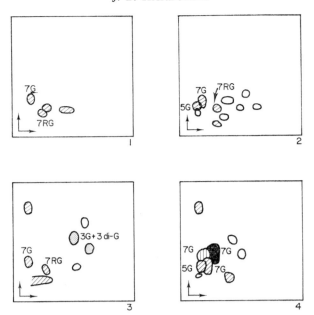

FIGURE 1. Two-dimensional chromatograms of *Daucus* and *Torilis* species

KEY: (1) *Torilis leptophylla* 2056. (2) *Torilis nodosa* 3123. (3) *Daucus littoralis* 2948. (4) *Daucus aureus* 3402. ▨ Luteolin; ▥ Chrysoeriol; ▦ Apigenin; ▦ Quercetin; ▢ Unidentified flavonoid; G 7-Glucoside; RG 7-Rutinoside. Chromatograms developed in the upward direction in *n*-butanol-acetic acid-water (4:1:5) and from left to right in 15% aqu. acetic acid. Phenylpropanoid constituents omitted for simplicity, but these appear as blue, mauve and green spots in the top right-hand corner of each chromatogram.

luteolin. Thus, *T. arvensis* and *T. japonica* have the 7-glucoside (and the 7-rutinoside which is common to all *Torilis*); *T. nodosa* and *T. tenella* have a 7-diglucoside; while *T. leptophylla* contains the 7-mono-, 7-di- and 7-triglucoside of luteolin.

Finally, in a chemotaxonomic analysis of this type, one must consider the question of intraspecific variation, i.e. of the possible presence of chemical races within the species studied. This has been looked for where possible and most of the results given in Table 5 refer to data obtained by screening several accessions of any given species. The one species which does show significant intraspecific variation is, not unexpectedly, *Daucus carota*. According to *Flora Europaea*, plants of this species can be separated into twelve interrelated and interhybridized subspecies (Heywood, 1968). In Table 5, results are shown for only one wild plant, subspecies *carota*, and for one cultivated form, subspecies *sativus*. As can be seen, these two forms are distinctly different in their flavonoids. A range of seeds from other subspecies have been screened by two-dimensional chromatography, with the results as summarized in Table 7. Again, there are differences at the subspecies level, and also some variation within different accessions of subspecies *carota*.

Daucus carota subsp. *carota* also shows considerable variation in leaf flavonoids, as illustrated by the two-dimensional chromatographic pattern of Fig. 2. It can be seen that three characters are universal, one is present in 73% of the forty specimens examined, while another five are much rarer (12–28% frequency). No obvious

Table 7. Chemical variation in *Daucus carota* fruit flavonoids

Flavonoid component	Identity or description*	Presence/absence in subspecies†				
		gadecaei	*gingidium*	*gummifer*	*drepanensis*	*carota*
1	Yellow/orange, 45/13	+	—	—	—	—
2	Luteolin 4'-glucoside	+	tr	—	—	+
3	Luteolin 7-rutinoside	+	+	+	+	+
4	Luteolin 7-diglucoside	+	+	+	+	+
5	Yellow/yellow, 47/26	+	—	—	—	—
6	Quercetin 3-glucoside	+	tr	—	tr	(+)
7	Apigenin 7-rutinoside (?)	+	+	—	+	(+)
8	Dark/yellow, 23/12	+	—	+	+	(+)
9	Dark/dark, 38/61	+	—	—	—	—
10	Dark/dark, 25/59	+	—	—	—	—
12	Dark/yellow, 40/55	tr	+	tr	+	tr
13	Dark/yellow, 36/54	—	+	—	—	—
14	Dark/yellow, 44/62	—	+	tr	tr	(+)
15	24/52	—	tr	+	+	tr
16	Dark/yellow, 42/10	—	tr	+	+	+
17	Dark/yellow, 49/29	tr	tr	+	tr	tr
18	19/20	tr	—	+	+	tr

* Colours are those of the spots on 2-dimensional chromatograms examined under ultraviolet light, without and with NH_3 vapour and R_fs refer to values in *n*-butanol-acetic acid-water (4:1:5) and 15% acetic acid respectively.

† +, present; —, absent; (+) variably present. Based on an analysis of six *carota* accessions, three *gadecaei* accessions and single accessions of the others. Components 11, 19 and 20 were trace constituents in one or two of the *carota* accessions.

correlations have yet emerged between chemistry and geography, although the samples screened came from the U.K., Europe and North America.

Essential oils and proteins

The phytochemical investigation of the Caucalideae has included a survey of other chemical characters, besides the flavonoids. The taxonomically most rewarding of these were the essential oils, proteins and enzymes present in the fruits. Detailed

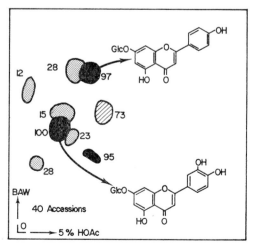

FIGURE 2. Leaf flavonoid variation in *Daucus carota sensu lato*. Figures are percentage occurrences of the individual flavonoid components in forty accessions.

discussion of these results will be reserved for publication elsewhere. However, it is worth considering the results here very briefly in view of the fact that these data do correlate rather well with the flavonoid results.

The results of surveying the spiny-fruited umbellifers for essential oils are summarized in Table 8. Three points are worth noting. First, the patterns are most useful, as are the flavonoid patterns, for separating the different genera. For example, *Daucus*, which is, incidentally, richer in essential oils than the other taxa, can be distinguished by the presence of geranyl acetate. Second, the chemical similarity already noted between *Daucus* and *Pseudorlaya* is supported by the essential oil data; these two genera have α- and β-pinene and limonene in common (Table 8).

Table 8. Distribution of monoterpenes and sesquiterpenes in the Caucalideae fruits

Terpenoid	Presence/absence in*					
	Torilis	*Orlaya*	*Pseudorlaya*	*Daucus*	*Caucalis*	*Turgenia*
α-Pinene	—	—	+	+	—	—
β-Pinene	—	—	+	+	+	—
Limonene	—	—	+	+	—	—
Biphenyl	+	+	—	—	—	—
Geranyl acetate	—	—	—	+	—	—
Caryophyllene	—	+	—	+	—	—
Humulene	+	—	—	+	—	—
Carotol	+	—	—	+	+	+
Unknown T_1	—	+	—	+	—	—
Unknown T_2	+	+	—	+	—	+

* Based on an analysis of fruit essential oils from six *Torilis* spp., twelve *Daucus* spp. and three *Orlaya* spp.; remaining genera analysed from a single accession. Components present in only a few taxa omitted from this table for simplicity. Unknown T_2 has mol.wt of 204. Analysis was by GLC on SE30 and 10% Carbowax columns, programmed from 60–260° at 5°/min with N_2 as carrier gas (J. B. Harborne & C. A. Williams, unpublished results).

Third, the substance carotol (34), a characteristic sesquiterpene of *Daucus* (present in all but one of twelve species surveyed) is apparently also present in *Caucalis*, *Turgenia* and in *Torilis*. Its presence in the latter genera is only based on retention times; the low concentrations present have prevented more rigorous identification. However, it is significant that a related sesquiterpene caucalol (35), has been isolated from one of the *Torilis* species not available to us, *T. scabra* (syn. *Caucalis scabra* Makino) by Sasaki *et al.*, 1966.

(34) Carotol

(35) Caucalol

Some of the results of surveying umbellifer fruits for proteins and enzymes are illustrated in Fig. 3, and are taken from a more extensive study of the whole family (Crowden *et al.*, 1969; and unpublished). The point to note again that the major

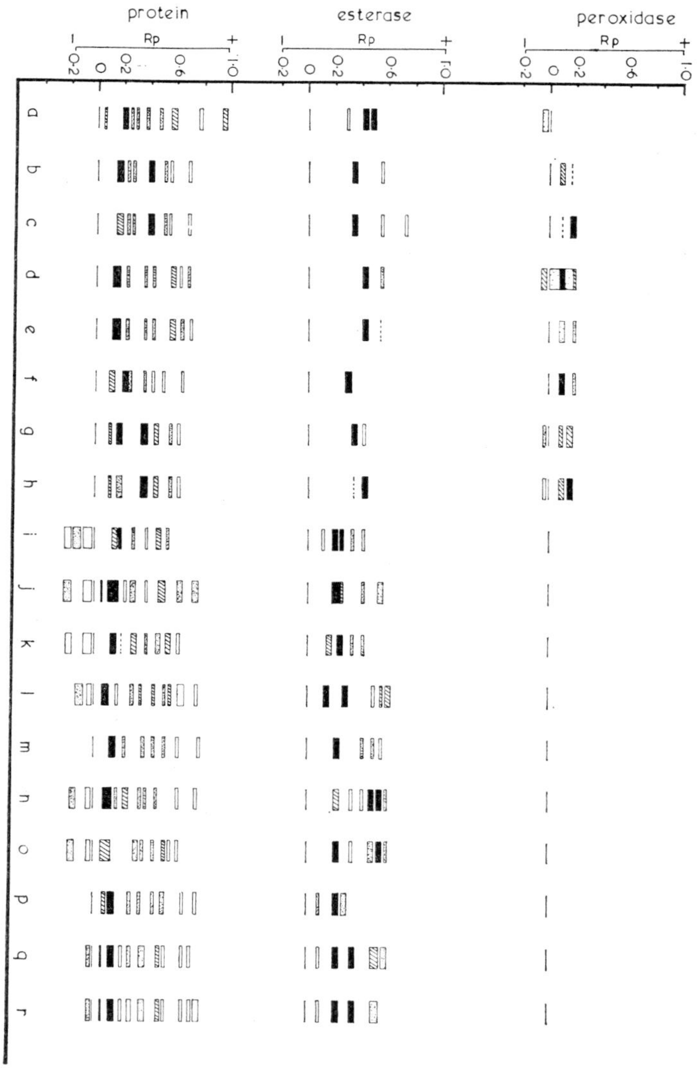

FIGURE 3. Protein, esterase and peroxidase electrophoretic patterns in seeds of the Umbelliferae.
KEY: Tribe I. Echinophoreae (a) *Echinophora sibthorpiana* Guss. Tribe II. Scandiceae. (1) Scandicinae (b) *Anthriscus nemorosa* (Bieb.) Sprengel; (c) *A. sylvestris* (L.) Hoffm.; (d) *Chaerophyllum aromaticum* L.; (e) *C. hirsutum* L.; (f) *Molopospermum peleponnesiacum* (L.) Koch; (g) *Scandix iberica* Bieb. (h) *S. pecten-veneris* L. (2) Caucalinae (i) *Torilis nodosa* (L.) Gaertner; (j) *T. japonica* (Houtth.) DC.; (k) *T. tenella* (Delile) Reichenb. fil.; (l) *Caucalis platycarpos* L.; (m) *Pseudorlaya pumila* (L.) Grande; (n) *Orlaya kochii* Heyw.; (o) *O. grandiflora* (L.) Hoffm.; (p) *Turgenia latifolia* (L.) Hoffm.; (q) *Astrodaucus littoralis* (Bieb.) Drude; (r) *A. orientalis* (L.) Drude.

differences in patterns do occur at the generic level. It is also worth pointing out the clear distinction in patterns between the taxa of the Scandicinae and of the Caucalinae, supposedly in the same tribe according to Drude (1898). Not only are peroxidases completely absent from the Caucalinae, but the positions of the major esterase and protein bands are also different. Within the Caucalinae, one may note again that *Turgenia*, distinctive in its flavonoid complement (see p. 306), is also distinctive in its gel electrophoretic pattern.

CONCLUSION

An account has been given here of the flavonoids of the Umbelliferae and it should be apparent that our knowledge of the distribution and structure of these constituents is still very superficial at the family level. For example, hardly any of the new world taxa, so ably surveyed by Dr Mildred Mathias elsewhere in this volume (pp. 13–29), have been analysed for their flavonoids. Our limited knowledge of the family is also apparent from the fact that a concerted attack on identifying the flavonoids in just one small group of taxa within the Caucalideae has revealed a whole new series of glycosides, many of them new to the family. Similar studies in other umbellifer groups would certainly reveal novel substances, some of which would undoubtedly be of taxonomic interest now that the basic pattern within the family has been established.

Table 9. Distribution of chemicals in spiny-fruited Umbellifers

Boissier classification:	Caucalideae		Scandiceae
Drude classification:	Scandiceae— subtribe Caucalineae	Dauceae	Scandiceae— subtribe Scandicinae
Flavonoids			
Chrysoeriol	In *Torilis, Turgenia*	In *Daucus, Pseudorlaya*	
Luteolin 5-glucoside	In *Chaetosciadium, Torilis*	In *Daucus*	⎫
Luteolin 4'-glucoside	In *Turgenia*	In *Daucus*	⎬ Not detected
Myristicin	Absent	In *Daucus, Pseudorlaya*	⎭
Terpenoids			
Carotol	In *Caucalis, Torilis?*	In *Daucus*	⎫ Not studied
Caryophyllene	In *Orlaya*	In *Daucus*	⎭
Macromolecules			
Peroxidases	Absent	Weak bands	Strong bands
Major esterases	Low or high R_p	Low R_p	Medium R_p
Major proteins	Low R_p	Low R_p	Medium R_p

It is also too early to claim that knowledge of the flavonoids has contributed significantly to taxonomic revision. Even in the Caucalideae, the analyses of the results are still proceeding and this evidence must be weighed in the balance along with all the other data that is accumulating (see p. 215) on this group. However, if one takes the question of whether in classifying the spiny-fruited umbellifers, one should follow the system of Drude or the system of Boissier, it is clear that the weight of the chemical evidence is in favour of the latter system. This evidence is summarized in Table 9, but it should be remembered that this is to some extent biased towards uniting the Caucalineae and the Dauceae, since the Scandicinae have not yet been analysed so thoroughly as the other taxa.

One area where flavonoid patterns seem to make a unique contribution to systematics is in studies of plant populations (see e.g. Moore *et al.*, 1970) and it is clear that studies of this type in the *Daucus carota* complex at present in progress in our laboratory should be most rewarding taxonomically.

ACKNOWLEDGEMENTS

The author thanks Professor V. H. Heywood for his interest and encouragement and Miss Christine A. Williams for expert experimental assistance. He is grateful to the Science Research Council for financial support.

REFERENCES

BATE-SMITH, E. C., 1962. The Phenolic Constituents of Plants and their taxonomic significance—I. Dicotyledons. *Bot. J. Linn. Soc.*, **58**: 95–173.

BENTHAM, G. & HOOKER, J. D., 1867. Umbelliferae. In *Genera Plantarum*, **1**: 859.

BOHLMANN, F. & ZDERO, C., 1969. A new isoeugenol epoxide from *Pimpinella saxifraga*. *Tetrahedron Letters* (13), 1003–1004.

BOISSIER, E., 1872. Umbelliferae. In *Flora Orientalis* 2, pp. 819–1090. Geneva & Basle: H. Georg.

BRACCONNET, L., 1843. Apiin from celery. *Justus Liebigs Annalen*, **48**: 349.

BRIESKORN, C. H. & MOSANDL, A., 1970. A caffeic acid-containing protein from umbellifer fruits. *Tetrahedron Letters* (1), 109–111.

BUTTERY, R. G., SEIFERT, R. M., GUADAGNI, D. G., BLACK, D. R., & LING, L. C., 1968. Some volatile constituents of carrots. *J. Agric. Fd Chem.*, **16**: 1009–1015.

CAGLIOTI, J., NAEF, H., ARIGONI, D. & JEGER, O., 1958. Farnesiferol B from *Ferula asafoetida*. *Helv. chim. Acta*, **41**: 2278–2285.

CALESTANI, V., 1905. Contributo alla sistematica delle Ombrellifere d'Europa. *Webbia*, **1**: 89–280.

CIAMICIAN, G. & SILBER, D., 1896. A new Apiole derivative. *Chem. Ber.*, **29**: 1799–1811.

CRONQUIST, A., 1968. *The Evolution and Classification of Flowering Plants*. London and Edinburgh: Nelson.

CROWDEN, R. K., HARBORNE, J. B. & HEYWOOD, V. H., 1969. Chemosystematics of the Umbelliferae—A general survey. *Phytochemistry*, **8**: 1963–1984.

DAVIS, P. H. & HEYWOOD, V. H., 1963. *Principles of Angiosperm Taxonomy*. Edinburgh & London: Oliver & Boyd.

DRUDE, C. G. O., 1898. Umbelliferae. In Engler, A. & Prantl, K. (eds), *Die natürlichen Pflanzenfamilien*, **3** (8).

DUMAS, M. J., 1833. The isolation of 'Aniskamfer' from Anise oil (the seed oil of *Pimpinella anisum*). *Justus Liebigs Annalen*, **6**: 245–253.

FAROOQ, M. O., GUPTA, S. R., KIAMMUDDIN, M., RAHMAN, W. & SESHADRI, T. R., 1953. Chemical Examination of celery seeds. *J. Sci. Ind. Res. India*, **12**B: 400–401.

GEISSMAN, T. A., 1958. Constituents of *Melicope sarcococca*. *Aust. J. Chem.*, **2**: 376–382.

GEISSMAN, T. A. (ed.), 1962. *Chemistry of Flavonoid Compounds*. Oxford: Pergamon Press.

GLENNIE, W. C. & HARBORNE, J. B., 1971. Flavone and Flavonol 5-glucosides. *Phytochemistry*, **10**: 1325–1329.

HARBORNE, J. B., 1966. Evolution of Flavonoid Pigments in Plants. In Swain, T. (ed.), *Comparative Phytochemistry*, pp. 271–295. London & New York: Academic Press.

HARBORNE, J. B., 1967a. *Comparative Biochemistry of the Flavonoids*. London & New York: Academic Press.

HARBORNE, J. B., 1967b. Luteolin 5-glucoside and its occurrence in the Umbelliferae. *Phytochemistry*, **6**: 1569–1573.

HARBORNE, J. B., HEYWOOD, V. H. & WILLIAMS, C. A., 1969. Distribution of myristicin in the seeds of the Umbelliferae. *Phytochemistry*, **8**: 1729–1732.

HARBORNE, J. B. & SALEH, N. A. M., 1971. Flavonol glycoside variation in fennel *Foeniculum vulgare*. *Phytochemistry*, **10**: 399–400.

HARBORNE, J. B., 1971. Evolution of Flavonoid Pigments. In *Recent Advances in Phytochemistry*, **4** (in press). New York: Appleton-Century-Crofts.

HEYWOOD, V. H., 1968. *Daucus*. In Tutin, T. G. *et al.* (eds.), *Flora Europaea*, **2**, pp. 373–375. Cambridge University Press.

KAPOOR, S. K., SHARMA, Y. N. & KIDWAI, A. R., 1968. Chemical Investigation of *Seseli sibiricum*. *Phytochemistry*, **7**: 147–149.

McCLURE, J. M., 1970. Secondary constituents of Aquatic Angiosperms. In Harborne, J. B. (ed.), *Phytochemical Phylogeny*, pp. 233–268. London & New York: Academic Press.

McNEILL, J., PARKER, P. F. & HEYWOOD, V. H., 1969. A taximetric approach to the classification of the spiny-fruited members (tribe Caucalideae) of the flowering plant family Umbelliferae. In Cole, A. J. (ed.), *Numerical Taxonomy*. London & New York: Academic Press.

MAKSYUTINA, N. P. & LITVINENKO, V. I., 1966. Chemical investigation of Pasternoside. *Chem. Abstr.*, **65**: 788.

MATSUSHITA, A. & ISEDA, S., 1965. Flavonoids of the flowers of *Oenanthestolonifera*. *Nippon Nogei Kaguku Kaishr.*, **39**: 317–318.

MINAEVA, V. G. & VOLKHONSKAYA, T. A., 1964. Flavonoids of *Bupleurum multinerve*. *Dokl. Akad. Nauk, S.S.S.R.*, **154**: 956–959.

MOORE, D. M., HARBORNE, J. B. & WILLIAMS, C. A., 1970. Chemotaxonomy, variation and geographical distribution of the Empetraceae. *Bot. J. Linn. Soc.*, **63**: 277–293.

OHTA, T. & MIYAZAKI, T., 1959. Foenicularin, a quercetin 3-arabinoside from *Foeniculum vulgare*. *J. Pharm. Soc. Japan*, **76**: 323–324.

NORDSTRÖM, C. G., SWAIN, T. & HAMBLIN, A. J., 1953. The Flavone Glycosides of Parsley. *Chemy. Ind.*, 85–86.

PLAT, M., LE MEN, J. & JANOT, M. M., 1963. Structure of crocatone, an aromatic ketone from *Oenanthe crocata*. *Bull. Soc. Chim. Biol.*, **45**: 1119–1123.

PLOUVIER, V., 1969. Glycosides and polyalcohols of some Umbelliferae. *Compt. r. Acad. Sci., Paris*, **268D**: 86–88.

RABATÉ, J., 1930. Rutoside in the leafy stems of *Bupleurum falcatum*. *Bull. Soc. Chim.-Biol.*, **12**: 974–977.

RAHMAN, W., ILYAS, M. & KHAN, A. W., 1963. Flower pigments—Flavonoids from *Daucus carota*. *Naturwissenschaften*, **50**: 477.

SALEH, N. A. M., BOHM, B. A. & ORNDUFF, R., 1971. Flavonoids of *Lasthenia conjugens* and *L. fremontti*. *Phytochemistry* **10**: 611–614.

SASAKI, S., ITAGAKI, Y., MORIYAMA, H., NAKANISHI, K., WATANABLE, E. & AOYAMA, T., 1966. Mass spectra of caucalol diacetate and related compounds. *Tetrahedron Letters*, 623–632.

SESHADRI, T. A. & SOOD, M. S., 1967. Selinone, a new flavanone from *Selinum vaginatum*. *Tetrahedron Letters*, (9), 853–855.

SHULGIN, A. T., 1966. Possible implications of myristicin as a psychotropic substance. *Nature, Lond.*, **210**: 380–384.

STARKOVSKY, N. A., 1962. Constituents of *Daucus carota*—2,4,5-trimethoxybenzaldehyde. *J. org. Chem.*, **27**: 3733–3736.

TAKHTAJAN, A., 1969. *Flowering Plants, Origin and Dispersal*. Edinburgh & London: Oliver & Boyd.

VONGERICHTEN, E., 1876. About Apiole. *Chem. Ber.*, **9**: 1477–1479.

WAGNER, H. & HÖLZL, J., 1968. Microscopic and chromatographic studies of Fructus petroselini and Fructus Ajowani. *Dtsch. Apotheker-Zeit.*, **42**: 1620–1624.

The use of serological data in a comparison of tribes in the Apioideae*

JERRY L. PICKERING† AND DAVID E. FAIRBROTHERS

Botany Department, Rutgers University, New Brunswick, New Jersey, U.S.A.

To provide additional taxonomic data serological analyses of nine genera representing five tribes of Apioideae, and nine taxa of the tribe Peucedaneae were undertaken. Precipitin techniques of agar gel double diffusion and liquid turbidity measurements were used to compare extracted fruit proteins. Five serological groupings were detected from the comparison of nine genera belonging to the Apioideae. These five serological groupings corresponded to the tribes Scandiceae, Coriandreae, Ammineae, Peucedaneae and Dauceae. High serological similarity occurred among the taxa in the tribes Coriandreae, Ammineae and Peucedaneae; but distinct protein differences were detected in taxa placed in the tribes Scandiceae and Dauceae. Serological data supported the division of Peucedaneae into three subtribes: Angelicinae, Ferulinae and Tordyliinae. *Angelica* and *Archangelica* (Angelicinae) formed a very close serological unit. Although data suggested *Levisticum* should be placed in Angelicinae, some protein similarity with *Peucedanum* and *Pastinaca* (Ferulinae) was also indicated. The four tested *Heracleum* (Tordyliinae) species formed a distinct serological grouping, and the serological techniques employed did not detect differences among these species.

CONTENTS

INTRODUCTION

Macromolecular systematics involving comparative studies of proteins and polynucleotides has developed concurrently with the biochemical era of systematics (Turner, 1967). The value of comparative protein chemistry in reaching phenetic and phylogenetic conclusions has been discussed in various publications (Alston,

* Financial aid was from N.S.F. Grant GB-6686, Research Council of Indiana University of Pennsylvania, and the Linnean Society of London and is gratefully acknowledged.

† Present address: Biology Department, Indiana University of Pennsylvania, Indiana, Pennsylvania 15701, U.S.A.

1967; Bryson & Vogel, 1965; Fairbrothers, 1968; Watts, 1970). Drude's (1897–98) classification of the Umbelliferae into three subfamilies is recognized by most present-day taxonomists, and is partially supported by chemotaxonomic data (Crowden et al., 1969; Pickering & Fairbrothers, 1970).

Systematic serology involves the comparison of protein characteristics using serological procedures. Soon after the discovery of the precipitin reaction by Kraus (1897), Nuttall (1901) used the method in zoological classification. The pioneering phytoserological studies were started by Mez and Gilig in the 1920's (Chester, 1937). Recent publications have emphasized the values of the application of serological methods in contributing useful data in solving systematic problems (Fairbrothers, 1968, 1969; Hawkes, 1968; Hunziker, 1969; Vaughan, 1968). At the tribal and subtribal levels there is considerable disagreement due to the reticulate distribution of characteristics (Rodríguez, 1957) and differences in character weighing. Comparative protein chemistry utilizing acrylamide gel disc electrophoresis in analysing total proteins (Pickering, 1969) and selective enzymes (Crowden et al., 1969) has been shown to be of systematic value at the tribal and generic levels in the Umbelliferae. In our research, serological techniques were used to reveal similarities and differences in proteins extracted from the fruits of taxa belonging to nine genera representing five tribes of the subfamily Apioideae, and nine species representing the three subtribes of the tribe Peucedaneae. The study was undertaken to increase the systematic data for these taxa, and to determine the value of serological comparisons at the tribal and generic levels in the Umbelliferae.

METHODOLOGY

Protein extraction

Fruits were collected from native populations or purchased from seedsmen. Table 1 presents the seventeen taxa investigated, arranged according to the classification of Drude (1897–98). Available herbarium specimens are on file in the Chrysler Herbarium, Rutgers University. Voucher specimens for all fruit collections are filed in the Botany Seed and Fruit Collection, Rutgers University.

Fruits were cleaned and quick frozen in liquid nitrogen and then pulverized in a Prolabo Microbroyeur Quantitatif Dangoumau. Delipified meal was extracted at 4°C for 17 hr with 2·5% buffered NaCl (0·19 g KH_2PO_4 and 0·75 g $NaHPO_4$/litre distilled water, pH 7·0, merthiolate at 1/10,000) at a ratio of 2 g of meal to 100 ml of buffer. The extract was partially purified by precipitating with $(NH_4)_2SO_4$ (0·628 g/ml), dialysed against cold water and the precipitate dissolved in the 2·5% buffered NaCl. All experiments were conducted with only freshly prepared protein extracts.

Serological techniques

Antisera were produced in rabbits by injection with an emulsion prepared by mixing one part Freud's incomplete adjuvent with one part meal-buffer slurry (25 mg meal/ml buffered 2·5% NaCl). An injection series consisted of four subcutaneous injections, one given each day for four consecutive days, plus two intra-

Table 1. Taxa investigated arranged according to Drude in Engler & Prantl

Taxa	Abbreviations*
Subfamily APIOIDEAE	
Tribe 2. Scandiceae	
Myrrhis odorata (L.) Scop.	My. o.
Osmorhiza longistylis (Torr.) DC.	Om. l.
Torilis arvensis (Huds.) Link	Tor. a.
Tribe 3. Coriandreae	
Coriandrum sativum L.	Cor. s.
Tribe 5. Ammineae	
Carum carvi L.	Cm. c.
Foeniculum vulgare Mill.	Fo. v.
Tribe 6. Peucedaneae	
Subtribe Angelicinae	
Angelica sylvestris L.	Ang. s.
A. atropurpurea L.	Ang. at.
Archangelica officinalis Hoffm.	Arch. o.
Levisticum officinale Koch	Le. o.
Subtribe Ferulinae	
Peucedanum palustre (L.) Moench	Pe. p.
Pastinaca sativa L.	Pas. s.
Subtribe Tordyliinae	
Heracleum lanatum Michx	Her. l.
H. speciosum Weinmann	Her. se.
H. sphondylium L.	Her. sp.
H. sphondylium subsp.	Her. sp. a.
australe (Hartman) Neuman	
Tribe 8. Dauceae	
Daucus carota L.	Da. c.

* Abbreviations for taxa used in tables and figures.

venous injections, one given each day on the last two days of the 4-day series. Trial bleedings were made five days after the completion of the injection series by heart punctures. Animals received 2–8 series of injections depending on the quantity of detectable antibodies produced (summated turbidity determined by photron-reflectometer) and on the projected use of the antiserum. Following bleeding, the blood was centrifuged, merthiolate added (0·01%), and the antiserum stored in 5–10 aliquots at −27°C.

Upon combination of protein extract (antigen) and antiserum, the antigen-antibody complex precipitates (Boyd, 1966). In this research the reaction was measured quantitatively in liquid media and qualitatively in agar gel media.

Turbidity measurements of the precipitin reactions were performed according to the Boyden Procedure (Fairbrothers, 1968) which enabled the total serological reaction to be measured quantitatively (Boyden, 1958; Libby, 1938). Relative reacting values were obtained by summated turbidity of the reactions between an antiserum and a protein extract dilution series. Reference reactions (R–Re) were obtained by reacting antiserum and the protein extract used to produce the antiserum. Cross reactions (X–Re) were obtained by reacting antisera and protein extracts of other than the sensitizing material (Fairbrothers, 1966, 1968). These reactions provided data for determining groupings of taxa based upon serological correspondence percentage values (R–Re/X–Re × 100). Experimental error of the turbidity analyses were determined to be 9–10% for our experiments.

Double diffusion analyses of the precipitin reaction separated the different immunoprecipitating systems involved in the antigen-antibody reactions, and indicated the degree of serological relationship among the antigenic components of the taxa compared (Ouchterlony, 1968). The tests were performed in a 1% agar gel which had been dissolved in a 2·5% buffered NaCl (merthiolate, 0·01%). Wells were cut in the agar in a pattern which produced a centre well with four peripheral wells. The centre well was inoculated with 0·1 ml of antiserum and the four outer wells with 0·05 ml of protein extract. The reactions were observed every day for ten days and the results were recorded by preparing diagrams.

TRIBAL RELATIONSHIPS

Turbidimetric results

On the basis of turbidimetric analyses three serological groupings could be discriminated in the Apioideae (Table 2). Data indicated that *Torilis* and *Myrrhis* exhibit close serological similarity which supports Drude's (1897–98) placement of both these taxa in the tribe Scandiceae (RP-47, 58, 59, 76). *Osmorhiza* could not be compared because of difficulties in obtaining adequate protein concentrations for quantitative analyses. The second grouping consisting of *Coriandrum*, *Carum*, *Foeniculum*, *Peucedanum* and *Pastinaca* had a high correspondence among themselves (RP-31, 47, 48, 51, 59). Serological subgroupings among the five taxa could not be determined by turbidimetric analyses. Both the low cross reactivity of *Daucus*

Table 2. Per cent correspondence among eight genera in Apioideae

Antisera	Antigens							
	Tor. a.	My. o.	Cor. s.	Cm. c.	Fo. v.	Pe. p.	Pas. s.	Da. c.
Myrrhis odorata RP-76	51	100	45	—	29	36	—	17
Torilis arvensis RP-58	100	45	32	26	21	39	32	26
Coriandrum sativum RP-47	27	35	100	47	57	48	65	4
Carum carvi RP-48	36	41	61	100	62	72	71	32
Foeniculum vulgare RP-51	8	18	44	33	100	55	44	25
Peucedanum palustre RP-59	22	28	50	44	44	100	52	8
Pastinaca sativa RP-31	12	25	56	55	51	52	100	13
Daucus carota RP-36	8	9	20	8	11	13	10	100

protein extract with antisera against the other taxa and the low serological correspondence of the *Daucus* antiserum (RP-36) with the antigen extracts from seven
members of the subfamily indicated the serological distinctness of this genus.

Double diffusion results

Greater discrimination was possible using double diffusion data (Table 3) than
by quantitative data. Diffusion data indicated the division of the nine taxa compared into five serological units. Data supported Drude's grouping of *Osmorhiza*,
Torilis and *Myrrhis* in the tribe Scandiceae (RP-38, 58, 76). Consistent with the
turbidimetric analyses, double diffusion data also revealed protein similarity among
Coriandrum, *Carum*, *Foeniculum*, *Peucedanum* and *Pastinaca* (RP-18, 48). The data
also indicated that these five genera were separated into three serological groupings:
Coriandrum (Coriandreae); *Carum* and *Foeniculum* (Ammineae); *Peucedanum* and

Table 3. Data arranged from double diffusion tests of nine genera in Apioideae

Antisera	Antigens								
	Om. l.	My. o.	Tor. a.	Cor. s.	Cm. c.	Fo. v.	Pe. p.	Pas. s.	Da. c.
Osmorhiza longistylis RP-38	5	4	4	2	2	3	3	3	2
Myrrhis odorata RP-76	4	5	4	3	—	3	3	—	3
Torilis arvensis RP-58	4	4	6	3	3	3	3	3	3
Coriandrum sativum RP-18	3*	4	3	6	5	5	5	5	4
Carum carvi RP-48	—	3	3	4	5	4	4	4	2
Foeniculum vulgare RP-25	2	2	2	4	4	6	3	3	2
Peucedanum palustre RP-59	—	2	3	3	3	3	5	4	2
Pastinaca sativa RP-31	3	3	3	3	3	3	4	6	3
Daucus carota RP-36	2	2	2	2	2	2	2	2	5

* Numbers indicate the immunoprecipitating systems (bands) observed.

Pastinaca (Peucedaneae). Although the cross reaction of *Carum* and *Coriandrum*
with *Foeniculum* antiserum (RP-25) produced the same number of immunoprecipitin systems, Type I systems were observed between *Carum* and *Foeniculum*
and Type III systems between *Coriandrum* and *Foeniculum* (Fig. 1). Type I systems,
which show a complete fusion of bands, indicate that identical antigenic proteins are
present in both extracts. Type III systems show partial fusion of bands, indicating
only a partial similarity between antigenic proteins (Ouchterlony, 1968). Thus, on
the basis of the interaction of immunoprecipitin systems, *Foeniculum* and *Carum*
comprise a serological unit separate from *Coriandrum*. These data would support

Drude's (1897–98) placement of these taxa into Ammineae and Coriandreae respectively. The distinctness of the fourth group consisting of *Peucedanum* and *Pastinaca* was indicated by the strong cross reactions between these two taxa (RP-31, 59) and their similar reaction with *Foeniculum* (RP-25) antiserum. The fifth group

FIGURE 1. Diagrammatic representation of Ouchterlony type double diffusion patterns. The centre well contains antiserum (Fo. v., RP-25), and the outer wells contain antigens.

consisting of *Daucus* was suggested by the serological dissimilarity of this genus with the other taxa. Partial protein similarity among all the taxa compared was indicated by the occurrence of some cross reactivity among all the taxa and the appearance of almost all Type I systems in the double diffusion tests.

SUBTRIBAL RELATIONSHIPS

Turbidimetric results

Two groupings were differentiated among the nine taxa compared in Peucedaneae. Quantitative data (Table 4) indicated that *Angelica* and *Archangelica* (Angelicinae) form a distinct serological unit (RP-32, 33). The protein similarity of these two taxa

Table 4. Per cent correspondence among nine taxa in Peucedaneae

	Antigens								
Antisera	Ang. s.	Arch. o.	Le. o.	Pe. p.	Pas. s.	Her. se.	Her. l.	Her. sp.	Her. sp. a.
Angelica sylvestris RP-32	100	95	74	80	66	72	—	67	—
Archangelica officinalis RP-33	69	100	42	45	37	19	19	22	27
Levisticum officinale RP-62	51	59	100	57	65	55	—	—	—
Peucedanum palustre RP-59	68	70	—	100	52	26	28	30	24
Pastinaca sativa RP-31	29	45	49	52	100	58	50	48	—
Heracleum speciosum RP-65	64	63	49	59	79	100	90	95	96
Heracleum sphondylium RP-44	60	71	72	68	80	93	96	100	98

support recent treatments (Clapham *et al.*, 1962; Tutin *et al.*, 1968) which unite *Archangelica* with the genus *Angelica*. The second grouping consisting of the four *Heracleum* (Tordyliinae) taxa showed high serological similarity (RP-33, 44, 59, 65). No differences in species proteins could be detected. The relationships of *Levisticum*, *Peucedanum* and *Pastinaca* could not be ascertained by turbidimetric analyses. Data did indicate, however, that *Peucedanum* was more similar to Angelicinae than to Tordyliinae and *Pastinaca* was more similar to Tordyliinae than to Angelicinae.

Double diffusion results

Three serological groupings were observed among the ten taxa investigated in the Peucedaneae (Table 5). Double diffusion data supported the placement of *Angelica*, *Archangelica* and *Levisticum* in the Angelicinae (RP-44, 62, 65). Consistent with the quantitative data, double diffusion analyses supported the protein similarity between

Table 5. Data obtained from double diffusion tests of ten taxa in Peucedaneae

	Antigen										
Antisera	Ang. s.	Ang. at.	Arch. o.	Le. o.	Pe. p.	Pas. s.	Her. se.	Her. l.	Her. sp.	Her. sp.a.
Angelica sylvestris RP-63	5*	5	5	4	4	3	3	3	3	3
Archangelica officinalis RP-33	5	5	5	4	4	4	3	3	3	3
Levisticum officinale RP-62	4	4	4	5	3	3	3	3	3	3
Peucedanum palustre RP-30	4	4	4	3	6	4	3	3	3	3
Pastinaca sativa RP-60	3	3	3	3	4	6	3	3	3	3
Heracleum speciosum RP-65	3	3	3	3	4	4	5	5	5	5
Heracleum sphondylium RP-44	4	4	4	4	5	5	6	6	6	6

* Numbers indicate the immunoprecipitating systems (bands) observed.

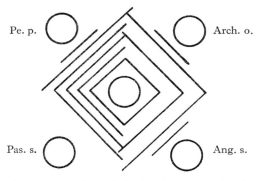

FIGURE 2. Diagrammatic representation of Ouchterlony type double diffusion patterns. The centre well contains antiserum (Pe. p., RP-30), and the outer wells contain antigens.

Angelica and *Archangelica*, and the somewhat less similarity of *Levisticum* with these two taxa (RP-30, 33, 63). The second grouping consisting of *Peucedanum* and *Pastinaca* (Ferulinae) was indicated by the strong cross reaction between these two taxa (RP-30, 60) based on the number and types (Fig. 2) of immunoprecipitin systems observed (RP-33, 44, 65). The third grouping consisting of the four *Heracleum* (Tordyliinae) taxa formed a distinct unit which showed a greater serological affinity to the Ferulinae than to the Angelicinae. Protein differences were not detected in the *Heracleum* species.

DISCUSSION

Serological methods provided data useful in interpreting taxonomic relationships among taxa in the Apioideae. Although the number of species examined in this investigation has been limited, certain conclusions are presented.

Serological analyses revealed protein differences among the five tribes investigated. In contrast to other serological taxonomic studies (Lee & Fairbrothers, 1969; Pickering & Fairbrothers, 1967) double diffusion analyses were more discriminatory than quantitative measurements. The tribes Coriandreae and Ammineae had the greatest protein similarity, but a close correspondence was also detected among the above two tribes and Peucedaneae. The Scandiceae and Dauceae were serologically the most distinct tribes. On the basis of morphological characteristics Scandiceae and Dauceae are considered to be advanced tribes in the subfamily. The serological distinctness of these two tribes would support the concept that in the more advanced tribes there has occurred greater changes in protein chemistry. The serological similarity between the more primitive Peucedaneae and Ammineae would also support this conclusion. However, the close serological relationship of the more advanced Coriandreae with Peucedaneae and Ammineae would not adhere to the preceding correlation.

Contrary to protein comparisons by acrylamide gel electrophoresis and flavonoid chemistry (Crowden *et al.*, 1969), serological evidence did not support Bentham's (1867) treatment of placing *Torilis* and *Daucus* in the tribe Caucalineae. This disagreement between the two methods of protein comparison cannot be completely resolved at this time. However, one explanation for this disagreement is that the two methods provide different information about the proteins. Serological specificity depends upon amino-acid residues located on the surface of the protein molecule. Therefore, the amino-acid sequence and the molecular configuration resulting from the coiling of the amino-acid chain are important in the specificity of the serological reaction (Boyd, 1966). Disk electrophoretic separation of proteins is dependent on the electrical charge, size and molecular weight of the proteins (Ornstein, 1964). Thus, the data obtained by the two methods may well indicate the relationships of the taxa compared on the basis of different protein characteristics. It is well known that different anatomical and morphological characters do not evolve at the same rate; similarly, different protein characters do not evolve at the same rate (Bryson & Vogel, 1965). These biochemical data may reveal the reticulate evolution of protein characteristics also revealed by morphological characteristics of the family.

Serological data supported Drude's placement of the taxa investigated into three subtribes of Peucedaneae. There was some difficulty in determining the relationship of *Levisticum* with the other genera in the tribe, and the comparison of other genera are required to delimit the serological relationship of this genus. In phytochemical research disk electrophoretic data have proven to be of greater taxonomic value than serological data for the comparison of species, while serological data have been of greater value than disk electrophoretic data for the comparison of genera, subtribes and tribes of the family Umbelliferae.

REFERENCES

ALSTON, R. E., 1967. Biochemical systematics, pp. 197–305. In Dobzhansky, T., Hecht, M. K. & Steere, W. C. (eds), *Evolutionary Biology*. Vol. 1, New York: Appleton-Century-Crofts.

BENTHAM, G., 1867. Umbelliferae. In Bentham, G. & Hooker, J. D., *Genera plantarum ad exemplaria imprimis in Herbariis Kewensibus servata definita*. **1**: 859–931, 1008–1009.

BOYD, W. C., 1966. *Fundamentals of Immunology*. 773 pp. 4th ed., New York: Interscience Publ.

BOYDEN, A., 1958. Comparative serology: aims, methods, and results, pp. 3–24. In Cole, W. H. (ed.), *Serological and Biochemical Comparisons of Proteins*. XIV Conf. Protein Metab. New Brunswick: Rutgers Univ.

BRYSON, V. & VOGEL, H. J. (eds), 1965. *Evolving Genes and Proteins*. 629 pp. New York: Academic Press.

CHESTER, K. S., 1937. A critique of plant serology. *Q. Rev. Biol.*, **12**: 19–46, 165–190, 294–321.

CLAPHAM, A. R., TUTIN, T. G. & WARBURG, E. F., 1962. *Flora of the British Isles*. 1269 pp., 2nd ed., Cambridge: Cambridge Univ. Press.

CROWDEN, R. K., HARBORNE, J. B. & HEYWOOD, V. H., 1969. Chemosystematics of the Umbelliferae—A general survey. *Phytochemistry* **8**: 1963–1984.

DRUDE, O., 1897–1898. Umbelliferae. In Engler, A. & Prantl, K., (eds), *Die natürlichen Pflanzenfamilien*, **3**: 63–150, 129–250, 271.

FAIRBROTHERS, D. E., 1966. Comparative serological studies in plant systematics. *Serol. Mus. Bull.*, **35**: 2–6.

FAIRBROTHERS, D. E., 1968. Chemosystematics with emphasis on systematic serology, pp. 141–174. In Heywood, V. H. (ed.), *Modern Methods in Plant Taxonomy*. London & New York: Academic Press.

FAIRBROTHERS, D. E., 1969. Plant serotaxonomic (Serosystematic) literature, '51–'68. *Serol. Mus. Bull.*, **41**: 1–11.

HAWKES, J. G. (ed.), 1968. *Chemotaxonomy and Serotaxonomy*. Systematic Association Special Vol., No. 2, 299 pp. London & New York: Academic Press.

HUNZIKER, J. H., 1969. Molecular data in plant systematics, pp. 280–312. In *Systematic Biology: Proc. Int. Conf. in 1967*. Washington, D.C. Nat. Acad. Sci. Publ. 1962.

KRAUS, R., 1897. Uber specifische Reactionen in keimfrein Filtraten aus Cholera, Typh und pest-bouillon Culturen, erzeugt durch homologes Serum. *Wiener klin. Wochenchr*. **10**: 736–738.

LEE, D. W. & FAIRBROTHERS, D. E., 1969. A serological and disc electrophoretic study of North American *Typha*. *Brittonia*, **21**: 227–243.

LIBBY, R. L., 1938. The photronreflectometer—An instrument for the measurement of turbid systems. *J. Immunol.*, **34**: 71–73.

NUTTALL, G. H. F., 1901. The new biological test for blood in relation to zoological classification. *Proc. R. Soc. London*, **69**: 150–153.

PICKERING, J. L., 1969. *A chemotaxonomic investigation of the Umbelliferae*. 63 pp. Ph.D. thesis Rutgers Univ., New Brunswick, New Jersey.

PICKERING, J. L. & FAIRBROTHERS, D. E., 1967. A serological and disc electrophoretic investigation of *Magnolia* taxa. *Bull. Torrey Bot. Club*, **94**: 468–479.

PICKERING, J. L. & FAIRBROTHERS, D. E., 1970. A serological comparison of Umbelliferae subfamilies. *Am. J. Bot.*, **57**: 988–992.

ORNSTEIN, L., 1964. Disc electrophoresis I. Background and theory. *Ann. N.Y. Acad. Sci.*, **121**: 321–349.

OUCHTERLONY, O., 1968. Handbook of *Immunodiffusion and Immunoelectrophoresis*. 215 pp. Ann Arbor Sci. Publ., Ann Arbor, Mich.

RODRÍGUEZ, R. L., 1957. Systematic anatomical studies of *Myrrhidendron* and other woody Umbellales. *Univ. Calif. Publ. Bot.*, **29**: 145–318.

TURNER, B. L., 1967. Plant chemosystematics and phylogeny. *Pure appl. Chem.*, **14**: 189–213.

TUTIN, T. G., HEYWOOD, V. H., BURGES, N. A., MOORE, D. M., VALENTINE, D. H., WALTERS, S. M. & WEBB, D. A., 1968. *Flora Europaea.* 455 pp., **2**. Cambridge: Cambridge Univ. Press.

VAUGHAN, J. G., 1968. Serology and other protein separation methods in studies of angiosperm taxonomy. *Sci. Prog. Oxf.*, **56**: 205–222.

WATTS, R. L., 1970. Proteins and plant phylogeny, pp. 145–178. In Harborne, J. B. (ed.). *Phytochemical Phylogeny*. London & New York: Academic Press.

Coumarin patterns in the Umbelliferae

B. EICHSTEDT NIELSEN

The Royal Danish School of Pharmacy, Chemical Laboratory B, 2100, Copenhagen, Denmark

A literature survey of the coumarins of Umbelliferous plants has shown that coumarins have been isolated from 161 umbellifer species, representing 33 genera of the family. About 125 different coumarins have been isolated and structurally characterized. A survey of the structural features is given.

In the assessment of the chemotaxonomic value of published data it should be realized that in some cases coumarins obtained from natural sources may be artifacts. Some examples are given to illustrate the possibilities of chemical changes that may occur during the isolation procedures.

So far, coumarins have only been isolated from the subfamily Apioideae, especially in the tribes Smyrnieae, Ammineae and Peucedanae, which are rich in coumarins. Distinct differences in coumarin patterns are found at the tribal, subtribal, and generic levels.

CONTENTS

INTRODUCTION

An insight into the increasing tempo of phytochemical research in the coumarin field may be obtained by a consideration of the number of recently discovered new coumarins. In 1963, Dean reviewed the literature and listed about 90 representatives. Today the number is approaching 200, of which about 125 have been obtained from Umbelliferous plants. Thus, in the past five to ten years, we have witnessed an extremely rapid development in coumarin chemistry.

Before turning to a discussion of the coumarin patterns in the Umbelliferae two subjects will be considered.

Firstly, a survey of the various types of coumarins is presented on the grounds that it is advantageous to use their chemical classification in the discussion of the coumarin patterns in the Umbelliferae. Thus, some differences in patterns are disclosed when the distribution of the various categories of coumarins is considered.

Secondly, the limitations of coumarin data for systematic purposes are discussed. Particular interest is devoted to isolation and identification methods because these subjects have some bearing on one of the fundamental questions in comparative biochemistry: how can the absence of a certain coumarin, in the taxon considered, be ascertained. From a chemosystematic point of view such information is basically as important as a positive discovery. Refinements in methods of isolation and purification as well as the development of effective analytical methods, of course, implies that many species would benefit from re-examination and in some cases this has already been very revealing. Furthermore, some of the earlier used methods might result in chemical changes or degradations, and such results would obscure rather than illuminate plant relationships.

SURVEY OF STRUCTURAL FEATURES

All members of the coumarin group, like coumarin itself, contain the 5,6-benz-2-pyrone skeleton as a distinguishing feature. With respect to naturally occurring coumarins, however, coumarin (1) is atypical, because it contains no oxygen atom at the 7-position. In the Umbelliferae only two coumarins lacking oxygen at the 7-position have been isolated, both having been obtained from *Ferula communis* L. (17, 18). On the basis of the structural features the coumarins of umbellifers have been divided into four major categories:

(1) *Coumarins substituted in the benzene ring only.* This group is comprised of hydroxylated (3), alkylated (4), alkoxylated (5, 6), and acylated (7) compounds derived from umbelliferone (2). Dean (1952) classifies coumarins in this category as 'Simple Coumarins'.

(2) *Furanocoumarins.* There are two basic forms of furanocoumarins in this group, namely the linear or psoralen type (8) and the angular or angelicin type (9). Both types are also found as their dihydroderivatives (10, 11). Similar types of substituents as noted in the category above are also found in the furanocoumarin group.

(3) *Pyranocoumarins.* Incorporation of the 7-oxygen atom into a fused six-membered ring produces the linear- or xanthyletin type (12) as well as the angular- or seselin-type (13) of coumarins, both of which occur naturally. The linear pyranocoumarins, however, have been demonstrated as naturally occurring in Umbelliferous plants only in the dihydro form. Only five coumarins of this type have been isolated, decursin (14) being a typical example. On the other hand, numerous dihydroderivatives of the angular pyranocoumarins (15, 16) have been obtained from Umbelliferous plants.

(4) *Coumarins substituted in the pyrone ring.* This type of coumarin, in general, has

(1) Coumarin   (2) Umbelliferone   (3) Aesculetin   (4) Osthenol

(5) Herniarin   (6) Umbelliprenin   (7) Glabralactone

(8) Psoralen   (9) Angelicin   (10) Marmesin

(11) Columbianadin   (12) Xanthyletin   (13) Seselin

(14) Decursin   (15) Lomatin

been observed to be substituted as follows: (a) 3-alkyl, (b) 4-alkyl, (c) 3-phenyl, (d) 4-phenyl, (e) 3-alkyl, 4-hydroxy (or alkoxy), (f) 3-phenyl, 4-hydroxy (or alkoxy), and (g) 3-phenoxy. Plant families providing these types of coumarins are Guttiferae (b, d), Papilionaceae (c, d, f, g), Rutaceae (a), Meliaceae (b), Ranunculaceae (e), and Umbelliferae (e). It may be noted that Umbelliferous plants have thus far been shown to contain only the 3-alkyl, 4-hydroxy type (17, 18).

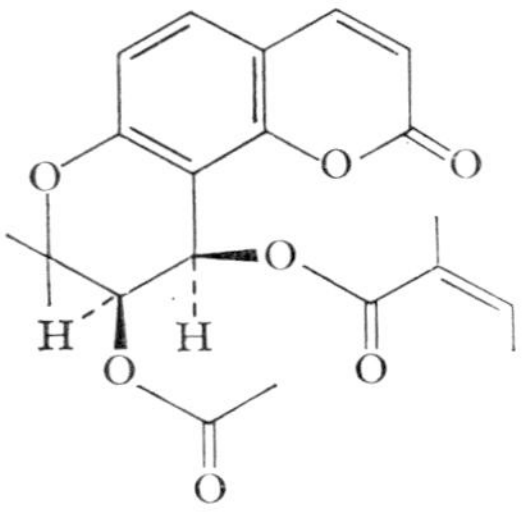

(16) Pteryxin

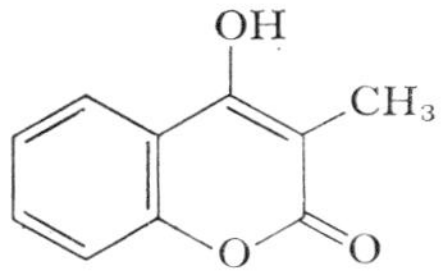

(17) 3-Methyl-4-hydroxy coumarin

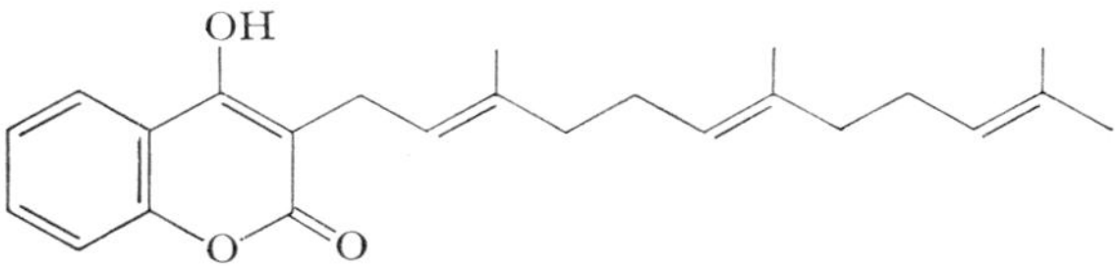

(18) Ferulenol

TAXONOMIC SIGNIFICANCE OF COUMARINS

The common structural characteristics of the coumarins argues in favour of a common biogenesis, which is recognized as proceeding from the shikimic acid pathway (see e.g. Steck, 1967), whereas the isoprenoid side chains originate from mevalonic acid (Steck *et al.*, 1969).

Isoprenoid chains involved in the formation of a fused heterocyclic ring system with adjacent phenolic groups are frequently found (10–16).

The dihydrofuranocoumarins and dihydropyranocoumarins may arise through cyclization of the 'precursors' (19)–(22)—or the corresponding epoxy compounds— as indicated in Scheme 1. This hypothesis is supported by the fact that the pair of isomers, nodakenetin (23) and decursinol (24), has been shown to co-occur in *Angelica decursiva* Fr. & Sav. (Hata & Sano, 1966). Furthermore, (23) and (24) have opposite configurations as would be expected if they arise from the same precursor (19). The same is true also for (+)-dihydro-oroselol (25) and lomatin (26), a pair of isomers shown to co-occur in *Lomatium nuttalii* (A. Gray) Macbr. (Lee & Soine, 1968).

Angelol (21) obtained from the roots of *Angelica pubescens* Maxim (Hata & Kozawa, 1965, 1967, 1968) may be looked upon as the precursor of (28) and (29). However, no linear dihydrofuranocoumarins containing two asymmetric centres (28) are known in the Umbelliferae, so far, and only one example of the isomeric dihydropyranocoumarins is known. The diester (29), xantalin, was recently obtained from *Xanthogalum purpurascens* Lall. (Sokolova *et al.*, 1968). On the other hand several examples of the angular types (30) and (31) are known in the Umbelliferae. The 'precursor' (22), however, has not been isolated. Thus, further investigations of the coumarins, their stereochemistry, biosynthesis and metabolism are needed in order to provide a more firm basis for the assessment of the chemosystematic value of coumarin data.

Mono- or bicyclic sesquiterpenes are infrequently found linked as ethers to the coumarin skeleton. This type of coumarin (e.g. 42, 43) has been found only in the genus *Ferula* where they may arise through cyclization of umbelliprenin (6).

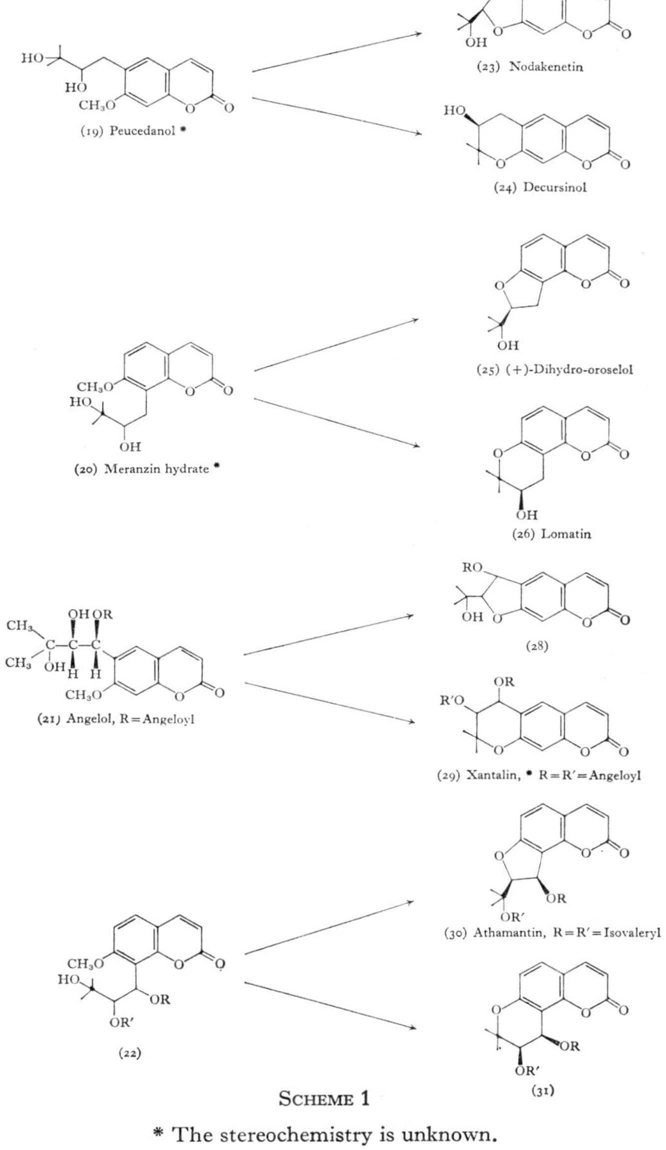

Scheme 1

* The stereochemistry is unknown.

Usually the coumarins are esterified with acetic acid or C_5-acids. However, from *Seseli gummiferum* Pall. subsp. *gummiferum*, Nielsen, Larsen & Lemmich (1970) have isolated three coumarins, which were shown to be esters of lomatin (15) with fatty acids. So these findings apparently break the above-mentioned pattern.

LIMITATIONS OF COUMARIN DATA FOR SYSTEMATIC PURPOSES

Most of the phytochemical results are not derived from extensive surveys but from isolated studies, often justified by an interest in work on structure elucidation, stereochemistry, medicinal chemistry, etc. Seldom have the plants been investigated because of their botanical interest. Accordingly, in several phytochemical papers, questions, important for the botanist concerned with classification, are unanswered, e.g. habitat, identification of plant material (herbarium specimens), time of harvest, genuine constituents or artifacts, etc.

Concerning the question whether a compound is genuine, a few examples will serve to illustrate the problem and provide an impression as to the difficulties engendered by earlier used isolation techniques. In the isolation of coumarins from other extracted constituents Späth & Socias (1934) took advantage of the lactonic nature of coumarins. Dilute alkali hydroxide solutions promote easy opening of the lactone ring to give a water-soluble neutral material. Acidification of the alkaline solution spontaneously cyclizes the lactone ring to regenerate the coumarin. This 'lactone separation' method became a standard method at that time and has even been used in more recent works (e.g. Nikonov *et al.*, 1964). However, the method should not be employed uncritically since it is well known that many coumarins are acid- and/or alkali-sensitive which could lead to isolation of artifacts rather than original coumarins. This is particularly true of compounds such as athamantin (30) and its congeners. One of the most characteristic features of athamantin (30) is the ease with which mineral acids expel two moles of isovaleric acid leaving oroselone. Furthermore, nearly all dihydropyrano- and dihydrofuranocoumarins which have ester groups are alkali-sensitive. Particular sensitivity is exhibited by an acyloxy group at the 4′-position of the dihydropyranocoumarins; such benzylic esters usually undergo rapid expulsion of the acyloxy group in the presence of alkali.

Some coumarins have epoxide structures in the side chain, and are therefore unusually sensitive to mineral acids which may cause opening of the epoxide ring even at room temperature (Nielsen & Lemmich, 1969). Sensitivity even to a silicic acid chromatographic column has been observed by Hata *et al.* (1963) who noted opening of the epoxide ring of byak-angelicol (32) under these conditions. Furthermore, cyclizations may occur on treatment of epoxide ring-containing coumarins with acid or alkali. For example, byak-angelicol (32) undergoes a cyclization reaction to yield isobyak-angelicolic acid (33) when treated with dilute aqueous alkali (Noguti & Kawanami, 1939; Chatterjee *et al.*, 1962). Another example of a cyclization is encountered during the acidic hydrolysis of vellein (34), the glycosidic coumarin from *Velleia discophore* (Goodeniaceae) to yield dihydroseselin (35), whereas emulsin hydrolysis of vellein yields osthenol (4). The role of acid in the production of dihydroseselin from vellein is clarified by the fact that treatment of osthenol with acid also gave dihydroseselin (Bottomly & White, 1951).

The search for effective means to purify coumarins led to frequent use of sublimation methods and fractional distillation in high vacuum, *vide* e.g. Späth *et al.* (1939) and Svendsen (1954). However, high vacuum sublimation or distillation techniques have inherent difficulties, the most significant being the real possibility of decomposition or isomeric change as may be seen from the following examples.

When bergamottin (36) is distilled in high vacuum it suffers cleavage at the ether linkage to yield bergaptol (37) (Chatterjee & Choudhury, 1955).

When imperatorin (38) is heated in high vacuum it isomerizes into alloimperatorin (39) (Bose & Choudhury, 1946; Kuznetsova, 1961). Byakangelicol (32), during high vacuum sublimation is degraded to 5-methoxy-8-hydroxy-psoralen (40) (Chatterjee *et al.*, 1962). Brown & Shyluk (1962) have reported that imperatorin (38) and umbelliprenin (6), coumarins of the isoprenoid ether type, could not be recovered from gas chromatography columns, presumably because of decomposition even at relatively low temperatures.

Recently, Hata & Kozawa (1967) reported that angelical (41) obtained from *Angelica glabra* Makino was an artifact produced by thermal decomposition of angelol (21) during vacuum distillation.

Until recently, for adsorption chromatography, aluminium oxide has been a preferred adsorbent. Although aluminium oxide is a useful adsorption material it may, especially in the case of the basic variety, cause degradation of the coumarins. Thus, Černobai & Kolesnikov (1960), in their studies of the coumarins of the fruits of *Cnidium dubium* (Schkur.) Thell., noted a great loss of coumarins when chromatographed on basic aluminium oxide.

DISTRIBUTION

A literature survey of phytochemical investigations of Umbelliferous plants has disclosed that coumarins have been isolated from 161 species representing 33 genera of this family (Nielsen, 1970). So far, coumarins have only been obtained from plants in the Apioideae, and within this subfamily the tribes Smyrnieae, Ammineae and Peucedaneae are especially rich in coumarins. While such studies may give useful taxonomic information, they must await more definitive studies of the enzyme systems involved before conclusions concerning the hereditary significance of the distribution patterns of these compounds may be formulated.

The coumarin patterns in the Apioideae are illustrated in Tables 1A–D. The figures in Tables 1A–C are the number of coumarins of each category isolated from the species in question. In Table 1D the left-hand column shows the number of species investigated in the genus considered. The figures in this table represent the number of species from which the various categories of coumarins have been obtained. Thus, the figures indicate the frequency of occurrence in the various genera.

Smyrnieae

Table 1A shows that linear furanocoumarins have been isolated from all members

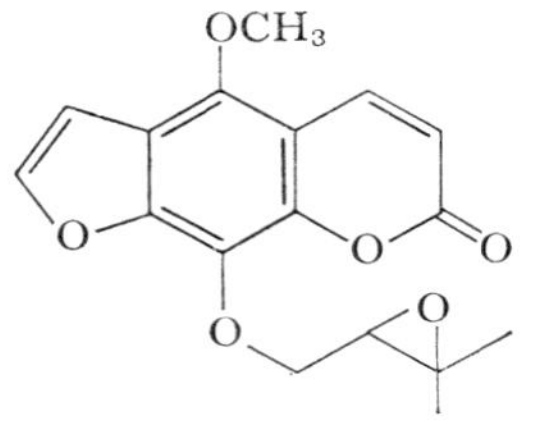

(32) Byakangelicol

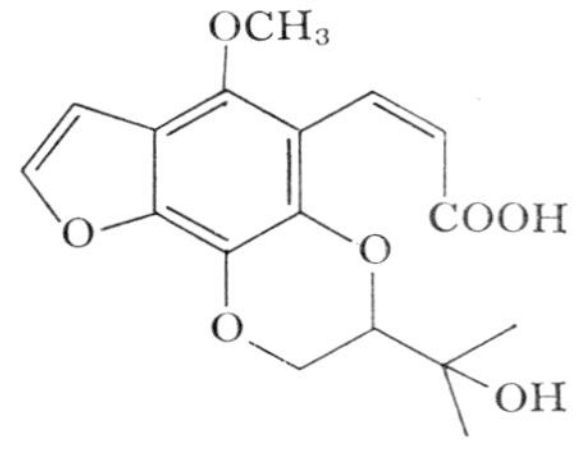

(33) Isobyak-angelicolic acid

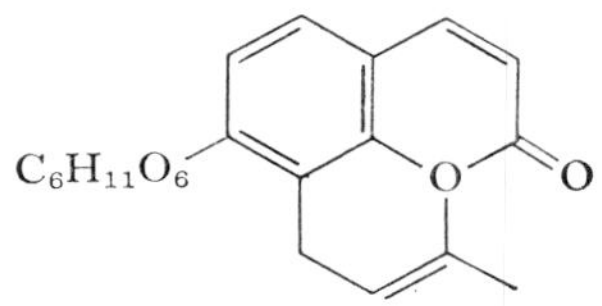

(34) Vellein

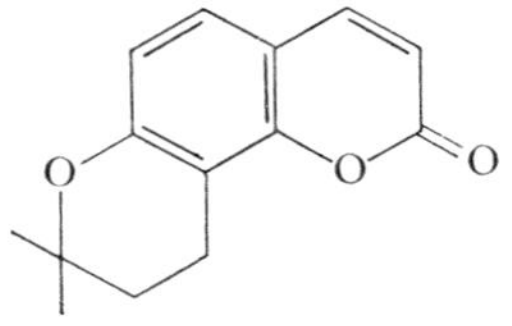

(35) 3,4′,-Dihydroseselin

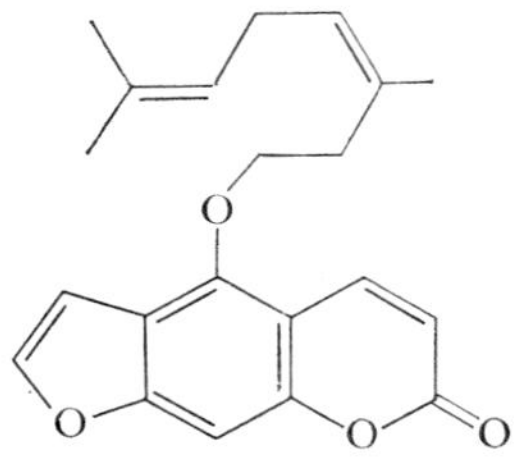

(36) Bergamottin

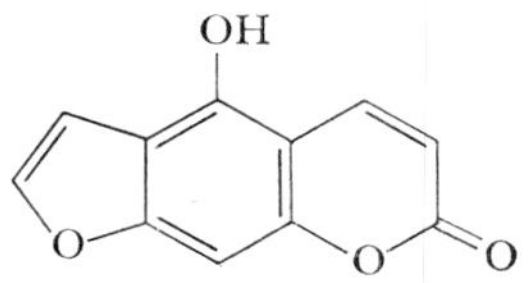

(37) Bergaptol

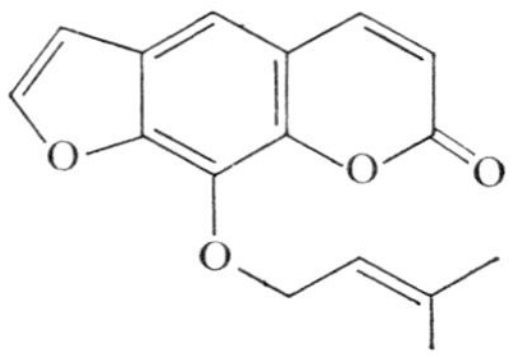

(38) Imperatorin

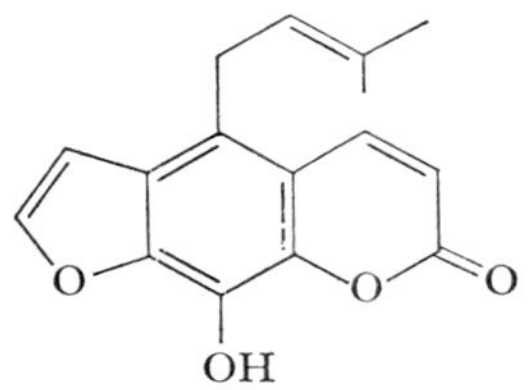

(39) Alloimperatorin

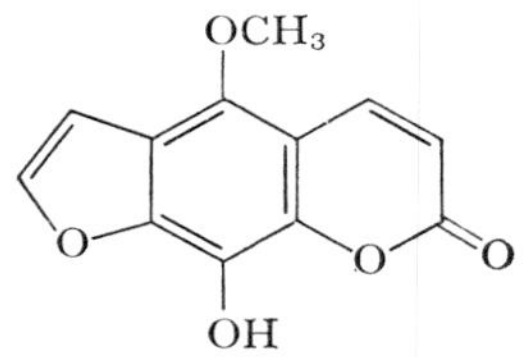

(40) 5-Methoxy-8-hydroxy-psoralen

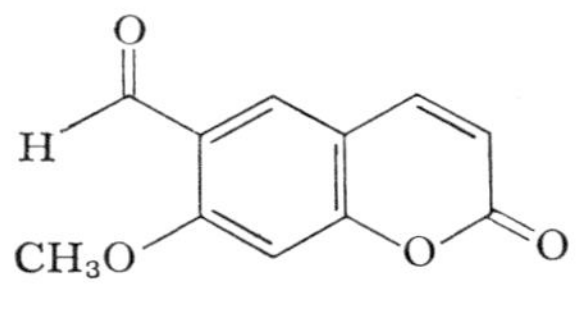

(41) Angelical

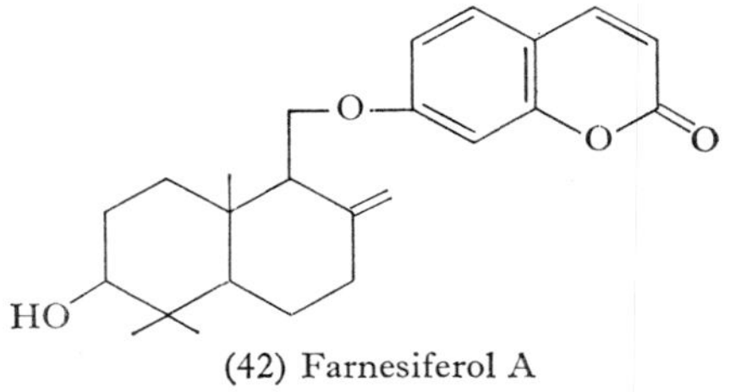

(42) Farnesiferol A

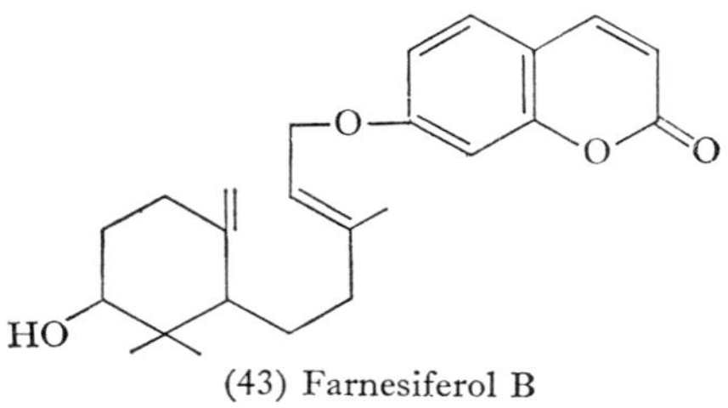

(43) Farnesiferol B

of this tribe and that the majority of plants in the Smyrnieae elaborate several coumarins of this type. Furthermore, linear dihydrofuranocoumarins have been isolated only from the genus *Prangos*.

Table 1A. Coumarin patterns in the Apioideae

Tribe: Smyrnieae

Genus, species	Simple coumarins	Furanocoumarins		Dihydrofuranocoumarins		Dihydropyranocoumarins		Seselin
		Linear	Angular	Linear	Angular	Linear	Angular	
Conium maculatum L.	—	2	—	—	—	—	—	—
Hippomarathrum caspicum (DC.) Grossk.	2	8	—	—	—	—	—	—
H. microcarpum (H.B.) Fedtsch.	2	7	—	—	—	—	—	—
Prangos ferulacea (L.) Lindl.	2	4	—	—	—	—	—	—
P. isphairamica B. Fedtsch.	—	3	—	2	—	—	—	—
P. lipskyi Korov.	—	—	—	1	—	—	—	—
P. ornata Kuzm.	—	4	—	1	—	—	—	—
P. pabularia Lindl.	1	13	—	—	—	—	—	—
P. serawschanica (Regel & Schmalh.) Kor.	1	6	—	—	—	—	—	—
P. tschimganica B. Fedtsch.	—	2	—	1	—	—	—	—

Table 1B

Tribe: Ammineae

Subtribe, genus, species	Simple coumarins	Furanocoumarins		Dihydrofuranocoumarins		Dihydropyranocoumarins		Seselin
		Linear	Angular	Linear	Angular	Linear	Angular	
Carinae:								
Bupleurum falcatum L. var. *komorowii* Koso-Polj.	—	—	1	—	—	—	—	—
Apium graveolens L.	3	1	—	—	—	—	—	—
Petroselinum sativum Hoffm.	—	1	—	—	—	—	—	—
Ammi majus L.	—	5	1	2	—	—	—	—
A. visnaga (L.) Lam.	—	—	—	1	—	—	3	—
Pimpinella heyneana Wall.	—	1	—	—	—	—	—	+
P. magna (L.)	1	2	3	—	—	—	—	—
P. major (L.) Huds.	1	1	3	—	—	—	—	—
P. saxifraga L.	1	3	3	—	—	—	—	—

It is worth noting that angular furano- and angular dihydrofuranocoumarins, as well as both types of dihydropyranocoumarins, are lacking in this tribe.

Ammineae

Carinae

With a single exception (*Ammi visnaga* (L.) Lam.) the coumarin pattern in the Carinae (Table 1B), like that of the Smyrnieae, is characterized by the absence of angular dihydrofuranocoumarins and of linear and angular dihydropyranocoumarins. As opposed to the Smyrniae, angular furanocoumarins seem to be of frequent

Table 1C

Tribe: Ammineae

Subtribe, genus, species	Simple coumarins	Furanocoumarins		Dihydrofuranocoumarins		Dihydropyranocoumarins		Seselin
		Linear	Angular	Linear	Angular	Linear	Angular	
Seselinae:								
Seseli campestre L.	—	2	—	—	—	—	—	—
S. indicum Wight & Arn.	—	2	—	—	—	—	—	+
S. libanotis (L.) Koch subsp. *libanotis*	—	3	—	—	—	1	3	—
S. libanotis	1	—	—	—	—	—	1	—
S. sibiricum (Benth.)	2	2	—	—	—	—	—	—
S. gummiferum Pall.	—	—	—	1	—	—	7	—
Libanotis buchtormensis (Fisch.) DC.	—	2	—	—	—	—	2	—
L. buchtormensis	2	2	—	—	—	—	2	—
L. condensata (L.) Crantz	1	—	—	—	—	—	1	—
L. intermedia Rupr.	1	—	—	—	—	—	—	—
L. transcaucasica Schischk.	—	—	—	—	1	—	—	—
Anethum graveolens L.	1	—	—	—	—	1	—	—
Cnidium dubium (Schkuhr.) Thell.	1	4	—	—	—	—	—	—
C. monnieri (L.) Cuss.	1	4	—	—	1	—	—	—
Selinum monnieri L.	1	—	1	—	1	—	—	—
S. vaginatum C. B. Clarke	—	—	2	—	1	—	2	—
Sphenosciadium capitelulatum (A. Gray)	—	6	—	1	—	—	—	—
Ligusticum acutiloba Sieb. & Zucc.	—	2	—	—	—	—	—	—

occurrence in the Carinae. This is especially true of the genus *Pimpinella*.

The coumarin pattern in *Pimpinella heyneana* Wall., however, is somewhat different from the pattern found in the other *Pimpinella* species. In the first place simple coumarins and angular furanocoumarins have not been obtained from *P. heyneana*. Secondly, *P. heyneana* has been shown to elaborate seselin, which is lacking in the other species. In the Umbelliferae seselin has only been isolated from two plants: *P. heyneana* (= *Seseli zeylanicum* Herb. Rottler & Klein ex C. B. Clark), and *Seseli indicum* Wight & Arn.

The difference in the coumarin patterns in *Ammi majus* L. and *A. visnaga* is notable.

Seselinae

In contrast to the Carinae (and the Smyrnieae), all the categories of coumarins usually found in the Umbelliferae are represented in the Seselinae (Table 1C).

The patterns in the genera *Seseli* and *Libanotis* are very much alike. The majority of species in these genera elaborate linear furanocoumarins and angular dihydropyranocoumarins.

Peucedanae

Table 1D illustrates the distribution of the various categories of coumarins in subtribes and genera of the Peucedanae.

Table 1D

Tribe: Peucedanae

Subtribe, genus	No. of species investi- gated	Simple cou- marins	Furano- coumarins		Dihydrofurano- coumarins		Dihydropyrano- coumarins	
			Linear	Angular	Linear	Angular	Linear	Angular
Angelicinae:								
Angelica L.	29	17	16	6	2	4	1	4
Archangelica Hoffm.	2	2	2	—	—	—	—	—
Levisticum Hill	2	1	2	—	—	—	—	—
Agasyllis Spreng.	1	1	—	—	1	—	—	—
Phellopterus (?)	1	—	1	—	—	—	—	—
Ferulinae:								
Ferula L.	17	15	1	—	—	—	—	—
Lomatium Nutt.	3	1	—	—	—	3	—	1
Xanthogalum Avé-Lall.	1	1	—	—	—	—	1	1
Ferulago Koch	1	—	—	—	1	—	—	—
Leptotaenia Nutt.	1	—	—	—	—	1	—	—
Peucedanum L.	17	6	8	—	4	2	—	1
Pteryxia Nutt.	2	1	—	—	—	—	—	2
Pastinaca L.	3	—	3	1	—	—	—	—
Tordyliinae:								
Heracleum L.	29	19	29	22	—	—	—	—
Zozimia DC.	1	—	—	—	1	1	—	—

Angelicinae

All categories of coumarins known to occur in Umbelliferous plants have been found in the genus *Angelica*. Although dihydrofurano- and dihydropyranocoumarins have only been isolated from a few of the 29 species investigated, this may be due to the sensitivity of these compounds to acid and/or alkali. Furthermore, these types of coumarins often co-occur in complex mixtures of closely related compounds and therefore are difficult to isolate. Further investigations of the genus *Angelica* may very well change the present picture. An indication of the likely development in the future is obtained from the fact that the majority of the dihydrofurano- and dihydropyranocoumarins have been discovered in recent years.

Ferulinae

From a phytochemical point of view the genus *Ferula* is an interesting group. It was mentioned earlier that the only examples of coumarins lacking an oxygen atom at the 7-position and carrying substituents at the 3- and 4-positions are the compounds (17) and (18) obtained from *F. communis*. Furthermore, investigations of 17 species in this genus have disclosed that 15 species only elaborate umbelliferone (2) and/or umbelliferone ethers. These ethers, in which mono- or bicyclic sesquiterpenes are linked to the coumarin skeleton, represent chemical structures which have only been obtained from the genus *Ferula*.

The isolation of three linear furanocoumarins, but no simple coumarins, from the fruits of *F. aliacea* Boiss., break the above mentioned pattern.

F. purpurea Wats., which is synonymous with *Lomatium columbianum* Math. & Const., has been shown to contain two angular dihydrofuranocoumarins, whereas no simple coumarins were obtained. Thus, *F. purpurea* does not fit into the coumarin pattern in the genus *Ferula*. On the other hand, from a chemical point of view, *F. purpurea* is closely related to the genus *Lomatium*.

There is a remarkable difference in the coumarin patterns in the genus *Ferula* and in the other genera of this subtribe. Thus, a survey of 17 species of the genus *Peucedanum* shows that the majority of categories of coumarins are represented in this genus. So far, only angular furano- and linear dihydropyranocoumarins are lacking.

Tordyliinae

The coumarin pattern in the genus *Heracleum* is similar to that found in *Pimpinella*. Of 29 species investigated, all were shown to contain linear furanocoumarins. In addition, the majority of the species elaborated simple coumarins (19 of 29) and angular furanocoumarins (22 of 29). Furthermore, it should be noticed that none of the dihydro-derivatives have been isolated from the genus *Heracleum*. From *Heracleum absinthifolium* Vent., which is synonymous with *Zozimia absinthifolia* (Vent.) DC., two dihydrofuranocoumarins have been isolated, indicating that *H. absinthifolium* may be placed in the genus *Zozimia*.

REFERENCES

BOSE, P. K. & CHOUDHURY, J. C., 1946. *Ann. Biochem. Expl. Med. (Calcutta)*, **6**: 1–10.
BOTTOMLY, W. & WHITE, D. E., 1951. *Aust. J. Sci. Res.*, A4: 112–115.
BROWN, S. A. & SHYLUK, J. P., 1962. *Analyt. Chem.*, **34**: 1058–1061.
CHATTERJEE, A., BOSE, P. K. & SAHA, S. K., 1962. *Arch. Pharm.*, **295**: 248–255.
CHATTERJEE, A. & CHOUDHURY, A., 1955. *Naturwissenschaften*, **42**: 535–536.
ČHERNOBAI, V. T. & KOLESNIKOV, D. G., 1960. *Dokl. Akad. Nauk SSSR*, **133**: 233–235.
DEAN, F. M., 1952. In Zechmeister, L., *Fortschr. Chem. org. Naturst.*, **9**: 225.
DEAN, F. M., 1963. *Naturally Occurring Oxygen Ring Compounds*. London: Butterworth.
HATA, K. & KOZAWA, M., 1965. *Tetrahedron Letters*, No. **50**: 4557–4562.
HATA, K. & KOZAWA, M., 1967. *J. Pharm. Soc. Japan*, **87**: 210–211.
HATA, K. & KOZAWA, M., 1968. *J. Pharm. Soc. Japan*, **88**: 283–292.
HATA, K., KOZAWA, M. & YEN, K., 1963. *J. Pharm. Soc. Japan*, **83**: 606–610.
HATA, K. & SANO, K., 1966. *Tetrahedron Letters*, No. **14**: 1461–1465.
KUZNETSOVA, G. A., 1961. *Zh. Obshsch. Khim.*, **31**: 3818–3820.
LEE, K-H. & SOINE, T. O., 1968. *J. Pharm. Sci.*, **57**: 865–868.
NIELSEN, B. E., 1970. *Dansk Tidsskr. Farmac.*, **44**: 111–286.
NIELSEN, B. E., LARSEN, P. K. & LEMMICH, J., 1970. *Acta chem. scand.*, **24**: 2863–2867.
NIELSEN, B. E. & LEMMICH, J., 1969. *Acta Chem. Scand.*, **23**: 962–966.
NIKONOV, G. K., VEREMEI, R. K. & PIMENOV, M. G., 1964. *Zh. Obshch. Khim.*, **34**: 1353–1354.
NOGUTI, T. & KAWANAMI, M., 1939. *J. Pharm. Soc. Japan*, **59**: 755–757.
SOKOLOVA, N. I., NIKONOV, G. K., PEREL'SON, M. E., SIROVA, G. P. & SHEINKER, Yu. N., 1968. *Khim. Prir. Soedin.*, **4**: 280–283.
SPÄTH, E., BOSE, P. K., MATZKE, J. & GUHA, N. Ch., 1939. *Ber.*, **72**: 821–830.
SPÄTH, E. & SOCIAS, L., 1934. *Ber.*, **67**: 59–61.
STECK, W., 1967. *Can. J. Biochem.*, **45**: 1995–2003.
STECK, W., EL-DAKHAKNY, M. & BROWN, S. A., 1969. *Tetrahedron Letters*, No. **54**: 4805–4808.
SVENDSEN, A. B., 1954. *Zur Chemie Norwegischer Umbelliferen*. Oslo: Diss.

Dérivés furannocoumariniques du genre *Heracleum* et plus spécialement de *Heracleum sprengelianum* Wight & Arn. et *Heracleum ceylanicum* Gardn. ex C. B. Clarke Étude Phylogénique

D. MOLHO, P. JÖSSANG, M.-C. JARREAU ET J. CARBONNIER

Laboratoire de chimie du Muséum National d'Histoire Naturelle, Paris, France

La composition furannocoumarinique d'une vingtaine d'espèces d'*Heracleum* a été déterminée. La présence d'esters de dihydrofurannocoumarines: angélate de columbianétine et tiglate de (±) marmésine, uniquement dans *Heracleum sprengelianum* et *H. ceylanicum*, différencie ces deux espèces de toutes celles examinées.

L'hypothèse selon laquelle ces esters, formes de blocage des biosynthèses conduisant habituellement aux furannocoumarines angulaires et linéaires, seraient la marque d'un processus évolutif, est corroborée par des critères botaniques d'ordre palynologique et caryologique. Une classification phylogénique des *Heracleum*, fondée sur des pertes successives de voies biogénétiques a été avancée.

Twenty different species of the genus *Heracleum* were examined for their furanocoumarinic distribution.

The occurrence of esters of dihydrofuranocoumarins: angelic ester of columbianetin and tiglic ester of (±) marmesin within *Heracleum sprengelianum* and *H. ceylanicum* differentiate these two species from all the others as yet examined.

The esters are believed to be the factor causing the blockage of the biosynthetic pathways which usually lead to the angular and linear furanocoumarins.

They are also assumed to be an indication of an evolutionary process, confirmed by palynological and karyological data. A phylogenetic classification, based on the successive loss of biogenetic pathways is proposed.

TABLE DES MATIERES

INTRODUCTION

De tous temps, les systématiciens ont utilisé la grande diversité des formes pour subdiviser la monde végétal en taxa de hiérarchie déterminée. Les progrès techniques ont cependant permis de saisir des variations héréditaires plus fines. C'est ainsi que les caryologistes, palynologistes et ontogénistes créent des lignées à l'intérieur des familles, subdivisent des tribus et redistribuent les espèces dans les genres.

Quant à l'utilisation des constituants chimiques comme caractères taxonomiques, ce sont les botanistes eux-mêmes qui ont fait les premières tentatives. En effet, l'opposition des plantes herbacées aux plantes ligneuses est en fait basée sur l'absence ou la présence de lignine. De même la chlorophylle permet de distinguer les algues des champignons parmi les Thallophytes.

La phytochimie peut donc apporter sa contribution à la taxonomie. Ainsi les bétalaïnes, pigments azotés, ne se rencontrent que dans le groupe des Centrospermées et la colchicine dans la sous-famille des Colchicoïdées (Liliacées). Dans ces deux exemples, la chimiotaxonomie recoupe parfaitement la systématique classique. Par contre la berbérine est un alcaloïde largement réparti dans une douzaine de familles sans grands rapports entre elles. Il existe donc, de ce point de vue des 'bonnes' et des 'mauvaises' substances.

Certains auteurs (Nielsen, 1970: 109) pensent que seuls les produits peu répandus peuvent jouer un rôle taxonomique; d'autres comme Bate-Smith (1964, 1966) préfèrent utiliser dans ce but des ensembles de composés très largement dispersés dans le règne végétal, ce qui est le cas en particulier des dérivés polyphénoliques.

Enfin, il peut être important parfois en chimiotaxonomie de tenir compte également des relations biosynthétiques. Une substance donnée peut dépendre de deux mécanismes biosynthètiques différents et il serait hasardeux de rapprocher, sans précaution, les espèces végétales la contenant. Ainsi l'acide hiptagénique (acide β nitropropionique) apparaît chez les microorganismes (*Aspergillus flavus*, *Penicillium atravenatum*) par nitration directe et également chez des végétaux supérieurs (*Hiptagena mandoblata*, *Indigofera endocarpus*) mais cette fois, par oxydation d'un dérivé aminé précurseur.

C'est donc en envisageant, non seulement les constituants trouvés dans les plantes mais également leur biogénèse que nous allons classer quelques *Heracleum* et tenter de les relier aux autres genres de la famille des Ombellifères.

FURANNOCOUMARINES DE QUELQUES *HERACLEUM*

Résultats expérimentaux

Les furannocoumarines ont été rencontrées dans de nombreuses Rutacées et dans quelques Légumineuses, mais c'est surtout dans les Ombellifères qu'elles semblent devoir servir de critère taxonomique.

En effet, si l'on essaie d'analyser leur distribution en fonction des données de Nielsen (1970) on constate qu'il n'est signalé de furannocoumarines identifiées que dans la sous-famille des *Apioïdeae* (voir Tableau 1), et particulièrement dans quatre des douze tribus de Drude, avec un maximum de fréquence dans les *Peucedaneae*. Les *Heracleum* qui font l'objet du présent travail font partie de cette dernière tribu.

Tableau 1. Distribution des dérivés furannocoumariniques
dans les Ombellifères

Résultats relevés dans 'Coumarins of Umbelliferous Plants' (Nielsen, 1970)
Classement botanique de Drude (Engler & Prantl, 1895)

Sous-familles	Tribus	Distribution Furannocoumarinique*
Hydrocotyloideae	1 Hydrocotyleae	0/9
	2 Mulineae	0/15
Saniculoideae	3 Saniculeae	0/6
	4 Lagoecieae	0/3
Apioideae	5 Echinophoreae	0/5
	6 Scandicineae	0/21
	7 Coriandreae	0/4
	8 Smyrnieae	2/29
	9 Ammineae	9/85
	10 Peucedaneae	10/39
	11 Laserpitieae	1/9
	12 Dauceae	0/4

* Nombre de genres dans lequels il est actuellement signalé des dérivés furanno-coumariniques identifiés, par rapport au nombre de genres recencés par Drude.

Ayant pu nous procurer une vingtaine d'espèces d'*Heracleum* dont dix n'avaient jamais été étudiées du point de vue chimique,* nous avons recherché les diverses furannocoumarines† présentes (voir Tableau 2).

Il ressort de l'examen de ces analyses, qu'il existe chez les *Heracleum*, aussi bien des furannocoumarines linéaires qu'angulaires, substituées ou non sur le noyau aromatique. Le bergaptène‡ (19) l'isopimpinelline (21), l'isobergaptène (19′), la pimpinelline (21′) et la sphondine (13′) sont à quelques exceptions près des constantes du genre.

Nous avons pu montrer que le byak-angélicol (23), non signalé dans le genre *Heracleum*, s'y rencontre en fait assez souvent, de même que deux dihydro-furanno-coumarines: la columbianétine (6′) et la marmésine (6).

Nous avons enfin identifié dans *H. sprengelianum* et *H. ceylanicum* les esters respectivement angélique et tiglique de ces deux dihydro-furannocoumarines: (8) et (7).

Les variations dans la composition furannocoumarinique permettent d'effectuer un classement chimique des espèces en deux groupes différenciés par la présence ou l'absence des esters de dihydro-furannocoumarines.

* Les dix espèces étudiées par nous pour la première fois sont: *Heracleum alpinum* L., *H. ceylanicum* Gardn., *H. flavescens* DC., *H. leucocarpum* Aitch., *H. montanum* Schleich. *H. palmatum* Baumg., *H. platytaenium* Bois., *H. pyrenaicum* Lam., *H. rigens* Wall., et *H. sprengelianum* Wight & Arn.

† Nous avons vérifié que les furannocoumarines sont des éléments constants de la plante. Des lots de provenances diverses (fruits de *H. sosnowskyi* Manden. de deux stations différentes, racines d'*H. sprengelianum* Wight & Arn. cultivé à Paris ou récolté aux Indes) ont la même composition qualitative.

‡ La numérotation des substances citées dans le texte, renvoie aux formules données Figs 1 et 2.

Tableau 2. Dérivés furannocoumariniques*

Espèces ou sous-espèces d'Heracleum	Osthol	Phelloptérine	Byak-angélicol	Impératorine	Xanthotoxine	Isopimpinelline	Bergaptène	Isobergaptène	Pimpinelline	Sphondine	Angélicine	Psoralène	Columbianétine†	Marmésine(+)ou(−)ou(±)†	Columbianadine	Tiglate de (±)marmésine	Parties de plantes étudiées
H. ceylanicum Gardn.	—	—	—	●	—	—	—	—	—	—	—	—	●	●	●	●	Fruits
H. sprengelianum Wight & Arn.	—	●	—	—	—	—	—	—	—	—	—	—	●	●	●	●	Fruits
	—	—	—	—	—	—	—	—	—	—	—	—	●	●	●	●	Racines
H. mantegazzianum Som. et Lev. ('La Jaysinia')‡	—	—	—	—	●	●	—	—	●	—	●	—	—	—	—	—	Fruits
	—	—	—	—	●	●	—	—	●	●	●	—	—	—	—	—	Feuilles
	—	—	—	—	●	●	●	●	●	●	●	●	—	—	—	—	Racines
H. mantegazzianum (Kew)‡	—	—	●	●	●	●	●	—	—	●	—	—	—	—	—	—	Fruits
H. lehmanianum Bge	—	—	●	—	●	●	●	●	●	●	●	—	—	—	—	—	Fruits
	—	—	—	—	●	●	●	●	●	●	●	—	—	—	—	—	Racines
H. stevenii Manden.	—	●	—	—	●	●	●	●	●	●	●	—	—	—	—	—	Fruits
	●	—	—	—	●	●	●	●	●	●	●	—	—	—	—	—	Racines
H. leucocarpum Aitch.	—	—	—	—	●	●	●	●	●	—	—	—	—	—	—	—	Fruits
	—	—	—	—	●	●	●	●	●	—	●	—	—	—	—	—	Feuilles
	—	—	—	—	●	●	●	●	●	●	●	—	—	—	—	—	Racines
H. wilhelmsii Fisch. & Lallem.	—	—	●	—	●	●	●	●	●	●	●	—	—	—	—	—	Fruits
H. trachyloma Fisch. & Mey.	—	—	●	—	●	●	●	●	●	●	●	—	—	—	—	—	Fruits
H. sosnowskyi Manden.	●	●	—	—	●	●	●	●	●	●	●	—	—	—	—	—	Fruits
H. lanatum Michx	—	●	—	—	●	●	●	●	●	●	●	—	—	—	—	—	Fruits
H. pyrenaïcum Lam.	—	—	●	—	●	●	●	●	●	—	●	—	—	—	—	—	Fruits
	—	—	—	—	●	●	●	●	●	●	●	—	●	●	—	—	Racines
H. mantegazzianum (Brunoy)‡	—	—	●	●	●	●	●	●	●	●	—	—	—	—	—	—	Fruits
H. palmatum Baumg.	—	—	—	—	●	●	●	●	●	●	—	—	—	—	—	—	Fruits
H. platytaenium Boiss.	—	—	●	—	●	●	●	●	●	●	●	—	—	—	—	—	Fruits
H. rigens Wall.	—	—	●	—	●	●	●	●	●	●	●	—	—	—	—	—	Fruits
H. flavescens DC.	—	—	●	—	●	●	●	●	●	●	—	—	—	—	—	—	Fruits
	—	—	—	—	●	●	●	●	●	●	●	—	—	—	—	—	Racines
H. alpinum L.	—	—	—	—	●	●	●	●	●	●	—	—	—	—	—	—	Fruits
	—	—	—	—	●	●	●	●	●	●	●	—	—	—	—	—	Racines
H. montanum Schleich.	—	—	●	●	●	●	—	—	●	●	—	—	—	—	—	—	Fruits
	—	—	—	—	●	●	●	●	●	●	●	—	—	—	—	—	Racines
H. sphondylium L.	—	●	—	●	—	●	—	—	—	—	—	—	—	—	—	—	Fruits
	—	—	—	—	●	●	●	●	●	●	●	—	—	—	—	—	Racines

* Résultats expérimentaux—Répartition des constituants coumariniques dans 20 espèces ou sous-espèces d'*Heracleum* classées en fonction de la disparition progressive: du tiglate de (±) marmésine, de la columbianidine, de la marmésine, de la columbianétine, du psoralène et de l'angélicine. Les formules développées des substances citées figurent dans les Figs 2 et 3.

† Substances toujours à l'état de traces.

‡ Le cas de *Heracleum mantegazzianum* paraît complexe. Nous avons eu en mains des plantes portant ce nom en provenance de trois jardins botaniques différents (Botanic Gardens, Kew, station écologique de Brunoy-Muséum National d'Histoire Naturelle, jardin botanique de 'La Jaysinia'—Samoëns). L'analyse chimique de chaque échantillon a donné des résultats différents. Il y aurait peut-être lieu de revoir la détermination de ces exemplaires, car de nouvelles espèces d'*Heracleum* ont été définies par Mandenova (1950) à une époque probablement postérieure à la dispersion des *H. mantegazzianum* dans les jardins botaniques. Avant la mise au point de Mandenova, le qualificatif *mantegazzianum* couvrait un groupe d'espèces d'*Heracleum* géants de l'actuelle section *Pubescentia*, comprenant entre-autres *Heracleum sosnowskyi* Manden., *Heracleum sommieri* Manden., *Heracleum grossheimii* Manden. et *Heracleum mantegazzianum* Som. et Lev.

Implications phylogéniques des résultats relatifs à Heracleum
sprengelianum *et* H. ceylanicum (*Macro-évolution*)

Relation entre 'type de pollen' et 'présence d'esters de dihydro-furannocoumarines'.

Parmi les diverses espèces étudiées, deux d'entre elles: *H. sprengelianum* et *H. ceylanicum* apparaissent tout à fait remarquables (voir Tableau 2); ces deux plantes méritent d'être séparées des autres *Heracleum*. En effet:

(i) Elles ne contiennent aucune furannocoumarine angulaire régulièrement présente dans les autres espèces.

(ii) Elles ne renferment qu'une furannocoumarine linéaire et *O*-isoprénylée (phelloptérine: 22 ou impératorine: 14).

(iii) Elles accumulent en quantité importante de la columbianadine (6′) (angélate de columbianétine) et de la sprengelianine (7) (nom proposé pour désigner le tiglate de ($\pm$) marmésine).

Des esters de ce type,* sont signalés ici pour la première fois dans le genre *Heracleum*. Ils ont cependant été trouvés dans d'autres Ombellifères, en particulier dans les genres: *Angelica, Peucedanum, Prangos, Zozimia* et *Leptotaenia*.

Cerceau-Larrival (1962, 1963) a établi, d'après les modifications de la forme des grains de pollen,† des relations phylogéniques entre les différents genres d'Ombellifères.

Or nous constatons que tous les genres connus jusqu'ici dans lesquels se rencontrent des esters de dihydro-furannocoumarines (en particulier *Peucedanum* et *Zozimia*) sont, dans le schéma d'évolution donné par Cerceau-Larrival (Fig. 1), à la droite du genre *Heracleum*, et par conséquent plus avancés selon l'échelle de 'macro-évolution'.

Le fait qu'*H. sprengelianum* et *H. ceylanicum* renferment des esters de dihydro-furannocoumarines permet donc de présumer que ces deux espèces‡ ont un degré d'évolution supérieur à celui des autres *Heracleum* déjà examinés du point de vue palynologique.

Cette hypothèse a été confirmée par l'étude du pollen de *H. ceylanicum*, effectuée

* Des esters de dihydro-furannocoumarines ont déjà été isolés des Ombellifères. Il s'agit de: la columbianadine: angélate de columbianétine; deltoïne: angélate de marmésine; prantschimgine: sénécioate de marmésine.

† La forme des grains de pollen est établie d'après le contour interne de l'endexine. Les espèces les plus primitives possèdent un pollen de forme subrhomboïdal; les plus évoluées un pollen équatorialoconstricté. Entre ces deux types extrêmes, l'évolution se traduit par des variations de la forme des pollen qui deviennent successivement subcirculaires, ovales et subrectangulaires. Le passage d'un type à l'autre traduit la *macro-évolution*. A chacun de ces types correspond une *micro-évolution*, propre à la lignée considérée et dont le degré peut être apprécié par la taille du pollen. Toutes ces données sont étayées par des critères évolutifs plus conventionnels comme la morphologie foliaire, le développement des plantules et l'anatomie des fruits. Il s'ensuit que le simple examen palynologique d'une espèce peut nous donner une idée de son degré d'évolution par rapport aux autres espèces du genre ou même par rapport aux autres genres (voir Fig. 1.)

‡ La composition en dérivés furannocoumariniques de *H. sprengelianum* et de *H. ceylanicum* se rapproche de celle de *Zozimia absinthifolia* (Vent.) DC. (Nikonov & Baranauskaite, 1964, 1965). Il est à noter que cette dernière espèce est en synonymie avec *Heracleum absinthifolium* Vent. et *H. tomentosum* Sm. Cependant il est actuellement admis qu'il s'agit bien d'un *Zozimia*. D'ailleurs le pollen de cette espèce est très semblable à ceux de *Z. dichotoma* Boiss., *Z. frigida* Boiss. et Hausskn. et *Z. tragioides* Boiss (Cerceau-Larrival, 1963). Cette synonymie ne gêne donc en rien l'argumentation développée.

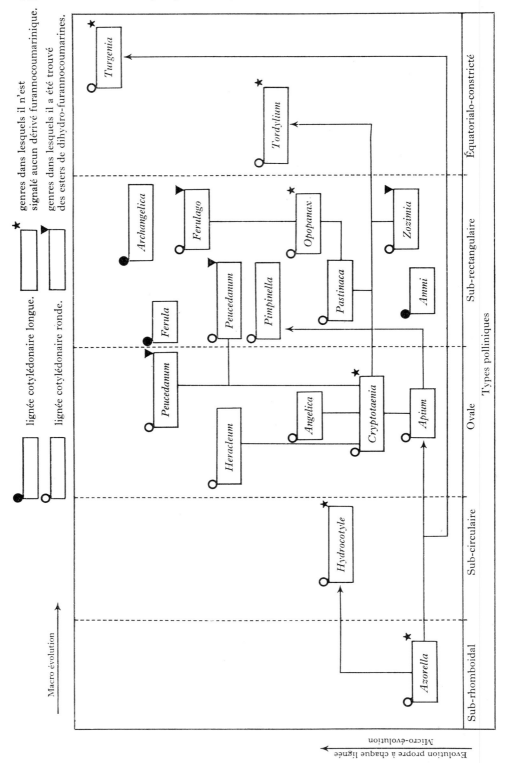

FIGURE 1. Représentation de l'évolution des Ombellifères d'après le type pollinique—(d'après Cerceau-Larrival, 1962, 1963, 1967) (reproduction partielle). Corrélation avec la présence de dérivés furannocoumariniques.

grâce à l'obligeance de Madame Cerceau-Larrival. Il s'avère que ce pollen est très particulier, en effet c'est le seul du genre à être subrectangulaire donc aussi évolué que ceux de genre *Zozimia.*

Une autre particularité de ces derniers *Heracleum* consiste en leur nombre chromosomique. Ces deux espèces sont en effet les seuls polyploïdes* connus du genre, ce qui à certains égards, peut être considéré comme un caractère d'évolution.

Nous avons donc pu montrer que la différenciation de caractères botaniques héréditaires de ces deux espèces existe parallèlement à une différenciation chimique.

Cette modification dans le chimisme de ces deux *Heracleum*, en particulier l'apparition d'esters et la disparition (à l'exception d'une seule) des furannocoumarines rencontrées habituellement dans ce genre fait nécessairement penser à un blocage des voies biogénétiques.

Biogénèse des furannocoumarines non substituées chez les Heracleum.

Des études détaillées (Floss & Mothes, 1966; Floss & Paikert 1969) ont montré que la biosynthèse des coumarines passe par la voie shikimique. La partie furannique résulte d'une isoprénylation de l'ombelliférone. Cette isoprénylation peut se faire de deux façons différentes aboutissant soit à la déméthyl-subérosine (2), soit à l'osthénol (2'), qui sont respectivement les intermédiaires de la biosynthèse des furannocoumarines linéaires et angulaires (voir fig. 2).

Steck *et al.* (1969) envisagent que l'osthénol (2') et la déméthyl-subérosine (2) subissent une époxydation (4') et (4). L'hydrolyse de l'époxyde conduit vraisemblablement au diol qui peut alors se cycliser de deux manières différentes:

(i) soit en dihydro-furannocoumarines: columbianétine (6') à partir de l'osthénol (2') ou marmésine (6) à partir de la déméthyl-subérosine (2).

(ii) soit en dihydro-pyrannocoumarines: lomatine (5') à partir de l'osthénol (2') ou décursinol (5) à partir de la déméthyl-subérosine (2).

Ces auteurs ont apporté la preuve, à l'aide de molécules marquées que la columbianétine (6') et la marmésine (6) sont bien les précurseurs respectifs des furannocoumarines linéaires et angulaires.

Bien que les intermédiaires de cette dernière biosynthèse n'aient pas été caractérisés nous pouvons admettre que l'hydroxy-9 columbianétine (9') résulte d'une hydroxylation benzylique en 9 de (6'); on trouve d'ailleurs ce dérivé [sous forme d'esters de type édultine (10) dans certaines Ombellifères (Nakazaki *et al.*, 1966).

L'étape suivante serait une rétroaldolisation avec départ d'acétone, puis une déshydratation qui conduirait à l'angélicine (11'). Le même mécanisme est envisageable pour la série linéaire.

De ce schéma, il ressort que les esters de la lomatine (5'), la columbianadine (8) et l'édultine (10) ou ses homologues résultent de l'estérification de leur précurseur immédiat. Ce sont là des formes de déviation de la voie normale de biosynthèse qui à partir des mêmes précurseurs conduit à l'angélicine (11') et à ses dérivés méthoxylés.

---

* Nous remercions Madame Cauwet qui a déterminé pour nous le caryotype de *H. sprengelianum* et le Professeur Constance qui nous a indiqué celui de *H. ceylanicum.*

Produits isolés dans les Ombellifères
Produits isolés dans les Heracleum

- - -> voies non démontrées

⟶ voies proposées par Steck et al. (1969)

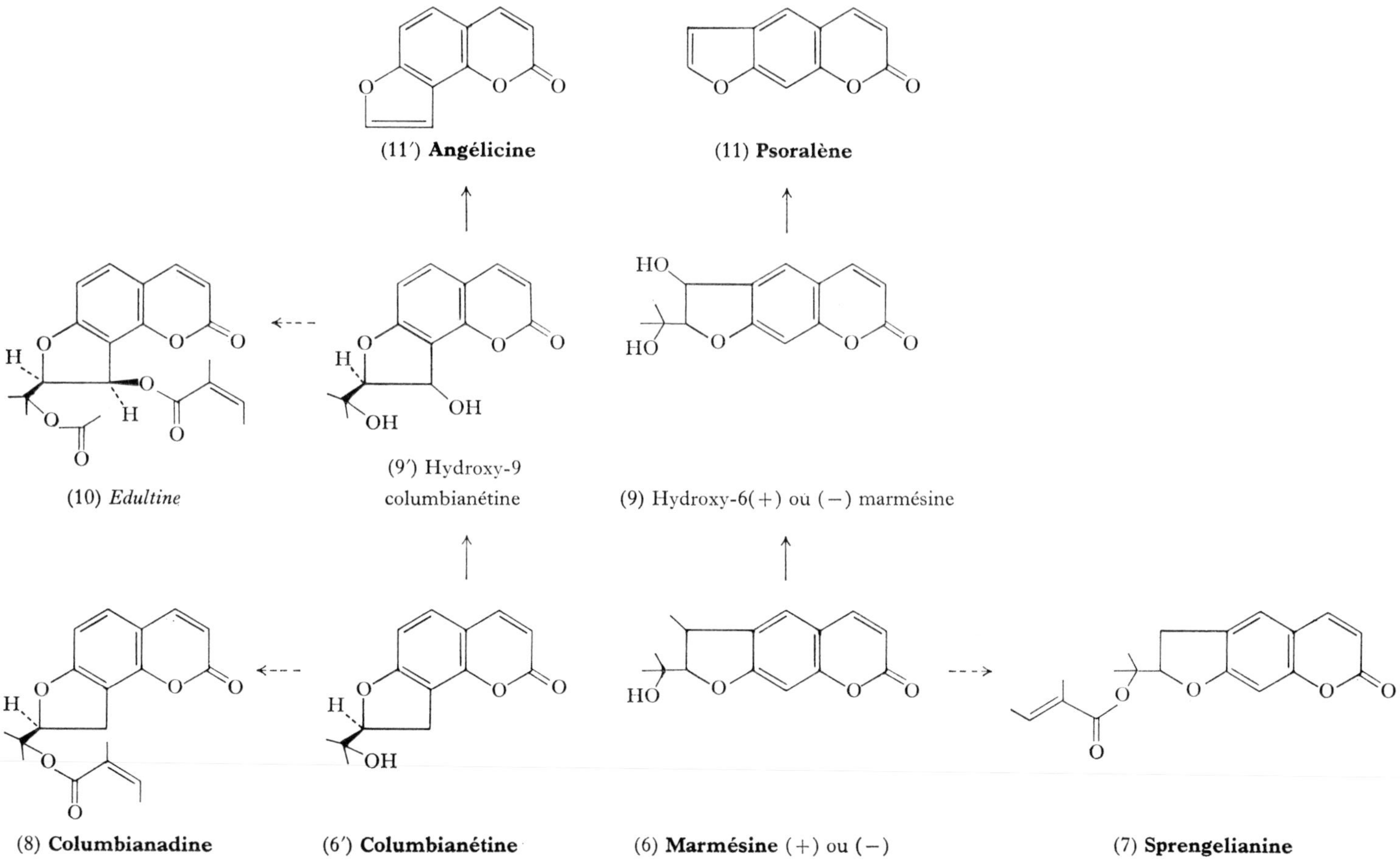

(7) **Sprengelianine**

(6) **Marmésine** (+) ou (−)

(9) Hydroxy-6(+) ou (−) marmésine

(11) **Psoralène**

(6') **Columbianétine**

(9') Hydroxy-9 columbianétine

(11') **Angélicine**

(10) *Edultine*

(8) **Columbianadine**

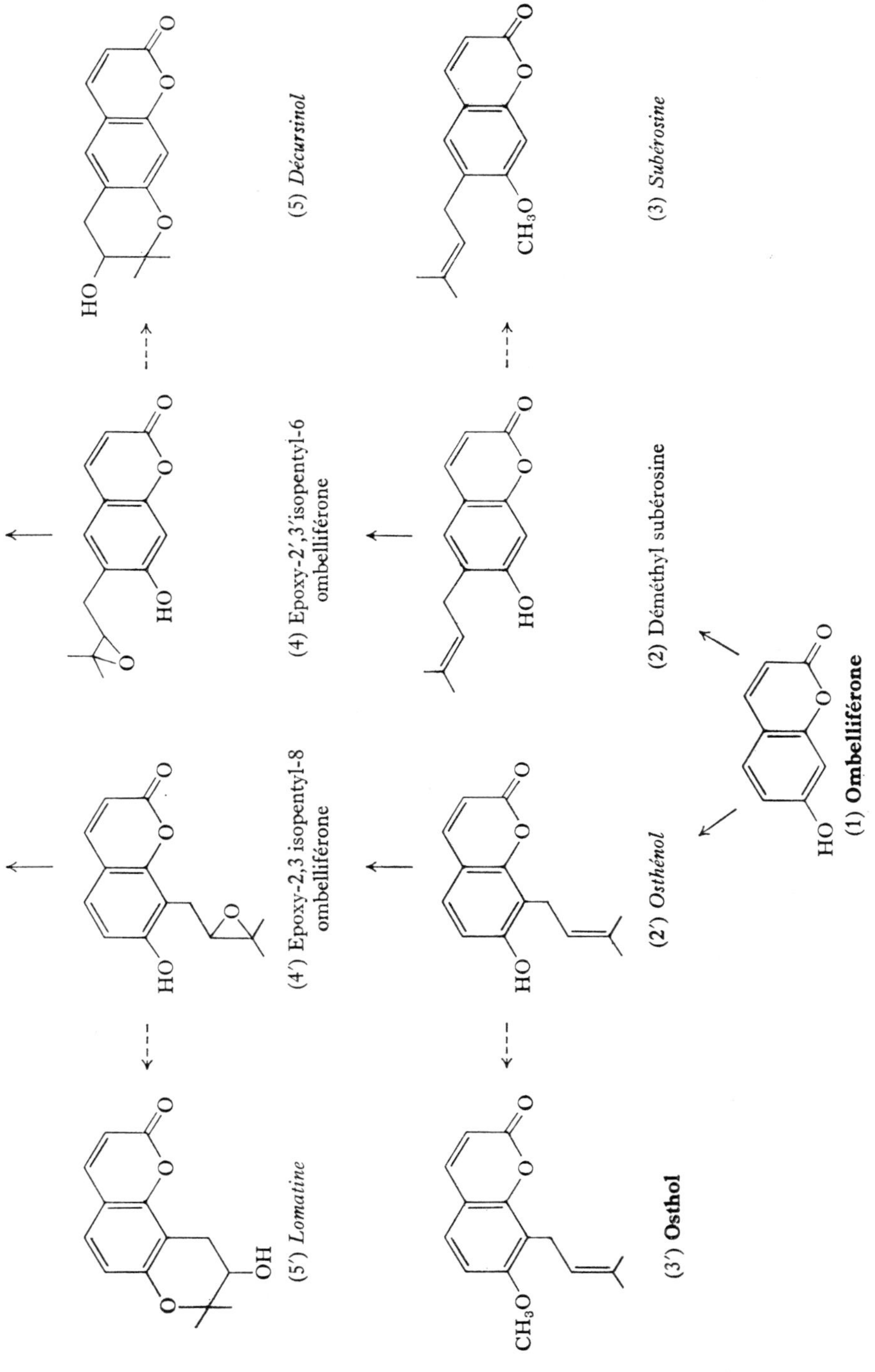

FIGURE 2. Schéma de la biosynthèse des dérivés furannocoumariniques.

(5) *Décursinol*

(3) *Subérosine*

(4) Epoxy-2',3'isopentyl-6 ombelliférone

(2) Déméthyl subérosine

(1) **Ombelliférone**

(4') Epoxy-2,3 isopentyl-8 ombelliférone

(2') *Osthénol*

(5') *Lomatine*

(3') **Osthol**

De même les esters du décursinol (5) et ceux de la marmésine (7) sont des produits de déviation de la biosynthèse du psoralène (11) et de toutes les autres furanno-coumarines linéaires.

Chez *H. sprengelianum* et *H. ceylanicum*, la présence de quantités importantes de columbianadine (8) et de sprengelianine (7) concrétise ce type de déviation et témoigne de la disparition de la biosynthèse de toutes les furannocoumarines angu-laires et d'une grande partie de celle de la série linéaire.

L'apparition d'une spécialisation par suppression de plusieurs potentialités bio-synthétiques semble donc être un caractère d'évolution; celà au même titre que les diverses spécialisations d'ordre morphologique qui sont reconnues par les botanistes comme étant des caractères évolutifs.

On constate ainsi un parallélisme entre la macro-évolution traduite par le passage des pollens de type ovale au type subrectangulaire et l'apparition de formes de blocage concomitantes de la suppression de plusieurs voies biosynthétiques.

Implications phylogéniques des résultats acquis avec les autres espèces du genre Hera-cleum (*micro-évolution*)

Nous avons essayé d'étendre à un ensemble d'espèces ayant le même type pol-linique et présentant une certaine homogénéité chimique, cette notion de régression des voies biogénétiques en tant que caractère d'évolution.

Résultats

Nous avons regroupé dans le Tableau 3 la composition globale (fruits et racines) en furannocoumarines des espèces du genre *Heracleum** étudiées tant par nous que par d'autres auteurs.

Les variations observées entre les diverses espèces traduisent des possibilités biosynthétiques différentes. Nous allons donc tenter de classer ces espèces en fonc-tion des processus biosynthétiques qu'elles utilisent. Par cette méthode, deux substances différentes, mais situées sur la même voie biogénétique, constitueront le même critère taxonomique.

Biosynthèse des furannocoumarines

Nous appuyant sur des données de la littérature nous avons représenté sur la Fig. 3 les diverses voies possibles par lesquelles les Ombellifères effectuent la synthèse des furannocoumarines les plus substituées à partir de l'angélicine (11′) et du psoralène (11).

(i) A partir de l'angélicine (11′), une hydroxylation sur le noyau aromatique, soit en 5, soit en 6, suivie d'une méthylation, conduit respectivement à l'isobergap-tène (19′) ou à la sphondine (13′).

Une seconde hydroxylation suivie de méthylation donne la pimpinelline (21′).

Seuls les dérivés méthoxylés des furannocoumarines angulaires ont été isolés. L'isoprénylation n'a pas lieu dans cette série.

---

* Les seules espèces considérées, sont celles dont à la fois les fruits et les racines, au moins, ont été étudiés de ce point de vue.

Tableau 3. Dérivés furannocoumariniques

Espèces ou sous-espèces d'*Heracleum*	Références bibliographiques†	Phelloptérine	Byak-angélicol	Impératorine	Xanthotoxine	Isopimpinelline	Bergaptène	Isobergaptène	Pimpinelline	Sphondine	Angélicine	Psoralène	Columbianétine*	Marmésine(+)ou(−)*	Columbianadine	Sprengelianine	Origine géographique des plantes étudiées
GROUPE I		*Utilisation de toutes les voies biogénétiques employées par le genre Heracleum*															
H. sphondylium L.	P, A, J	●	●	●	●	●	●	●	●	●	—	—	—	—	—	—	France
H. sosnowskyi Manden.	P, I	—	●	●	●	●	●	●	●	●	●	●	●	●	●	—	Caucase
GROUPE II		*Disparition de la xanthotoxine*															
H. wilhelmsii Fisch. & Lallem.	P, D	—	●	●	—	●	●	●	●	●	●	●	●	●	●	—	Caucase
GROUPE II'		*Disparition du byak-angélicol*															
H. alpinum L.	P	—	—	●	●	●	●	—	●	●	●	●	—	—	—	—	Jura, Alpes
H. montanum Schleich	P	—	—	●	●	●	●	—	●	●	●	—	—	—	—	—	Alpes
GROUPE III		*Disparition de la xanthotoxine et de l'impératorine*															
H. asperum M. B.	J, D, E	●	—	—	—	●	●	●	●	●	●	—	—	—	—	—	Caucase
H. stevenii Manden.	P, G	—	●	—	—	●	●	●	●	●	●	●	●	●	●	—	Caucase
H. pyrenaicum Lam.	P	—	●	—	—	●	●	●	●	●	●	●	—	●	●	—	Pyrénées
H. flavescens DC.	P	—	●	—	—	●	●	●	●	●	●	—	—	—	—	—	France
GROUPE III'		*Disparition de la xanthotoxine et du byak angélical*															
H. lanatum Michx	P, C	—	—	●	—	●	●	●	●	●	●	●	—	●	●	—	Amér. Nord
H. lehmanianum Bge	P, G	—	—	●	—	●	●	●	●	●	●	●	●	●	—	—	Pamir
GROUPE IV		*Disparition de toutes O-isoprénylations*															
H. leucocarpum Aitch.	P	—	—	—	—	●	●	●	●	●	●	●	●	●	●	—	Afghanistan
H. sibiricum L.	G, K, B	—	—	—	—	●	●	●	●	●	●	—	—	—	—	—	Caucase, Asie
H. mantegazzianum Som. et Lev.‡	G	—	—	—	—	●	●	●	●	●	—	●	●	●	—	Caucase

Analyse globale (fruits et racines) des dérivés furannocoumariniques des espèces d'*Heracleum*. Les formules développées des substances citées figurent dans les Figs 2 et 3.

A: Beyrich, 1968; B: Brown *et al.*, 1970; C: Fujita *et al.*, 1954; D: Giorgobiani *et al.*, 1968; E: Giorgobiani *et al.*, 1969; F: Jössang *et al.*, 1969 et complété par le présent travail; G: Komissarenko *et al.*, 1961; H: Komissarenko *et al.*, 1965; I: Kreier 1963; Kreier et Sokolov, 1965; J: Späth *et al.*, 1936; K: Baerheim-Svendsen *et al.*, 1957; 1959; P: Présent travail.

(1) furannocoumarines méthoxylées en 5 et isoprénylées en 8; (2) furannocoumarines monosubstituées en 8; (3) furannocoumarines angulaires.

* Produits toujours à l'état de traces.

† Nos résultats confirment ou complètent ceux de la littérature. Il y a cependant deux exceptions: (a) Beyrich a trouvé de la phelloptérine dans les fruits d'*Heracleum sphondylium*, l'exemplaire que nous avons étudié n'en contenait pas. (b) Kreier a trouvé de la xanthotoxine dans les feuilles de *Heracleum sosnowskyi*, (organe que nous n'avons pas eu en mains).

‡ Parmi toutes les études portant sur *Heracleum mantegazzianum* nous n'avons retenu présentement que celles qui remplissaient les deux conditions suivantes: (a) Etudes complètes concernant à la fois les fruits et les racines. (b) Analyses pratiquées sur des espèces dont l'identification nous a paru certaine (voir légende du Tableau II).

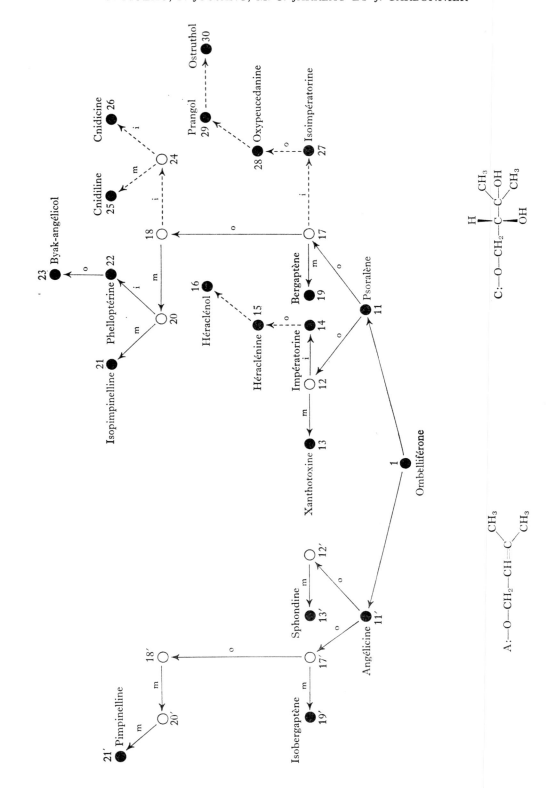

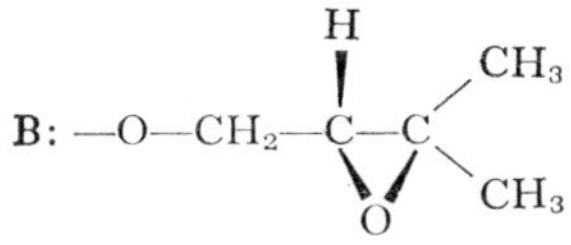

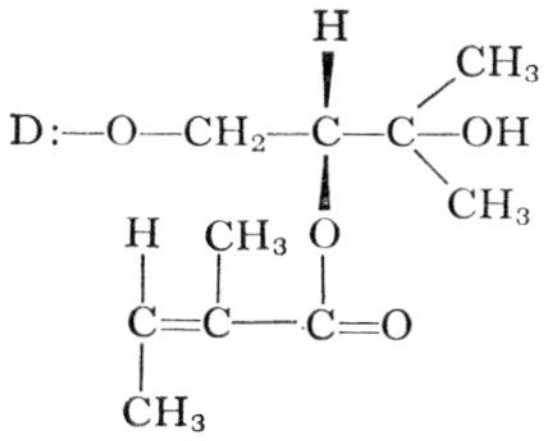

SÉRIE ANGULAIRE

$R_1 = OCH_3$; $R_2 =$

(19) H: Bergaptène
(20) OH: Hydroxy-8 bergaptène
(21) OCH₃: Isopimpinelline
(22) A: Phelloptérine
(23) B: Byak-angélicol

$R_1 = A$; $R_2 =$

(24) OH: Hydroxy-8 cnidine
(25) OCH₃: Cnidiline
(26) A: Cnidicine

$R_2 = H$; $R_1 =$

(27) A: Isoimpératorine
(28) B: Oxypeucedanine
(29) C: Prangol
    (configuration absolue non déterminée)
(30) D: Ostruthol

$R_1 = OH$; $R_2 =$

(17') H: Isobergaptol
(18') OH: Dihydroxy-5,6 angélicine

$R_1 = OCH_3$; $R_2 =$

(19') H: Isobergaptène
(20') OH: Hydroxy-6 isobergaptène
(21') OCH₃: Pimpinelline

SÉRIE LINÉAIRE

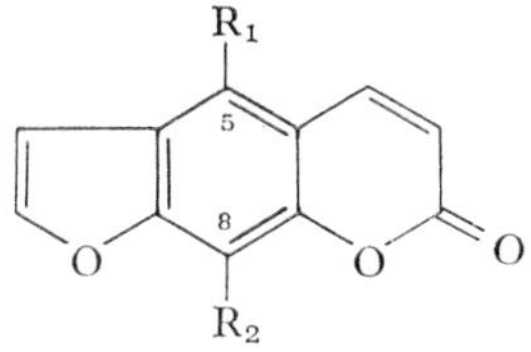

$R_1 = H$; $R_2 =$

(11) H, Psoralène
(12) OH: Xanthotoxol
(13) OCH₃: Xanthotoxine
(14) A: Impératorine
(15) B: Héraclénine
(16) C: Héraclénol

$R_1 = OH$; $R_2 =$

(17) H: Bergaptol
(18) OH: Dihydroxy-5,8 psoralène

SÉRIE ANGULAIRE

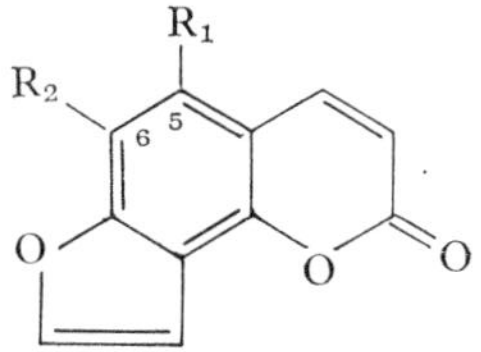

$R_1 = H$; $R_2 =$

(11') H: Angélicine
(12') OH: Hydroxy-6 angélicine
(13') OCH₃: Sphondine

FIGURE 3. Voies biosynthétiques relatives aux furannocoumarines chez les Ombellifères.
Légende: m = méthylation
         i = isoprénylation
         o = oxydation
         ● : produits isolés des Ombellifères
         → : voies biogénétiques utilisées par les *Heracleum*

(ii) A partir du psoralène (11), les mêmes réactions se retrouvent: monohydroxylation soit en 5, soit en 8. Mais ensuite, deux possibilités:

(a) méthylation donnant soit la xanthotoxine (13), soit le bergaptène (19);
(b) isoprénylation conduisant soit à l'impératorine (14) et à ses dérivés, soit à l'isoimpératorine (27) et à ses dérivés.

La seconde hydroxylation peut se faire sur une furannocoumarine monosubstituée soit en 5 soit en 8. La constante présence du bergaptène (19) nous incline à penser que la voie du bergaptol (17) est suivie de préférence à celle du xanthotoxol (12). Le précurseur ainsi formé pourrait conduire:

(a) à l'isopimpinelline (21) par deux méthylations successives;
(b) à la phelloptérine (22) et ses dérivés par méthylation puis isoprénylation (suivie d'oxydation sur la chaine);
(c) à la cnidicine (26) par deux isoprénylations successives;
(d) à la cnidiline (25) par isoprénylation en 5 suivie d'une méthylation en 8.

Ces processus ne sont pas tous démontrés; néanmoins des résultats expérimentaux récents ont apporté des confirmations partielles au schéma proposé. C'est ainsi que Steck *et al.* (1970) viennent de montrer que le xanthotoxol (12) est un précurseur de la xanthotoxine (13) et de l'impératorine (14). Cette expérimentation est d'ailleurs en faveur de l'existence d'intermédiaires hydroxylés comme précurseurs des furannocoumarines.

La Figure 3 est un schéma global de la biosynthèse furannocoumarinique chez les Ombellifères. Cependant toutes ces voies ne sont pas utilisées par le genre *Heracleum*:

(a) En effet l'isoprénylation, qui à partir du bergaptol (17), donne l'isoimpératorine (27) et ses dérivés n'existe pas dans ce genre, alors qu'elle est très fréquente dans les genres *Angelica* et *Peucedanum*.
(b) De même l'isoprénylation en 5 qui conduit à la cnidicine (26) et à la cnidiline (25) est une voie très peu courante dans les *Heracleum*. Ces dérivés, caractéristiques du genre *Cnidium*, ne se rencontrent que chez *Heracleum antasiaticum* Manden. (Buziashvili & Komissarenko, 1967).
(c) Enfin les dérivés d'oxydation de l'impératorine (14): héraclénine (15) et héraclénol (16) n'ont été signalés que dans *H. nepalense* D. Don (Bhar, 1947).

Nous ne tiendrons donc pas compte de ces trois processus qui ne sont pas utilisés par les espèces étudiées ici.

Phylogénie fondée sur la 'micro-évolution'

Dans la Fig. 4, nous avons schématisé les silhouettes des voies biosynthétiques suivies par chacune des espèces (ou groupe d'espèces) étudiées.

(i) *Heracleum sphondylium* et *H. sosnowskyi*, qui composent le groupe I, utilisent le plus grand nombre de voies biosynthétiques.

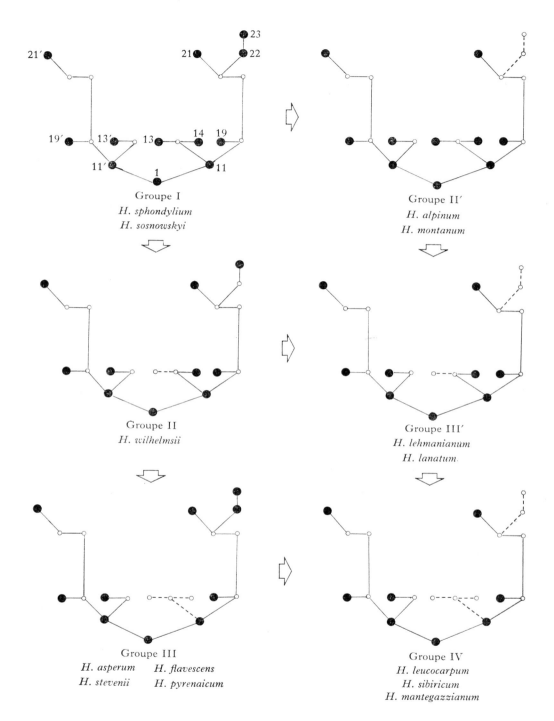

FIGURE 4. Silhouettes des voies biosynthétiques relatives aux furannocoumarines chez les *Heracleum*. Légende: ● Produits isolés dans le groupe concerné; — Voies utilisées par le groupe considéré.

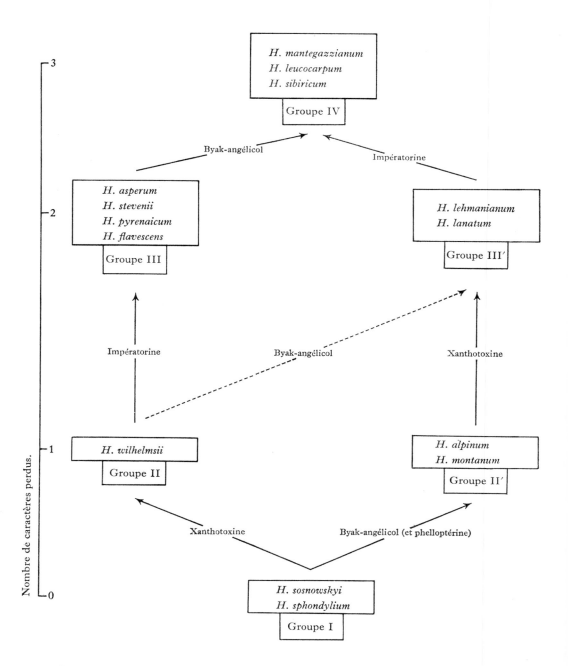

FIGURE 5. Phylogénie de quelques *Heracleum* (micro-évolution). Les espèces d'*Heracleum* sont classées par groupes, en fonction des pertes successives des voies biogénétiques utilisées par le plus primitif: *H. sphondylium*.

(ii) Le groupe II représenté par *H. wilhelmsii* se caractérise par la perte de la xanthotoxine (13).

(iii) Le groupe II′ comprenant *H. alpinum* et *H. montanum*, a perdu un caractère: la voie: phélloptérine-byak-angélicol (22) et (23).

(iv) Le groupe III (*H. asperum, H. stevenii, H. pyrenaicum, H. flavescens*) se signale par la perte de deux voies de synthèse: celle de la xanthotoxine (13) et celle de l'impératorine (14). Ce groupe ne pratique plus de mono-substitution en 8.

(v) Le groupe III′ (*H. lanatum, H. lehmanianum*) a également perdu deux caractères: la xanthotoxine (13) et le byak-angélicol (23).

(vi) Enfin le groupe IV, composé de *H. mantegazzianum, H. leucocarpum, H. sibiricum*, a perdu trois caractères: la xanthotoxine (13), l'impératorine (14) et le byak-angélicol (23). Ce groupe présente en outre la particularité de ne plus effectuer d'isoprénylation. La seule présence de furannocoumarines méthoxylées le rapproche beaucoup du genre *Pimpinella*.

En résumé, la régression progressive des voies de biosynthèse des furanno-coumarines correspond à des phyllums qui partant du groupe I nous mènent aux groupe II et II′; de II à III et III′; de II′ à III′; et de III et III′ à IV. (voir Fig. 5).

Cerceau-Larrival (1962, 1963) a montré que les *Heracleum* possèdent en général un pollen de type ovale. Dans ce type la 'micro-évolution' se traduit par une augmentation progressive de la taille du pollen. C'est ainsi que la distance qui sépare les deux pôles des grains de pollen (P) est de 38·4 μm pour *H. sphondylium* (le plus primitif du genre), de 60 μm pour *H. lehmanianum* et de 64 μm pour *H. mantegaz-zianum*. Il se trouve que cette gradation en niveaux de 'micro-évolution' correspond à celle obtenue par la perte successive des caractères chimiques considérés.

Incidences biogéographiques

La marmésine (6), la columbianétine (6′), le psoralène (11) et l'angélicine (11′) bien qu'intermédiaires indispensables à la synthèse de furannocoumarines plus complexes (voir Figs 1 et 2), sont souvent absents de plusieurs espèces d'*Heracleum* examinées (voir Tableau 1). Leur présence peut donc signifier un certain ralentissement dans les séquences biogénétiques, par analogie avec ce que nous avons montré dans le cas des esters.

Si au sein de chaque groupe, nous distinguons les espèces qui n'accumulent pas de précurseur, nous constatons que ce sont toutes des espèces européennes. (voir Fig. 6).

Nous remarquons enfin sur cette Fig. 6 que les espèces caucasiennes présentent l'éventail le plus complet des différentes étapes de cette micro-évolution. Cette région apparaît donc comme un foyer très important de la diversification des *Heracleum*.

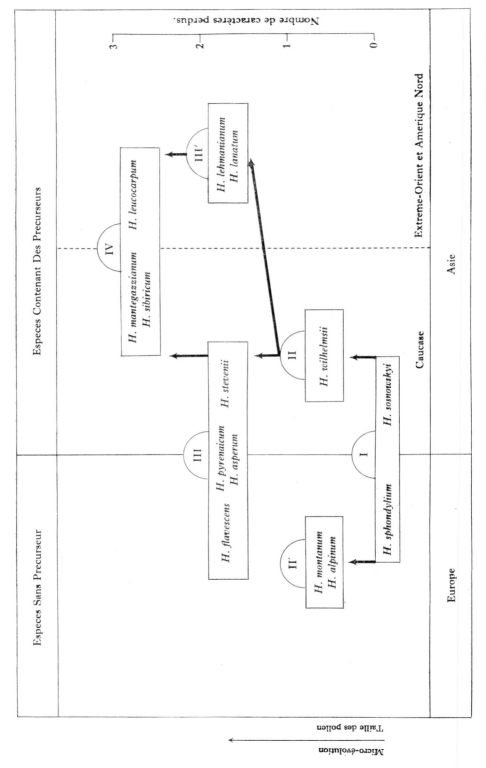

FIGURE 6. Distribution géographique des espèces d'*Heracleum* ayant un pollen de type ovale (micro-évolution) en fonction de l'accumulation des précurseurs de la biosynthèse furannocoumarinique.

CONCLUSIONS

Ces diverses constatations montrent que l'étude des dérivés furannocoumariniques est une voie d'approche pour la compréhension des phénomènes liés à l'évolution. Ce n'est cependant pas un exemple isolé puisque Bate-Smith (1966) a constaté que la présence de leucoanthocyanes est un caractère primitif chez les *Iridaceae* et que la diminution du degré d'hydroxylation, dans la série polyphénolique est un critère d'évolution.

Présentement nous avons pu montrer que l'examen des furannocoumarines peut conduire raisonnablement à la taxonomie des espèces du genre *Heracleum*. Elle peut en outre mettre en évidence des relations phylogéniques en plein accord avec les données palynologiques. C'est ainsi que l'évolution du genre *Heracleum* se traduit par une régression de biosynthèse des dérivés furannocoumariniques.

Néanmoins, pour qu'il soit possible de dresser la phylogénie des divers genres d'Ombellifères, il conviendrait qu'un nombre plus grand d'espèces soit étudié tant au point de vue ontogénique que caryologique, palynologique et chimique.

PARTIE EXPÉRIMENTALE

Matériel végétal

Les difficultés d'identification botanique, les très nombreuses synonymies des espèces du genre *Heracleum* et l'absence d'une monographie botanique de ce genre, nous engagent à noter avec précision l'origine du matériel végétal.

H. alpinum L.
 = *H. juranum* Genty (toutes les Flores)
 sous-espèce de *H. sphondylium* L. (Brummitt, 1968)
 espèce pour Coste (1937) et Mandenova (1950)
 récolté par nos soins au col de la Rochette-Jura, France.

H. ceylanicum Gardn.
 = *H. sprengelianum* Thw. (*Index Kewensis*)
 fruits fournis par l'institut français de Pondichéry.

H. flavescens DC.
 = *H. lecokii* Gren. & Godr. (Bonnier, 1934)
 mis en partie en synonymie avec *H. sibiricum* (Brummitt, 1968)
 sous-espèce de *H. sphondylium* L. (Brummitt, 1968)
 H. sibiricum L. élevé au rang d'espèce par Mandenova (1950)
 H. lecokii Gren. & Godr. élevé au rang d'espèce par Coste (1934)
 récolté par nos soins, en juillet, le Bleymard, le long de la rivière Lot—Cevennes, France.

H. lanatum Michx
 fruits provenant du jardin botanique de Cluj, Roumanie—mis en culture à la station écologique de Brunoy, Muséum National d'Histoire Naturelle, Paris.

H. lehmanianum Bge
 fruits provenant du jardin botanique de Coimbra, Portugal, mis en culture à la station écologique de Brunoy.

H. leucocarpum Aitch.

    = *H. afghanicum* Kitam. (Rechinger, 1963)

    récolté par nos soins sur le versant est du col de Shibar (Shibar kotal), Indou-Kouch, Afghanistan.

H. mantegazzianum Som. & Lev.

    groupe d'*Heracleum* géants subdivisés par Mandenova (1950) en:

    H. mantegazzianum Som. & Lev.

    H. sommieri Manden.

    H. grossheimsii Manden.

    (a) récolté par nos soins au jardin botanique de la Jaysinia-Samoëns, France;

    (b) fruits provenant du Royal Botanic Gardens, Kew;

    (c) fruits fournis par la station écologique de Brunoy.

H. montanum Schleich.

    = *H. panaces* Gren. & Godron en partie (Coste, 1937)

    = *H. dubium* Ten. (Bonnier, 1934)

    = *H. dissectum* Ledeb., *H. setosum* Lapeyr., *H. granatense* Boiss. (Brummitt, 1968)

    sous-espèce de *H. sphondylium* L. (Brummitt, 1968; Coste, 1937)

    élevé au rang d'espèce (Coste, 1937; Mandenova, 1950)

    récolté par nos soins au 'Clos de Sales'-1800m-Alpes savoyardes-environs de Samoëns, France.

H. palmatum Baumg.

    fruits provenant du jardin botanique de Cluj, Roumanie, mis en culture à la station écologique de Brunoy.

H. platytaenium Boiss.

    = *H. eminens* Lange (*Index Kewensis*)

    fruits provenant du jardin botanique de Cluj, Roumanie, mis en culture à la station écologique de Brunoy.

H. pyrenaicum Lam.

    = *H. amplifolium* Lapeyr. (Bonnier, 1934)

    = *H. pollianum* Bertol. (Brummitt, 1968)

    sous-espèce de *H. sphondylium* L. (Brummitt, 1968; Bonnier, 1934)

    élevé au rang d'espèce par Mandenova (1950) et Coste (1937)

    récolté par nos soins aux abords de la station de Jouéou-Bagnères de Luchon-Pyrénées.

H. rigens Wall.

    = *H. sprengelianum* Dalz. & Gibs. (*Index Kewensis*)

    herbier du laboratoire de phanérogamie, Muséum National d'Histoire Naturelle, Paris.

H. sosnowskyi Manden.

    envoi de I. Mandenova. Récolté en Arménie, district de Kalininsky. Caucase, U.R.S.S.

H. sphondylium L.

    récolté par nos soins aux Allamands, 600m d'altitude, environs de Samoëns, France.

H. sprengelianum Wight & Arn.

= *Pastinaca sprengeliana* (*Index Kewensis*)

fourni par l'Institut français de Pondichéry

Récolté en septembre à Palni, Indes, 2100 m d'altitude.

H. stevenii Manden.

fruits provenant du jardin botanique de Cluj, Roumanie, mis en culture à la station écologique de Brunoy.

H. trachyloma Fisch. & Mey.

envoi de I. Mandenova, récolté en Arménie, district d'Idschevan, Caucase, U.R.S.S.

H. wilhelmsii Fisch. & Lallem.

envoi de I. Mandenova, récolté en Georgie Orientale, Caucase, U.R.S.S.

Nos études ont toujours porté sur du matériel frais (récolté moins d'un an avant son étude), excepté *H. rigens* qui provient d'un herbier. Les fruits étudiés sont toujours des fruits mûrs. Les racines ont toujours été prélevées sur des exemplaires fleuris ou en fruits, entre le premier juillet et le 15 août.

Méthodes d'analyse

Le matériel après sèchage à 40° est pulvérisé, puis épuisé au soxhlet durant 48 h., par de l'éther de pétrole. L'extrait brut, après évaporation du solvant, est chromatographié analytiquement au moyen des systèmes suivants:

A: silice G: cyclohexane-acétate d'éthyle 75:25

B: alumine G: benzène

C: alumine G: chloroforme

D: alumine G: éther dibutylique-acétate d'éthyle 88:12

Puis, lorsque les conditions chromatographiques sont définies, on transpose directement, en chromatographie préparative sur couche épaisse non liée, selon une technique décrite en détail par ailleurs (Jössang & Molho 1967). Cette méthode nous permet d'isoler pondéralement les furannocoumarines. Celles-ci sont ultérieurement purifiées soit par une nouvelle chromatographie préparative soit par recristallisation.

Les furannocoumarines sont alors identifiées à la fois par leurs critères physiques: point de fusion, spectres uv (bande caractéristique à 250 nm) et ir, pouvoir rotatoire, *Rf* chromatographique, couleur de fluorescence, et par comparaison avec un échantillon de référence.

La structure de la sprengelianine (7) (tiglate de (±) marmésine) a été définie par des analyses physiques (R.M.N., spectrographie de masse) et des dégradations chimiques (à paraître).

Notons que c'est la première fois qu'il est isolé un tiglate de dihydro-furannocoumarine. Jusqu'à maintenant les substances de ce type isolées des Ombellifères étaient des angélates ou des sénécioates de la (+) marmésine, respectivement deltoïne et prantschimgine. Bien que la (—) marmésine (ou nodakénétine) ait déjà été isolée, il n'a pas été trouvé d'ester correspondant. Il était donc intéressant de signaler l'existence d'un ester du racémique.

A l'exception des deux dihydro-furannocoumarines et du psoralène, toutes les furannocoumarines identifiées ont été isolées. Cependant, lorsque nous ne disposons pas de quantités suffisamment importantes de matériel végétal, nous avons été contraints de caractériser les constituants par chromatographie. C'est le cas *H. rigens, H. trachyloma, H. wilhelmsii, H. ceylanicum,* et *H. mantegazzianum* (de Kew).

Certaines identifications chromatographique sont difficiles dans le cas de substances ayant des R_f voisins dans le système A. (voir Tableau 4).

Tableau 4. Furannocoumarines identifiées dans le genre *Heracleum*

Substances	R_f	f	SO_4H_2	F	S
(±) Marmésine	0·05	bleu-violet	bleu-violet	166°	benzène
Columbianétine	0·15	bleu-violet	bleu ciel	163°	méthanol
Byak-angélicol	0·20	brun		106°	ac. d'éthyle
Sphondine	0·25	bleu ciel	jaune	192°	éthanol
Isopimpinelline	0·32	brun		150°	éthanol
Xanthotoxine	0·35	brun-jaune		145°	méthanol
Psoralène	0·38	bleu livide	beige	162°	eau
Bergaptène	0·40	jaune-vert		190°	méthanol
Sprengelianine	0·40	bleu-violet	bleu-violet	105°	méthanol
Impératorine	0·45	brun-jaune		102°	benzéne
Phelloptérine	0·45	brun		102°	éthanol
Pimpinelline	0·52	brun		118°	éthanol
Angélicine	0·60	bleu livide	beige	139°	éthanol
Columbianadine	0·60	bleu-violet	bleu ciel	119°	ligroine-benzène
Isobergaptène	0·60	jaune-vert		224°	méthanol
Osthol	0·62	bleu-violet	bleu-violet	84°	

R_f: R_f dans le système de solvants A. Nous remarquerons que dans ce système chromatographique, les furannocoumarines angulaires ont des R_f toujours plus élevés que ceux de leur équivalent linéaire.

f: fluorescence en uv.

SO_4H_2: fluorescence en uv après pulvérisation par SO_4H_2 concentré.

F: points de fusion.

S: solvants de recristallisation.

Nous avons résolu ces difficultés de la manière suivante:

L'angélicine: très bonne séparation dans le système B., traces jaunes de décomposition après quelques heures sur la chromatoplaque de silice.

La phelloptérine et l'impératorine: séparation dans le système B. Caractérisation par leur fluorescence en uv courts.*

La xanthotoxine lorsqu'elle coexiste avec l'isopimpinelline: chromatographie bidimensionelle sur couche mince selon Karlsen (1969)—(alumine G. avec respectivement les systèmes de solvants C et D.)

Une pulvérisation de SO_4H_2 concentré modifie la fluorescence sous uv de certaines substances et permet de les identifier. C'est le cas de la columbianadine, de la columbianétine, de l'angélicine et du psoralène. Ces deux derniers produits peuvent être caractérisés par ce traitement: en effet la fluorescence des autres furannocoumarines dont les Rf. interfèrent disparaît dans ces conditions.

* Mineral light ultraviolet lamp—UVSL25—long–short wave. U.V. Product Inc. San Gabriel, California, U.S.A.

La fluorescence de la marmésine, de la sprengelianine et de l'osthol n'est pas modifiée dans ces conditions.

REMERCIEMENTS

Nous tenons à remercier les Professeurs Kuznetsova et Komissarenko qui ont bien voulu nous faire parvenir des échantillons de référence.

Nous avons gré aux autorités afghanes de nous avoir permis certaines récoltes sur leur territoire.

Nous remercions très vivement le Professeur Delamare-Deboutteville, qui a bien voulu autoriser l'utilisation des serres du laboratoire d'écologie du Muséum National d'Histoire Naturelle.

Nous remercions par ailleurs les Professeurs Deferré, et Hamel ainsi que Messieurs Lebrun†, Delerisse et Farille de nous avoir indiqué des stations botaniques.

Enfin que le Professeur Mandenova, Madame Cerceau-Larrival, Messieurs Blasco et Dechavassigne trouvent ici l'expression de notre gratitude pour nous avoir fourni du matériel végétal.

BIBLIOGRAPHIE

BAERHEIM-SVENDSEN, A. & OTTESTAD, E., 1957. Coumarins of the fruits of *Heracleum panaces* and *H. sibiricum. Pharm. Acta. Helv.*, **32**: 457–461.

BAERHEIM-SVENDSEN, A., OTTESTAD, E. & BLYBERG, C., 1959. Coumarins in roots of *Heracleum sibiricum. Planta Med.*, **7**: 113–117.

BATE-SMITH, E. C., 1964. The phenolic constituents of plants and their taxonomic significance. I—Dicotyledons. *J. Linn. Soc. (Bot.)*, **58**: 95–173.

BATE-SMITH, E. C., 1966. The phenolic constituents of plants and their taxonomic significance. II—Monocotyledons. *J. Linn. Soc. (Bot.)*, **60**: 325–356.

BEYRICH, T., 1968. Vergleichende Untersuchung über das Vorkommen an Furocumarinen in einigen Arten der Gattung *Heracleum. Pharmazie*, **23** (6): 325–38.

BHAR, CH., 1947. Crystalline components of seeds of *Heracleum nepalense. Sci. Cult. (Calcutta)*, **12**: 504–505.

BONNIER, G., 1934. *Flore complète de France.* IV: 97–98. Paris: Librairie générale de l'Enseignement.

BROWN, S. A., EL-DAKHAKHNY, M. & STECK, W., 1970. Biosynthesis of linear furanocoumarins. *Can. J. Biochem.*, **48**: 863–871.

BROWN, S. A. & SHYLUK, J. P., 1962. Gas-liquid chromatography of some naturally occurring coumarins. *Analyt. Chem.*, **34**: 1058–1061.

BRUMITT, R. K., 1968. *Heracleum.* In Tutin, T. G. *et al.* (eds), *Flora Europaea* 2: 364–366. Cambridge: University Press.

BUZIASHVILI, I. SH. & KOMISSARENKO, N. F., 1967. Coumarins of the roots of *Heracleum antasiaticum. Khim. Prir. Soedin.*, **3** (1): 56.

CERCEAU-LARRIVAL, M.-TH., 1962. *Plantules et pollen d'Ombellifères. Leur intérêt systématique et phylogènique.* Paris: Muséum National d'Histoire Naturelle.

CERCEAU-LARRIVAL, M.-TH., 1963. Le pollen d'Ombellifères méditerranéennes. II—*Tordylinae* Drude. *Pollen Spores*, **5** (2): 297–323.

CERCEAU-LARRIVAL, M.-TH., 1967. Corrélation de caractères chez les grains de pollen d'Ombellifères. *Rev. paleobot. palynol.*, **4**: 311–324.

COSTE, H., 1937. *Flore de France*, 2: 181–183. Paris: Librairie des Sciences et des Arts.

ENGLER, A. & PRANTL, K., 1898. *Die natürlichen Pflanzenfamilien*, 3 (8): 63–250. Leipzig.

FLOSS, H. G. & MOTHES, U., 1966. Biosynthesis of furanocoumarins in *Pimpinella magna. Phytochemistry*, **5**: 161–169.

FLOSS, H. G. & PAIKERT, H., 1969. Biosynthesis of furanocoumarins in *Pimpinella magna. Phytochemistry*, **8**: 589–596.

FUJITA, M. & FURAYA, T., 1954. Furocoumarins from the roots of *Heracleum lanatum. J. pharm. Soc. Japan*, **74**: 795.

GIORGOBIANI, E. D., KOMISSARENKO, N. F. & KEMERTELIDZE, E. F., 1968. Coumarins of roots of *Heracleum wilhelmsii* and *Heracleum asperum. Khim. Prir. Soedin.*, **4**: (1) 47–48.

GIORGOBIANI, E. D., KOMISSARENKO, N. F. & KEMERTELIDZE, E. F., 1969. Coumarins from the roots of *Heracleum sommieri* and fruits of *H. asperum*. *Khim. Prir. Soedin.*, **5** (1): 53–54.

JÖSSANG, P. T., CARBONNIER, J. & MOLHO, D., 1969. Etude des constituants de l'*Heracleum mantegazzianum* cultivé à 'La Jaysinia'. *Travaux du laboratoire de 'La Jaysinia'*, **3**: 187–195.

JÖSSANG, P. T. & MOLHO, D., 1967. Chromatographie sur couche épaisse non liée des constituants du rhizome de *Piper methysticum* Forst. *J. Chromatog.*, **31**: 375–383.

KARLSEN, J., BOOMSMA, L. E. J. & BAERHEIM-SVENDSEN, A., 1969. Thin-layer chromatography of furanocoumarins. *J. Chromatog.*, **42** (4): 550–551.

KOMISSARENKO, N. E., CHERNOBAI, V. T. & KOLESNIKOV, D. G., 1965. Coumarins in roots of *Heracleum mantegazzianum* and *H. dissectum*. *Tr. Botan. Inst. Akad. Nauk SSSR, Ser. 5: Rast. Syr'e*, **12**: 58–60.

KOMISSARENKO, N. F., ZOZ, I. G., CHERNOBAI, V. T. & KOLESNIKOV, D. G., 1961. Coumarins of cowparsnip fruits and taxonomy. *Biokhimia*, **26**: 980–983.

KREIER, V. G., 1963. Isolation of furocoumarins from *Heracleum sosnowskyi*. *Zh. Prikl. Khim.*, **36** (11): 2517–2522.

KREIER, V. G. & SOKOLOV, V. S., 1965. Furanocoumarins of *Heracleum sosnowskyi*. *Tr. Botan. Inst. Akad. Nauk SSSR, Ser. 5: Rast. Syr'e*, **12**: 61–65.

MANDENOVA, I. P., 1950. Monographie: *Espèces caucasiennes du genre Heracleum*. 103 pp. U.R.S.S.: Acad. Sci. Georgie, Tbilissi.

NAKAZAKI, M., HIROSE, Y. & IKEMATSU, K., 1966. The absolute configuration of athamantin and edultin. *Tetrahedron Letters*, **39**: 4735–4738.

NIELSEN, B. E., 1970. *Coumarins of Umbelliferous plants*. 191 pp. Copenhagen: The Royal Danish School of Pharmacy.

NIKONOV, G. K. & BARANAUSKAITE, D. I., 1964. Coumarins of *Zozimia absinthifolia*. *Zh. Obshch. Khim.*, **34**: 3854.

NIKONOV, G. K. & BARANAUSKAITE, D. I., 1965. Lactones of *Zozimia absinthifolia*. *Khim. Prir. Soedin.*, **1** (3): 220–223.

RECHINGER, K. H. & RIEDL, H., 1963. *Symbolae Afghanicae*. V: KIE, M. & RECHINGER, K. H., Umbelliferae. *Biol. skrift.*, **13** (4).

SPATH, E. & SIMON, A. F. J., 1936. Über die Cumarine der Wurzel von *Heracleum sphondylium* L. *Monat. Chem.*, **67**: 344–351.

STECK, W. & BROWN, S. A., 1970. Biosynthesis of angular furanocoumarins. *Can. J. Biochem.*, **48**: 872–880.

STECK, W., EL-DAKHAKHNY, M. & BROWN, S. A., 1969. The role of marmesin and columbianetin in the biosynthesis of furanocoumarins. *Tetrahedron Letters*, **54**: 4805–4808.

The alkaloids of hemlock (*Conium maculatum* L.)* (or *Conium maculatum* L: The Odd Man Out)

J. W. FAIRBAIRN

The School of Pharmacy, University of London, London, England

Conium maculatum is probably the only member of the Umbelliferae which produces alkaloids. It is also one of the few members which are devoid of vittae in the fruits and sometimes it is associated taxonomically with other species with poorly developed vittae. However, 'pro-vittae' occur in early stages of fruit development and are associated with translocation of alkaloids into the fruit. It is suggested that at an even earlier stage volatile oil is produced in these ducts but that later there is a switch to alkaloid production. Biosynthetic studies present a surprisingly confused picture for such simple alkaloids. The possible route seems to be from acetate to lysine, compound D, γ-coniceine, coniine and N-methylconiine. The alkaloidal pattern shows remarkably rapid changes during the phase of active growth in the developing fruit and it is suggested that the major alkaloids, coniine and γ-coniceine, function in this plant as parts of co-enzymes involved in oxidation-reduction processes.

CONTENTS

INTRODUCTION

The poison hemlock (*Conium maculatum* L.) holds a unique place in history as it is claimed to be responsible for the death of Socrates. The main ingredient of the Athenian State poison was 'Koneion' and from the description of this plant given by Dioscorides (A.D. 100) it could well be *Conium maculatum*. Furthermore, the details given by Plato on the effects of the poison cup on his friend are consistent with the known effects of *Conium* extracts (Tyler, 1942: 44). In these extracts the main alkaloids are coniine (1) and γ-coniceine (2), and recent work (Bowman & Sanghvi, 1963) has confirmed that their action could be responsible for the toxic

(1) Coniine   (2) γ-Coniceine

* Dedicated to Herr Prof. Dr Kurt Mothes on the occasion of his 70th birthday, 3 November, 1970.

effects. It was also shown that γ-coniceine is seven to eight times more toxic than coniine. Our own work showed that the proportions of these two alkaloids varied considerably (see later) no doubt leading to the inconvenient variation in toxicity noted by the Greeks and which later led them to fortify the poison cup with such things as opium. As a wet season favours the production of the more toxic γ-coniceine (Fairbairn & Challen, 1959), Socrates' comparatively rapid death may have resulted from using plants collected during a wet season, if such seasons ever occurred in Greece!

To the botanist *Conium maculatum* also holds a unique place as it is one of the few, if not the only member of the Umbelliferae which produces alkaloids. From this point of view, it is very much an 'odd man out'. Other umbelliferous plants are said to contain coniine; for instance, Clapham, Tutin & Warburg (1962: 524) state that *Aethusa* 'usually contains coniine, and is consequently poisonous' but the chemical evidence for its occurrence here and in certain members of the Araceae (Manske & Holmes, 1950) is not satisfactory. Our own preliminary attempts to detect alkaloids in these plants have been unsuccessful, but obviously we cannot say categorically that they are absent at all stages of growth. The object of this chapter therefore is to consider this unusual member of the family in detail, especially the occurrence and biosynthesis of the alkaloids in relation to their taxonomic position.

TAXONOMIC POSITION

Taxonomists are faced with a very formidable task in attempting to subdivide this comparatively homogeneous family into subgroups and genera, and as far as I can see, have not used the presence of alkaloids as a character in placing *Conium maculatum*. The most popular system (Drude, 1897) places *Conium* in the subfamily Apioideae, tribe Smyrnieae, because of its grooved endosperm, lack of crystals in the pericarp and absence of volatile oil. *Conium* shares its place in this tribe with 28 other genera. Calestani (1905) placed *Conium* in the subfamily Ferulineae, tribe Ligusticeae, and closely associated it with *Anisum* and *Bupleurum*. Cerceau-Larrival (1962) associates it with various groups of species according to leaf-shape, inflorescence, fruit-section, etc., but not on alkaloid content. Although the *Index Kewensis* lists several species under the genus *Conium* most are synonyms and *C. maculatum* is certainly the best known species. Early writers have referred to the variability of this species however and Bentley & Trimen (1880) describe two varieties, the fruits of one of which (the Eastern) have ridges not very crenated. This would correspond to our 'Bowles' variety in which the predominant alkaloid of the fruit is methylconiine (3), whereas the more common variety with crenated

$$\text{N}\!-\!C_3H_7$$
$$|$$
$$CH_3$$

(3) *N*-Methylconiine

ridges on the fruits would correspond to our 'Chelsea' variety whose major alkaloid is coniine (Fairbairn & Challen, 1959).

ANATOMICAL STUDIES

Although the presence of alkaloids is not referred to in the above classification system, there is reference to another chemotaxonomic feature, namely, the presence or absence of vittae and volatile oils in the pericarp. In some of the species associated with *Conium*, vittae are poorly developed, e.g. *Bupleurum*, and in *Conium* itself Clapham, Tutin & Warburg (1962: 510) state that 'vittae are absent'. Tschirch and Oesterlie (1900) also state that vittae are absent but Moll & Janssonius (1923) claim that schizogenous ducts occur abundantly in the ovary though none are present in the mature fruit. Our own studies (Fairbairn & Challen, 1959) showed that fairly numerous schizogenous ducts form in the valleculae of the very young fruit and continue to develop for the first three or four weeks after fertilization; afterwards, they cease further growth into normal vittae and at fruit maturity are considerably compressed tangentially. These observations correspond closely to those of Bentley & Trimen (1880). Piperideines (almost certainly mainly γ-coniceine) were present in these ducts throughout fruit development, reaching a maximum about three weeks after fertilization, then falling off in amount. This period (two to four weeks after fertilization) was also marked by other anatomical and chemical changes. Temporary collenchyma formed in the mesocarp and the inner two layers of the pericarp developed into distinct lignified structure containing alkaloids. At this stage also, the alkaloid content and its fluctuation (see later) was at a maximum.

If vittae are thought of as fully developed schizogenous ducts, it is strictly correct to state that they are absent in *Conium*. However, 'pro-vittae' are present which, at a critical stage in the development of the fruit, are particularly associated with transport of alkaloids or their precursors. These alkaloids seem then to be transferred to the 'coniine' layer and used during further development of the fruit. It may even be possible that in the early stages, the 'pro-vittae' behave like the vittae of other umbelliferous plants and produce volatile oil. To test this out, I recently (1970) steam distilled some young fruits and was able to isolate a small amount of volatile oil, in contrast to none from the more mature fruits. Is it possible, therefore, that in this plant the vittae develop like all other members of the family, but that after fertilization, there is a switch to production or translocation of alkaloids rather than volatile oil?

BIOSYNTHETIC STUDIES

Robinson (1955) suggested that the piperidine ring of the *Conium* alkaloids could be formed in the plant from lysine in the analogous way in which the pyrrolidine ring of the tropane alkaloids is formed from ornithine. Schiedt & Höss (1962) and Cromwell & Roberts (1964) attempted to confirm this theory by feeding radioactive lysine to the plant, but very little incorporation into the alkaloids resulted. Later, Leete (1964) suggested an entirely different route, namely from four acetate units followed by cyclization of the resulting eight carbon polyketide. This would give the carbon framework of the *Conium* alkaloids; at a certain stage nitrogen would be incorporated to give the alkaloids. To test out this theory, he fed sodium acetate $-1\text{-}^{14}C$ to two year old hemlock plants and after eight days harvested the plants and extracted the alkaloids, coniine and conhydrine (4). Systematic degradation of

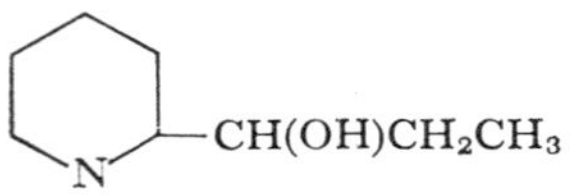

$-\text{CH(OH)CH}_2\text{CH}_3$

(4) Conhydrine

the molecules showed that all the radioactivity was on the even-numbered carbon atoms and was equally divided between the four positions. This is very impressive evidence for the theory that the alkaloids are formed by direct condensation of four acetate units and further confirmation (Leete, 1970) was attempted by feeding eight carbon radioactive compounds to the plant. Quite surprisingly the aliphatic acid, octanoic acid (without keto groups) was incorporated into coniine. He also found, on this occasion that feeding acetate $-2\text{-}^{14}C$ led to coniine *equally* labelled on all its carbons. The acetate pathway clearly needs further detailed study. Conceivably, acetate could be incorporated by a more indirect route via lysine then to the alkaloids. Cromwell & Roberts (1964) suggested two routes from lysine, one involving decarboxylation to cadavarine with subsequent amine oxidation and cyclization. However, they failed to detect diamine oxidase activity in hemlock plants. Furthermore, Dietrich & Martin (1969) were unable to find even traces of cadaverine in the plant, so that this route is probably not used. Cromwell and Roberts did find transaminases, whose presence would be consistent with another route from lysine. The story of the biosynthetic route is further complicated by the recent work of Deitrich & Martin (1969). Young plants were exposed to $^{14}CO_2$ for varying periods of time and the rate of incorporation into the alkaloids studied. The results were consistent with the sequence $CO_2 \rightarrow \gamma$-coniceine $\rightarrow$ coniine $\rightarrow$ *N*-methylconiine, but a new important intermediate prior to γ-coniceine was isolated (and also found in such dissimilar plants as *Sedum sarmentosum* and *Punica granatum* which, however, produce *Conium*-like alkaloids). This compound D was shown to have the following structure:

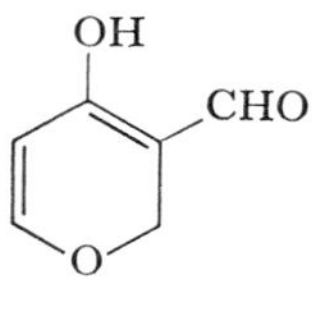

OH

CHO

O

Some ingenuity and much experimental work will be necessary to fill the gaps between acetate, lysine, compound D and γ-coniceine. Koleoso, Dietrich & Martin (1969) refer to an earlier paper by Bickel (1947) on the ease of amination of pyrones with ammonia, and this certainly makes a useful start in postulating the progress from compound D to the alkaloids.

POSSIBLE FUNCTION OF THE ALKALOIDS

As a contribution to the investigation of this problem we decided, some years ago, to study the changes in alkaloidal content during the development of flowers to fruit. This was obviously a metabolically active phase in the life of the plant and as the fruits occurred in numerous compound umbels adequate numbers could be collected for each sample involved. Analysis of samples collected at weekly intervals showed that the two major alkaloids, coniine and γ-coniceine, slowly increased in amount up to the half-ripe stage then gradually decreased as the fruits matured (Fig. 1). This was consistent with results published by other workers, not only in

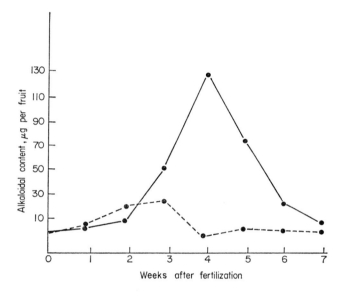

FIGURE 1. Alkaloidal content during development of the fruit: upper curve coniine, lower curve (dotted) γ-coniceine.

Conium but also in other alkaloid-containing plants, and supported one idea that the alkaloids are merely waste products of active metabolism: a sort of slowly accumulating heap of metabolic sludge which later disappeared as the plant matured. However, when samples collected at four and two hourly intervals were examined a very different picture emerged. Figure 2 shows the results on samples collected during a 24-hour period about two weeks after fertilization. From this figure it can be seen that (a) the alkaloidal pattern at this stage showed rapid fluctuation at short intervals, (b) as the coniine content fell the γ-coniceine content rose and vice versa. Since these two alkaloids differ only by two hydrogen atoms a reversible inter-conversion involving oxidation-reduction may be taking place. However, a significant amount of coniine seems to 'disappear' from the fruits without being replaced by a corresponding amount of γ-coniceine. Thus between 10.00 and 12.00 hr the coniine content fell from 175% to 28% of the daily average of 110 mg/fruit; this represented a loss of 162 mg/fruit. During the same period the γ-coniceine content rose from

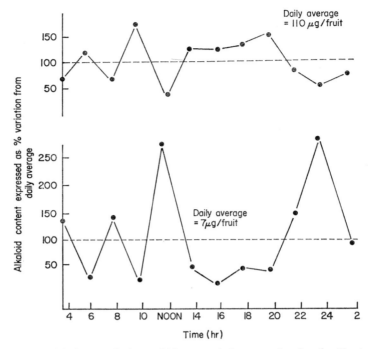

FIGURE 2. Alkaloidal changes during a 24-hour period two weeks after fertilization. Upper curve coniine (average content for 24-hour period = 110 μg/fruit); lower curve γ-coniceine (average content for 24-hour period = 7 μg/fruit).

zero to 280% of the daily average of 7 mg/fruit; this represented an increase of only 19 mg/fruit (Fairbairn & Suwal, 1961).

The use of radioactive isotopes confirmed and extended these conclusions. When radioactive γ-coniceine was fed to the plant it was converted to coniine and ψ-conydrine (5) (Leete & Adityachaudhury, 1967). Similarly, radioactive coniine was

(5) ψ-Conhydrine

converted into γ-coniceine. Furthermore, a series of bound forms of both alkaloids have been detected, so that when radioactive γ-coniceine was fed to the fruits not only did the coniine, but also the bound forms became radioactive (Fairbairn & Ali, 1968a). Our experiments also suggested a re-cycling system so that the 'disappearance' of the coniine, already referred to, could be explained by its temporary conversion to bound forms. Later it would be released to enter the cycle again. These remarkable changes in the alkaloidal pattern occurred mainly in fruits two to three weeks after flower fertilization; at earlier and later stages the fluctuations were much less marked.

Dietrich & Martin's work (1969: 4167) on biosynthesis happens to include alkaloidal analysis of the vegetative parts at short intervals and their results indicate a variation of $+70\%$ to -62% of the day's average for γ-coniceine and $+100\%$ to -50% for coniine. These are significant variations but not so marked as those we found in the developing fruits two to three weeks after fertilization. A more important difference was that they found no evidence for a re-cycling system in the vegetative parts. As we have found repeatedly that the alkaloids are readily translocated from the pedicel to the developing fruits the absence of a re-cycling system in the vegetative parts may be due to the fact that the alkaloids here are in transition rather than in storage (as in the 'coniine layer' of the fruit). Cromwell's work (1956) showed that only small amounts of alkaloid (mainly γ-coniceine) occurred in the roots and leaves during the first year but larger amounts occurred in the second year, when the flowers are formed, and still larger concentrations (mainly as coniine) were found in the developing fruit.

To try and summarize this information I am tempted to give a very tentative picture of the possible role of the alkaloids in this plant. During the vegetative phase small amounts are formed, especially the piperideine γ-coniceine. These are translocated to the flowers and young fruits via the schizogenous ducts which, in their early stages of development, may behave similarly to normal umbelliferous vittae in producing volatile oil compounds. However, as the very young fruits develop, increasing amounts of piperideines are translocated in these ducts and are stored (mainly as the saturated, energy-richer, alkaloid coniine) in the two inner layers of the pericarp, the coniine layers. During active metabolism in the fruit the alkaloids, especially coniine and γ-coniceine are involved in oxidation-reduction processes. We have already suggested (Fairbairn & Ali 1968b) that this may result from the bound forms acting as co-enzymes in a manner analogous to the bound forms of nicotinic acid (NAD, etc.) which also involves a re-cycling system (Gholson, 1966). As the fruit reaches maturity the alkaloids cease to function and decrease considerably in amount.

REFERENCES

BENTLEY, R. & TRIMEN, H., 1880. *Medicinal Plants*, **2**: 259–265. London: J. A. Churchill.

BICKEL, A. F., 1947. On the Structure of Leucaenine from *Leucaena glauca* Benth. *J. Am. chem. Soc.*, **69**: 1801.

BOWMAN, W. C. & SANGHVI, I. S., 1963. Pharmacological actions of Hemlock alkaloids. *J. Pharm. Pharmacol.*, **15**: 1–25.

CALESTANI, V., 1905. *Contributo alla Sistematica delle Ombrellifere d'Europa. Webbia*, **1**: 89–373.

CERCEAU-LARRIVAL, M.-T., 1962. Plantules et Pollens d'Ombellifères. *Mem. Mus. natn. Hist. nat. Paris, Series B*. **14**.

CLAPHAM, A. R., TUTIN, T. G. & WARBURG, E. F., 1962, *Flora of the British Isles*. 2nd ed. Cambridge: Cambridge University Press.

CROMWELL, B. T., 1956. The separation, micro-estimation and distribution of the alkaloids of Hemlock (*Conium maculatum*). *Biochem. J.*, **64**: 259–266.

CROMWELL, B. T. & ROBERTS, M. F., 1964. The Biogenesis of γ-coniceine in Hemlock. *Phytochemistry*, **3**: 369–375.

DIOSCORIDES (A.D. 100). *Greek Herbal*. Gunther, R. (ed.), Oxford: Oxford University Press (1934).

DIETRICHS, S. M. C. & MARTIN, R. O., 1969. The biosynthesis of *Conium* alkaloids using carbon-14 dioxide. *Biochemistry*, **8**: 4163–4172 and 4172–4177.

FAIRBAIRN, J. W. & ALI, A. A. E. R., 1968a. The alkaloids of Hemlock. The presence of bound forms in the plant. *Phytochemistry*, **7**: 1593–1597.

FAIRBAIRN, J. W. & ALI, A. A. E. R., 1968b. Isotopic studies of the bound forms of alkaloids in the plant. *Phytochemistry*, **7**: 1599–1603.

FAIRBAIRN, J. W. & CHALLEN, S. B., 1959. The alkaloids of Hemlock. Distribution in relation to the development of the fruit. *Biochem. J.*, **72**: 556–561.

FAIRBAIRN, J. W. & SUWAL, P. N., 1961. The alkaloids of Hemlock. Evidence for a rapid turnover of the major alkaloids. *Phytochemistry*, **1**: 38–46.

GHOLSON, R. K., 1966. The pyridine nucleotide cycle. *Nature, Lond.*, **212**: 934–935.

KOLEOSO, O. A., DIETRICH, S. M. C. & MARTIN, R. O., 1969. The Biosynthesis of *Conium* alkaloids. Identification of a novel non-nitrogenous base. *Biochemistry*, **8**: 4172–4177.

LEETE, E., 1964. Biosynthesis of the Hemlock alkaloids. The incorporation of Acetate-1-C^{14} into coniine and conhydrine. *J. Am. chem. Soc.*, **86**: 2509–2513.

LEETE, E. & ADITYACHAUDHURY, N., 1967. Biosynthesis of the Hemlock alkaloids—II. The conversion of γ-coniceine to coniine and conhydrine. *Phytochemistry*, **6**: 219–223.

LEETE, E., 1970. Biosynthesis of coniine from octanoic acid in Hemlock plants. *J. Am. chem. Soc.*, **92**: 3835.

MANSKE, R. H. F. & HOLMES, H. L., 1950. *The Alkaloids*. New York & London: Academic Press.

MOLL, J. W. & JANSSONIUS, H. H., 1923. *Botanical Pen Portraits*. The Hague: N. Nijhoff.

ROBINSON, R., 1955. *The structural relations of Natural Products*. Oxford: Clarendon Press.

SCHIEDT, U. & HÖSS, H. G., 1962. The Biosynthesis of Alkaloids III. Lysine as a precursor of Coniine. *Hoppe-Seyler's Z. Physiol. Chem.*, **330**: 74–83.

TSCHIRCH, A. & OESTERLIE, O., 1900. *Anatomischer Atlas der Pharmakognosie und Nahrungsmittelkunde*. Leipzig: Tauchnitz.

TYLER, M. L., 1942. *Homeopathic Drug Pictures*. London: Homeopathic Publishing Co.

Chemosystematics of the Saniculoideae

K. HILLER

Humboldt-Universität zu Berlin, Sektion Chemie, Bereich Pharmazie, 112, Berlin, Germany

Es wurden die noch ungenügend bekannten Inhaltsstoffe der Saniculoideae (Fam. Umbelliferae) untersucht. Hierbei fanden besondere Berücksichtigung die in der Volksmedizin verwendeten Species *Sanicula europaea* L., *Astrantia major* L., *Eryngium campestre* L., *-maritimum* L. und *-planum* L.

Es wurden in Ergänzung zu bisher bekannten Inhaltsstoffen aufgefunden:

1. Aliphatische Säuren
2. Phenolcarbonsäuren
3. Saccharide
4. Saponine.

Zu 1. Die Identifizierung der aliphatischen Säuren ergab in sämtlichen überprüften Species das Vorhandensein von Äpfel-, Malon- und Oxalsäure. Die Isolierung von Malonsäure erfolgte aus den Blättern von *A. major* L. und *S. europaea* L. Darüberhinaus konnte in *A. major* und den Eryngiumarten Glykolsäure aufgefunden werden. Ferner wurde aus den unterirdischen Teilen von *A. major* Angelicasäure isoliert, die auch in den Blüten sowie in Spuren in den Blättern nachweisbar war, dagegen in den Gattungen *Sanicula* und *Eryngium* nicht beobachtet werden konnte.

Zu 2. Die Überprüfung der Phenolcarbonsäuren zeigte das Vorhandensein von Chlorogen- und Rosmarinsäure in sämtlichen bearbeiteten Arten. Ihre Isolierung erfolgte aus den unterirdischen Teilen von *S. europaea*, die den höchsten Gehalt aufweisen. Die bisher nur in Labiaten aufgefundene Rosmarinsäure wurde damit in einigen Vertretern der Umbelliferen nachgewiesen. Somit gilt als sicher, daß ihr Vorkommen nicht auf die Familie der Labiaten beschränkt ist.

Zu 3. In allen überprüften Arten wurde Saccharose nachgewiesen. Ein ungewöhnlich hoher Saccharosegehalt war in den Wurzeln von *S. europaea* (c. 23%) auffallend. Nachgewiesen wurde außerdem in *A. major* das Trisaccharid Umbelliferose (2^G-α-Galaktosylsaccharose), das aus den Früchten isoliert wurde. Die Eryngiumarten enthalten, vermutlich in den Wurzeln, neben Saccharose (1^F-β-Fructosylsaccharose), die damit zum ersten Mal in Vertretern der Familie Umbelliferae nachgewiesen werden konnte.

Zu 4. Die aus *S. europaea* sowie aus *E. campestre*, *-maritimum* und *-planum* isolierten Saponine sind Saponinkomplexe mit unterschiedlich starker hämolytischer Aktivität. Die Saponinkomplexe sind vorwiegend Estergemische. Die Esterstruktur ist stets im Geninanteil lokalisiert und ist verantwortlich für die Hämolyseeigenschaften.

Als Zuckerkomponenten ließen sich beim Saniculasaponingemisch Arabinose und Glucose, beim *E. maritimum* Saponingemisch Arabinose, Xylose und Glucose, beim *E. maritimum* Saponingemisch Arabinose, Xylose und Glucose, beim *E. campestre*-Saponingemisch Arabinose, Rhamnose, Xylose und Glucose, dagegen bei den aus *E. planum* gewonnen Saponingemischen lediglich Glucose nachweisen.

Nach eingehender Überprüfung der sehr komplexen Sapogeningemische aus *Sanicula europaea* L. und *Eryngium planum* L. sowie orientierenden Untersuchungen weiterer Eryngiumarten kann festgestellt werden, daß Estergenine des R_1- und A_1-Barrigenols in dieser Unterfamilie der Umbelliferen vorherrschen. Als dominierende Esterkomponente wurde 3,3-Dimethylacrylsäure festgestellt. Daneben konnten in *Sanicula europaea* L. bisher nur geringe Mengen unveresterter Genine, nämlich Barringtogenol C und 16-Desoxybarringtogenol C, gefunden werden.

Die Estersapogenine können in folgende Gruppen eingeteilt werden: (a) Monoester des A_1-Barrigenols mit ungesättigten C_5-Säuren; (b) Monoester des R_1-Barrigenols mit gesättigten C_5-Säuren; (c) Monoester des R_1-Barrigenols mit ungesättigten C_5-Säuren; (d) Diester des R_1-Barrigenols mit Essigsäure und ungesättigten C_5-Säuren.

Members of the Saniculoideae (Umbelliferae) have been surveyed for aliphatic acids, hydroxycinnamic acids, sugars and saponins. Special attention was devoted to *Sanicula europaea* L., *Astrantia major* L., *Eryngium campestre* L., *E. maritimum* L., and *E. planum* L., all plants used in classic medicine.

The study of the aliphatic acids showed the presence of malic acid, malonic acid and oxalic acid in all species examined. Malonic acid was isolated in crystalline form from the leaves of *A. major* and *S. europaea*. In addition, glycollic acid was found in *A. major* and in the three *Eryngium* species. Moreover, angelic acid was isolated from the roots, petals and leaves (in traces) of *A. major*, but was absent from *Sanicula* and *Eryngium*.

Examination of the hydroxycinnamic acids revealed the presence of chlorogenic acid and rosmarinic acid in all species. They were isolated from the roots of *S. europaea*, which showed the highest content. Rosmarinic acid, which up to now has been found mainly in the Labiatae, is reported in the Umbelliferae for the first time.

Sucrose, detected in all species tested, was present in very high concentration (c. 23%) in the roots of *S. europaea*. The trisaccharide umbelliferose (2^G-α-galactosylsucrose), which has been isolated from fruit of *S. europaea* was also detected in *A. major*. Apart from sucrose the *Eryngium* species also contain, primarily in the roots, 1-kestose (1^F-β-fructosylsucrose), a trisaccharide new to the Umbelliferae.

The saponins isolated from *S. europaea* as well as *E. campestre*, *E. maritimum* and *E. planum* are saponin complexes with haemolytic activity of different intensities. Saponin complexes are predominantly ester mixtures; the ester structure is always localized in the genin component and is responsible for the haemolytic properties.

Arabinose and glucose were found as sugar components in the *Sanicula* saponin mixture; arabinose, xylose, and glucose in *E. maritimum* saponin mixture; arabinose, rhamnose, xylose, and glucose in *E. campestre* saponin mixture; and glucose alone in saponin mixtures extracted from *E. planum*.

A thorough analysis of the saponins from *Sanicula europaea* and *Eryngium planum* L., showed that the ester genins of R_1 and A_1 barrigenol predominate in this subfamily of the Umbelliferae. 3,3-dimethyl acrylic acid was found to be the predominant ester component. In addition, only small quantities of unesterified genins, i.e. barringtogenol C and 16-desoxy-barringtogenol C, are present in *Sanicula europaea*. The ester saponins can be subdivided into the following groups: (a) monoesters of A_1-barrigenol with unsaturated C_5 acids; (b) monoesters of R_1-barrigenol with saturated C_5 acids; (c) monoesters of R_1-barrigenol with unsaturated C_5 acids; (d) diesters of R_1-barrigenol with acetic acid and unsaturated C_5 acids.

CONTENTS

INTRODUCTION

The subfamily Saniculoideae of the *Umbelliferae* is subdivided into the tribe Saniculeae comprising the genera *Actinolema*, *Alepidea*, *Astrantia*, *Eryngium*, *Hacquetia* and *Sanicula*, and the tribe Lagoecieae including the genera *Arctopus*, *Lagoecia* and *Petagnia*. These 9 genera contain a total of 280 species, of which the genus *Eryngium* with its 220 species is the most varied, *Sanicula* coming in second place with 40 species (Engler, 1964). Despite the diversity of Saniculoideae the only native members of this subfamily, found in East Germany (GDR) are *Astrantia major* L., *Eryngium campestre* L., *E. maritimum* L., *E. planum* L. and *Sanicula europaea* L.

S. europaea (Sanicle) is of special interest as a medicinal plant. The above ground parts of this plant have been utilized since ancient times to heal wounds and to treat diseases of the respiratory system (Madaus, 1938). Occasionally the dried above ground parts of *Astrantia major* are used for the same purpose, mostly by mistake.

As to the species of *Eryngium*, it is chiefly the roots of *E. campestre* that are employed in popular medicine. It should be mentioned, however, that no strict separation is made between the three species *E. campestre, maritimum* and *planum*. The indications are much the same for the three plants. They are recommended primarily as diuretics (Madaus, 1938). There are also reports about the underground parts of *E. planum* exerting a soothing effect on whooping cough.

The fact that these plants, especially *S. europaea*, are highly regarded as household remedies prompted us to subject the substances contained in this and closely related plants to a thorough examination.

SUBSTANCES KNOWN TO DATE

Data about the substances contained in these medicinal plants are of a more general nature in those cases where they refer to older literature. Table 1 lists the substances detected so far in these plants.

Table 1. Substances detected to date

Sanicula europaea	Astrantia major	Eryngium campestre	Eryngium maritimum	Eryngium planum
Saponins (Luft, 1926; Boitchinow, 1931; Constantinescu, 1968)	Choline, (Klein, 1932)	Saponins (Kofler, 1927; Klein, 1932; Koczwara, 1949; Boywa & Drayanovska-Noninska, 1961)	Saponins (Luft, 1926)	Saponins (Peyer, 1934; Manta & Weinrich, 1934; Roberg, 1937; Boywa & Drayanovska-Noninska, 1961)
Bitter principles (Thoms, 1929)	Quercetin (Hörhammer et al., 1958)		Kaempferol (Crowden et al., 1969)	
Tannins (Thoms, 1929)	Kaempferol (Hörhammer et al., 1958; Crowden et al., 1969)	Essential oils (Schimmel, 1905)		Tannins (Peyer, 1934)
Ascorbic acid (Kühn & Schäfer, 1939)		Chlorogenic acid (Baerheim-Svendsen, 1951)		Essential oils (Peyer, 1934)
Essential oils (Kroeber, 1948)		Caffeic acid (Baerheim-Svendsen, 1951)		Polyacetylene (Bohlmann et al., 1961)
Caffeic acid (Baerheim-Svendsen, 1951)		Fisetin (?) (Crowden et al., 1969)		Kaempferol (Hörhammer et al., 1958; Crowden et al., 1969)
Quercetin (Crowden et al., 1969)				

INVESTIGATIONS AND RESULTS

Screening of the above-mentioned plants by means of the conventional chromatographic methods led to the results listed in Table 2.

Table 2. Present investigations—screening

Plant	Essential oils	Alkaloid	Aliphatic acids	Phenolcarboxylic acid	Tannins	Flavonoids	Coumarins	Saccharides	Saponins
					Class of Compound				
S. europaea	Tr.*	—	+	+ +	—	—	—	+ +	+ +
A. major	+ +	—	+	+ +	—	+	—	+ +	****
E. campestre	Tr.**	—	+	+	—	+	?	+ +	+
E. maritimum	+	—	+	+	—	+	?	+ +	+
E. planum	Tr.***	—	+	+	—	+	?	+ +	+

Notes:

+ +	Present in substantial quantities.	*	Exception: Flowers = 0·70%
+	Clearly detectable.	**	Exception: Fruit = 0·53%
Tr.	Traces.	***	Exception: Flower = 0·25%
—	Not detectable.		Fruit = 0·42%
?	Identification doubtful.	****	Chiefly non-haemolysing saponins.

Paying special attention to *S. europaea* it was found that the predominant substances were acids—chiefly of the phenolic type—saccharides and saponins. The following investigations discuss, therefore, these three categories of compounds in respect of the species mentioned above. In addition, some other *Eryngium* species were examined.

Acids

Aliphatic carboxylic acids (cf. Hiller et al., 1967).

Introduction. The presence of aliphatic acids in species of the Saniculoideae has not been reported so far, though a large number of such compounds are ubiquitous in the vegetable kingdom (cf. Bonner, 1950; Hegnauer, 1966; Karrer, 1958; Paech, 1950).

Free aconitic, angelic, malic, succinic, fumaric, malonic, oxalic and citric acid were repeatedly detected or even isolated (Baerheim-Svendsen, 1953) in umbelliferous plants, most of which are also found in other plant families. Unbound angelic acid, however, has been observed so far only in a few genera, among others in *Angelica* and *Laserpitium* species (cf. Deryng & Parczewski, 1963; Hata & Kozawa, 1961; Hegnauer, 1966; Nielsen & Kofod, 1963).

Apart from the compounds resulting from the basic metabolism of the plants, such as citric and malic acid, those substances which are present only in certain genera or even families of plants or which are found in a quantity sharply differing from that in other plants were the centre of interest in the following investigations.

Results and discussion. Table 3 indicates the occurrence of the acids in the different organs of the species examined. No differences were observed between fresh and dried plant material.

Malic, citric, malonic and oxalic acid, the latter existing as calcium oxalate (microscopic investigation; presence in the ether extract), were detected in all of the plants. It must be emphasized, however, that the acids mentioned are not found in every organ. To give an example, malic acid was not observed in the fruits of the *Eryngium* species examined. On the other hand, it was found to exist in substantial quantities in the fruits of *S. europaea*. As to *E. maritimum*, malic and citric acid are present only in the roots, citric acid being detectable only in traces.

Table 3. Aliphatic carboxylic acids detected to date

Plant or plant organ		Angelic acid	Malic acid	Citric acid	Glycolic acid	Malonic acid	Oxalic acid
S. europaea	Root	—	+	+	—	Tr.	+
	Rhizome	—	+	+	—	Tr.	+
	Leaf	—	+ +	+	—	+ +	+
	Flower	—	+	+	—	+	+
	Fruit	—	+ +	+	—	+	+
A. major	Root	+ +	+	+	—	Tr.	+
	Rhizome	+ +	+	+	Tr.	Tr.	+
	Leaf	Tr.	+ +	+	—	+ +	+
	Flower	+	+ +	+	+	+	+
	Fruit	—	+	+	—	+	+
E. campestre	Root	—	+	+	+	Tr.	+
	Leaf	—	+	Tr.	+	+	+
	Flower	—	+	Tr.	+	+	+
	Fruit	—	—	—	—	—	Tr.
E. maritimum	Root	—	+ +	Tr.	+	+	+
	Leaf	—	Tr.	—	+	Tr.	+
	Flower	—	Tr.	—	—	Tr.	+
	Fruit	—	—	—	Tr.	—	Tr.
E. planum	Root	—	+	+	+	—	+
	Leaf	—	+	Tr.	+	+ +	+
	Flower	—	+ +	+	Tr.	+ +	+
	Fruit	—	—	—	—	—	Tr.

Notes:
— Negative.   Tr. Traces.   + Low quantities.   + + Substantial quantities.

All of the plants investigated contain malonic acid, except for the fruits of the *Eryngium* species and the roots of *E. planum*, where this compound was not detected. This confirms the view held by Lesaint *et al.* (1962) that malonic acid is widespread in the plant kingdom and the observation made by Bentley (1952) according to which malonic acid frequently occurs in the mature leaves of leguminous and umbelliferous plants.

In the plant's metabolism the malonic acid obviously assumes the role of a competitive inhibitor of the dehydrogenase of succinic acid (cf. Bentley, 1952; Bonner, 1950; Korte & Behner, 1956). After it has been established that malonate can be assimilated and processed by the plant by transforming it into acetyl-CoA with the aid of the co-enzyme A, it has also been possible to confirm the relation of this compound with the tricarboxylic acid cycle (Kretowitsch, 1965).

The formation of malonic acid may also be obtained through oxidation of oxalacetic acid and through the degradation of quinic acid (Wolf, 1960). It is necessary to conduct further experiments before one can demonstrate whether there is a correlation between the relatively high level of chlorogenic acid (Hiller & Kothe, 1967) and the high malonic acid content of the leaves of *A. major* and *S. europaea*.

Whereas the presence of malic and citric acid is not unusual because of their function as energy-supplying intermediate products in the oxidative degradation of D-glucaric and fatty acid, malonic acid also not being unusual, it was rather surprising to detect glycolic acid in nearly every organ of the *Eryngium* species examined as well as in the flowers of *A. major*. Opinions about its biosynthesis vary (cf. Reinbothe, 1958), but the oxidation of acetic acid to glycolic acid seems to be very probable (cf. Kretowitsch, 1965). It must also be considered possible that it is formed during the oxidative degradation of sugar. An oligosaccharide which we isolated from *Eryngium* species and which represents a fructoside not occurring in *S. europaea* might be of interest here.

Oxalic acid was discovered in all the plants investigated. It is evidently present only as calcium oxalate. Owing to its low energy content it is very likely to represent the final link of a metabolic process of degradation, of which sugar or other carboxylic acids might be the starting material (cf. Paech, 1950). Attention should be paid in the first line to the formation of acetic acid via glycolic and glyoxylic acid.

The presence of angelic acid in *A. major* is also noteworthy. It was the first time that this compound was discovered in a species of the Saniculoideae and thus in another genus of umbelliferous plants. The acid was isolated from underground parts of *A. major*.

Beside the acids described above we observed an acid which it was not possible to identify with conventional methods, in the root extracts of *E. campestre* and leaves of *E. planum*.

Phenol carboxylic acids

Introduction. The number of plants where phenol carboxylic acids were detected or even occasionally isolated has considerably increased over the past few years, so that these compounds must be considered today as belonging to the ubiquitous vegetable substances (cf. among others Harborne, 1966; Herrmann, 1958; Hiller, 1965). The most widely spread arrangement of the hydroxy groups in the aromatic nucleus, both free and esterified, is the 3,4-dihydroxy grouping as found among others in the caffeic and ferulic acids. The phenyl ring may however be non-substituted (e.g. in cinnamic acid) or bear only a single hydroxy group the orientation of which is *para* (e.g. *p*-coumaric acid).

In the plants of the Saniculoideae it was established by means of a paper chromatography test on old herbarium samples that caffeic acid is the probable representative of this class of compound in the foliage of *S. europaea*, and caffeic and chlorogenic acid those in the roots and foliage of *E. campestre* (Baerheim-Svendsen, 1951).

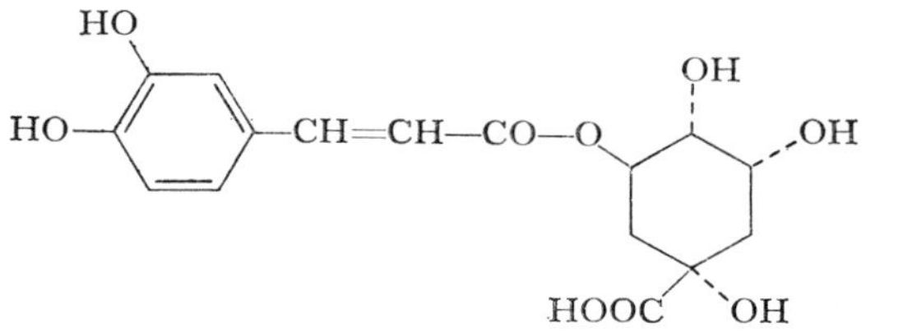

Chlorogenic acid

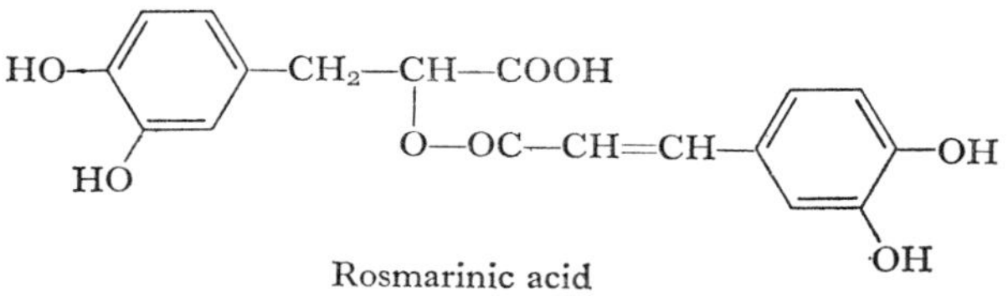

Rosmarinic acid

FIGURE 1

Investigations and results. When examining the methanolic extracts of *S. europaea*, *A. major*, *E. campestre*, *maritimum* and *planum* it was possible to detect chlorogenic and rosmarinic acid in every organ. On the other hand, in none of the plants examined was caffeic acid observed. The two acids were isolated from leaves and underground parts of *S. europaea* (Hiller, 1965) (Fig. 1).

Table 4. Content of chlorogenic and rosmarinic acid

Plant		Plant organ/content in %				
		Rhizome	Root	Leaf	Flower	Fruit
S. europaea L.	1	2·30	1·40	1·70	3·10	1·10
	2	1·20	0·80	0·60	0·95	1·05
A. major L.	1	0·57	0·40	0·41	1·06	0·48
	2	0·90	0·37	0·50	1·10	0·65
E. amethystinum L.	1		0·15	0·60*	0·25	(+)
	2		0·08	1·10*	0·27	(+)
E. bourgatii Gouan	1		0·21	0·66*	0·22	(+)
	2		0·07	0·56*	0·16	(+)
E. bromeliifolium Delar.	1		0·38	0·93	0·37	(+)
	2		0·20	0·39	0·28	(+)
E. campestre L.	1		0·32	0·12	0·17	(+)
	2		0·07	(—)	0·16	(+)
E. dichotomum.	1		0·05	0·32*	(+)	(+)
	2		(+)	(+)	(+)	(+)
E. giganteum M.B.	1		0·08	(+)	(+)	(+)
	2		(+)	(+)	(+)	(+)
E. maritimum L.	1		0·30	(—)	0·85	0·35
	2		0·17	0·21	0·23	0·20
E. planum L.	1		0·08	(+)	(+)	(+)
	2		(+)	(+)	(+)	(+)

Note:

All the material, except for the flowers, was collected in autumn.

1 = Rosmarinic acid.   2 = Chlorogenic acid.

(+) = Occurrence proven. Content less than 0·05%.

* = This figure refers to the young, basal autumn leaves. The older leaves on the stems contained only traces of these compounds.

Chlorogenic and rosmarinic acid were likewise detected in other species of the *Eryngium* genus (*E. amethystinum* L., *bourgatii* Gouan, *bromeliifolium* Delar., *dichotomum* L., *giganteum* M.B.). Quantitative analysis of the two phenol carboxylic acids by means of spectrophotometry yielded the results listed in Table 4 (Hiller & Kothe, 1967).

Discussion of the results. While caffeic and chlorogenic acid are widespread in the plant kingdom, rosmarinic acid has been isolated so far only from labiates. After Scarpati & Oriente (1958) isolated this depside from *Rosmarinus officinalis* L. and elucidated its structure, Herrmann (1960) supposed that it might also be present in *Melissa officinalis* L., *Salvia officinalis* L. and *Mentha piperita* L. The author suggests that the general designation 'labiatic acid' should be adopted as soon as its identity has been proven. The isolation of rosmarinic acid from *S. europaea* and the proof that the compound is found in other species of the Saniculoideae demonstrates that it is not limited to the Labiatae.

As rosmarinic and caffeic acid are hardly distinguishable in many of the development systems employed in paper chromatography, the possibility cannot be excluded that the presence of rosmarinic acid has often been mistaken for caffeic acid. The caffeic acid attributed by Baerheim-Svendsen (1951) to *S. europaea* may well be due to the age of the material used, so that it seems to be, rather, the product of a process of degradation. Since the author has not been able to discover chlorogenic acid, it is probable that the substance concerned is a product of degradation, all the more so as the detection of the α-hydroxyhydrocaffeic acid as the second product of the degradation of rosmarinic acid is more difficult because of its much weaker fluorescence.

Although all the plants investigated contained both chlorogenic and rosmarinic acid, the quantitative distribution within the species and within the organs varies to a considerable extent. *S. europaea* L. stands out in having the highest content of phenolcarboxylic acid. The two substances are also found in a relatively high amount in the *Astrantia major* which is closely related to *S. europaea*. On the other hand, the *Eryngium* species, which are taxonomically much further removed, showed a much lower concentration of chlorogenic and rosmarinic acid, sometimes only traces of them (cf. Table 4).

The rosmarinic acid content of *S. europaea*, e.g. 2·3% in the rhizome, is remarkable considering that Scarpati & Oriente (1958) found only 0·02 to 0·03% in a fresh sample of *Rosmarinus officinalis*, although this was during the preliminary examination.

Saccharides

Introduction. No exact data are available about the presence of saccharides in plants of the subfamily Saniculoideae, although saccharides must be expected because of the basic metabolism of the plant, especially in the storage organs, and have been clearly shown to exist during preliminary examinations (see Table 2).

Investigations and results. When we investigated the presence of saccharides in the Saniculoideae, firstly in *S. europaea*, we only succeeded in detecting sucrose as well as traces of fructose and glucose. The subsequent quantitative analysis, however, showed an unusually high sucrose content, attaining as much as 23.1% in the roots, which was even higher than the average figure for sugar beets (15 to 20%) (cf. Table 5). As is known, sucrose is a dominant factor because of its role as the plant's reserve substance. It obviously assumes this role in *S. europaea*, where it represents a final product in the biosynthetic pathway of the saccharides. In numerous plants it also provides the starting material for the formation of higher oligosaccharides. Unlike *S. europaea* we observed a higher sugar level in addition to relatively high quantities of sucrose in *A. major* and in the *Eryngium* species (see Table 5). The so-called *Astrantia* oligosaccharide obtained from the fruits of *A. major* turned out to be a trisaccharide during hydrolysis, the substance containing a mole of fructose, a mole of galactose and a mole of glucose. By means of a paper chromatographic comparison with authentic saccharides containing galactose, partial hydrolysis and periodate oxidation, the isolated trisaccharide was identified as umbelliferose [O-α-D-galacto-pyranosyl $(1 \rightarrow 2)$-O-α-D-gluco-pyranosyl-$(1 \rightarrow 2)$-O-β-D-fructo-furanoside] (Hiller & Kothe, 1969) (Fig. 2).

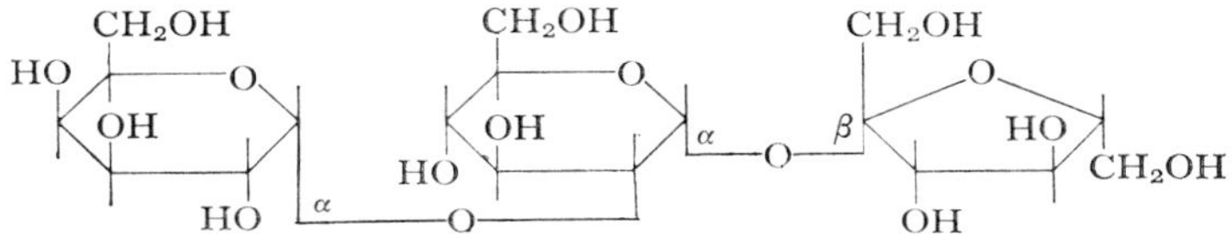

Umbelliferose

FIGURE 2

Umbelliferose has been obtained so far by Baerheim-Svendsen (1953, 1956) from some umbelliferous genera. Now that it has been discovered in *A. major*, proof has been furnished that it is also present in the subfamily Saniculoideae.

As far as we can judge at present it is probable that the presence of oligosaccharides containing galactose and differing from the obviously most usual $1 \rightarrow 6$ linkage of the galactose to the glucose half of the saccharose (the so-called raffinose family, Täufel, Täufel & Ruttloff, 1962), is limited to a few genera.

The composition of the saccharides in the *Eryngium* species examined was characterized by the fact that apart from a high amount of sucrose there were two oligosaccharides provisionally called *Eryngium* oligosaccharides A and B. Of these two it was possible to isolate the quantitatively prevalent saccharide, *Eryngium* oligosaccharide A, and to define it as glucodifructoside by means of a quantitative analysis of the monosaccharide components (Hiller, 1969a).

A paper chromatographic comparison with corresponding authentic trisaccharides, periodate oxidation, partial fermentative and acid hydrolysis as well as the mixed melting point permitted the identification of the *Eryngium* oligosaccharide A as 1-kestose [O-α-D-gluco-pyranosyl-$(1 \rightarrow 2)$-O-β-D-fructo-furanosyl$(1 \rightarrow 2)$-O-β-D-fructo-furanoside] (Fig. 3).

It was also possible to detect 1-kestose by means of a paper chromatographic test in the roots of *E. amethystinum* L., *bourgatii* Gouan, *bromeliifolium* Delar. and *giganteum* M.B.

Bacon & Bell (1953) were the first to obtain 1-kestose by allowing 'takadiastase' to react on sucrose, and the first to elucidate its structure. In the plant also the saccharide is formed by way of fermentation, i.e. by transfructosidation on carbon atom 1 of the fructose half of the sucrose (cf. Allen & Bacon, 1956; Feingold

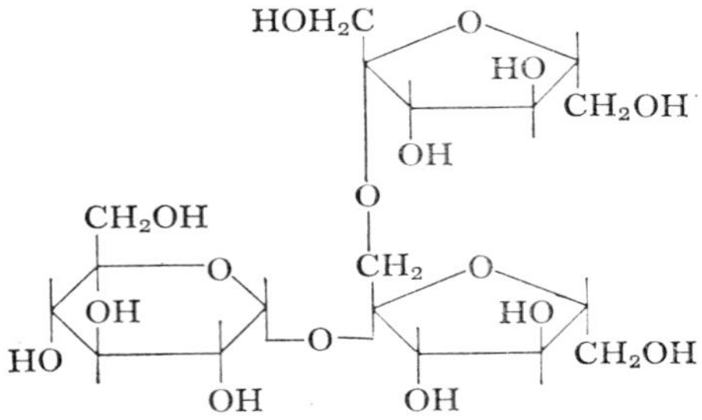

HOH_2C ... HO ... CH_2OH ... OH ... O ... CH_2OH ... O ... OH ... HO ... CH_2 ... O ... HO ... O ... CH_2OH ... OH ... OH

1-Kestose (Isokestose)

FIGURE 3

et al., 1956; Schlubach & Koehn, 1958). The compound, which is sometimes known as isokestose, has been found meanwhile in higher plants as well. The isolation of 1-kestose from *Eryngium* species signifies that this trisaccharide was observed for the first time in an umbelliferous genus.

Table 5. Saccharides detected and their quantitative analysis

Plant and part		Sugar in %					
		Fructose	Glucose	Sucrose	*Astrantia* oligosaccharide	*Eryngium* oligosaccharide	
						A	B
S. europaea	rhizome	—	—	13·9	—	—	—
	root	—	—	23·1	—	—	—
	leaf	+	+	12·8	—	—	—
	flower	+	+	6·0	—	—	—
	fruit	—	—	5·2	—	—	—
A. major	rhizome	—	—	7·8	—	—	—
	root	—	—	11·8	—	—	—
	leaf	+	+	7·8	—	—	—
	flower	+	+	3·3	—	—	—
	fruit	—	—	2·4	3·2	—	—
E. campestre	root	0·48	0·32	8·88	—	5·56	+
	leaf	0·12	0·16	0·90	—	+	—
	flower	0·38	0·48	2·26	—	+	—
	fruit	+	0·12	0·92	—	+	—
E. maritimum	root	1·0	0·73	14·0	—	14·8	+
	leaf	0·46	1·2	1·5	—	+	—
	flower	3·16	8·7	3·7	—	+	—
	fruit	0·73	2·06	0·56	—	+	—
E. planum	root	2·46	1·73	12·26	—	14·33	+
	leaf	0·04	0·38	1·08	—	+	—
	flower	3·50	3·20	2·8	—	0·65	—
	fruit	0·12	0·78	+	—	+	—

Note:
+ = Compound detected, but quantity not determined because of low content.
— = Compound not detectable.
    Astrantia oligosaccharide (=umbelliferose).
    Eryngium oligosaccharide (=1-kestose).

As regards the presence of saccharides, there are considerable differences between the genera *Sanicula*, *Astrantia* and *Eryngium*, despite their close relationship within the taxonomic system. The differences observed in the biogenesis of oligosaccharides suggest that there are different enzymatic systems.

Saponins

Introduction. Saponins, it is known, are glycosidic vegetable substances that develop soap-like foam when they enter into contact with water, which in fact earned them their name (*sapo* = soap, Lat.). Beside their surface activity it is their toxicity with regard to fishes and their haemolytic activity that characterize these compounds. Substances found in nature are assigned to the class of the saponins when they present these properties, although one or other of these characteristic features may be absent in some cases (cf. Hiller *et al.*, 1966).

Investigations and results. The first part of the investigation was devoted to the determination of the haemolytic index (h.i.) of the different plant organs of *Sanicula europaea*, *Astrantia major*, *Eryngium campestre*, *maritimum* and *planum* on the basis of methods specially elaborated for this purpose (Hiller & Linzer, 1966). It could be shown that the plants (see Table 6) present saponins at least in some of their organs. The least haemolytic activity was observed in certain parts of *A. major*, whereas the highest values were recorded for *S. europaea*. In the latter case only the fruits had a weak haemolytic effect.

Table 6. Haemolytic behaviour of plants of Saniculoideae

Plant	Haemolytic index				
	Rhizome	Root	Leaf	Flower	Fruit
S. europaea L.	862	417	417	719	125
A. major L.	208	154	(—)	86	(—)
E. planum L.		500	588	120	(—)
E. campestre L.		173	(—)	50	(—)
E. maritimum L.		125	173	500	154
E. giganteum M.B.		145	1150	100	50
E. amethystinum L.		100	333*	50	50
E. dichotomum L.		72	475*	(—)	(—)
E. bourgatii Gouan		(—)	(—)	(—)	(—)
E. bromeliifolium Delar.		(—)	(—)	(—)	(—)

Notes:

(—) = h.i. < 25.

* = These figures refer to young basal leaves collected in autumn. The older leaves on the shoot showed a much lower haemolytic activity (h.i. between 50 and 60).

An additional investigation of some cultivated *Eryngium* species not found in the native German flora showed that in two plants there was no pronounced haemolysis in any organ (see Table 6). We must conclude from this that saponins are not present in all plants of a genus, but the possibility cannot however be excluded that non-haemolysing saponins exist. The highest saponin content was recorded in the leaves of the spring-time drug of *S. europaea* (c. 13·5%) (Hiller & Linzer, 1967). Following the isolation of saponin complexes from the four haemolytically active, closely related plants *Sanicula europaea, Eryngium campestre, maritimum* and *planum* we succeeded, as far as the main components were concerned, in splitting these four mixtures up into spots of the same R_f value (see Table 7), but of different intensity.

Table 7. The distribution of the saponins

Plant	R_f values			Quantitative inter-relation of the saponins
S. europaea				
(root)	0·26	0·37	—	(10 to 20)
(leaf)	0·26	0·37	—	(20 to 10)
E. campestre	0·26	0·37	0·45	(20 to 1 to 10)
E. maritimum	0·26	0·37	0·43	(15 to 0·5 to 1)
E. planum	0·26	0·37	—	(1 to 20)

After an acid hydrolysis of the saponin complexes we were able to detect the following monosaccharides: glucose in the *E. planum* saponin, arabinose and glucose in the *Sanicula* saponin, arabinose, xylose and glucose in the *E. maritimum* saponin, and arabinose, rhamnose, xylose and glucose in the *E. campestre* saponin (see Table 8). It thus turned out that it was an error to predict the identity of the different saponin complexes.

Table 8. Sugar components of the saponins

S. europaea	glucose, arabinose
E. campestre	glucose, arabinose, rhamnose, xylose
E. maritimum	glucose, arabinose, xylose
E. planum	glucose

The investigations of the saponin portion led to a splitting into ten components in the case of the *Sanicula* sapogenin mixture. The multitude of the sapogenins proves that the splitting of the saponin mixture is not yet identical with the separation into the individual saponins.

Six of the *Sanicula* sapogenins (A, B, C, D, E and F) and four of the sapogenins from *E. planum* (*Eryngium* sapogenins A, B, C and D) were isolated and their structure was partly cleared up by means of dc and gc techniques as well as ir, nmr and mass spectroscopy (Hiller, 1968, 1969b, 1970).

Sanicula sapogenin C was identified as 16-desoxy-barringtogenol C and *Sanicula* sapogenin D as barringtogenol C (cf. Hiller, 1969b) (see Fig. 4). So far the 16-desoxy-barringtogenol C has been detected only in the Japanese horse-chestnut, *Aesculus turbinata* Blume (Yosioka, 1967). In most cases, however, they are ester sapogenins. The ester structure is the decisive factor determining the haemolytic properties of the saponins. (cf. Segal *et al.*, 1966; Schlösser & Wulff, 1969). The principal sapogenin from *S. europaea*, saniculagenin A, was defined as a diester mixture of the $3\beta.15\alpha.16\alpha.21\beta.22\alpha.28$-hexahydroxy Δ^{12}-oleanene ($=R_1$-barrigenol). It is an ester sapogenin mixture, in which the 3,3-dimethyl-acrylic acid was observed for the first time as an ester component of a sapogenin. The 3,3-dimethyl-acrylic acid is partly replaced by angelic and tiglic acid. The proportion between the 3,3-dimethyl-acrylic acid, the angelic acid and the tiglic acid is 7·5 : 2·0 : 0·5. The same sapogenin complex was also isolated from *E. planum* (= *Eryngium* sapogenin D), in this case however the proportion between the three ester components 3,3-dimethyl-acrylic acid, angelic acid and tiglic acid being 3·5 : 4 : 2.

The *Sanicula* sapogenins B, E and F as well as the *Eryngium* sapogenin C were also identified as ester mixtures of the R_1-barrigenol. *Sanicula* sapogenin F is a monoester mixture of the R_1-barrigenol with a saturated C_5 acid, α-methyl-butyric acid, as the dominant ester component. By isolating the *Eryngium* sapogenin A we were the first to isolate an ester of the A_1-barrigenol (3β.15α.16α.22α.28-penta-hydroxy Δ^{12}-oleanene). This compound is found in traces also in *S. europaea*. Although it is not possible to clearly define the position of the ester acids, it is very

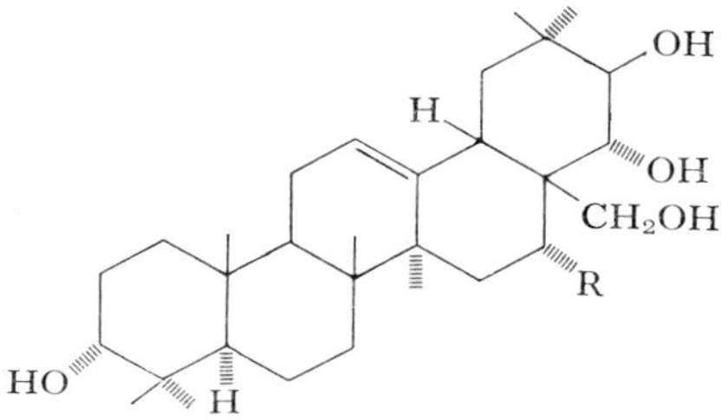

Barringtogenol C: R = OH
16-Desoxybarringtogenol C: R = H

FIGURE 4

probable that they must be regarded as a 22α substituent. The *Eryngium* sapogenin A is a monoester mixture of the A_1-barrigenol which contains 3,3-dimethyl acrylic acid, angelic acid, tiglic acid and small amounts of iso-valeric acid in the proportion of 4·9 : 3·7 to 0·9 : 0·4. *Eryngium* sapogenin B is likewise an ester mixture of the A_1-barrigenol, the ester components of which could not be identified unequivocally (cf. Table 9).

Our examinations revealed that, unlike the *Sanicula* and *Eryngium* saponins described above, the saponin from *A. major* (see Table 2) is predominantly a non-haemolysing saponin mixture without an ester structure.

Ester saponins or sapogenins with organic acids are only seldom found in nature (cf. Woitke *et al.*, 1970). Their presence, as described up to now, is limited to plant families not related to umbelliferous plants in the system.

Except for some older reports that deal exclusively with *S. europaea* and *Eryngium* species, reports on the occurrence of saponins in the Umbelliferae family, even of a more recent date, are very rare. These are practically restricted to the asiaticoside from *Centella asiatica* L. (Boiteau *et al.*, 1964) and to the saponins or their sapogenins, namely the saikogenins A, B, C, D and E isolated from *Bupleurum falcatum* L. (Shibata *et al.*, 1965; Kubota *et al.*, 1966). Serova (1961) reports the isolation of a saponin from *Eryngium incognitum*, a shrub found in the Kurdai mountains (Kazakhistan). Oleanolic acid has been named as the sapogenin. As the

Table 9. Main components of the ester sapogenin complexes
of Saniculoideae species

No.	R^1	R^2	Sapogenin complex
I	H	CO—C—CH$_3$ ‖ H C—CH$_3$	
II	H	CO—C—CH$_3$ ‖ H$_3$C—C—H	Eryngiumgenin A
III	H	CO—CH=C⟨CH$_3$ / CH$_3$⟩	
IV	H	CO—C$_4$H$_9$ or CO—C$_4$H$_7$	Eryngiumgenin B
V	OH	CO—C—CH$_3$ ‖ H C—CH$_3$	
VI	OH	CO—C—CH$_3$ ‖ H$_3$C—CH	Eryngiumgenin C
VII	OH	CO—CH=C⟨CH$_3$ / CH$_3$⟩	
VIII	OH	CO—C$_4$H$_9$	
IX	COOCH$_3$	CO—C—CH$_3$ ‖ H—C—CH$_3$	
X	COOCH$_3$	CO—C—CH$_3$ ‖ H$_3$C—CH	Eryngiumgenin D Saniculagenin A
XI	COOCH$_3$	CO—CH=C⟨CH$_3$ / CH$_3$⟩	

sapogenin spectrum is identical for all the *Eryngium* species examined (*E. campestre*, *maritimum* and *planum*), it is rather surprising to learn that oleanolic acid is present in *Eryngium incognitum*.

The structures now described of the *Sanicula* and *Eryngium* sapogenins differ greatly in structure from those found so far in umbelliferous plants.

As regards the complexity of the *Sanicula* and *Eryngium* saponins or sapogenins, including their ester structure, there are certain structural similarities with the saponin complex aescine (Wulff & Tschesche, 1969) obtained from *Aesculus hippocastanum* L. (Hippocastanaceae) as well as with the theasapogenols (Tschesche, Weber & Wulff, 1969) obtained from *Thea sinensis* L. (Theaceae).

REFERENCES

ALLEN, P. J. & BACON, J. S. D., 1956. Oligosaccharides formed from Sucrose by Fructose-transferring Enzymes of Higher Plants. *Biochem. J.*, **63**: 200–206.

BACON, J. S. D. & BELL, D. J., 1953. A New Trisaccharide produced from Sucrose by Mould Invertase. *J. chem. Soc.*, 2528–2530.

BAERHEIM-SVENDSEN, A., 1951. Über das Vorkommen der Chlorogen- und Kaffeesäure in der Pflanzenfamilie der Umbelliferen. *Pharmac. Acta Helvetiae*, **26**: 253–256.

BAERHEIM-SVENDSEN, A., 1953. *Thesis: Zur Chemie Norwegischer Umbelliferen*, Oslo.

BAERHEIM-SVENDSEN, A., 1956. La Structure d'un Isomère du Raffinose Isolé des Racines de l'*Angelica archangelica* L. subsp. *norvegica*. *Acta chem. scand.*, **10**: 1500–1501.

BENTLEY, L. E., 1952. Occurrence of Malonic Acid in Plants. *Nature, Lond.*, **170**: 847–848.

BOITEAU, P., PASICH, B. & RATSIMANANGA, A. R., 1964. *Les Triterpénoides en physiologie végétale et animale*. Paris: Gauthier-Villars.

BOITCHINOW, A., 1931. *Thesis*, Vienna.

BOHLMANN, F., BOINOWSKI, H. & KLEINE, K. M., 1961. Über Polyine aus der Familie der Umbelliferen. *Chem. Ber.*, **94**: 958–967.

BONNER, J., 1950. *Plant Biochemistry*, New York & London: Academic Press.

BOYWA, A. & DRAYANOVSKA-NONINSKA, L., 1961. Saponin content of some indigenous plants. *Pharmacy (Sofia)*, **11**: 19–26.

CONSTANTINESCU, E., PISLARASU, N. & FORSTNER, S., 1968. Über Inhaltsstoffe von *Sanicula europaea* L. *Pharmazie*, **23**: 34–35.

CROWDEN, R. K., HARBORNE, J. B. & HEYWOOD, V. H., 1969. Chemosystematics of the Umbelliferae — A General Survey. *Phytochemistry*, **8**: 1963–1984.

DERYNG, J. & PARCZEWSKI, A., 1963. The isolation from angelic acid from the essential oil of *Laserpitium hispidum*. *Dissertat. pharmac. (Warsaw)*, **14**: 513–516.

ENGLER, A., 1964. *Syllabus der Pflanzenfamilien*. 12th ed. (H. Melchior) 2. Berlin: Verlag Gebr. Borntreyer.

FEINGOLD, D. S., AVIGAD, G. & HESTRIN, S., 1956. The mechanism of Polysaccharide Production from Sucrose. *Biochem. J.*, **64**, 351–361.

HARBORNE, J. B., 1966. Caffeic Acid Ester Distribution in Higher Plants. *Z. Naturf.*, **21B**: 604–605.

HATA, K. & KOZAWA, M., 1961. On the Constituents of the Roots of *Angelica Keiskei* Koidzumi. *J. pharmac. Soc. Japan (Yakugaku zasshi)*, **81**: 1647 (1961); ref. taken from *Chem. Abstr.*, **56**: 10281–10283 (1962).

HEGNAUER, R., 1964, 1966. *Chemotaxonomie der Pflanzen*. Basel & Stuttgart: Birkhäuser Verlag.

HERRMANN, K., 1958. Über Oxyzimtsäuren in Pflanzen. *Planta med. (Stuttgart)*, **6**: 35–39.

HERRMANN, K., Über den Gerbstoff der Labiatenblätter. *Arch. Pharmaz. Ber. dtsch. pharmaz. Ges.*, **293/65**: 1043–1048.

HILLER, K., 1965. *Sanicula europaea*—Isolierung und quantitative Erfassung von Chlorogen- und Rosmarinsäure. *Pharmazie* **20**: 574–579.

HILLER, K., 1968. Über die Saponine von *Sanicula europaea* L. *Pharmazie*, **23**: 376–387.

HILLER, K., 1969a. Oligosaccharide in *Eryngiumarten*. *Z. Naturf.*, **24b**: 36–38.

HILLER, K., 1969b. Zur Struktur der Saniculagenine C und D. *Pharmazie*, **24**, 178–179.

HILLER, K., 1970. Zur Struktur der Eryngiumsayogenine. *Pharmazie*, **25**, 769–774.

HILLER, K. & LINZER, B., 1966. Saponine der Saniculoideae und deren hämolytische Aktivität. *Pharmazie*, **21**: 245–250.

HILLER, K., KEIPERT, M. & LINZER, B., 1966. Triterpensaponine. *Pharmazie*, **21**: 713–751.

HILLER, K. & KOTHE, N., 1967. Chlorogen- und Rosmarinsäure—Vorkommen und quantitative Verteilung in Pflanzen der Saniculoideae. *Pharmazie*, **22**: 220–221.

HILLER, K. & LINZER, B., 1967. Hämolytische Aktivität von Eryngium-Species sowie jahreszeitliche Schwankungen im hämolytischen Index von *Sanicula europaea* L. und *Eryngium planum* L. *Pharmazie*, **22**: 321.

HILLER, K., KOTHE, N. & PFEIFER, S., 1967. Aliphatische Carbonsäuren in Saniculoideae. *Pharmazie*, **22**: 718–722.

HILLER, K. & KOTHE, N., 1969. Über die Saccharide in *Astrantia major* L. *Planta med. (Stuttgart)*, **17**: 79–86.

HÖRHAMMER, L., WAGNER, H. & GÖTZ, 1958. Über das Vorkommen von Flavonen in einheimischen Umbelliferen. *Arch. Pharmaz.*, **291/63**: 44–52.

KARRER, W., 1958. *Konstitution und Vorkommen der organischen Pflanzenstoffe*. Basel & Stuttgart: Birkhäuser-Verlag.

KLEIN, G., 1932. *Handbuch der Pflanzenanalyse* III. Vienna: Springer-Verlag.

KOCZWARA, M., 1949. Polish saponin containing plants. *Dissertat. pharmac. (Warsaw)*, **1**: 65–69.

KOFLER, L., 1927. *Die Saponine*. Vienna: Springer-Verlag (and works cited therein).

KORTE, F. & BEHNER, O., 1956. Zur Konfiguration der Tiglin- und Angelicasäure. *Chem. Ber.*, **89**, 2675–2677.

KRETOWITSCH, V. L., 1965. *Grundzüge der Biochemie der Pflanzen*. Jena: Gustav-Fischer-Verlag.

KROEBER, L., 1948. *Das neuzeitliche Kräuterbuch*. **1**: 317–318, Stuttgart: Hippokrates-Verlag.

KUBOTA, T., TONAMI, F. & HINOH, H., 1966. The Structure of Saikogenins A, B, C and D, triterpenoid alcohols of *Bupleurum falcatum* L. *Tetrahedron Letters (London)*, 701–710.

KUHN, A. & SCHÄFER, G., 1939. Zur Kenntnis des Vitamin C-Gehalts frischer Arzneipflanzen. *Madaus Jahrb.*, **3**: 52–54.

LESAINT, C., TENDILLE, C. & PAPIN, J. L., 1962. Malonic acid, predominant acid in dahlia petals. *Cr. hebd. Séanc. Acad. Sci., Paris*, **255**: 1002–1005.

LUFT, G., 1926. Verteilung der Saponine und Gerbstoffe in der Pflanze. *S.-B. Akad. Wiss. Wien, math.-naturwiss. Kl.*, Abt. I, **135**: 259–264.

MADAUS, 1938. *Lehrbuch der biologischen Heilmittel*. Leipzig: Verlag G. Thieme.

MANTA, J. & WEINRICH, C., 1934. Über *Eryngium planum* L. *Pharmaz. Mh.*, **15**: 187–189.

NIELSEN, B. E. & KOFOD, H., 1963. Constituents of the Root of *Angelica archangelica* L. *Acta chem. scand.*, **17**: 1161–1163.

PAECH, K., 1950. *Biochemie und Physiologie der sekundären Pflanzenstoffe*. Berlin-Göttingen-Heidelberg: Springer-Verlag.

PEYER, W., 1934. Die Isolierung des Saponins aus den Wurzeln von *Eryngium planum* L. *Dtsch. Apotheker-Ztg.*, **49**: 353–355.

REINBOTHE, H., 1958. Genese und Stoffwechselschicksal der 2-Kohlenstoffsäuren Glykol-, Glyoxyl- und Oxalsäure in der Pflanze. *Pharmazie*, **13**: 693–707, 740–747.

ROBERG, M., 1937. Über das Vorkommen und die Verteilung von Saponinen in Samendrogen. *Arch. Pharmaz.*, **275**: 84–103, 145–166.

SCARPATI, M. L. & ORIENTE, G., 1958. Isolation and Constitution of rosmarinic acid from *Rosmarinus officinalis* L. *Ric. Sci.*, **1958**: 2329–2333.

SCHIMMEL, M. B., 1905. Öl von *Eryngium campestre*. *Ber. Oct.*, **1905**: 73–74.

SCHLÖSSER, E. & WULFF, G., 1969. Structural Specificity of Saponin Hemolysis. *Z. Naturf.* **24B**: 1284–1290.

SCHLUBACH, H. H. & KOEHN, H. O. A., 1958. Die Bildung der verzweigten Polyfructosane in den Roggenhalmen. *Liebigs Annln. Chem.*, **614**: 126–136.

SEGAL, R., MANSOUR, M. & ZAITSCHEK, D. V., 1966. Effect of Ester Groups on the Haemolytic Action of some Saponins and Sapogenins. *Biochem. Pharmacol.*, **15**: 1411–1414.

SEROVA, N. A., 1961. On the Sapogenins of the roots of *Eryngium incognitum* Pavl. *Med. Ind. USSR*, **15**: 26–27.

SHIBATA, S., KITAGAWA, I. & FUJIMOTO, H., 1965. The Structure of Saikogenin A—a Sapogenin of Bupleurum Species. *Tetrahedron Letters (London)*, 3783–3788.

TÄUFEL, K., TÄUFEL, A. & RUTTLOFF, H., 1962. Physiologisch-chemische Studien über die Raffinose-Familie. *Planta*, **58**: 127–129.

THOMS, H., 1929. *Handbuch der praktischen und wissenschaftlichen Pharmazie*, **5**: Berlin-Vienna.

TSCHESCHE, R., WEBER, A. & WULFF, G., 1969. Über die Struktur des 'Theasaponins', eines Gemisches von Saponinen mit stark antiexsudativer Wirkung. *Liebigs Annln. Chem.*, **721**: 209–219.

WOITKE, H.-D., KAYSER, J.-P. & HILLER, K., 1970. Fortschritte in der Erforschung der Triterpensaponine. *Pharmazie*, **25**: 213–241.

WOLF, J., 1960. In: Ruhland, W. *et al.* (eds). *Handbuch der Pflanzenphysiologie*, **XLI/2**. Berlin-Göttingen-Heidelberg: Springer-Verlag.

WULFF, G. & TSCHESCHE, R., 1969. Über die Struktur der Roßkastaniensaponine (Aescin) und die Aglykone verwandter Verbindungen. *Tetrahedron Letters (London)*, 415–436.

YOSIOKA, I., 1967. Saponine aus Roßkastanien-Saponinen durch Bodenbakterien-Hydrolyse. *Tetrahedron Letters (London)*, 2577–2580.

Ethnobotany of the Umbelliferae

DAVID H. FRENCH

Department of Anthropology, Reed College, Portland, Oregon, U.S.A.

Uses, names and beliefs for members of the family are considered, especially for recent years, without excluding any part of the world.

Many uses for food and in beverages are described; often flavour, rather than nutritional value, is important. Umbels are also eaten by other animals. These plants have been widely used as medicines. The fact that some of them are highly poisonous has affected attitudes toward the family, as well as uses of them as medicines and as food.

Less frequent ways in which these plants have been important to humans are discussed, e.g. as fuel or for ornament. Sometimes they are regarded as weeds.

In passing, comparisons are made with other plant families.

An annotated list of the Umbels of greatest importance has been compiled as a supplement to the paper.

CONTENTS

INTRODUCTION

There are between two and three thousand species in the Umbelliferae, and they grow in all the major regions of the earth regularly inhabited by humans. These plants are relatively unimportant in moist, tropical areas and in true deserts; they are common and best-known in temperate and mountainous areas, especially in the Northern Hemisphere (Mathias & Constance, 1962: 3). In these pages, including the accompanying list, between two and three hundred species are taken into account; it would be difficult to estimate how many more would be included in a complete ethnobotanical study of the Umbelliferae. In a general work on the useful plants of the world, 20 to 30 such species and varieties might be discussed (cf. Hill, 1952). No particular significance is attached to these ratios; they are offered to provide one kind of perspective on the material to follow. The intention here is to take a naïve look at the ethnobotany of the family as a whole. This task is divided between a simple general discussion and a list of some of the species of concern to human beings.

In a broad sense, ethnobotany is concerned with *any* relationship, from conceptual to gastronomic, between men and plants. Frequently, ethnobotany is limited to the uses and naming of plants by non-literate peoples; the term 'economic botany' is often used for the study of those plants which are involved in the money economies of the world. I have not observed this distinction; no relationship between men and Umbels is excluded, but agricultural products—as such—are not stressed.

There are reasons for the lack of a sharp distinction here between economic botany and ethnobotany. While it is true that some Umbels are planted in large fields on a commercial basis, those same plants may also be grown in simple gardens. This contrasts with many other crops, for example, most cereals. Nowadays, does anyone grow his own wheat? At the same time, many of the Umbels that have been grown in gardens, and even as field crops, also grow wild and can be gathered for human use.

ETHNOBOTANY OF THE UMBELLIFERAE

An interesting question is why certain, scattered members of a plant family should manifest the characteristic of swelling, e.g. tuber formation, in the roots—or an analogous swelling just above the roots. The puzzle lies in the fact that such plants may not be closely related to each other. Nevertheless, a significant number of Umbels do have such swellings, and they may become staple foods.

Carrots (*Daucus carota* L.) are not a bad starting point for our discussion. They are a near-staple food and a food for animals. They have been used to flavour other foods and to flavour drinks. They have sometimes been used as medicine and in a variety of other ways. For this species, and others below, additional details are included in the accompanying list.

Beyond carrots and parsnips (*Pastinaca sativa* L.), no Umbels have international reputations as root foods. Yet, others have been used in Europe, and elsewhere. Among them, cultivated or not, have been: *Bunium bulbocastanum* L., caraway (*Carum carvi* L.), *Chaerophyllum bulbosum* L., *Conopodium majus* (Gouan) Loret, *Cryptotaenia canadensis* (L.) DC., *Cymopterus* spp., *Eryngium campestre* L., and parsley (*Petroselinum crispum* (Miller) A. W. Hill).

In northwestern South America, together with potatoes and other underground foods, an Umbel, *Arracacia xanthorrhiza* Bancroft, has been long cultivated for its large, tasty, tuberous roots (Hodge, 1954). In North America, roots of members of the genus *Perideridia* are still eaten by Indians in the interior parts of the Pacific states. Today, the most important plant is *Perideridia gairdneri* ssp. *borealis* Chuang & Constance. Foods of even greater importance have been the tubers and aboveground parts of plants of the genus *Lomatium*. Oddly, in terms of how little known it is even by botanists, this is the largest genus of Umbels in the United States. Furthermore, some species have constituted true plant staples for many Indian groups in the northwestern part of the United States and in western Canada (French, 1965: 380). Among the most important are *Lomatium canbyi* Coult. & Rose, *L. cous* (S. Wats.) Coult. & Rose, and *L. piperi* Coult. & Rose.

Neither *Lomatium* nor *Perideridia* spp. have been cultivated. (In my own experience, few of them are easy to transplant or grow from seed.) Furthermore, no native American species of Umbel has come to be of any real international importance as food, medicine, or whatever. The same holds for much of Africa and large areas of Asia. It is North Africa, Europe, and western and southern Asia that have provided our best-known foods and other cultivated plants of this family.

With exceptions already noted, Umbels rarely constitute one of the staple foods of a people. Although a few are annuals and others are harvested as if they were annuals, the economically important Umbel species in the world tend to be biennials or perennials. Ames, in his work lauding annual angiosperms in human history (1939), mentions no Umbels. Cereal grasses are typical staples for large human populations; no known civilization has been based on the cultivation of parsnips or carrots.

Root foods have now been discussed; there are other kinds of food. Wild or cultivated, fresh or preserved, the exposed parts of many Umbels are also eaten. Some are a major or minor food item on their own account, and many others are used as flavouring for some other food.

Among those plants whose stems, petioles, and/or leaves can provide food are: *Aegopodium podagraria* L., *Angelica* spp., *Apium graveolens* L. (celery), *Cryptotaenia canadensis*, *Cymopterus* spp., *Heracleum lanatum* Michx, *Heracleum sphondylium* L., *Levisticum officinale* Koch, *Ligusticum scoticum* L., *Lomatium* spp., especially *L. nudicaule* (Pursh) Coult. & Rose, and *Smyrnium olusatrum* L.

English-speaking people have a pair of linked concepts: 'herbs' and 'spices'; the two are not consistently differentiated. Herbs can often be grown in one's own garden, are preferably used fresh, and may be medicinal as well as used in flavouring foods and drinks. Spices are more often exotic and are ordinarily limited to flavouring. Both categories, of course, can include parts of Umbel plants.

Most of the food plants already listed are not typical 'herbs'. Various species whose leaves are used in flavouring other foods would, however, qualify; among these are: *Anthriscus cerefolium* (L.) Hoffm. (chervil), *Foeniculum vulgare* Miller (fennel), and *Petroselinum crispum*. Parsley is interesting because it can also be a special kind of ornamental. In America, at least, it is served with food, it decorates the plate, but it is rarely eaten (cf. Harrison *et al.*, 1969: 146).

'Spices' are more likely than 'herbs' to consist of fruits or seeds, though this distinction is not absolute. In either case, it is generally the so-called 'essential oils' that provide the desired flavours, which are usually actually odours. Even a small collection of spices in a European or Europe-derived kitchen is likely to contain a goodly percentage of items from Umbels. They are the major rivals of non-umbelliferous species from tropical areas. Yet, in the tropics, Umbel fruits are also used.

The species whose fruits or whose oils are, or were, used for flavouring include: *Anethum graveolens* L. (dill), *Apium graveolens*, *Bunium bulbocastanum*, *Carum carvi*, *Coriandrum sativum* L. (coriander), *Cuminum cyminum* L. (cumin), *Daucus carota*, *Eryngium foetidum* L., *Heracleum persicum* Desf. ex Fischer, *Lagoecia cuminoides* L., and *Pimpinella anisum* L. (anise).

Beverages, as well as foods, are flavoured by Umbel products. *Angelica archan-gelica* L., *Laserpitium* spp., and many of the species just listed (notably anise), are used this way. In addition, a few plants, such as *Heracleum sphondylium*, are made into alcoholic beverages, rather than just being used to flavour them.

Not many plantings are made only as food for animals or are regarded as especially suitable wild forage for them. *Daucus carota*, *Pastinaca sativa*, and scattered other species are cultivated plants that have been fed to animals. Pastures, meadows and forests spontaneously provide forage. Animals of only indirect importance to man also eat Umbels. Schaller tells us (1963: 158, *et passim*) that mountain gorillas eat species of *Peucedanum*. (I was delighted a few years ago while doing some work in the herbarium at Stanford University to note that Schaller had deposited certain voucher specimens of gorilla food; ethnobotanists do not always remember to document their work so well.)

The medicinal uses of the plants of any family are likely to be more numerous and diverse than, for example, the food uses. The Umbelliferae are no exception; many species are involved, and they have been employed as remedies for an amazing variety of complaints. Neither the plants nor their past and present uses will be discussed in detail here. More information can be found in the accompanying list, but it, too, is in no sense complete.

Remedies for problems of the gastro-intestinal tract are probably the medicines of greatest importance derived from Umbels; fennel has been used for nausea, and there are many plants described as stomachic and/or carminative (e.g. *Ammi majus* L.). Species of *Ferula* have been used for constipation and *Cuminum cyminum* for diarrhoea.

Upper respiratory complaints have also had many kinds of medication; examples: anise for catarrh, *Ferula* spp. for coughs and coriander for halitosis.

There are many diuretics, e.g. *Eryngium* spp., and other remedies for genito-urinary problems. These include menstrual disturbances (*Daucus carota* is one medication) and syphilis (*Centella asiatica* (L.) Urban has been used).

Umbels have also been employed for cardio-vascular ailments and as tonics, stimu-lants, sedatives, antispasmodics, aphrodisiacs, and sudorifics. In addition, many topical applications for wounds, boils, bites and stings, and skin eruptions are re-ported. Some interesting, though less common, uses include treatments for baldness, warts, hiccoughs, hypochondriasis, mental disorders, poor memory and habitual drunkenness.

Veterinary medicine would be included in a complete discussion of Umbel uses; *Laser trilobum* (L.) Borkh. is one of the plants that would receive attention.

It now seems worth while to consider further what kinds of species have provided medicines. For Europeans and Americans, certain plants which are exotic—even romantic—are those long used as sources of gum-resins and resins. Some of these plant exudations are obtained in Mediterranean areas; others come from farther east, e.g. Iran and India. Various plant families are represented in this commerce, but certain Umbels are among the sources which have been most important (Howes, 1950).

Gum-resins are mixtures of gums and resins. Asafetida, from *Ferula assa-foetida*

L., and other members of the genus, is collected from cuts made low on the stem or at the top of the root. Like other such gum-resins, it has been used principally as medicine (e.g. as a carminative, antispasmodic and stimulant); when these remedies were common in the West some years ago, asafetida had such fame as being foul-smelling that it would have surprised many to learn that it was also used in Asia to flavour food.

Galbanum is a gum-resin (or oleo-gum-resin, in that it includes oil) which is similar to asafetida in properties; it is available in the same areas, sometimes as a result of natural exudation. It is derived from *Ferula galbaniflua* Boiss. & Buhse and one or more other species of *Ferula*. Ammoniacum, another oleo-gum-resin, is medicinal and is derived from *Dorema ammoniacum* D. Don, *Ferula tingitana* L., and perhaps other species. Sagapen and/or sagapenum (from *Ferula* spp.) and opopanax (from *Opopanax chironium* (L.) Koch), are similar (Howes, 1950: 314–315).

It is of interest that the sources of resins and gum-resins which were once of such importance are, after all, wild plants. It would be impossible to characterize in a general way the scores or hundreds of other wild Umbels that have been used in non-European medicine and as home remedies. This is not true, however, for the cultivated plants that have been sources of medicine: in general, they are the same plants that are used for food and flavouring. It was suggested earlier that 'spice' plants were not important in medicine. This is generally true for 'home remedies', but many of the species which have produced spices have also yielded oils and other products of importance in the traditional commercial drug trade. Fruits, roots, and sometimes leaves have been used; flowers are rarely, if ever, utilized. We are dealing here with anise, carrots, caraway and the like. Even parsnips have been used as medicine (Courchet, 1882: 160).

Although Umbels are still used in Western healing, it appears that no materials derived from them are constituents of *major* contemporary medicines. Also, there seems to be less current research on possible future medicinal uses than for many other plant families. This may in part be due to the scarcity of alkaloids in Umbels.

The fact that there are poisonous plants in the family is frightening enough to cause some people to avoid any Umbel they do not know well. Among the less famous species said to contain poisons are: *Aethusa cynapium* L., *Chaerophyllum temulentum* L., *Oenanthe crocata* L. (and perhaps other *Oenanthe* spp.), and *Sium* spp. (possibly). There is no doubt, of course, about the poisonous qualities of *Conium maculatum* L. and various species of *Cicuta*. Not only humans but also cattle and other animals are sometimes poisoned.

At times, poisonous Umbels are also useful. *Oenanthe crocata*, and probably other plants, have been used to stupefy fish; there are reports of arrow poisons made from one or another Umbel. *Cicuta douglasii* (DC.) Coult. & Rose has been used for suicide. *Conium maculatum* is one of the poisonous Umbels that has been used as medicine; it can also be used to kill criminals or philosophers.

We need not linger here over the weeds among the Umbels. Some are in lawns, some in gardens and fields; some are seen as weeds because they are poisonous. In general, however, other plant families supply the most important weeds of the world.

A fair number of species have been used at one time or another in the making of perfume or other scented products. These plants include: *Angelica archangelica*, *Carum carvi*, *Coriandrum sativum*, *Cuminum cyminum*, *Daucus carota*, and *Ferula sumbul* (Kauffmann) Hook. f.

Certain Indians in the western United States used fruits of *Lomatium nudicaule* to scent buckskin, and the leaves of *Steganotaenia araliacea* Hochst. have been employed in tropical Africa to scent clothing.

Some plants are sources of incense, for example in religious services; included are: *Dorema ammoniacum*, *Ferula galbaniflua*, and *Ferula sumbul*.

Umbels are not typical garden flowers, but members of diverse genera are sometimes grown for their ornamental value. These include species of *Astrantia*, *Eryngium*, *Heracleum*, and *Trachymene*. Most of these are probably not domesticated but, rather, are wild plants which can grow in gardens. They may be showy, or unusual, e.g. conspicuously large. Like many plants, wild Umbels are gathered for bouquets; it is not unusual for flowering stalks to form a part of dry bouquets, displayed in the winter.

At times, depictions of Umbels are included in paintings, in drawings, in seals, or in craft work. I have seen them in a still life painting of no great distinction, and *Daucus carota*, for example, has been the subject of more than one commercial embroidery design.

Sometimes to understand an item or an assemblage, it is helpful to consider what is not true, or is scarcely true, about it. For example, Umbel wood is not ordinarily used to build furniture. Woodiness is, of course, not absent in the family (Rodríguez, 1957), though it may be ignored when there are alternatives. Yet, *Steganotaenia araliacea* is locally important in Africa for its woodiness; *Azorella compacta* Phil., while quite different in form, is used in South America as fuel. There are trivial uses: the pedicels or rays of *Ammi visnaga* (L.) Lam. are said to have been sold in Egypt as toothpicks (Uphof, 1968: 31). No commercial fibre sources evidently exist in the family.

Umbels are not important in providing pigments, though *Daucus carota* has been used to colour butter, and *Heracleum lanatum* roots are reported as a dye source.

It is in foods, flavourings, and medicines that we have found Umbels to be especially useful. Nevertheless, there are the other uses, and one of the more startling characteristics of the family, when one thinks about it, is the number of ways in which the plants have been utilized. The uses range from foods to poisons and from fodder to perfumery. Furthermore, all parts of one or another species are used.

All the major groupings and many subgroups in the family are represented in the plants of ethnobotanical importance. Among the cultivated species some stabilized variability has developed in the form of horticultural varieties. There is, however, more of this variability in other kinds of crops and among garden flowers. Actually, human modification appears not to have taken any Umbel species especially far from its wild ancestors. As for wild species, we are using them less as substitutes have become available; this is true, of course, of wild plants in general.

Before turning to beliefs about Umbels, I would like to consider briefly how well they are known and how common names are used. To select an extreme, most Americans of European ancestry know practically nothing about wild Umbels and use none of them, except possibly in bouquets. There are almost no common names in general use and few ever really existed. 'Queen Anne's Lace', for *Daucus carota* (and any other white-flowered, medium-sized plant) would be the only exception, and most people do not connect the name with carrots. In Britain, there are many established common names, but I assume that they are no longer widely known and used. In France (and in the rest of Europe, I presume), there are comparable old names for wild species which could be used, but people do not understand the plants well enough to use the names consistently (French & French, 1966, 1968). It is among non-European peoples (including American Indians) who still gather wild plants regularly that names are used in a consistent manner.

Ignorance and mistakes can be interesting as well as dangerous. For example, *Apium nodiflorum* (L.) Lag. has been mistaken for watercress, with which it often grows, and apparently there are no ill effects when it is eaten (Clapham *et al.*, 1962: 513). Thus, the scope of ethnobotany is widened by accident.

Deceit, as well as error, can add to the number of plants actually in use. Evidently, in the traditional European, American and Asiatic drug plant trade, materials have sometimes been adulterated with other species, or one species has been offered in place of another. Included are both fruits and gum-resins (Culbreth, 1917: 435–448; cf. Aitchison, 1890: 74).

Of course, all of ethnobotany is replete with what can be called beliefs and 'belief systems', e.g. 'I believe parsnips are edible'. Those beliefs which lack an empirical basis can be more interesting and are sometimes considered separately. To illustrate: *Sanicula bipinnata* Hook. & Arn. yields good luck, and *Angelica archangelica* is among the species useful against witches.

Many more examples of such beliefs could be added, including those concerning the numerous medicines that lack empirical support. A single example will suffice: in Belgium, France and Poland, carrots or carrot juice once were used for jaundice because these are all yellow (Hermant & Boomans, n.d.: 6–7).

References to Umbels in mythology and symbolism do not seem to be especially common or significant, though it would have been pleasant to spend more time searching for them. American Indian mythology includes Umbels, and we are told that Prometheus concealed his stolen fire in a hollow Umbel stalk.

S. M. Walters is among those who have considered the development of taxonomy in relationship to the 'historical' (or socio-cultural and geographic) situation of the men who did the work (Walters, 1961). Specifically, he asserts that angiosperm taxonomy would have been quite different had not the systems we all use originated in Europe at a particular time. This is interesting, especially to an anthropologist with curiosity about the nature and history of science. The issues involved would not especially concern us here, however, were it not that he selects the Umbelliferae as his principal example to establish certain points. He reminds us that a number of Umbels, with names, were in use in Europe as foods or medicines (or feared as poisons) prior to Linnaeus. These became small genera, because it seemed important to differentiate them; Walters speculates that a 'New Zealand Linnaeus' might have treated the family as a single genus, or a few genera, in the Araliaceae.

Anthropologists have been increasingly interested in the taxonomic systems of non-European peoples. Not surprisingly, they find relationships between the ways plants and animals are used and the ways they are conceptualized. Following Walters, our neo-Latin taxonomy is also relative to human concerns and not just to the nature of the plants themselves. Nevertheless, this perspective—still following Walters—does not require us to dump existing taxonomies and build new ones.

A final thought: for many humans, Umbels are just a bit like mushrooms. In both groups, some are poisonous, some are not—in fact, they can add flavour or spice to our lives. Yet, it can be difficult to tell them apart, e.g. to differentiate between the dangerous ones, the indifferent ones, and the delightful or useful ones. Contrasts and ambiguities are prevalent. Despite the parallels, Umbels, however, do not evoke the same extremes of dread and delight as do fungi.

AN ANNOTATED LIST:
UMBELLIFERAE OF ETHNOBOTANICAL IMPORTANCE

This list probably includes the Umbels best known (to ethnobotanists) in the world, but there are limitations in the coverage and in the presentation. For example, there are species not known to the compiler, and there are others which could not be included for one or another reason. Perhaps African species were especially slighted (see Watt & Breyer-Brandwijk, 1962, for some missing ones). There was also a problem about how many synonyms to include and to cross-reference; those within the same genus are not cross-referenced.

The common names are, of necessity, only a few of those used in English and a few others likely to be known to speakers of English. Sometimes the same name is listed for more than one species; common names are not always consistent with botanical names.

In general, the geographical notations indicate where the plants are said to grow, but not necessarily where they are known or used today. Quite a few of the listed species are no longer used, whether as food, as medicine, or otherwise. No consistent distinction has been made between folk medicine and other medicinal uses.

The citation of sources used in compiling the list could not be complete; certain species are widely known, and the relevant citations are general ones. Others are those that seem to be representative. In short, there are many possible additional references to human uses and beliefs regarding these plants.

Abbreviations used in the list

A	annual	N	north, northern
Afr.	Africa	P	perennial
Amer.	America	S	south, southern
B	biennial	temp.	temperate
C	central	trop.	tropical
E	east, eastern	US	United States
Eur.	Europe	W	west, western
Medit.	Mediterranean		

Aegopodium podagraria L. Goutweed, Bishop's Elder, Bishop's Weed, Ground Elder, Dwarf Elder, Herb Gerard. P. Eur. (except parts of S), Asia, naturalized in N Amer. Perhaps once cultivated. Eaten like spinach or as salad. Folk medicine: for gouty and sciatic pains; externally as fomentation; diuretic and sedative (Clapham, *et al.*, 1962: 520; Uphof, 1968: 14).

Aethusa cynapium L. Fool's Parsley, Small Hemlock, Dog Parsley, Dog Poison. A, B or P. Eur., N Asia, N Amer. (naturalized). Among medicinal uses: gastro-intestinal troubles; convulsions; sedative (Uphof, 1968: 15; Garnaud, 1942: 67). Poisonous, within certain limits (Harborne, 1970: 14; Paris & Moyse, 1961: 111; cf. Clapham *et al.*, 1962: 524).

(*Aethusa mutellina* (L.) St. Lag. Syn. for *Ligusticum mutellina* (L.) Crantz.)

Alepidea amatymbica Eckl. & Zeyh. P. S Afr. Uses: for stomach pain, colic; as laxative, tonic (Uphof, 1968: 22).

Aletes anisatus (A. Gray) Theobald & Tseng (*Pseudocymopterus aletifolius* Rydb., *Pteryxia anisata* (A. Gray) Math. & Const.). P. Colorado, US. Leaves said (Uphof, 1968: 432) to be eaten by Indians in New Mexico, where evidently it does not grow.

(*Ammi copticum* L. Syn. for *Trachyspermum copticum* (L.) Link.)

Ammi majus L. Bishop's Weed. A. Medit. region (introduced northward) to Iran, Ethiopia; other temp. regions (introduced). Said to have been cultivated since the Middle Ages. Seeds aromatic; used as tonic, stomachic, carminative, and diuretic; also for angina pectoris and asthma (Uphof, 1968: 31).

Ammi visnaga (L.) Lam. (with many syns.). Khella, El Viellah. A or B. Eurasia, N Afr.; introduced in the Americas. Emetic, purgative, anti-spasmodic; for urinary disorders, angina pectoris, asthma, gastric ulcers (Courchet, 1882: 108–110; Paris & Moyse, 1961: 106–107; Uphof, 1962: 31).

Ammodaucus leucotrichus Coss. & Dur. A. NW and N Afr. Seeds used as condiment, leaves for chest complaints (Uphof, 1968: 32).

(*Anethum foeniculum* L. Syn. for *Foeniculum vulgare* Miller.)

Anethum graveolens L. (with various syns.; cf. next entry and *Peucedanum graveolens*). Dill. A. S Asia, Eur., N Amer., W Indies. Widely cultivated; sometimes naturalized. Fruits and other plant parts (or oil from either) used for flavouring pickles and other foods (Sievers, 1947: 152–153). Seeds: stomachic, carminative, stimulant, other uses (Courchet, 1882: 158).

Anethum sowa Roxb. ex Flem. (perhaps best regarded as a syn. for *A. graveolens* L.). Sowa, Indian Dill, Dill. A. Trop. Asia. India: cultivated as vegetable and for flavouring; carminative and stomachic (The Wealth of India, 1948–: 1: 78–79).

Angelica acutiloba (Sieb. & Zucc.) Kitagawa (*Ligusticum acutilobum* Sieb. & Zucc.). P. China and Japan. As medicine: for dizziness, easy childbirth.

Angelica archangelica L. (*Archangelica officinalis* Hoffm.). Angelica, Garden Angelica. P. Temp. Eur. to Greenland and N Asia; naturalized in other parts of Eur.; Himalayas. Often cultivated; candied, in pastries, flavouring other foods and certain drinks; young shoots eaten. Perfumery. Dental preparations; tonic, antispasmodic, stomachic, carminative, stimulant, expectorant, diaphoretic, for painful and swollen parts, other medicinal uses (Héraud, 1949: 91–93). Once used against devils and witches (cf. Grieve, 1959: 36).

Angelica atropurpurea L. Purple Angelica. P. Labrador to Delaware and to Midwest US. Food: vegetable and salad; candied (Uphof, 1968: 37). Medicine: many uses, often the same as those for *A. archangelica* L. (Culbreth, 1917: 439; Vogel, 1970: 272).

Angelica breweri A. Gray. P. Calif. and Nevada, US. Indians used root for colds, chest ailments, and headaches (Barrett & Gifford, 1933: 166; Uphof, 1968: 37).

Angelica decursiva (Miq.) Franch. & Sav. (*Porphyroscias decursiva* Miq., *Peucedanum decursivum* (Miq.) Maxim.). P. E Asia. Vietnam: rheumatism (Uphof, 1968: 398).

Angelica edulis Miyabe. P. Japan. Food: stalks eaten by the Ainu (Uphof, 1968: 37).

Angelica glauca Edgew. P. W Himalayas. Flavouring agent; also stimulant, and for flatulence and dyspepsia (The Wealth of India, 1948–: 1: 79).

Angelica hendersonii Coult. & Rose. P. W US, coastal. Panacea and talisman for certain Indians (Schneider, 1906: 64).

Angelica koreana Maxim. P. China, Korea: rheumatism (Uphof, 1968: 37).

(*Angelica levisticum* All. Syn. for *Levisticum officinale* Koch.)

Angelica lucida L. (*Coelopleurum actaeifolium* (Michx) Coult. & Rose, *Archangelica gmelini* DC.). P. N Pacific, Asia to Calif.; also Labrador to New York. Food, tonic and ceremonial plant for Alaskan Eskimos; food on N Atlantic Coast, N Amer. (Heller, 1953: 11; Oswalt, 1957: 31–32, 36; cf. Uphof, 1968: 45).

Angelica polymorpha Maxim. var. *sinensis* Oliv. (Syn. for *A. polymorpha* Maxim.?). P. E Asia. China: root used for contraction of the uterus, as diuretic, and to stimulate blood pressure (Uphof, 1968: 38).

(*Angelica rosaefolia* Hook. Syn. for *Scandia rosaefolia* (Hook.) Dawson.)

Angelica sylvestris L. Wild Angelica, Woodland Angelica. P. Most of Eur. to Siberia; N America (introduced). Vegetable. Fruits used to kill head parasites (Uphof, 1968: 38).

Angelica tenuissima Nakai. P. China, Korea. Carminative (Uphof, 1968: 38).

Angelica tomentosa S. Wats. (*A. californica* Jepson). P. Coast Ranges, Oregon and Calif., US. Used by Calif. Indians, e.g. by Karoks as food and as purification after funerals (Schenck & Gifford, 1952: 387).

Angelica uchiyama Nakai. P. China. Root used for women's ailments (Uphof, 1968: 38).

Angelica venenosa (Greenway) Fernald (*A. villosa* (Walt.) B.S.P.). P. E US. Leaves used to discourage use of tobacco (Uphof, 1968: 38).

(*Anisum vulgare* Gaertner. Syn. for *Pimpinella anisum* L.)

Anthriscus cerefolium (L.) Hoffm. (*A. longirostris* Bertol., *Cerefolium cerefolium* (L.) Schinz & Thell., *Chaerefolium cerefolium* (L.) Schinz, *Chaerophyllum sativum* Lam., *Scandix cerefolium* L.). Chervil, Garden Chervil. A. E Eur. and W Asia; introduced in the rest of Eur., E Asia, N Afr., the Americas and New Zealand. Cultivated. Leaves a well-known flavouring. Medicine: diuretic, depurative, e.g. for cancer (Courchet, 1882; 206–208; Uphof, 1968: 41).

Anthriscus sylvestris (L.) Hoffm. (*A. torquata* Coste, *Chaerophyllum sylvestre* L., *Cerefolium sylvestre* (L.) Besser.). Cow Parsley, Keck. B or P. Much of Eur.;

Siberia; N Afr.; Ethiopia; N Amer. (introduced). Roots and young shoots once eaten (Courchet, 1882: 208). Remedy for skin diseases (Uphof, 1968: 121).

Apium australe Thouars (*Apium prostratum* Labill. may be syn.). S Atlantic; also Pacific areas? *A. australe* is from Tristan da Cunha; Fuegian plants, antiscorbutic, may be the same.

(*Apium carvi* (L.) Crantz. Syn. for *Carum carvi* L.)

Apium graveolens L. (with vars.). Celery; Celeriac, Turnip-rooted Celery; Smallage, Wild Celery. B. Old and New World, widely cultivated. Var. *dulce* (Miller) DC. is the familiar celery; var. *rapaceum* (Miller) DC., Celeriac, with a tuberous base, is another vegetable; leaves of var. *silvestre* Presl are used for flavouring food. Oil from seeds used for flavouring, for perfume, as fixative. Medicine: stimulant, stomachic, carminative, febrifuge, emmenagogue, other uses (The Wealth of India, 1948–: 1: 87–88).

Apium leptophyllum (Pers.) F. Mueller ex Bentham. A. W S Amer., to Atlantic and Pacific coasts of US; Eur. (introduced). Formerly a carminative in Amer. (Courchet, 1882: 98). Niue Island (introduced?): used to scent oil (Yuncker, 1943: 92–93).

Apium nodiflorum (L.) Lag. Fool's Watercress. P. W, C and S Eur. to Iran, N Afr., Ethiopia; introduced in N and S Amer. Eaten as salad in W Eur., sometimes in mistake for watercress; medicine: diuretic, chronic skin disorders (Clapham *et al.*, 1962: 513; Courchet, 1882: 98).

(*Apium petroselinum* L. Syn. for *Petroselinum crispum* (Miller) A. W. Hill.)

Apium prostratum Labill. B or P. W Pacific; evidently also coastal S Amer. Australia: vegetable (Irvine, 1937: 120). New Zealand: in vapour baths; as antiscorbutic (Brooker & Cooper 1961: 7). (*A. australe* Thouars, from S Amer. and S Atlantic may be the same.)

(*Archangelica actaeifolium* Michx. Listed by Uphof (1968: 45); evidently a syn. for *Angelica lucida* L.)

(*Archangelica gmelini* DC. Syn. for *Angelica lucida* L.)

(*Archangelica officinalis* Hoffm. Syn. for *Angelica archangelica* L.)

Arctopus echinatus L. P. S Afr. Roots used for 'cleaning the blood', as diuretic, and for skin diseases (Uphof, 1968: 45).

Arracacia xanthorrhiza Bancroft (*Conium arracacia* Hooker). Arracacha. P. Northern S Amer.; C Amer. Cultivated in highlands for edible, fleshy roots (Hodge, 1954: 3: 195–221). Can yield an alcoholic drink; has been recommended as an analeptic (Courchet, 1882: 217).

Astrantia major L. P. S and C Eur. to the Caucasus. Purgative; same uses as *Peucedanum ostruthium* (L.) Koch (Courchet, 1882: 87).

(*Athamanta cervaria* L. Syn. for *Peucedanum cervaria* (L.) Lapeyr.)

Athamanta cretensis L. Candy Carrot. P. S Eur., Mediterranean region. Flavouring liqueurs (Uphof, 1968: 58). Diaphoretic, diuretic, stimulant (Courchet, 1882: 136).

Athamanta macedonica (L.) Sprengel. P. E Medit., Balkans. Once a medicine (Courchet, 1882: 135–136).

(*Athamanta roxburghiana* Wall. Syn. for *Carum roxburghianum* Bentham.)

(*Aulospermum* spp. See *Cymopterus* spp.)

Azorella caespitosa Lam. P. Patagonia and temp. Andean S Amer. Also Falkland Islands, where used for kidney and liver ailments; source of bolax resin (Uphof, 1968: 61).

Azorella compacta Phil. (*A. prismatoclada* Domin, *A. yareta* Hauman). Yareta. P. Highland S Amer. Locally important fuel. For colds and pains; astringent and absorbent (Hodge, 1960: 112–118).

Azorella diapensioides A. Gray. P. Peru to Bolivia. Fuel (Hodge, 1960: 113). Possible medicine (Uphof, 1968: 61).

Berula erecta (Hudson) Coville (*Sium angustifolium* L., *S. erectum* Hudson, *S. thunbergii* DC.). P. Most of Eur.; Canada, US, Mexico (widespread); S Afr. In S Afr.: reported as poisonous to cattle; root used for toothache (Uphof, 1968: 487).

Bowlesia flabilis Macbr. A. W S Amer., Mexico, Peru: styptic; for lung ailments (Mathias & Constance, 1962: 29–30). *Bubon galbanum* L. Syn. for *Peucedanum galbanum* (L.) Bentham.

Bunium bulbocastanum L. (*Carum bulbocastanum* (L.) Koch, *Apium bulbocastanum* (L.) Carvel, *Ligusticum bulbocastanum* (L.) Crantz). Great Earthnut. P. W and S Eur., S Asia. Once cultivated. Fruits as flavouring; leaves and tubers eaten (Aitchison 1890: 34); has been an emergency food (French & French, 1966, 1968); food for animals. Tubers: astringent (Uphof, 1968: 91).

Bupleurum falcatum L. P. Eur. to E Asia. India: roots used for liver and stomach ailments (The Wealth of India 1948–: 1: 250). Var. *octoradiatum* Tourn. used in China to stimulate perspiration (Uphof, 1968: 90).

Bupleurum jucundum Kurz. P. India: (same as preceding sp.).

(*Cachrys* sp. See *Prangos pabularia* Lindl.)

(*Carum* spp. For native N Amer. species attributed to *Carum*, see *Perideridia* spp.)

(*Carum bulbocastanum* (L.) Koch. Syn. for *Bunium bulbocastanum* L.)

Carum capense (Thunb.) Sond. (has been referred to *Chamarea capensis* (Thunb.) Eckl. & Zeyh.). P. S Afr. Roots eaten in some areas (Uphof, 1968: 109).

Carum carvi L. (*Apium carvi* Crantz, *Seseli carvi* Lam.). Caraway. B or P. Much of Eur. and Asia. Morocco. Introduced elsewhere. Seeds used to flavour many foods, certain drinks, e.g. kümmel; roots said to be eaten as vegetable. Fruits or oil: stimulant, stomachic, carminative, diaphoretic, diuretic, anthelmintic, for scabies (e.g. Uphof 1968: 109).

(*Carum copticum* (L.) Bentham ex C. B. Cl. Treated here as a syn. for *Trachyspermum copticum* (L.) Link.)

Carum roxburghianum Bentham. Ajmud. A. Trop. Asia. Cultivated: seeds: condiment, stimulant, carminative (Uphof, 1968: 109).

Caucalis microcarpa Hook. & Arn. A. W US. Poultice used by Indians for rattlesnake bites (Schneider, 1906: 65).

Centella asiatica (L.) Urban (*Hydrocotyle asiatica* L.). P. S and SE Asia, SW Pacific. Eaten in some areas (Uphof, 1968: 118). Recommended as a cover crop. Many medicinal uses in India, e.g. as tonic, diuretic, for skin diseases and leprosy (*The Wealth of India*, 1948–: 2: 116–118; Dastur, 1951: 79–81). Niue Island: in medicine (Yuncker, 1943: 93).

(*Cerefolium cerefolium* (L.) Schinz & Thell. Syn. for *Anthriscus cerefolium* (L.) Hoffm.)

(*Cerefolium sylvestre* (L.) Besser. Syn. for *Anthriscus sylvestris* (L.) Hoffm.)

Chaerophyllum bulbosum L. (*C. laevigatum* Vis.). Turnip-rooted Chervil. P. Eur., except parts of W. Sometimes cultivated. Roots eaten. Medicinal (French, 1960).

(*Chaerophyllum sativum* Lam. Syn. for *Anthriscus cerefolium* (L.) Hoffm.)

(*Chaerophyllum sylvestre* L. Syn. for *Anthriscus sylvestris* (L.) Hoffm.)

Chaerophyllum temulentum L. Rough Chervil. B. Most of Eur., W N Afr; introduced elsewhere. Poisonous.

Changium smyrnioides Wolff. P. China. Medicinal.

(*Cicuta* spp. Many, perhaps all, species are poisonous; not all are listed here (cf. Kingsbury, 1964: 373–379).)

(*Cicuta amomum* (L.) Crantz. Syn. for *Sison amomum* L.)

Cicuta douglasii (DC.) Coult. & Rose (*C. occidentalis* Greene, *C. vagans* Greene). Water Hemlock. P. W N Amer. Toxic. Used by certain Indians for suicide (Schneider, 1906: 65). Roots with oil as medicine (Steedman, 1930: 513).

Cicuta mackenziana Raup. P. Hudson Bay to the Mackenzie Basin. Leaves eaten by W Alaskan Eskimos (though roots considered poisonous), according to Oswalt (1957: 21); this would be outside the range as given by Mathias & Constance (1944–45: 146).

Cicuta maculata L. P. E N Amer. Cherokee Indian contraceptive (Vogel, 1970: 239n, 241, 243, 244).

Cicuta virosa L. Cowbane. P. W, N and E Eur. to Japan. Poisonous. Formerly used in the same ways as *Conium maculatum* L. (Courchet, 1882: 90–94).

Cnidium monnieri (L.) Cusson (*Selinum monnieri* L.). A. E Asia, formerly cultivated and naturalized in Europe. Perhaps cultivated as condiment in Viet Nam (Uphof, 1968: 312, under the heading *Ligusticum monnieri* Celast.).

(*Coelopleurum actaeifolium* (Michx) Coult. & Rose. Syn. for *Angelica lucida* L.)

(*Coelopleurum gmelini* (DC.) Ledeb. Syn. for *Angelica lucida* L.)

(*Cogswellia* spp. See *Lomatium* spp.)

(*Conium arracacia* Hooker. Syn. for *Arracacia xanthorrhiza* Bancroft.)

Conium maculatum L. Poison Hemlock, Hemlock. A or B. Temp. Eurasia (widely introduced into N and S Amer., also New Zealand). Very poisonous; said to have been used to put criminals to death in ancient Greece (Uphof 1968: 148); believed to have been used to poison Socrates. Unripe fruit has been used as medicine: anodyne, sedative, antispasmodic; for cancer and other diseases.

Conopodium majus (Gouan) Loret (*C. denudatum* Koch). Pignut, Earthnut. P. W Eur. to Italy. Tubers edible.

Coriandrum sativum L. Coriander. A. Mediterranean region; adventive in Asia, N Afr., and the Americas. Cultivated. Fruits or oil used to flavour foods and beverages; foliage for soups (China). Used in soap and perfumes. Fruits as medicine: carminative, diuretic and aphrodisiac; once used for nervous disorders (Héraud, 1949: 228–230).

Crithmum maritimum L. Samphire, Rock Samphire. P. Coastal Eur. Leaves used as food and condiment; they 'make a good pickle' (Clapham *et al.*, 1962: 521). Leaves also seen as: aromatic, depurative, diuretic and possibly anthelmintic (Courchet, 1882: 139).

Cryptotaenia canadensis (L.) DC. P. E and Midwest US and Canada; naturalized in E Asia. Cultivated in Japan for food (Uphof, 1968: 161).

Cuminum cyminum L. Cumin. A. E and S Asia, N and E Afr.; more or less naturalized in S Eur. Widely cultivated. Condiment for many foods (e.g. cheese) and in drinks; ingredient of curry powders; largely replaced by caraway in Europe. Perfumery. Traditional uses: antispasmodic, astringent, stimulant, carminative, stomachic, diuretic; emmenagogue; veterinary medicine (The Wealth of India, 1948–: 2: 396–398; Héraud, 1949: 243–245).

Cymopterus acaulis (Pursh) Raf. P. N Amer., Great Plains westward. Eaten by Indians (Uphof, 1968: 168).

Cymopterus bulbosus A. Nelson. P. S Rocky Mt. area. Acc. to Uphof (1968: 168), Indians used leaves of *C. bulbosus* L. (error regarding auth.?) for flavouring food.

Cymopterus fendleri A. Gray. P. SW US. Leaves and roots eaten by Indians (Castetter & Opler, 1936: 47–48, 59).

Cymopterus globosus (S. Wats.) S. Wats. P. SW US. Certain Indians: roots and leaves as food (Uphof, 1968: 168).

Cymopterus longipes S. Wats. (*Aulospermum longipes* (S. Wats.) Coult. & Rose). P. Rocky Mt. area, US. Leaves eaten by Indians (Chamberlin, 1911: 338, 367).

Cymopterus montanus (Nutt.) Torr. & Gray (*Phellopterus montanus* Nutt.). P. Plains to SW, US. Roots and other parts eaten by Indians and others (Medsger, 1967: 200, Chamberlin, 1911: 338, 367).

Cymopterus purpureus S. Wats. (*Aulospermum purpureum* (S. Wats.) Coult. & Rose). P. Great Basin and SW US. Certain Indians: seasoning and food.

(*Dasyloma javanica* Miq. Syn. for *Oenanthe javanica* (Blume) DC.)

Daucus carota L. (with many subspecies). Carrot; Wild Carrot, Queen Anne's Lace. B or A. Eur. to Siberia and E India; widely introduced elsewhere. Young shoots of ssp. *maritimus* (Lam.) Britt. (*D. maritimus* Lam.) are sometimes eaten (Courchet, 1882: 204). Ssp. *sativus* (Hoffm.) Arcangeli (with horticultural vars.) is cultivated, principally as the familiar vegetable. Some vars. fed to animals. Sweetening; other flavouring (e.g. of liqueurs). Roots as coffee substitute. Sometimes colouring for butter. Perfumery. Medicine: diuretic, for other urinary problems, excitant, stimulant, deobstruant, useful in skin afflictions, jaundice, dropsy, and in uterine ailments (The Wealth of India, 1948–: 3: 19–23; Harborne, 1970: 13–16; many other sources).

Daucus pusillus Michx. A. Widely distributed, N Amer. Indians: talisman in gambling; root said to be a food; remedy for snake bite (Uphof, 1968: 174).

(*Didiscus glaucifolius* F. Muell. Syn. for *Trachymene glaucifolia* Bentham.)

Dorema spp. A number of species, in addition to the next one below, have been mentioned as possible sources of ammoniac or gum ammoniacum. An example is *D. aucheri* Boiss. (Courchet, 1882: 186–191; Culbreth, 1917: 448).

Dorema ammoniacum D. Don. (*Diserneston gummiferum* Jaub. & Spach.). Ammoniacum. P. W Asia. The principal source of ammoniac. Perfumery. Medicine: antiseptic, carminative, expectorant, stimulant, antispasmodic; for bronchial, liver, and spleen ailments. Root as incense (The Wealth of India, 1948–: 3: 111–112).

Echinophora spinosa L. P. Medit. region. Root edible (Polunin, 1969: 278).

Eryngium spp. Many species of *Eryngium* have been grown as ornamentals because of 'their coloured stems, prickly foliage, teasel-like heads and often brilliant involucre' (The Wealth of India, 1948–: 3: 194).

Eryngium aquaticum L. (*E. virginianum* Lam.). B. Atlantic coast, US. Certain Indians: emetic, diaphoretic, and expectorant (Uphof, 1968: 204; Vogel, 1970: 371).

Eryngium caeruleum Bieb. (possible syn. for *E. dichotomum* Desf., acc. to Tutin *et al.*, 1968: 322). P. SE Russia to W Himalayas. India: tonic, aphrodisiac; for haemorrhoids (The Wealth of India, 1948–: 3: 194).

Eryngium campestre L. Field Eryngo, Snakeroot. P. W Eur. to Afghanistan; N Afr.; N Amer. (introduced). Roots sometimes candied. Diaphoretic, expectorant, emetic; for urinary and uterine ailments (Uphof, 1968: 204).

Eryngium carlinae Delar.f. P. Mexico to Central Amer. Digestive disturbances in children (Uphof, 1968: 204).

Eryngium dichotomum Desf. (cf. *E. caeruleum*). P. W Medit. (local); SE Russia and possibly to the Himalayas. Sudorific (Courchet, 1882: 85).

Eryngium dilatatum Lam. P. Spain and Portugal. Sudorific (Courchet, 1882: 85).

(*Eryngium fluitans* M. E. Jones. See *E. mexicanum*.)

Eryngium foetidum L. B. Mexico to Bolivia, W Indies; other areas, e.g. S Asia. Condiment (substitute for coriander). Cattle fodder in Java. Stomachic (The Wealth of India, 1948–: 3: 194).

Eryngium graecum L. P. SE Eur. Leaves eaten by ancient Greeks; sudorific (Uphof, 1968: 204; Courchet, 1882: 85).

Eryngium longifolium Cav. P. Mexico. Diuretic, emmenagogue, antidote or remedy for poisoning (Courchet, 1882: 85).

Eryngium maritimum L. Sea Holly. P. Coasts of much of Eur.; Ellis Island, NY (introduced). Eaten; sometimes candied. Formerly a medicine, sometimes as a substitute for *E. campestre* (Courchet, 1882: 84–85).

Eryngium mexicanum [auth?]. (If this is *sensu* H. Wolff, it is a syn. for *E. fluitans* M. E. Jones; if the authority is S. Wats., it is a syn. for *E. phyteumae* Delar.f.) P. Mexico (to Arizona?). Diuretic, emmenagogue and treatment for poisoning (Courchet, 1882: 85).

Eryngium monocephalum Cav. (*E. bromeliaefolium* Delar. f.) P. Mexico. Diuretic, emmenagogue and treatment for poisoning (Courchet, 1882: 85).

(*Eryngium phyteumae* Delar.f. See *E. mexicanum*.)

Eryngium planum L. P. C and SE Eur.; E Afr.?; US (introduced). Diuretic, sudorific (Uphof, 1968: 204; Courchet, 1882: 85).

Eryngium ternatum Poiret. P. Crete. Sudorific; aphrodisiac (Courchet, 1882: 85; Uphof, 1968: 204).

Eryngium viride Lam. [Data insufficient.] Evidently provided salad for ancient Greeks (Uphof, 1968: 204, together with *E. graecum*).

Eryngium yuccifolium Michx (including var. *synchaetum* A. Gray (E. *synchaetum* (A. Gray) Rose). Rattlesnake Master, Button Snakeroot. P. E half of US. Medicine of Indians and others: diuretic, diaphoretic, expectorant and emetic. Seminole Indians: ceremonial drink (Uphof, 1968: 204; Vogel, 1970: 371).

(*Eulophus ambiguus* Nutt. Syn. for *Lomatium ambiguum* (Nutt.) Coult. & Rose.)

(*Eulophus bolanderi* (A. Gray) Coult. & Rose. Syn. for *Perideridia bolanderi* (A. Gray) Nelson & Macbr.)

Ferula spp. A number of species of *Ferula* have been mentioned as sources of gum-resins called asafetida and galbanum. The botanical status of some of them could not be determined at the time of writing; not all have been listed separately below.

Ferula alliacea Boiss. Probably P. Iran. Perhaps a source of asafetida (Courchet, 1882: 180–181). Carminative, intestinal antiseptic; for scorpion stings, hysteria and epilepsy (Uphof, 1968: 222).

Ferula assa-foetida L. (with varying spellings and many synonyms). Asafetida. P. SW Asia. Flavouring for sauces and other food. Widely-known medicine: expectorant, carminative, laxative, antispasmodic, stimulant, emmenagogue and anthelmintic; for hypochondriasis (Courchet, 1882: 179–180, 182-185; Uphof, 1968: 222; Héraud, 1949: 286–290). Veterinary medicine (Howes, 1950: 314).

Ferula communis L. (with sspp. and vars.). P. Medit. region. Once used as an antihysteric and for dysentery (Courchet, 1882: 166).

(*Ferula dissoluta* S. Wats. Syn. for *Lomatium dissectum* (Nutt.) Math. & Const.)

Ferula foetida (Bunge) Regel. P. SW Asia. Medicine: Same uses as *F. assa-foetida* (Uphof, 1968: 222) and possibly synonymous with it.

Ferula galbaniflua Boiss. & Buhse. Galbanum. P. SW Asia. The principal source of galbanum, a gum-resin (or oleo-gum-resin). Antispasmodic, expectorant, carminative, stimulant; for hysteria, amenorrhea, tumours, boils, swellings (Uphof, 1968: 222; Courchet, 1882: 172–179). Church incense (Culbreth, 1917: 443). Perfumery (Paris & Moyse, 1961: 110).

Ferula jaeschkeana Vatke. Probably P. C Asia, Afghanistan, W Pakistan, Kashmir. Source of a gum-resin, used for wounds and bruises (Uphof, 1968: 222).

Ferula marmarica Asch. & Taub. P. N Africa. Source of ammoniac of Cyrenaica, a gum (Uphof, 1968: 222).

Ferula narthex Boiss. P. Pakistan and Iran. Possibly a spice in ancient E Medit. areas (Uphof, 1968: 222). Yields one of the gum-resins called asafetida, with the same properties and uses as *F. assa-foetida* or *F. foetida* (Dastur, 1951: 118–119).

Ferula persica Willd. P. Iran. A source of sagapenum, a resin or gum-resin. Uses: like those of *F. assa-foetida* and *F. galbaniflua* (Howes, 1950: 315; Héraud 1949: 289).

Ferula rubricaulis Boiss. P. Iran. A source of galbanum (Courchet, 1882: 172–179) or possibly asafetida (Howes, 1950: 313). See *F. galbaniflua* for uses of galbanum.

Ferula schair Borszcz. P. Turkestan. Possible source of galbanum (Courchet, 1882: 172; Uphof, 1968: 222). See *F. galbaniflua*.

Ferula suaveolens Aitchison & Hemsley. Probably P. C. Asia. May be a source of sumbul (see next entry) or used to adulterate it (Holland, 1937: 201; Culbreth, 1917: 446; Aitchison 1890: 74, 182, 200).

Ferula sumbul (Kauffmann) Hook f. Sumbul, Muskroot. Probably P. C. Asia. Antispasmodic, stimulant, nervous system disorders, carminative; has been used for many other ailments, such as cholera, delirium tremens and gleet (Courchet, 1882:

168–170; Culbreth, 1917: 446–447). Iran: perfume, ceremonial incense (Uphof, 1968: 222) (cf. *F. suaveolens*).

Ferula szowitziana DC. P. Iran. A source of sagapen (?), used for rheumatism and other ailments (cf. *F. persica*) (Holland, 1937: 71, 172; Uphof, 1968: 222).

Ferula tingitana L. African Ammoniac. P. Medit. area, incl. SW Eur. A source of ammoniac, an oleo-gum-resin, used in medicine (see *Dorema ammoniacum*) (Culbreth, 1917: 448; Uphof, 1968: 222).

Foeniculum vulgare Miller (*F. officinale* All., *F. dulce* Miller, *Anethum foeniculum* L.). Fennel. P or B. Most of Eur.; naturalized in most temperate countries. Ssp. *vulgare* is widely cultivated for flavouring foods and beverages and as a vegetable (var. *azoricum* (Miller) Thell. of this ssp. is cultivated for its large tuberous stock and used as a vegetable in some Medit. countries (Tutin *et al.*, 1968: 341)). An old medicine in Eur.: stimulant, tonic, carminative, stomachic (Courchet, 1882: 132–134; Uphof, 1968: 230).

Glehnia littoralis (A. Gray) F. Schmidt ex Miq. (*Phellopterus littoralis* (A. Gray) Bentham). P. E Asia to NW N Amer., maritime. Said to be cultivated in Asia as a condiment (Uphof, 1968: 400). Medicinal plant (Mathias, 1928: 95).

(*Helosciadium californicum* Hook. & Arn. Syn. for *Oenanthe sarmentosa* Presl.)

Heracleum lanatum Michx Cow Parsnip. P. E Asia, Canada, US. Eskimos and many Indian groups ate tender parts and possibly roots. Medicine for Indians, e.g. on the Plains (Gilmore, 1919: 107) and for Whites (Wood & Bache, 1858: 401; Vogel, 1970: 334). Roots as dye (Schenck & Gifford, 1952: 287). Considering food, medicine, and ceremonies, this was probably the most widely used native Umbel in N Amer.

Heracleum mantegazzianum Sommier & Levier. Giant Hogweed. B or P. Caucasus; naturalized elsewhere. Sometimes planted in Europe and the US as an ornamental. May cause dermatitis.

(*Heracleum panaces* L. Possibly a syn. for *H. sphondylium* L., according to Tutin *et al.*, 1968: 436.)

Heracleum persicum Desf. ex Fischer. Probably P. Iran. Cultivated in Eur., occasionally naturalized. Seeds as condiment for pickles in Iran (Uphof 1968: 266).

Heracleum sphondylium L. Common Cow Parsnip, Hogweed, Keck. B or short-lived P. Eur., W and N Asia; W N Afr.; N Amer. (introduced). Young shoots eaten in Siberia. Leaves esteemed by animals. Made into an alcoholic beverage in some European and Asian areas; used for a liqueur in France. Once used medicinally (Uphof, 1968: 266; Courchet, 1882: 161–162).

Heracleum wallichii DC. P. Himalayan area. Tonic, aphrodisiac (Uphof, 1968: 266).

Heteromorpha arborescens (Thunb.) Cham. & Schlecht. P. S, E Afr. Many medicinal uses (Watt & Breyer-Brandwijk, 1962: 1038–1039).

Heteromorpha trifoliata (Wendl.) Eckl. & Zeyh. P. Widespread, Trop. and S Afr. Many medicinal uses; also for making fire (Cannon, 1970: 341–342; Cannon, personal communication).

Hydrocotyle alchemilloides Rich. (*H. citriodora* R. & P.). P. Peru to Ecuador. Peru: aromatic (Courchet, 1882: 81).

(*Hydrocotyle asiatica* L. Syn. for *Centella asiatica* (L.) Urban.)

Hydrocotyle bonariensis Lam. P. Argentina to N Carolina; trop. Afr. (naturalized). S Amer.: for skin diseases and toothache (Courchet, 1882: 81; Mathias & Constance, 1962: 67).

Hydrocotyle bupleurifolia Rich. (Has been referred to *Centella glabrata* L.) P. S Afr.: astringent; for diarrhoea (Courchet, 1882: 81).

Hydrocotyle moschata Forster. P. New Zealand: aromatic (Courchet, 1882: 81). (Introduced in US and probably elsewhere.)

Hydrocotyle sibthorpioides Lam. (*H. hirsuta* Blume, *H. latisecta* Zell., *H. puncticulata* Miq., *H. rotundiflora* Roxb.) P. SE Asia to Indonesia; trop. Afr.; Americas (introduced). Leaves eaten. Cough remedy; has been substitute for *Centella asiatica* (L.) Urban (Courchet, 1882: 81; Uphof, 1968: 275).

Hydrocotyle umbellata L. P. Coastal S and N Amer.; Old World (introduced). S Amer.: used for liver, kidney ailments (Courchet, 1882: 81).

Hydrocotyle vulgaris L. Pennywort, White-rot. P. W and S Eur., NW Afr.; (possibly introduced, New Zealand). Medicine: aperitive and detergent (Courchet, 1882: 84); Danish home remedy for whooping cough (Brøndegaard, 1970).

(*Imperatoria ostruthium* L. Syn. for *Peucedanum ostruthium* (L.) Koch.)

Lagoecia cuminoides L. A. Medit. region. Occasionally used as flavouring in place of *Cuminum cyminum* (Uphof, 1968: 298).

Laser trilobum (L.) Borkh. (*Siler trilobum* (L.) Crantz). C Eur. to Iran. Veterinary medicine: carminative (Uphof, 1968: 485, as *S. trilobum* (L.) Borkh.).

Laserpitium latifolium L. Laserwort, Woundwort, White Gentian. P. Much of Eur. Used in beer. Locally: stomachic. Veterinary medicine (Uphof: 1968: 302). Var. *asperum* (Crantz) Soyer-Willemet (*L. asperum* Crantz): root formerly used as tonic, emmenagogue, diuretic, purgative (Courchet 1882: 202).

Laserpitium prutenicum L. (*L. selenoides* Crantz). B, though sometimes longer-lived. Widespread in Eur. Root used in home remedies for skin diseases (Uphof, 1968: 302).

Laserpitium siler L. (*L. montanum* Lam., *Siler montanum* Crantz). Sermountain. P. C and SC Eur. Condiment and in liqueur. Formerly as medicine: emmenagogue, stomachic, diuretic, vulnerary and for toothache (Uphof, 1968: 302; Courchet 1882: 202).

Laretia acaulis Gill & Hook. P. Chile, Argentina. Source of a resin, a substitute for galbanum (Uphof 1968: 304).

(*Leptotaenia* spp. See *Lomatium* spp.)

Levisticum officinale Koch (*Angelica levisticum* Baill.). Garden Lovage, Bladder Seed, Lovage Angelica. P. Iran, most of Eur. (often cultivated). Eaten like celery; flavouring for foods and drinks. Medicine: aromatic, stimulant, diaphoretic, emmenagogue, carminative (Courchet 1882: 147–148; Uphof, 1968: 310).

(*Libanotis daucoides* Scop. Syn. for *Seseli libanotis* (L.) Koch.)

Lichtensteinia interrupta E. Mey. P. S Afr. Root: febrifuge (Uphof, 1968: 311).

Lichtensteinia pyrethrifolia Cham. & Schlecht. P. S Afr. Hottentots: for making an intoxicating drink (Uphof, 1968: 311).

(*Ligusticum acutilobum* Sieb. & Zucc. Syn. for *Angelica acutiloba* (Sieb. & Zucc.) Kitagawa.)

Ligusticum apiifolium (Nutt.) A. Gray (*L. apiodorum* (A. Gray) Coult. & Rose). P. Pacific states, US. Medicine of Indians, e.g. the Karok used for stimulation of appetite (Schenck & Gifford, 1952: 387).

(*Ligusticum bulbocastanum* (L.) Crantz. Syn. for *Bunium bulbocastanum* L.)

Ligusticum diffusum Roxb. (Has been referred to *Seseli indicum* W. & A.) A. India. Said to be used in India for treatment of sick farm animals (Courchet 1882: 148).

Ligusticum filicinum S. Wats. P. W US. Medicine: many uses by Indians (e.g. Smith, 1923: 55).

Ligusticum grayi Coult. & Rose. P. W US. Possibly eaten by Indians. Stimulant (French & French, n.d.).

(*Ligusticum monnieri* (L.) Calest. Syn. for *Cnidium monnieri* (L.) Cusson, evidently, but there has been confusion in the nomenclature.)

Ligusticum mutellina (L.) Crantz (*Meum mutellina* (L.) Gaertner, *Aethusa mutellina* (L.) St. Lag.). P. Mountains, C and S Eur. Used like parsley and as tea. Fodder for livestock. Sometimes a stomachic (Uphof, 1968: 312).

(*Ligusticum nodiflorum* Vill. Syn. for *Trochiscanthes nodiflora* (Vill.) Koch.)

Ligusticum porteri Coult. & Rose. P. Mountains, W US. SW Indians eat as vegetable (Castetter & Opler, 1936: 46–47).

Ligusticum scoticum L. (*L. hultenii* Fernald). Lovage, Scotch Lovage, Alexanders. P. Eurasia, W and E coasts of northern N Amer. Eaten as a vegetable in Scotland (formerly) and by Alaskan Eskimos; also candied like *Angelica archangelica* (Uphof, 1968: 312).

Lomatium ambiguum (Nutt.) Coult. & Rose (*Cogswellia ambigua* (Nutt.) M. E. Jones). P. NW US, British Columbia. Eaten by Indians (Uphof, 1968: 143).

Lomatium californicum (Nutt.) Math. & Const. (*Leptotaenia californica* Nutt. ex Torr. & Gray). P. Calif. and S Oregon. Indians: eaten, smoked; used ceremonially and to stimulate appetite (Schenck & Gifford, 1952: 387).

Lomatium canbyi (Coult. & Rose) Coult. & Rose (*Cogswellia canbyi* (Coult. & Rose) M. E. Jones, *Peucedanum canbyi* Coult. & Rose). P. NW US. Roots eaten by Indians (French, 1965: 380).

Lomatium cous (S. Wats.) Coult. & Rose (*Cogswellia cous* (S. Wats.) M. E. Jones, *Peucedanum cous* S. Wats.). Cous. P. NW US. Roots eaten by many Indian groups (French, 1965: 380).

Lomatium dissectum (Nutt.) Math. & Const. (*Ferula dissoluta* S. Wats., *Leptotaenia dissecta* Nutt. ex Torr. & Gray, *L. multifida* Nutt. ex Torr. & Gray) (with vars.). P. SW Canada and W US. Roots and young shoots sometimes eaten by Indians; medicine for humans (e.g. lung diseases) and for horses; root used in making buckskin (French & French, n.d.; Constance, 1963; Steedman, 1930; 480, 513).

Lomatium farinosum (Geyer) Coult. & Rose (*Cogswellia farinosa* (Geyer) M. E. Jones). P. NW US. Indians: roots eaten (Medsger, 1967: 190–191).

Lomatium foeniculaceum (Nutt.) Coult. & Rose (*Cogswellia daucifolia* (Nutt.) M. E. Jones, *C. foeniculacea* (Nutt.) Coult. & Rose). P. W US and Canada. Love charm among Plains Indians (Gilmore, 1919: 107). Possibly eaten (cf. Uphof, 1968: 143).

Lomatium geyeri (S. Wats.) Coult. & Rose. P. S British Columbia to C Washington and to Idaho. Roots eaten by Indians (Constance, 1963; Medsger, 1967: 190–191).

Lomatium gormanii (Howell) Coult. & Rose. P. NW US. Roots eaten by Indians (Constance, 1963; French & French, n.d.).

Lomatium grayi Coult. & Rose. P. W US, except the coastal regions. Young shoots and roots eaten by Indians (French, 1965: 380; Constance, 1963).

Lomatium leptocarpum (Torr. & Gray) Coult. & Rose. NW US (interior). Roots eaten by Indians (Constance, 1963).

Lomatium macrocarpum (Hook. & Arn.) Coult. & Rose (*Peucedanum macrocarpum* Nutt. ex Torr. & Gray). P. W Canada and US. Roots once eaten by many Indian groups, e.g. Thompson (Steedman, 1930: 479).

Lomatium nudicaule (Pursh) Coult. & Rose (*Peucedanum leiocarpum* Nutt. ex Torr. & Gray). P. W Canada and US. Stems and leaves (also roots formerly) eaten by Indians; used as tea; sometimes used as medicine, e.g. among the Thompson (Steedman, 1930: 473, 479, 483, 484, 494); fruits to perfume buckskin (French, 1965: 381).

Lomatium parryi (S. Wats.) F. Macbr. (*Peucedanum scopulorum* M. E. Jones). P. Calif. to Utah. Eaten by Paiute Indians (Schneider, 1906: 97).

Lomatium piperi Coult. & Rose. P. Interior of NW US. Roots eaten by Indians (French, 1965: 380).

Lomatium salmoniflorum (Coult. & Rose) Math. & Const. P. Snake River area, W US. Indians ate root (Constance, 1963).

Lomatium triternatum (Pursh) Coult. & Rose (with vars.). P. NW US and adjacent Canada. Roots formerly eaten by Indians (Constance, 1963; French & French, n.d.).

Lomatium utriculatum (Nutt.) Coult. & Rose (*Peucedanum utriculatum* Nutt. ex Torr. & Gray). P. Pacific Coast areas of US and Canada. Young leaves eaten by Indians (Chesnut, 1902: 373).

Malabaila pumila Boiss. P. Sahara, E Nile region. Roots eaten by Bedouins (Uphof, 1968: 327).

Malabaila sekakul (Russ.) Boiss. (*Pastinaca sekakul* Russ.). Sekakul. P. E Medit. Aphrodisiac (Uphof, 1968: 327; Courchet, 1882: 160).

Meum athamanticum Jacq. Spignel, Meu, Baldmoney. P. W and C Eur., local in S and E. Once cultivated in N England. Roots formerly eaten as vegetable by Scottish Highlanders. The herb as medicine: tonic, aromatic, stomachic, diuretic and stimulant; used for flatulence, cattarh, hysteria, amenorrhea, dysmenorrhea, other uterine ailments (Uphof, 1968: 344).

(*Meum mutellina* (L.) Gaertner. Syn. for *Ligusticum mutellina* (L.) Crantz.)

Myrrhis odorata (L.) Scop. Sweet Cicely, Garden Myrrh. P, occasionally cultivated. Much of Eur.; Chile (probably introduced). Flavouring. Forage plant. Expectorant, carminative, stomachic; home remedy for 'cleaning the blood' (Uphof, 1968: 356).

Neonelsonia acuminata (Bentham) Coult. & Rose. P. NW S Amer. Intestinal ailments; after childbirth (Uphof, 1968: 359).

(*Oenanthe* spp. A number of species of *Oenanthe* are said to be poisonous, at least to a degree; only one such is listed here (cf. Courchet, 1882: 125; Kingsbury, 1964: 377).)

Oenanthe aquatica (L.) Poiret (*O. phellandrium* Lam., *Phellandrium aquaticum* L.). Fine-leaved Water Dropwort, Water Fennel. Winter A or B, becoming P by offsets. Eur., except the extreme N; W Asia. Medicine: expectorant, diuretic, alterative; for laryngitis, catarrh, and asthma (Uphof, 1968: 367; Courchet, 1882: 121–123).

Oenanthe crocata L. Hemlock Water Dropwort. P. W Eur.; Morocco. Roots poisonous; used in Sardinia for stupefying fish (Uphof, 1968: 367); formerly a medicine, e.g. for epilepsy (Courchet, 1882: 125).

Oenanthe javanica (Blume) DC. (*O. laciniata* Zoll., *O. stolonifera* Wall., *Dasyloma javanica* Miq.). Water Dropwort. P, sometimes cultivated. E Asia, Indonesia. Food (Barrau, n.d.: 67; Uphof, 1968: 367).

Oenanthe pimpinelloides L. Water Dropwort. P. W and S Eur. to Asia Minor. Tubers said to have been eaten in parts of France (Courchet, 1882: 125).

Oenanthe sarmentosa Presl. (*Helosciadium californicum* Hook. & Arn.). P. Pacific Coast, Canada and US. Stems and roots eaten by various Indians; laxative (Gunther, 1945: 42; Medsger, 1967: 200).

Opopanax chironium (L.) Koch (*Pastinaca opopanax* L.). Opopanax. P. Balkans, Medit. region, Iran. Used in perfumery. Once medicinal: antispasmodic and expectorant (Courchet, 1882: 163–165; Howes, 1950: 315).

Osmorhiza brachypoda Torr. P. Calif. and Arizona. Indian use: cough medicine (Schneider, 1906: 97).

Osmorhiza chilensis Hook. & Arn. (*O. nuda* Torr., *Washingtonia nuda* Heller). P. N Amer. (widespread); W S Amer. Roots and shoots eaten by certain Indian groups; many medicinal uses (Steedman, 1930: 480; Schenck & Gifford, 1952: 386–387).

Osmorhiza claytonii (Michx) Clarke. P. E, Midwest US, Canada. Menomini Indians: for gaining weight (Smith, 1923: 55).

Osmorhiza longistylis (Torr.) DC. (*Washingtonia longistylis* (Torr.) Britton). P. E and C Canada and US. Indian medicine: e.g. tonic and for lesions (Gilmore, 1919: 107).

Osmorhiza occidentalis (Nutt.) Torr. P. W Canada and US. Indians used for colds (Uphof, 1968: 378).

(*Pastinaca opopanax* L. Syn. for *Opopanax chironium* (L.) Koch.)

Pastinaca sativa L. (with ssp. and/or vars.). Parsnip; Wild Parsnip. B. W Eur. to Altai Mts; many temperate countries (introduced). Cultivated (frequently escapes). Roots well-known as food. Food for animals. Fruits: tonic and carminative; said to be emmenagogue (Courchet, 1882: 159–160).

(*Pastinaca sekakul* Russ. Syn. for *Malabaila sekakul* (Russ.) Boiss.)

Perideridia bolanderi (A. Gray) Nelson & Macbr. (*Eulophus bolanderi* (A. Gray) Coult. & Rose). P. Great Basin and Sierra Nevada Mts, W US. Roots eaten by Miwok and other Indians (Chuang & Constance, 1969: 23–24).

Perideridia gairdneri (Hook. & Arn.) Mathias (*Carum gairdneri* (Hook. & Arn.) A. Gray). P. Calif. to British Columbia, east to S Dakota, US. The roots of ssp. *borealis* Chuang & Constance, at least, have been an important food of many Indian groups (Chuang & Constance, 1969: 23–24, 57–63; French & French, n.d.; Medsger, 1967: 191–192).

Perideridia kelloggii (A. Gray) Mathias (*Carum kelloggii* A. Gray). P. California.

Roots eaten by Indians; seeds as flavouring; root fibres in hair grooming (Chesnut, 1902: 372; Chuang & Constance, 1969: 23–24).

Perideridia lemmonii (Coult. & Rose) Chuang & Constance. P. Calif. and adjacent Oregon. Probably eaten by certain Calif. Indians (Chuang & Constance, 1969: 23–24).

Perideridia oregana (S. Wats.) Mathias (*Carum oreganum* S. Wats.). P. Calif. and Oregon. Eaten by Indians (Chuang & Constance, 1969: 23–24).

Perideridia parishii (Coult. & Rose) Nelson & Macbr. P. Calif. to New Mexico. Evidently eaten by Indians (Chuang & Constance, 1969: 23).

Petroselinum crispum (Miller) A. W. Hill (*P. hortense* auct., *P. sativum* Hoffm., *Apium petroselinum* L.). Parsley. B. Much of Eur., W Asia (also widely cultivated elsewhere). Some plants form enlarged, edible roots. Leaves well known for flavouring soups, foods; oil of parsley used similarly. Aperitive, carminative, stimulant, diuretic (Courchet, 1882: 99–103; Garnaud, 1942: 111–112; Uphof, 1968: 398).

(*Peucedanum* spp. For native N American species attributed to *Peucedanum*, see *Lomatium* spp.)

Peucedanum alsaticum L. P. Much of Eur. Once used for epilepsy (Courchet, 1882: 150–151).

(*Peucedanum araliaceum* (Hochst.) Bentham ex Vatke for *Steganotaenia araliacea* Hochst.)

Peucedanum aucheri Boiss. P. SW Asia. Seeds and leaves used in Baluchistan for indigestion (Uphof, 1968: 398).

Peucedanum cervaria (L.) Lapeyr. (*Selinum cervaria* L., *Athamanta cervaria* L.). Hart's Wort, Much-good. P. S and C Eur. to the Urals. Once cultivated. Traditional European uses: for dropsy, gout, epilepsy, gastrointestinal ailments, fever; as emmenagogue and diuretic (Uphof, 1968: 398; Courchet, 1882: 151).

(*Peucedanum decursivum* (Miq.) Maxim. Syn. for *Angelica decursiva* (Miq.) Franch. & Sav.)

Peucedanum dhana Buch.-Ham. ex D. Don. P. W. Himalayas, N Bengal. Root as tonic (Uphof, 1968: 398).

(*Peucedanum fraxinifolium* Hiern. ex Oliv. Syn. for *Steganotaenia araliacea* Hochst.)

Peucedanum galbanum (L.) Benth. & Hook. (*Bubon galbanum* L.). P. S Afr. Diuretic (Uphof, 1968: 399; cf. Courchet, 1882: 157).

(*Peucedanum graveolens* Bentham. Probably the same as *Anethum graveolens*.)

Peucedanum magaliesmontanum Sond. P. S Afr. Root in baths to refresh the body (Watt & Breyer-Brandwijk, 1962: 1041).

Peucedanum officinale L. (*P. altissimum* Desf., *Selinum officinale* Vest). Hog's Fennel, Sea Hog's Fennel, Sulphurweed. P. Much of Eur.; W Siberia. Expectorant, sudorific, diuretic emmenagogue, antiscorbutic (Uphof, 1968: 399).

Peucedanum oreoselinum (L.) Moench. Mountain Parsley, Mountain Stone Parsley. P. Much of Eur. Once medicinal: stimulant, diaphoretic, febrifuge (Courchet, 1882: 150–151).

Peucedanum ostruthium (L.) Koch (*Imperatoria ostruthium* L., *Selinum ostruthium* Wallr.). Master-wort, Hogfennel, Herb Gerard. P. C and S Europe; many temperate countries (introduced). Formerly cultivated. Flavouring for cheese and beverages. Stimulant (Courchet, 1882: 152–154; Uphof, 1968: 399).

Peucedan umpalustre (L.) Moench (*Selinum palustre* L., *S. sylvestre* L.). Hog's Fennel (cf. other *Peucedanum* spp.), Milk Parsley. B. W Eur. to Altai Mts. Slavic countries: substitute for ginger (Uphof, 1968: 399). Once used medicinally, e.g. for epilepsy (Courchet, 1882: 151–152).

(*Peucedanum sativum* S. Wats. Syn. for *Pastinaca sativa* L.)

(*Phellandrium aquaticum* L. Syn. for *Oenanthe aquatica* (L.) Poiret.)

(*Phellopterus littoralis* Bentham. Syn. for *Glehnia littoralis* (A. Gray) F. Schmidt ex Miq.)

(*Phellopterus montanus* Nutt. Syn. for *Cymopterus montanus* (Nutt.) T. & G.)

Pimpinella alpina Koord. P. Java: diuretic, aphrodisiac (Uphof, 1968: 406; cf. Courchet, 1882: 117, under *P. panatjan*).

Pimpinella anisum L. (*Anisum vulgare* Gaertner). Anise. A. Asia; long cultivated—often naturalized—elsewhere. Fruits for flavouring foods, beverages. Medicine: aromatic, stimulant, carminative, diaphoretic, emmenagogue; for pulmonary afflictions, to stimulate the secretion of milk; externally for ecchymosis (Uphof, 1968: 406–407; Courchet, 1882: 113–115; Héraud, 1949: 95–97).

Pimpinella diversifolia DC. P. Himalayan region. Carminative (Uphof, 1968: 407).

Pimpinella platyphylla Welw. ex Hiern. B to P. Angola and Rhodesia. Stimulant and antispasmodic (Cannon, 1970: 346–347).

Pimpinella major (L.) Hudson (*P. magna* L.). Great Burnet Saxifrage. P. Much of Eur. Has been used as diuretic, antispasmodic, vulnerary (Courchet, 1882: 115–116).

Pimpinella saxifraga L. (*P. alpestris* (Sprengel) Schultes, *P. dissecta* Retz., *P. laconica* Halácsy, *Carum nigrum* Baill.). Burnet Saxifrage, Black Caraway. P. Most of Eur.; Asia Minor; W Siberia; possibly E Asia. Limited use as condiment. Medical uses have been like those for *P. anisum* and *P. major* (Courchet, 1182: 116–117; Culbreth, 1917: 434).

(*Porphyroscias decursiva* Miq. Syn. for *Angelica decursiva* (Miq.) Franch. & Sav.)

Prangos pabularia Lindl. (Has been referred to a species of *Cachrys*.) P. Iran, Kashmir. Stimulant, stomachic, carminative, diuretic, emmenagogue; expulsion of foetus. Veterinary medicine (Uphof, 1968: 428).

(*Pseudocymopterus aletifolius* Rydb. Syn. for *Aletes anisatus* (A. Gray) Theobald & Tseng.)

(*Pteryxia anisata* (A. Gray) Math. & Const. Syn. for *Aletes anisatus* (A. Gray) Theobald & Tseng.)

(*Ptychotis* spp. Various species believed to be sources of Ajowan and Ammi have been assigned to this genus. See *Trachyspermum copticum* (L.) Link.)

Sanicula bipinnata Hook. & Arn. P. Calif. Indians ate young greens; believed to grow near water which can bring good luck; used for snake bite (Schenck & Gifford, 1952: 386; Barrett & Gifford, 1933: 172).

Sanicula bipinnatifida Dougl. ex Hook. P. SW Canada to NW Mexico. Miwok Indians: decoction of root as cure-all (Barrett & Gifford, 1933: 172, 173).

Sanicula canadensis L. B. E half of US. Said to have had the same uses as *S. europaea* L. (Courchet, 1882: 87). Once used as medicine by Indians (Vogel, 1970: 62).

Sanicula crassicaulis Poepp. ex DC. (*S. menziesii* Hook. & Arn.). P. Vancouver Is. to

Baja California; Chile. Calif. Indians: for rattlesnake bites; good luck in gambling (Barrett & Gifford, 1933: 173; Chesnut, 1902: 373).

Sanicula europaea L. European Wood Sanicle, Sanicle. P. Eur. to E Asia and E Indies; Afr. Has been used as astringent, stomachic; for leukorrhea, dysentery, lung diseases, contusions (Courchet, 1882: 85–86; Uphof, 1968: 468).

Sanicula marilandica L. Black Snake Root, Sanicle. P. From E N Amer. to Br. Columbia and New Mexico. Astringent, antispasmodic, periodic, antisyphilitic (Uphof, 1968: 468; Vogel, 1970: 212, 368).

Sanicula tuberosa Torr. P. Oregon to S Calif. Tuberous root eaten by certain Calif. Indians (Chesnut, 1902: 374).

Scandia rosaefolia (Hook.) Dawson (*Angelica rosaefolia* Hook.). P. New Zealand. Diuretic; for syphilis (Brooker & Cooper, 1961: 7).

Scandix australis L. A. S Eur. May once have been medicinal (cf. Courchet, 1882: 206). Subsp. *grandiflora* (L.) Thell. (*S. grandiflora* L.) eaten as salad in Greece (Uphof, 1968: 473).

(*Scandix cerefolium* L. Syn. for *Anthriscus cerefolium* (L.) Hoffm.)

Scandix pecten-veneris L. Shepherd's Needle, Venus's Comb, Lady's Comb. A. Eur. to Himalayas. Temp. zones elsewhere (introduced). A weed. Young tops of stems sometimes used in salads (Uphof, 1968: 474). Once used for bleeding, amenorrhea, bladder afflictions (Courchet, 1882: 206).

(*Scorodosma foetidum* Bunge. Syn. for *Ferula assa-foetida* L.)

(*Selinum cervaria* L. Syn. for *Peucedanum cervaria* (L.) Lapeyr.)

(*Selinum monnieri* L. Syn. for *Cnidium monnieri* (L.) Cusson.)

(*Selinum officinale* Vest. Syn. for *Peucedanum officinale* L.)

(*Selinum ostruthium* Wallr. Syn. for *Peucedanum ostruthium* (L.) Koch.)

(*Selinum palustre* L. Syn. for *Peucedanum palustre* (L.) Moench.)

(*Selinum sylvestre* L. Syn. for *Peucedanum palustre* (L.) Moench.)

Seseli hippomarathrum Jacq. P. C and E Eur. May have had the same uses as *S. tortuosum* L. (cf. Courchet, 1882: 134–135).

(*Seseli indicum* W. & A. Possibly the same as *Ligusticum diffusum* Roxb.)

Seseli libanotis (L.) Koch (*Libanotis daucoides* Scop.). B or P. Much of Europe. Switzerland: aromatic and vulnerary (Courchet, 1882: 155).

Seseli tortuosum L. B. S Eur. Has been a carminative and a component of an antidote for animal poisons (Courchet, 1882: 134).

(*Siler montanum* Crantz. Syn. for *Laserpitium siler* L.)

(*Siler trilobum* (L.) Crantz. Syn. for *Laser trilobum* (L.) Borkh.)

Sison amomum L. (*Cicuta amomum* (L.) Crantz, *Sium amomum* Roth, *S. aromaticum* Lam., *Seseli amomum* (L.) Scop.). Stone Parsley, Hedge Sison. B. W Eur., Medit. region, Caucasus. Food and flavouring. Once as medicine: diuretic, stomachic, carminative, diaphoretic (cf. Courchet, 1882: 106–107; Uphof, 1968: 486).

(*Sium* spp. Various species of *Sium*, not all listed here, have been reported as poisonous.)

(*Sium angustifolium* L. Syn. for *Berula erecta* (Hudson) Coville.)

(*Sium aromaticum* Lam. Syn. for *Sison amomum* L.)

(*Sium erectum* Hudson. Syn. for *Berula erecta* (Hudson) Coville.)

Sium latifolium L. P. Most of Eur., except certain peripheral regions. Once: diuretic, antiscorbutic, aperitive (Courchet, 1882: 118). Root-stock said to be poisonous (Grieve, 1959: 617–618).

Sium sisarum L. (with vars.). Skirret, Chervin. P. C, S, SE Eur.; E Asia? Roots of var. *sisarum* have been cultivated: food, coffee substitute (Uphof, 1968: 487). Once used for a tonic and a digestive liqueur (Courchet, 1882: 118–119).

Sium suave Walt. (*S. cicutaefolium* Schrank, *S. latifolium* A. Gray, non L., *S. lineare* Michx.). P. N Amer., widespread; E Asia. Roots and leaves eaten by Indians (e.g. Uphof, 1968: 487).

(*Sium thunbergii* DC. Syn. for *Berula erecta* (Hudson) Coville.)

Smyrnium cordifolium Boiss. SW Asia. Eaten as a vegetable, raw or cooked (Aitchison, 1890: 195, 217).

Smyrnium olusatrum L. Maceron, Alexanders. B. W, S Eur. to Caucasus, Syria, Canary Is. Formerly cultivated as a pot-herb; fed to animals; fruits used for scurvy (Courchet, 1882: 217; Uphof, 1968: 488).

Sphenosciadium capitellatum A. Gray. P. W US (interior). Root as syphilis medication (Steward, 1933: 317).

Steganotaenia araliacea Hochst. (*Peucedanum araliaceum* (Hochst.) Bentham ex Vatke f., *P. fraxinifolium* Hiern. ex Oliv.). P. Trop. Afr. Leaves for scenting clothes (Uphof, 1968: 398). Gateposts, etc.: Uganda (R. N. Lester, personal communication). Root for sore throat, bark for asthma (Watt & Breyer-Brandwijk, 1962: 1042). Diuretic, depurative, vermifuge, for lotions (Uphof, 1968: 398).

Tauschia arguta (Torr. & Gray) J. F. Macbride (*Velaea arguta* (Torr. & Gray) Coult. & Rose). P. Coastal S Calif. to Baja Calif. Luiseño Indians: roots used medicinally (White, 1955).

Thapsia garganica L. P. Medit. region. Medicine: epispastic, revulsive, purgative; for thinness, chest ailments, sterility, rheumatism, gout (Courchet, 1882: 194–201; Héraud, 1949: 584–586).

Thapsia villosa L. P. W Medit. Moors: purgative (Courchet, 1882: 201).

Tordylium apulum L. A. Medit. region. Greece: young plants as vegetable (Uphof, 1968: 522).

Tordylium officinale L. A. E Medit. Fruits: emmenagogue; component of an antidote for animal (e.g. snake) poisons (Courchet, 1882: 163).

Trachymene glaucifolia Bentham (*Didiscus glaucifolius* F. Muell.). A or B. Australia. Root may have been eaten (Cleland & Johnston, 1937–1938: 338).

Trachyspermum copticum (L.) Link (*Ammi copticum* L., *Carum copticum* (L.) Bentham). (Perhaps a syn. for *Ammios* sp.) Ammi; Ajowan. A. S and SE Asia, NE Afr. Condiment. Industrial uses for oil. Antiseptic, aromatic, carminative, many other uses (Holland, 1937: 214; Dastur, 1951: 71–72).

Trochiscanthes nodiflora (Vill.) Koch (*Ligusticum nodiflorum* Vill.). P. SC Eur. Carminative and emmenagogue; said to be sometimes substituted for *Angelica archangelica* L. (Courchet, 1882: 148–149).

(*Velaea arguta* (Torr. & Gray) Coult. & Rose. Syn. for *Tauschia arguta* (Torr. & Gray) J. F. Macbride.)

(*Washingtonia* spp. See *Osmorhiza* spp.)

Zizia aurea (L.) Koch. P. E N Amer. to Saskatchewan and Texas. Certain Indians: febrifuge (Vogel, 1970: 175).

Zozima absinthiifolia (Vent.) Link. (Aitchison, 1890: 225, lists *Zozimia absinthifolia* Vent., which is clearly the same, as a common herb, eaten in SW Asia.)

ACKNOWLEDGEMENTS

Thanks for assistance that made this paper possible is owed to many; among them are: Bert G. Brehm, Robert Campbell, J. F. M. Cannon, Lincoln Constance, Lori Cronyn, Kathrine S. French, I. C. Hedge, V. H. Heywood, Patricia Honchar, Mildred E. Mathias, Robert Ornduff, Rafael L. Rodríguez and Katherine Verdery. Numerous useful suggestions were made by participants in the symposium at Reading; they are not all acknowledged here.

Grants to Reed College from the National Science Foundation (GY-4746, GU-3664) supported student assistance in the preparation of the manuscript. A National Institutes of Health grant (GM-11287) to the author financed earlier ethnobotanical research, which proved to be useful in this undertaking.

REFERENCES

AITCHISON, J. E. T., 1890. *Notes on the Products of Western Afghanistan and of Northeastern Persia.* 228 pp. Reprinted from Transactions of the Botanical Society, Edinburgh.

AMES, O., 1939. *Economic Annuals and Human Cultures.* 153 pp. Cambridge: Botanical Museum of Harvard University.

AREY, L. B. *et al.* (eds), 1957. *Dorland's Illustrated Medical Dictionary.* Philadelphia & London: W. B. Saunders Company. 23rd ed., 1598 pp.

BARRAU, J., n.d. *An Ethnobotanical Guide for Anthropological Research in Malayo-Oceania* (*Preliminary Draft*). 149 pp. UNESCO Science Cooperation Office for Southeast Asia.

BARRETT, S. A., & GIFFORD, E. W., 1933. Miwok material culture. *Bull. Publ. Mus. Milwaukee,* **2**: 117–376.

BRØNDEGAARD, V. J., 1970. Personal communication.

BROOKER, S. G. & COOPER, R. C., 1961. New Zealand medicinal plants. *Econ. Bot.,* **15**: 1–10.

CANNON, J. F. M., 1970. Umbelliferae. *Conspectus Flor. angol.,* **4**: 334–360.

CASTETTER, E. F. & OPLER, M. E., 1936. Ethnobiological studies in the American Southwest. III. The ethnobiology of the Chiricahua and Mescalero Apache. A. The use of plants for foods, beverages, and narcotics. *Univ. New Mex. Bull., Biol. Ser.,* **4**, No. 5, 63 pp.

CHAMBERLIN, R. V., 1911. The ethno-botany of the Gosiute Indians of Utah. *Mem. Amer. Anthrop. Ass.,* **2**: 329–405.

CHESNUT, V. K., 1902. Plants used by the Indians of Mendocino County, California. *Contrib. U.S. natn. Herb.,* **7**: 295–408.

CHUANG, T.-I. & CONSTANCE, L., 1969. *A Systematic Study of Perideridia* (*Umbelliferae-Apioideae*). 74 pp. Berkeley and Los Angeles: University of California Publs.

CLAPHAM, A. R., TUTIN, T. G. & WARBURG, E. F., 1962. *Flora of the British Isles.* 2nd ed., 1269 pp. Cambridge: University Press.

CLELAND, J. B. & JOHNSTON, T. H., 1937–1938. Notes on native names and uses of plants in the Musgrave Ranges region. *Oceania,* **8**: 208–215, 328–342.

CONSTANCE, L., 1963. Notes on uses of Umbelliferae by Indians of the Pacific Northwest, from collectors' notations at Kew and the British Museum of Natural History. Unpublished.

COURCHET, L., 1882. *Les Ombellifères en général et les espèces usitées en pharmacie en particulier.* 221 pp. Montpellier: Imprimerie Cristin, Serre & Ricome.

CULBRETH, D. M. R., 1917. *A Manual of Materia Medica and Pharmacology.* 6th ed., 1001 pp. Philadelphia & New York: Lea & Febiger.

DASTUR, J. F. [1951]. *Medicinal Plants of India and Pakistan.* 317 pp. Bombay: D. B. Taraporevala Sons & Co., Ltd.

FRENCH, D. H., 1960. Ethnobotanical notes taken at the Jardin des Plantes, Muséum National d'Histoire Naturelle, Paris. Unpublished.

FRENCH, D. H., 1965. Ethnobotany of the Pacific Northwest Indians. *Econ. Bot.*, **19**: 378–382.

FRENCH, D. H. & FRENCH, K. S., n.d. Ethnobotanical notes on Indians of the Pacific Northwest. Unpublished.

FRENCH, D. H. & FRENCH, K. S., 1966, 1968. Ethnobotanical notes collected in France, especially in the Massif Central. Unpublished.

FULLING, E. H. (ed.), 1950. Some potential sources of important plant products in California. *Econ. Bot.*, **4**: 3–36.

GARNAUD, P., 1942. Les principales plantes médicinales du Massif Central. *Mém. Société d'Histoire Naturelle d'Auvergne*, No. 2, 115 pp.

GILMORE, M. R., 1919. Uses of plants by the Indians of the Missouri River region. *Bur. Amer. Ethnol. Ann. Rep.*, **33**: 43–154.

GRIEVE, M., 1959. *A Modern Herbal* (first published 1931), 2 vols., 888 pp. New York: Hafner Publishing Co.

GUNTHER, E., 1945. Ethnobotany of western Washington. *Univ. Wash. Publ. Anthropol.*, **10**: 1–61.

HARBORNE, J. B., 1970. Editorial review: chemotaxonomy of the carrot. *Chemical Plant Taxonomy Newsletter*, **14**: 13–16.

HARRISON, S. G., MASEFIELD, G. B. & WALLIS, M., 1969. *The Oxford Book of Food Plants*. 206 pp. London: Oxford University Press.

HELLER, C. A., 1953. *Edible and Poisonous Plants of Alaska*. 167 pp. Cooperative Extension Work in Agriculture and Home Economics Extension Service, University of Alaska and U.S. Department of Agriculture College, Alaska.

HÉRAUD, A., 1949. *Nouveau dictionnaire des plantes médicinales*. 7th ed., 657 pp. Paris: Librairie J.-B. Baillière et Fils.

HERMANT, P. & BOOMANS, D., n.d. La médecine populaire. *Bulletin du Service de Recherches Historiques et Folkloriques du Brabant*, 240 pp. Bruxelles.

HILL, A. F., 1952. *Economic Botany, a Textbook of Useful Plants and Plant Products*. 2nd ed., 560 pp. New York: McGraw-Hill Book Company, Inc.

HODGE, W. H., 1954. The edible Arracacha, a little-known root crop of the Andes. *Econ. Bot.*, **8**: 195–221.

HODGE, W. H., 1960. Yareta—fuel umbellifer of the Andean puna. *Econ. Bot.*, **14**: 112–118.

HOLLAND, J. H., 1937. *Overseas Plant Products*. 279 pp. London: John Bale, Sons & Curnow, Ltd.

HOWES, F. N., 1950. Age-old resins of the Mediterranean region and their uses. *Econ. Bot.*, **4**: 307–316.

IRVINE, F. R., 1957. Wild and emergency foods of Australian and Tasmanian aborigines. *Oceania*, **28**: 113–142.

KINGSBURY, J. M., 1964. *Poisonous Plants of the United States and Canada*. 626 pp. Englewood Cliffs, New Jersey: Prentice-Hall, Inc.

MATHIAS, M. E., 1928. Studies in the Umbelliferae. I. *Annls Mo. Bot. Gdn*, **15**: 91–108.

MATHIAS, M. E. & CONSTANCE, L., 1944–1945. Umbelliferae. *N. Amer. Flora*, **28B**: 43–295.

MATHIAS, M. E. & CONSTANCE, L., 1962. Flora of Peru. Umbelliferae. *Field Mus. nat. Hist., Bot. Ser.*, **13**, Part 5-A, No. 1, pp. 3–97.

MEDSGER, O. P., 1967. *Edible Wild Plants* (first published 1939), 323 pp. New York: The Macmillan Company.

OSWALT, W. H., 1957. A Western Eskimo ethnobotany. *Anthrop. Pap. Univ. Alaska*, **6**: 16–36.

PARIS, M. R. & MOYSE, H., 1961. *Abrégé de matière médicale: matière premières d'origine végétale*. 188 pp. Paris: Vigot Frères.

POLUNIN, O., 1969. *Flowers of Europe: a Field Guide*. 662 pp. London: Oxford University Press.

RODRÍGUEZ, R. L., 1957. Systematic anatomical studies on Myrrhidendron and other woody Umbellales. *Univ. Calif. Publs Bot.*, **29**: 2: 145–292.

SCHALLER, G. B., 1963. *The Mountain Gorilla: Ecology and Behavior*. 431 pp. Chicago: The University of Chicago Press.

SCHENCK, S. M. & GIFFORD, E. W., 1952. Karok ethnobotany. *Anthrop. Rec.*, **13**: 377–392.

SCHERY, R. W., 1952. *Plants for Man*. 564 pp. New York: Prentice-Hall.

SCHNEIDER, A., 1906. The medicinal plants of the California Indians. *Merck's Rep.*, **15**: 63–128.

SIEVERS, A. F., 1947. The production of minor essential oils in the United States. *Econ. Bot.*, **1**: 148–160.

SMITH, H. H., 1923. Ethnobotany of the Menomini Indians. *Bull. Publ. Mus. Milwaukee*, **4**: 1–174.

STEEDMAN, E. V. (ed.), 1930. Ethnobotany of the Thompson Indians of British Columbia, based on field notes by James A. Teit. *Bur. Amer. Ethnol. Ann. Rep.*, **45**: 441–522.

STEWARD, A. N., 1958. *Manual of Vascular Plants of the Lower Yangtze Valley, China*. 621 pp. Corvallis: Oregon State College.

STEWARD, J. H., 1933. Ethnography of the Owens Valley Paiute. *Univ. Calif. Publs. Amer. Archaeol. Ethnol.*, **33**: 233–350.

TUTIN, T. G. *et al.* (eds), 1968. *Flora Europaea*. Vol. **2**, 455 pp. Cambridge: University Press.

UPHOF, J. C. Th., 1968. *Dictionary of Economic Plants*. 2nd ed., 591 pp. Lehre: Verlag von J. Cramer.

VOGEL, V. J., 1970. *American Indian Medicine*. 583 pp. Norman: University of Oklahoma Press.

WALTERS, S. M., 1961. The shaping of Angiosperm taxonomy. *New Phytol.*, **60**: 74–84.

WATT, J. M. & BREYER-BRANDWIJK, M. G., 1962. *The Medicinal and Poisonous Plants of Southern and Eastern Africa*. 2nd ed., 1457 pp. Edinburgh and London: E. & S. Livingstone Ltd.

THE WEALTH OF INDIA, 1948–. *The Wealth of India: a Dictionary of Indian Raw Materials and Industrial Products*. Many vols. Delhi & New Delhi: Council of Scientific and Industrial Research [and other agencies].

WHITE, R. C., 1955. Ethnobotany of the Luiseño. University of California, Los Angeles, unpublished ms.

WOOD, G. & BACHE, F., 1858. *The Dispensatory of the United States of America*. 11th ed., 1583 pp. Philadelphia: J. B. Lippincott & Co.

YUNCKER, T. G., 1943. The flora of Niue Island. *Bishop Mus. Bull.* No. 178, 126 pp.

Author Index

Numbers in italics refer to the page on which the references appear.

413

Subject Index

Figures printed in bold type are references to plates.

Index to Scientific Names of Organisms

Figures printed in bold type are references to plates.

425